Nonequilibrium Phenomena in Strongly Correlated Systems

Nonequilibrium Phenomena in Strongly Correlated Systems

Editors

David Blaschke
Alexandra Friesen
Vladimir Morozov
Nikolay Plakida
Gerd Röpke

MDPI • Basel • Beijing • Wuhan • Barcelona • Belgrade • Manchester • Tokyo • Cluj • Tianjin

Editor
David Blaschke
Institute of Theoretical Physics
University of Wroclaw
Poland
Bogoliubov Laboratory of Theoretical Physics
Joint Institute for Nuclear Research Dubna
Russia
National Research Nuclear University (MEPhI) Moscow
Russia

Alexandra Friesen
Bogoliubov Laboratory of
Theoretical Physics,
Joint Institute for Nuclear
Research Dubna
Russia

Vladimir Morozov
MIREA-Russian Technological
University Moscow
Russia

Nikolay Plakida
Bogoliubov Laboratory of
Theoretical Physics,
Joint Institute for Nuclear
Research Dubna
Russia

Gerd Röpke
Institut für Physik
Universitat Rostock
Germany
National Research Nuclear
University (MEPhI) Moscow
Russia

Editorial Office
MDPI
St. Alban-Anlage 66
4052 Basel, Switzerland

This is a reprint of articles from the Special Issue published online in the open access journal *Particles* (ISSN 2571-712X) (available at: https://www.mdpi.com/journal/particles/special_issues/nonequilibrium_phenomena_in_strongly_correlated_systems).

For citation purposes, cite each article independently as indicated on the article page online and as indicated below:

LastName, A.A.; LastName, B.B.; LastName, C.C. Article Title. *Journal Name* **Year**, *Article Number*, Page Range.

ISBN 978-3-03936-814-3 (Pbk)
ISBN 978-3-03936-815-0 (PDF)

Cover image courtesy of Galina Rudolfovna Zubareva.

Contents

About the Editor vii

Preface to "Nonequilibrium Phenomena in Strongly Correlated Systems" ix

Vladimir Morozov and Vasyl' Ignatyuk
Energy Conservation and the Correlation Quasi-Temperature in Open Quantum Dynamics
Reprinted from: *Particles* **2018**, *1*, 285–295, doi:10.3390/particles1010023 1

Gerd Röpke
The Source Term of the Non-Equilibrium Statistical Operator
Reprinted from: *Particles* **2019**, *2*, 309–338, doi:10.3390/particles2020020 13

Francesco Becattini, Matteo Buzzegoli and Eduardo Grossi
Reworking Zubarev's Approach to Nonequilibrium Quantum Statistical Mechanics
Reprinted from: *Particles* **2019**, *2*, 197–207, doi:10.3390/particles2020014 43

Masaru Hongo and Yoshimasa Hidaka
Anomaly-Induced Transport Phenomena from Imaginary-Time Formalism
Reprinted from: *Particles* **2019**, *2*, 261–280, doi:10.3390/particles2020018 55

Mykhailo Tokarchuk and Petro Hlushak
Unification of Thermo Field Kinetic and Hydrodynamics Approaches in the Theory of Dense Quantum–Field Systems
Reprinted from: *Particles* **2019**, *2*, 1–13, doi:10.3390/particles2010001 75

Arus Harutyunyan, Armen Sedrakian and Dirk H. Rischke
Relativistic Dissipative Fluid Dynamics from the Non-Equilibrium Statistical Operator
Reprinted from: *Particles* **2018**, *1*, 155–165, doi:10.3390/particles1010011 89

Mikhail Veysman, Gerd Röpke and Heidi Reinholz
Application of the Non-Equilibrium Statistical Operator Method to the Dynamical Conductivity of Metallic and Classical Plasmas
Reprinted from: *Particles* **2019**, *2*, 242–260, doi:10.3390/particles2020017 101

David Blaschke, Gerd Röpke, Dmitry N. Voskresensky and Vladimir G. Morozov
Nonequilibrium Pion Distribution within the Zubarev Approach
Reprinted from: *Particles* **2020**, *3*, 380–393, doi:10.3390/particles3020029 121

Georgy Prokhorov, Oleg Teryaev and Valentin Zakharov
Calculation of Acceleration Effects Using the Zubarev Density Operator
Reprinted from: *Particles* **2020**, *3*, 1–14, doi:10.3390/particles3010001 135

Yuri G. Rudoy and Yuri P. Rybakov
Generalizing Bogoliubov–Zubarev Theorem to Account for Pressure Fluctuations: Application to Relativistic Gas
Reprinted from: *Particles* **2019**, *2*, 150–165, doi:10.3390/particles2010011 149

Stanislav A. Smolyansky, Anatolii D. Panferov, David B. Blaschke and Narine T. Gevorgyan
Nonperturbative Kinetic Description of Electron-Hole Excitations in Graphene in a Time Dependent Electric Field of Arbitrary Polarization
Reprinted from: *Particles* **2019**, *2*, 208–230, doi:10.3390/particles2020015 167

David B. Blaschke, Lukasz Juchnowski and Andreas Otto
Kinetic Approach to Pair Production in Strong Fields—Two Lessons for Applications to Heavy-Ion Collisions
Reprinted from: *Particles* **2019**, *2*, 166–179, doi:10.3390/particles2020012 . . . . **191**

Brent Harrison and Andre Peshier
Bose-Einstein Condensation from the QCD Boltzmann Equation
Reprinted from: *Particles* **2019**, *2*, 231–241, doi:10.3390/particles2020016 . . . . **205**

Elizaveta N. Nazarova, Lukasz Juchnowski, David B. Blaschke and Tobias Fischer
Low-Momentum Pion Enhancement from Schematic Hadronization of a Gluon-Saturated Initial State
Reprinted from: *Particles* **2019**, *2*, 140–149, doi:10.3390/particles2010010 . . . . **217**

Ivan Dadić and Dubravko Klabučar
Causality and Renormalization in Finite-Time-Path Out-of-Equilibrium ϕ^3 QFT
Reprinted from: *Particles* **2019**, *2*, 92–102, doi:10.3390/particles2010008 . . . . **227**

Ludwik Turko
NA61/SHINE Experiment—Program beyond 2020
Reprinted from: *Particles* **2018**, *1*, 296–304, doi:10.3390/particles1010024 . . . . **239**

About the Editors

David Blaschke (Prof. Dr. Dr. h.c. mult.) obtained his PhD in theoretical physics from Rostock University in 1987 and habilitated in 1995. From 2001 to 2007, he was Vice Director of the Bogoliubov Laboratory of Theoretical Physics at the Joint Institute for Nuclear Research in Dubna. Since 2006, he has been a professor at the University of Wroclaw. His works are mainly devoted to topics in quantum field theory at finite temperatures, dense hadronic matter and QCD phase transitions, quark matter in heavy-ion collisions and in compact stars, as well as in pair production in strong fields, with applications to high-intensity lasers. He has published more than 380 articles, most of them in peer-reviewed international journals, edited more than 12 books, and currently has an h-index of 44. He has obtained honorary doctorates from Dubna State University (2017) and Russian-Armenian University in Yerevan (2019).

Alexandra Friesen (Dr.) obtained her PhD in theoretical physics from the Bogoliubov Laboratory of Theoretical Physics at the Joint Institute for Nuclear Research in 2016. Since then, she has worked as a scientific researcher at the laboratory. Her scientific interests are centered around topics in quantum field theory at finite temperature, dense hadronic matter, QCD phase transitions and quark matter in heavy-ion collisions. She has published more than 20 articles in peer-reviewed journals. She was awarded scholarships for Young Scientists and Specialists, named after D.I. Blokhintsev (2015, 2016) and L.D. Soloviev (2017).

Vladimir Morozov (Prof., Dr. phys.-math. Sciences) obtained his PhD (1973) and Doctor of Science degree (1988) in theoretical physics from Steklov Mathematical Institute of the Soviet Academy of Sciences in Moscow. He is currently a full professor at the MIREA—Russian Technological University. His works are mainly devoted to the statistical mechanics of nonequilibrium processes and its applications to different many-particle systems, in particular open quantum systems in solid state physics. He has published more than 100 articles in peer-reviewed international journals and contributed to several books on statistical mechanics.

Nikolay Plakida (Prof., Dr. phys.-math. Sciences) graduated at Moscow State University in 1960, obtained his PhD in theoretical physics from Steklov Mathematical Institute RAS in Moscow in 1966, Doctor of Science in 1976, and the Professor rank in 1991. In 1963—1966 he was a lecturer at the Physics faculty of Moscow State University. From 1966, he has been working at the Bogoliubov Laboratory of Theoretical Physics of the Joint Institute for Nuclear Research in Dubna, presently as a chief scientific researcher. He has been a supervisor of 15 PhD students. Between 1992 and 2007, he was a Visiting Professor at MPIF (Stuttgart), RAL (Didcot, UK), CPT CNRS (Marseille), Yukawa Institute (Kyoto), Tohoku University (Sendai), and MPIPKS (Dresden). His works are devoted to statistical physics, many-body systems, and the theory of solid state. In particular, he has developed a theory of highly anharmonic crystals —the theory of self-consistent phonons and the theory of structural phase transitions. In recent years, he has developed, with his coworkers, a theory of spin fluctuations and superconductivity in strongly-correlated electronic systems, such as cuprates, based on the application of Hubbard's operator technique to the t-J and Hubbard models. He has published more than 300 articles in peer-reviewed international journals, has written three books, and several contributions to monographs. He currently has an h-index of 30. In 2003, he became an honored worker in the science of Russia.

Gerd Röpke (Prof. Dr. Dr. h.c.) obtained his PhD in theoretical physics from Leipzig University in 1966 and habilitated at the Technical University Dresden in 1973. He visited the Steklov Institute of the Soviet Academy of Science in Moscow from 1968–1970. From 1977 to 2009 he was docent, later on professor at the Rostock University. From 1994 to 1997, he was Vice Director of the Bogoliubov Laboratory of Theoretical Physics at the Joint Institute for Nuclear Research in Dubna. His works are mainly devoted to quantum statistics of many-particle systems, in particular dense plasmas and nuclear systems in equilibrium and non-equilibrium. He has published about 400 articles in peer-reviewed international journals and contributed to several books. He worked in different administrative committees and is a member of several scientific societies.

Preface to "Nonequilibrium Phenomena in Strongly Correlated Systems"

Dmitrii Nikolaevich Zubarev was born in November 27, 1917, in Moscow, Russia. On the occasion of his 100th birthday, a honorary colloquium was performed at April 18/19, 2018, at the Bogoliubov Laboratory of Theoretical Physics at the Joint Institute of Nuclear Research, Dubna, Russia. Former coworkers and followers (see Figure 5) contributed with talks:

BLASCHKE, David (Wroclaw)	Nonequilibrium pion distribution in heavy-ion collisions from the Zubarev approach
DADIC, Ivan (Zagreb)	Damping rate and collision integral from finite-time-path out-of-equilibrium field theory
HONGO, Masaru (RIKEN)	Revisiting hydrodynamics from quantum field theory
KUZEMSKY, Alexandr (JINR)	Neutron scattering on the nonequilibrium statistical medium and generalized Van Hove's formula
MOROZOV, Vladimir (MIREA)	Kinetic theory of correlated quantum systems in the framework of Zubarev's nonequilibrium statistical operator method
PLAKIDA, Nikolay (JINR)	Charge fluctuations in strongly correlated electronic systems
REINHOLZ, Heidi (Rostock)	Dielectric function and dynamical collision frequency from the Zubarev approach
RÖPKE, Gerd (Rostock)	Electrical conductivity of charged particle systems and the Zubarev NSO method
RUDOY, Yurii/ RYBAKOV, Yurii (Moscow, RUDN)	Generalized form of the Bogoliubov - Zubarev theorem for pressure fluctuations. Possible applications to ultra-relativistic gases.
SEDRAKIAN, Armen (Frankfurt)	Transport coefficients of QCD from Zubarev formalism
SMOLYANSKY, Stanislav (Saratov)	Magnetic moment of the e-e+ plasma generated from vacuum under action of a rotating E-field
TROPIN, Timur (JINR)	On the theoretical description of polymers glass transition kinetics in a wide range of cooling rates
TURKO, Ludwik (Wroclaw)	Finite size effects, intermolecular forces and effective virial expansion

The organizers decided to collect contributions to prepare this Special Issue. Following the open call, there were, in addition to the contributions from the above speakers, also contributions from colleagues who could not participate in the seminar:

BECATTINI, Francesco (Firenze)	Reworking Zubarev's approach to nonequilibrium quantum statistical mechanics
HARRISON, Brent (Cape Town)	Bose–Einstein condensation from the QCD Boltzmann equation
JUCHNOWSKI, Lukasz (Wroclaw)	Kinetic approach to pair production in strong fields—Two lessons for applications to heavy-ion collisions
NAZAROVA, Elizaveta (Wroclaw)	Low-momentum pion enhancement from schematic hadronization of agluon-saturated initial state
PROKHOROV, Georgy (JINR)	Calculation of acceleration effects using the Zubarev density operator
TOKARCHUK, Mykhailo (Kiev)	Unification of thermo-field kinetic and hydrodynamics approaches in the theory of dense quantum field systems

Figure 1. Photo taken on April 18, 2018, at the honorary colloquium for D. N. Zubarev's 100th birthday. From left to right: Vladimir Morozov (MIREA, Moscow), Heidi Reinholz (Rostock), David Blaschke (Wroclaw and JINR Dubna), Nikolay Plakida (JINR Dubna), Gerd Röpke (Rostock), Yurii Rybakov (RUDN, Moscow). Background: Hermann Wolter (Munich).

We will now outline the biography and scientific legacy of D. N. Zubarev; for details see [1–3].

D. N. Zubarev studied physics at Moscow State University. In 1941, he graduated from the Department of Physics. His academic advisor was N. N. Bogoliubov, who was also the promotor of his PhD thesis work. From 1954 to the end of his life, D. N. Zubarev worked at the V. A. Steklov Institute of Mathematics of the Russian Academy of Sciences. From 1969 to 1971, he was also head of the Statistical Mechanics and Theory of Condensed Matter Group at the

Laboratory of Theoretical Physics, JINR, Dubna. He died in Moscow, July 29, 1992, after a traffic accident.

D. N. Zubarev successfully contributed to statistical physics. In 1957, he obtained, together with N.N. Bogoliubov and Yu.A. Tserkovnikov, the asymptotically exact solution of the BCS model Hamiltonian [4], which was an essential contribution to the theory of superconductivity.

Figure 2. Photo taken at an excursion to Mzcheta during the Tiflis Conference on Low-Temperature Physics in 1959. From left to right: Dmitry Vasil'evich Shirkov (JINR Dubna), Dmitrii Nikolaevich Zubarev (Steklov Inst. Moscow), Anatoly Alekseevich Logunov (JINR Dubna), Yurii Aleksandrovich Tserkovnikov (Steklov Inst. Moscow), Zygmunt Galasiewicz (JINR Dubna & Wroclaw), Albert Nikifirovich Tavkhelidze (JINR Dubna).

Figure 3. Photo taken when the group of D. N. Zubarev visited Vladimir in June 1969. From left to right: John Shepherd (UK), Karl-Hartmut Müller (GDR), Celia Shepherd (UK), Wolfgang Götze (FRG), Gerd Röpke (GDR), Dmitrii Nikolaevich Zubarev.

He considered himself as a "father of methods", in particular he published the highly cited review article entitled: "Double-time Green Functions in Statistical Physics" [5], and wrote the well known monography "Neravnovesnaya statisticheskaya termodinamika" [6], translated from Russian to English by P. J. Shepherd. He made very fundamental contributions to statistical physics published in many scientific articles, based on a sound mathematical approach. His very general approach to nonequilibrium processes with applications in different fields was presented in the Monography [7].

Figure 4. D. N. Zubarev at the 6-th Winter School on Theoretical Physics in Karpacz (Poland) 1969. From left to right, back row: Nikolay Maksimilianovich Plakida, Elmar Grigorievich Petrov, Dmitrii Nikolaevich Zubarev, ?, Władysława Rybarska (Nawrocka); front row: ?, Tadeusz Paszkiewicz, Jerzy Stęślicki, Andrzej Pękalski, Valery Leonidovich Pokrovsky.

As a leading scientist in statistical physics, D. N. Zubarev had many active collaborations within the former Soviet Union and abroad. Many close relations to colleagues and guests were long-standing and are determined by his open-minded, tolerant and clear scientific position, also his accurate and precise work and discussions. He attracted and educated young scientists, including G. O. Balabamyan, V. P. Kalashnikov, V. G. Morozov, T. Paszkiewicz, N. M. Plakida, L. Pokrovsky, S. Tishchenko, M. V. Tokarchuk and others. He also hosted guests from abroad (see Figure 3), and visited them to give series of lectures, like at the Karpacz Winter School in Poland 1969 (see Figure 4) and at the Miniworkshop on Quantum Statistics in Ahrenshoop (GDR) in 1987 (see Figure 5).

Figure 5. D. N. Zubarev and M.V. Tokarchuk during a visit at the University of Rostock in November 1987, when Dmitri Nikolaevich was giving a lecture series on the NSO method during a Miniworkshop with the group of Gerd Röpke in Ahrenshoop.

The personality of D. N. Zubarev was formed also by the WWII. On June 25, 1941 he volunteered for duty in the Eighth Division of the People's Militia and participated in the defense of Moscow. At the end of the war D. N. Zubarev was in Berlin with the 47th Army of the First Belorussian Front. He was awarded the Red Star for participation in mine clearing in Berlin. Many of his fellow students died during the war. After war, he worked with G. Hertz who was made head of Institute G, in Agudzery, about 10 km southeast of Sukhumi and a suburb of Gulrip'shi, on separation of isotopes by discussion in a ow of inert gases. After this he worked for several years on important defense problems at the "object," now known as Arzamas-16. His association during this period with N. N. Bogoliubov and A. D. Sakharov greatly influenced his scientific career. His wife, Galina Rudolfovna, participated in the Leningrad blockade.

Despite the very hard history, and under the restrictions of the soviet time, he developed an open-minded and complaisant atmosphere in the contact with physicists around the world. D. N. Zubarev had an unusual talent for social intercourse, which attracted people to him. He exhibited the traits of a true Russian intellectual live interest and openness to anything new in science and in life, honesty and fairness, softness, delicacy, unselfishness and constant readiness to help people, but at the same time he was strict and uncompromising in the search for scientific truth and he unfailingly adhered to strict scientific ethics.

D. Blaschke, A.V. Friesen, V. G. Morozov, N. K. Plakida, G. Röpke.
Wroclaw, Dubna, Moscow, Rostock, in July 2020

Figure 6. Photo taken at the honorary colloquium for D. N. Zubarev's 100th birthday in the Conference Hall of the Bogoliubov Laboratory of Theoretical Physics at the JINR Dubna. From left to right: D. Blaschke (Wroclaw & JINR Dubna), H. Reinholz (Rostock), V.G. Morozov (MIREA, Moscow), G. Röpke (Rostock), N.M. Plakida (JINR Dubna). Background: Bust of N.N. Bogoliubov.

References

1. Bogoliubov, N.N.; Vladimirov, V.S. *Usp. Mat. Nauk* **1988**, *43*, 235–236.
2. Byishvili, L.L.; Vladimirov, V.S.; Kalashnikov, V.P.; Klimontovich, Yu.L.; Morozov, V.G.; Moskalenko, V.A.; Plakida, N.M.; Tserkovnikov, Yu.A.; Shirkov, D.V.; Yukhnovskii, I.R. *Usp. Fiz. Nauk* **1993**, *163*, 107–108.
3. Slavnov, A.A.; Pogrebkov, A.K.; Tareyeva, E.E.; Zharinov, V.V.; Aref'eva, I.Ya.; Dobrokhotov, S.Yu.; Gal'tsov, D.V.; Gershtein, S.S.; Holevo, A.S.; Kazakov, D.I.; Krichever, I.M.; Libanov, M.V.; Manin, Y.I.; Marshakov, A.V.; Maslov, V.P.; Morozov, A.Yu.; Plakida, N.M.; Rubakov, V.A.; Semikhatov, A.M.; Shabat, A.B.; Slavnov, N.A.; Slavyanov, S.Yu.; Tyutin, I.V. (Editorial Board) *Theor. Mat. Phys.* **2018**, *194*, 2–3.
4. Bogolyubov, N.N.; Zubarev, D.N.; Tserkovnikov, Yu.A. On the phase transition theory. *Dokl. Akad. Nauk SSSR* **1957**, *117*, 788–791.
5. Zubarev, D.N. Double-time Green Functions in Statistical Physics. *Usp. Fiz. Nauk* **1960**, *71*, 71–116; [*Sov. Phys. Uspekhi* **1960**, *3*, 320–345].
6. Zubarev, D.N. *Neravnovesnaya statisticheskaya termodinamika*; Nauka: Moscow, Russia, 1971; Engl. Translation: *Nonequilibrium Statistical Thermodynamics*; Consultants Bureau: New York, NY, USA, 1974.
7. Zubarev, D.; Morozov, V.; Röpke, G. *Statistical Mechanics of Nonequilibrium Processes*; Akademie-Verlag: Berlin, Germany, 1996/1997; Volume I/II.

particles

MDPI

Article

Energy Conservation and the Correlation Quasi-Temperature in Open Quantum Dynamics

Vladimir Morozov [1] **and Vasyl' Ignatyuk** [2,*]

[1] MIREA-Russian Technological University, Vernadsky Av. 78, 119454 Moscow, Russia; vladmorozov45@gmail.com

[2] Institute for Condensed Matter Physics, Svientsitskii Str. 1, 79011 Lviv, Ukraine

* Correspondence: ignat@icmp.lviv.ua; Tel.: +38-032-276-1054

Received: 25 October 2018; Accepted: 27 November 2018; Published: 30 November 2018

Abstract: The master equation for an open quantum system is derived in the weak-coupling approximation when the additional dynamical variable—the mean interaction energy—is included into the generic relevant statistical operator. This master equation is nonlocal in time and involves the "quasi-temperature", which is a non- equilibrium state parameter conjugated thermodynamically to the mean interaction energy of the composite system. The evolution equation for the quasi-temperature is derived using the energy conservation law. Thus long-living dynamical correlations, which are associated with this conservation law and play an important role in transition to the Markovian regime and subsequent equilibration of the system, are properly taken into account.

Keywords: open quantum system; master equation; non-equilibrium statistical operator; relevant statistical operator; quasi-temperature; dynamic correlations

1. Introduction

In this paper, we continue the study of memory effects and nonequilibrium correlations in open quantum systems, which was initiated recently in Reference [1]. In the cited paper, the nonequilibrium statistical operator method (NSOM) developed by Zubarev [2–5] was used to derive the non-Markovian master equation for an open quantum system, taking into account memory effects and the evolution of an additional "relevant" variable—the mean interaction energy of the composite system (the open quantum system plus its environment). This approach allows one to describe systematically the long-living nonequilibrium correlations associated with the total energy conservation. However, the price paid for this possibility is the need to solve the system of coupled evolution equations for the statistical operator of the open system and the additional nonequilibrium state parameters. In the present paper, our main concern is the time behaviour of the so-called quasi-temperature, which is a parameter conjugated to the mean interaction energy [1].

The structure of the paper is as follows. In Section 2, we show how a scheme for deriving master equations in open quantum dynamics can be formulated within NSOM and introduce the auxiliary "relevant" statistical operator describing correlated nonequilibrium states of the composite system. This relevant statistical operator is then used in Section 3 to derive the non-Markovian master equation in the limit of weak interaction between the open system and the environment. Nonequilibrium correlations associated with the energy conservation introduce additional relaxation terms in the master equation. These terms contain the state parameter (quasi-temperature) thermodynamically conjugated to the mean interaction energy. In Section 4, we derive the general evolution equation for the quasi-temperature and consider its modification in the weak-coupling limit. Finally, conclusions and outlook are given in Section 5.

2. The Reduced Statistical Operators and the Relevant Statistical Operator

Let us assume that the open quantum system of interest (S) interacts with another (as a rule, much larger) system (E)—the environment, and the Hamiltonian of the composite system has the form

$$H = H_S + H_E + V \equiv H_0 + V, \tag{1}$$

where H_S and H_E are the Hamiltonians of the open quantum system and the environment, and V is the interaction Hamiltonian. For the sake of simplicity, we restrict ourselves to the case when the composite system $(S+E)$ is isolated and, consequently, H_S and H_E do not depend on time. It is an easy matter to generalize the main results and conclusions to the case when the open quantum system (or the environment) is affected by some alternating fields.

Nonequilibrium states of the open quantum system and the environment are completely described by the *reduced statistical operators*

$$\varrho_S(t) = \mathrm{Tr}_E\{\varrho_{SE}(t)\}, \qquad \varrho_E(t) = \mathrm{Tr}_S\{\varrho_{SE}(t)\}, \tag{2}$$

where the symbol Tr_E (Tr_S) means the trace over all degrees of freedom of the environment (of the open quantum system), and $\varrho_{SE}(t)$ is the statistical operator of the composite system at time t. The evolution of the composite system is described by the von Neumann equation (in units with $\hbar = 1$)

$$\frac{\partial \varrho_{SE}(t)}{\partial t} = i[\varrho_{SE}(t), H]. \tag{3}$$

The first step in deriving the master equation for the reduced statistical operator $\varrho_S(t)$ is to apply the operation Tr_E to both sides of Equation (3). This gives

$$\frac{\partial \varrho_S(t)}{\partial t} - i[\varrho_S(t), H_S] = -i\mathrm{Tr}_E[V, \varrho_{SE}(t)]. \tag{4}$$

For this formal equality to have the meaning of a closed evolution equation for the subsystem (S), the statistical operator $\varrho_{SE}(t)$ is to be expressed in terms of ϱ_S.

Let us now consider how a scheme for deriving the master equation can be formulated within NSOM [3,4]. As usual, we start from the decomposition of the statistical operator $\varrho_{SE}(t)$:

$$\varrho_{SE}(t) = \varrho_{\mathrm{rel}}(t) + \Delta\varrho(t), \tag{5}$$

where $\varrho_{\mathrm{rel}}(t)$ is the relevant part of the statistical operator for the composite system. We recall that the problem posed in NSOM is to derive evolution equations (generalized kinetic equations) for some set of observables $\langle P_i \rangle^t$ characterizing the nonequilibrium state of the system, where $\{P_i\}$ is the set of the corresponding basic dynamical variables, and the average is taken with the nonequilibrium statistical operator of the system (in the present case with $\varrho_{SE}(t)$). The problem now is to construct a proper relevant statistical operator that is a functional of the observables. It is commonly required that $\varrho_{\mathrm{rel}}(t)$ corresponds to the extremum of the information entropy $S(t) = -\mathrm{Tr}_{S,E}\{\varrho_{\mathrm{rel}}(t) \ln \varrho_{\mathrm{rel}}(t)\}$ under the supplementary conditions that the mean values $\langle P_i \rangle^t$ be equal to given quantities and the normalization condition $\mathrm{Tr}_{S,E}\{\varrho_{\mathrm{rel}}(t)\} = 1$. Under these conditions we have [3]

$$\varrho_{\mathrm{rel}}(t) = \exp\Big\{-\Phi(t) - \sum_i F_i(t) P_i\Big\}. \tag{6}$$

The Massieu-Planck function $\Phi(t)$ is determined by normalization,

$$\Phi(t) = \ln \mathrm{Tr} \exp\left\{ -\sum_i F_i(t) P_i \right\}, \tag{7}$$

where the parameters $F_i(t)$ (Lagrange multipliers) are found from the self-consistency conditions

$$\langle P_i \rangle^t = \mathrm{Tr}\{ P_i \varrho_{\mathrm{rel}}(t) \}, \tag{8}$$

which can be considered as the nonequilibrium equations of state.

The answer to which set of the dynamic variables P_i is preferable depends on the kind of the system and the required level of its description. For instance, the "hydrodynamic" description corresponds to taking the densities of conserved quantities as a basic set of the dynamical variables [4]. An extension of this set at the expense of higher derivatives allows one to obtain equations of the generalized hydrodynamics and to widen the timescale of the description of the system evolution. Such a scheme underlies the generalized collective mode theory (GCM) [6–8], which has proven its efficiency at the study of variety of the condensed matter systems.

Conversely, the GCM can be extended by taking into account the "ultraslow" processes (defined by the time integrals of corresponding densities) [9–11]) , which allows one to approach the problems of account for slow structural relaxation and study the ageing processes in the glassy forming system on equal footing with the extended hydrodynamics [12].

Thus, the main criterion for the choice of the dynamic variables of the abbreviated description of the system is a slowness of their variation on the chosen time scale. A closer examination of this point is given, e.g., in the books [2–4]. Leaving aside the problems connected with initial correlations, memory effects, and other special features of quantum dynamics, for a moment, we will consider the fundamental question about the possibility of deriving a master equation for an open quantum system within the framework of NSOM. The problem is to find dynamical variables P_i such as their mean values, calculated with the statistical operator $\varrho_{SE}(t)$, contain the same information about the state of the open system (S) as the reduced statistical operator $\varrho_S(t)$.

To this end, let us consider some complete and orthonormal set $\mathcal{G} = \{|n\rangle\}$ of quantum states in the Hilbert space of the open system (S). We introduce the so-called *Hubbard operators* [13]

$$X_{mn} = |m\rangle\langle n|, \tag{9}$$

which obey the following algebraic properties:

$$X_\alpha X_{\alpha'} = \sum_{\alpha''} g_{\alpha\alpha';\alpha''} X_{\alpha''}, \qquad [X_\alpha, X_{\alpha'}] = \sum_{\alpha''} c_{\alpha\alpha';\alpha''} X_{\alpha''} \tag{10}$$

with the structure constants

$$g_{\alpha\alpha';\alpha''} = \delta_{mm''}\delta_{nm'}\delta_{n'n''}, \qquad c_{\alpha\alpha';\alpha''} = g_{\alpha\alpha';\alpha''} - g_{\alpha'\alpha;\alpha''}. \tag{11}$$

To simplify some notations, we have introduced the ordered pairs of indexes $\alpha = (m,n)$, $\alpha' = (m',n')$, etc.

Let us show that the matrix elements of the reduced statistical operator $\varrho_S(t)$ of the open system (S) are expressed in terms of the mean values $\langle X_{mn} \rangle^t$, where the averaging is performed with the statistical operator of the composite system $(S+E)$. To do this we write the obvious chain of equalities:

$$\langle X_{mn} \rangle^t \equiv \mathrm{Tr}_{S,E}\{ X_{mn} \varrho_{SE}(t) \} = \mathrm{Tr}_S\{ X_{mn} \varrho_S(t) \} = \sum_{k,k'} \langle k | X_{mn} | k' \rangle \langle k' | \varrho_S(t) | k \rangle, \tag{12}$$

where relation (2) has been used. Since, in calculating the trace, we may take $|k\rangle \in \mathcal{G}$ and $|k'\rangle \in \mathcal{G}$, it follows from the definition (9) that $\langle k|X_{mn}|k'\rangle = \delta_{km}\delta_{k'n}$. Consequently,

$$\langle X_{mn}\rangle^t = \langle n|\varrho_S(t)|m\rangle. \tag{13}$$

Thus, there is a good reason to include the Hubbard operators into the basic set of dynamical variables $\{P_i\}$. Such an approach was used, for instance, in Reference [14] to study the role of initial correlations for a system consisting of many two-level atoms interacting with a common bath.

Before writing down the explicit form of the relevant statistical operator, we would like to emphasize that the first term appearing in Equation (5) is by itself an auxiliary operator, but it plays an important role in NSOM. First, the choice of the relevant statistical operator determines the initial (or boundary) condition for $\Delta\varrho(t)$ (see, e.g., Ref. [1]). Second, the choice of $\varrho_{\text{rel}}(t)$ determines the "structure" of approximations in solving the von Neumann Equation (3), since the scheme of NSOM works most effectively when the operator $\Delta\varrho(t)$ may in a sense be regarded as a small correction to the relevant part of the statistical operator (5).

To be sure that all slow variables are incorporated in the relevant statistical operator, let us recall that regardless of the structure of the open system and the properties of the environment, there is the quantity (namely the average energy of the composite system $\langle H\rangle^t$) which does not depend on time and, consequently, is "slowly varying" at all time scales. As shown in Reference [15], taking into account the energy conservation changes drastically the structure of non-Markovian kinetic equations even in the Born approximation and ensures the existence of the equilibrium solution for the statistical operator. Within NSOM, the additional "correlational" terms appearing in a kinetic equation can be found in an explicit form, if $\langle H\rangle^t$ is included into the set of observables to construct the relevant statistical operator. It is often convenient to take as a controlled parameter of state not the total energy of the system but the mean interaction energy since all the remaining contributions to $\langle H\rangle^t$ can be obtained by redefining the Lagrange multipliers for other basic dynamical variables [15].

Following Reference [1], we take the relevant statistical operator of the composite system in the form

$$\varrho_{\text{rel}}(t) = \exp\Big\{-\Phi(t) - \sum_\alpha \Lambda_\alpha(t)X_\alpha - \beta^*(t)V - \beta H_E\Big\}. \tag{14}$$

As usual, the Massieu-Planck function is determined from the normalization condition for the operator $\varrho_{\text{rel}}(t)$, and the Lagrange multipliers $\Lambda_\alpha(t)$, $\beta^*(t)$ are determined from the self-consistency conditions

$$\text{Tr}_{S,E}\{X_\alpha\,\varrho_{\text{rel}}(t)\} = \langle X_\alpha\rangle^t, \qquad \text{Tr}_{S,E}\{V\varrho_{\text{rel}}(t)\} = \langle V\rangle^t, \tag{15}$$

where the averages $\langle X_\alpha\rangle^t$ and $\langle V\rangle^t$ are calculated with the nonequilibrium statistical operator $\varrho_{SE}(t)$ of the composite system.

The relevant statistical operator (14) has some important properties. For example, if we set $\beta^* = \beta$, then ϱ_{rel} coincides with the exact equilibrium statistical operator at temperature $T = (k_B\beta)^{-1}$. In this connection, the quantity $T^* = (k_B\beta^*)^{-1}$ may be interpreted as a *correlational quasi-temperature* of the open system. On the other hand, if we put $\beta^* = 0$ (or $T^* = \infty$), then the relevant statistical operator (14) describes the state in which there are no correlations between the open system and the environment,

$$\varrho^{(0)}_{\text{rel}}(t) = \exp\Big\{-\Phi^{(0)}(t) - \sum_\alpha \Lambda_\alpha(t)X_\alpha - \beta H_E\Big\}. \tag{16}$$

This expression can be cast into the form

$$\varrho_{\mathrm{rel}}^{(0)}(t) = \varrho_S(t) \otimes \varrho_E, \tag{17}$$

where

$$\varrho_E = \exp\{-\Phi_E^{(0)} - \beta H_E\} \tag{18}$$

is the equilibrium statistical operator of the environment, and the statistical operator of the subsystem S is defined as

$$\varrho_S(t) = \exp\left\{-\Phi_S^{(0)}(t) - \sum_{\alpha} \Lambda_\alpha(t) X_\alpha\right\}. \tag{19}$$

As above, the Massieu-Planck function $\Phi_S^{(0)}(t)$ is determined from the normalization condition for the operator on the left-hand side.

The relevant statistical operator (16) can be used to determine the initial condition $\varrho_{SE}(0) = \varrho_{\mathrm{rel}}^{(0)}(0)$ if the evolution of the composite system starts from a non-correlated state. However, even in this simplest case, for all times—not just at time $t = 0$—the absence of correlations is not true and consequently nonequilibrium states are not adequate described by statistical operator (16).

3. The Weak-Coupling Master Equation

Starting from the description of nonequilibrium states of the composite system by the relevant statistical operator (14), one can derive the master equation for $\varrho_S(t)$. To explain the scheme of the derivation, we shall consider the case where the operator V in the Hamiltonian (1) describes weak interaction between the open quantum system and the environment, i.e., it is possible to expand at some stage the quantities of interest in a power series in the coupling constant to which the operator V is proportional.

First we substitute the expression (5) into Equation (4):

$$\frac{\partial \varrho_S(t)}{\partial t} - i[\varrho_S(t), H_S] = -i\mathrm{Tr}_E[V, \varrho_{\mathrm{rel}}(t)] - i\mathrm{Tr}_E[V, \Delta\varrho(t)]. \tag{20}$$

Now, following the logic of NSOM, the operator $\Delta\varrho$ is to be expressed in terms of ϱ_{rel}. Then the right-hand side of Equation (20) could, in principle, be considered as a functional of ϱ_S and β^*. For this purpose, we first derive the evolution equation for the operator $\Delta\varrho(t)$. Let us substitute the expression (5) into the von Neumann Equation (3) and then change to the interaction picture by setting

$$\tilde{A}(t) = e^{itH_0} A(t) e^{-itH_0} \tag{21}$$

for any operator $A(t)$. After simple manipulations we obtain

$$\frac{\partial}{\partial t}\Delta\tilde{\varrho}(t) - i[\Delta\tilde{\varrho}(t), \widetilde{V}(t)] = -\left(\frac{\partial}{\partial t}\tilde{\varrho}_{\mathrm{rel}}(t) - i[\tilde{\varrho}_{\mathrm{rel}}(t), \widetilde{V}(t)]\right). \tag{22}$$

Let us assume that the initial condition $\Delta\tilde{\varrho}(0) = \Delta\varrho(0) = 0$ is satisfied. It means that the evolution of the composite system starts from the state characterized by the condition $\varrho_{SE}(0) = \varrho_{\mathrm{rel}}(0)$. This is typical when the open quantum system is prepared in a particular way (e.g., by some quantum measurement [16]). Then Equation (22) can be written in the integral form

$$\Delta\tilde{\varrho}(t) - i\int_0^t d\tau\,[\Delta\tilde{\varrho}(\tau), \widetilde{V}(\tau)] = -\int_0^t d\tau\left(\frac{\partial}{\partial \tau}\tilde{\varrho}_{\mathrm{rel}}(\tau) - i[\tilde{\varrho}_{\mathrm{rel}}(\tau), \widetilde{V}(\tau)]\right). \tag{23}$$

If the interaction between the open subsystem and its environment is weak, then, as is clear from Formula (20), in the leading (Born) approximation it is sufficient to calculate $\Delta\varrho(t)$ up to terms linear in V. Apparently, in this approximation the second term on the left-hand side of Equation (23) may be omitted. Using interaction representation (21) once again, we obtain

$$\Delta\varrho(t) = -\int_0^t d\tau\, e^{-i(t-\tau)H_0}\left(\frac{\partial\varrho_{\rm rel}(\tau)}{\partial\tau} - i[\varrho_{\rm rel}(\tau), H]\right)e^{i(t-\tau)H_0}. \tag{24}$$

The commutator in (24) is transformed in a standard way using definition (14) for the relevant statistical operator, the Kubo identity for non-commuting operators [3] and the self-consistency conditions (15). As a result, up to terms linear in V, we have

$$\Delta\varrho(t) = -i\int_0^t d\tau\, e^{-i(t-\tau)H_0}R(\tau)\, e^{i(t-\tau)H_0}, \tag{25}$$

where

$$R(\tau) = [V, \varrho_S(\tau)\varrho_E] + \beta^*(\tau)\int_0^1 dx\,(\varrho_S(\tau)\varrho_E)^x\,[V, H_0](\varrho_S(\tau)\varrho_E)^{1-x}. \tag{26}$$

In Equation (26) the superscript, which emerges due to the Kubo identity, denotes the x-th power of the corresponding statistical operators.

Using Formula (25), we can bring Equation (20) to its final form

$$\frac{\partial\varrho_S(t)}{\partial t} - i[\varrho_S(t), H_S] = -i\mathrm{Tr}_E[V, \varrho_{\rm rel}(t)] - \int_0^t d\tau\,\mathrm{Tr}_E[V, e^{-i(t-\tau)H_0}R(\tau)\, e^{i(t-\tau)H_0}]. \tag{27}$$

It follows from the above analysis that both terms on the right-hand side of this equation are functionals of $\varrho_S(t')$ and $\beta^*(t')$, where $0 < t' \leq t$. However, Equation (27) is not itself a closed master equation for the reduced statistical operator ϱ_S because we need also the evolution equation for $\beta^*(t)$ or for the correlational quasi-temperature $T^*(t) = (k_B\beta^*(t))^{-1}$. A similar situation arises in the "standard" kinetic theory when nonequilibrium correlations are taken into account in non-Markovian kinetic equations. Within the weak coupling approximation, the equation for $\beta^*(t)$ was derived in the work [15] where a quantum system of particles with pair interaction was considered. As already noted, the approach to the dynamics of open systems presented here is formally quite analogous to NSOM in quantum kinetics, so that the equation for $\beta^*(t)$ can be derived by applying the scheme described in the work [15].

4. Equation for the Quasi-Temperature

Let us turn to the self-consistency conditions (15) and differentiate them with respect to time. Recalling the explicit form (14) of the relevant statistical operator and the definition (7) of the Massieu-Planck function leads to the set of equations

$$\begin{cases} (X_\alpha, V)\dfrac{d\beta^*(t)}{dt} + \sum\limits_{\alpha'}(X_\alpha, X_{\alpha'})\dfrac{d\Lambda_{\alpha'}(t)}{dt} = -\dfrac{d\langle X_\alpha\rangle^t}{dt}, \\ (V, V)\dfrac{d\beta^*(t)}{dt} + \sum\limits_{\alpha}(V, X_\alpha)\dfrac{d\Lambda_\alpha(t)}{dt} = -\dfrac{d\langle V\rangle^t}{dt}. \end{cases} \tag{28}$$

We have introduced the time-dependent correlation functions of dynamical variables in the relevant ensemble,

$$(A,B)=\int_0^1 dx\langle\Delta A\varrho_{\rm rel}^{x}\Delta B\varrho_{\rm rel}^{-x}\rangle_{\rm rel},\qquad \Delta A=A-\langle A\rangle_{\rm rel}^{t},\tag{29}$$

where $\langle\ldots\rangle_{\rm rel}\equiv{\rm Tr}_{S,E}\{\varrho_{\rm rel}(t)\ldots\}$ denotes averaging with the relevant statistical operator (14). It is easy to check that the correlation function (29) satisfies the symmetry condition $(A,B)=(B,A)$.

The chain of matrix Equations (28) can formally be solved for the derivatives $d\Lambda_\alpha(t)/dt$, yielding the evolution equation for the quasi-temperature:

$$C(t)\frac{d\beta^*(t)}{dt}=\sum_{\alpha,\alpha'}(V,X_\alpha)\,(X,X)^{-1}_{\alpha\alpha'}\,\frac{d\langle X_{\alpha'}\rangle^t}{dt}-\frac{d\langle V\rangle^t}{dt},\tag{30}$$

where (X,X) is a matrix whose elements are $(X_\alpha,X_{\alpha'})$, and the quantity

$$C(t)=(V,V)-\sum_{\alpha,\alpha'}(V,X_\alpha)(X,X)^{-1}_{\alpha\alpha'}(X_{\alpha'},V)\tag{31}$$

may be regarded as a generalized heat capacity.

Let us rewrite the right-hand side of Equation (30) in a more transparent form. First we eliminate the derivative $d\langle V\rangle/dt$ applying the energy conservation law

$$\frac{d\langle H_S\rangle^t}{dt}+\frac{d\langle H_E\rangle^t}{dt}+\frac{d\langle V\rangle^t}{dt}=0,\tag{32}$$

and then express the derivative $d\langle H_S\rangle/dt$ in terms of $d\langle X_\alpha\rangle/dt$ using the fact that, in general, the system Hamiltonian H_S can be written as

$$H_S=\sum_\alpha \mathcal{E}_\alpha X_\alpha\tag{33}$$

with $\mathcal{E}_\alpha\equiv\mathcal{E}_{mn}=\langle m|H_S|n\rangle$. After the above manipulations, Equation (30) takes the form

$$C(t)\frac{d\beta^*(t)}{dt}=\sum_\alpha\left(\mathcal{E}_\alpha+\sum_{\alpha'}(V,X_{\alpha'})\,(X,X)^{-1}_{\alpha'\alpha}\right)\frac{d\langle X_\alpha\rangle^t}{dt}+\frac{d\langle H_E\rangle^t}{dt}.\tag{34}$$

For the time derivatives on the right-hand side of this equation, we have the expressions

$$\begin{aligned}\frac{d\langle X_\alpha\rangle^t}{dt}&=-i\langle[X_\alpha,H_S]\rangle_S^t-i\langle[X_\alpha,V]\rangle^t_{\rm rel}+I_\alpha(t),\\ \frac{d\langle H_E\rangle^t}{dt}&=-i\langle[H_E,V]\rangle^t_{\rm rel}+I_E(t),\end{aligned}\tag{35}$$

where $\langle\ldots\rangle_S^t$ means averaging with the reduced statistical operator $\varrho_S(t)$, and

$$I_\alpha(t)=-i{\rm Tr}_{S,E}\left\{[X_\alpha,V]\,\Delta\varrho(t)\right\},\qquad I_E(t)=-i{\rm Tr}_{S,E}\left\{[H_E,V]\,\Delta\varrho(t)\right\}.\tag{36}$$

Formulas (35) follow directly from the von Neumann Equation (3) and Equation (5).

Let us show that the first term on the right-hand side of the evolution Equation (35) for $\langle H_E \rangle^t$ is equal to zero. To this end, we use the obvious identity

$$\mathrm{Tr}_{S,E}\left\{\varrho_{\mathrm{rel}}(t)[A, \ln \varrho_{\mathrm{rel}}(t)]\right\} = 0, \tag{37}$$

which is valid for any operator A. Taking $A = H_E$ and recalling the explicit form (14) of the relevant statistical operator, one readily obtains

$$\mathrm{Tr}_{S,E}\left\{\varrho_{\mathrm{rel}}(t)[H_E, V]\right\} = 0. \tag{38}$$

Substituting Equation (35) into Equation (34) leads, in general, to a rather cumbersome evolution equation for the quasi-temperature. However, this equation can be considerably simplified, if the system-environment coupling is weak. To do this, let us assume that $\langle V \rangle_E \equiv \mathrm{Tr}_E\,(V\varrho_E) = 0$, where ϱ_E is given by Equation (18). If the initial operator V does not satisfy this condition, then it suffices to redefine H_S and V by replacing $H_S \to H_S + \langle V \rangle_E$ and $V \to V - \langle V \rangle_E$. Then it is easy to check that the leading terms in the correlation functions (X_α, V) as well as in the mean values $\langle [X_\alpha, V] \rangle^t_{\mathrm{rel}}$ are of the second order in interaction. In this approximation, Equation (34) reduces to

$$C(t)\,\frac{d\beta^*(t)}{dt} = -i\sum_\alpha \left\{ \mathcal{E}_\alpha \langle [X_\alpha, V] \rangle^t_{\mathrm{rel}} + \sum_{\alpha'} (V, X_{\alpha'})\,(X, X)^{-1}_{\alpha'\alpha}\,\langle [X_\alpha, H_S] \rangle^t_S \right\} + \sum_\alpha \mathcal{E}_\alpha I_\alpha(t) + I_E(t), \tag{39}$$

where the generalized heat capacity $C(t)$ is to be evaluated with the relevant statistical operator (16) for a non-interacting composite system. This gives

$$C(t) = \int_0^1 dx\,\mathrm{Tr}_{S,E}\left\{ V \left(\varrho^{(0)}_{\mathrm{rel}}\right)^x V \left(\varrho^{(0)}_{\mathrm{rel}}\right)^{1-x} \right\}. \tag{40}$$

Note that the time dependence of the generalized heat capacity (40) arises from that of the relevant statistical operator (16).

We would like to note that the "coherent" term $\sum_\alpha \mathcal{E}_\alpha \langle [X_\alpha, H_S] \rangle^t_S$ in Equation (39) vanishes due to Equation (33). It can also be shown that within the leading weak coupling approximation the term in braces in Equation (39) vanishes, so that we finally arrive at the simplified equation for the quasi-temperature:

$$C(t)\,\frac{d\beta^*(t)}{dt} = \sum_\alpha \mathcal{E}_\alpha I_\alpha(t) + I_E(t). \tag{41}$$

Let us touch upon a physical meaning of the quasi-temperature in more detail. Of course, $1/\beta^*(t)$ cannot be treated as a temperature in its ordinary meaning since it cannot be even measured. Moreover, the quasi-temperature can even be negative if the system admits the dynamically induced inversion of the levels' population [17–19]. However, $1/\beta^*(t)$ can really be considered as the generalized temperature since: (i) it is introduced in a quasi-Gibbsian manner via the relevant statistical operator similarly (14), like the ordinary temperature is; (ii) it obeys the generalized thermodynamic relation (41), whose right-hand side is nothing but the derivative of the total kinetic energy of the composite $(S + E)$ system; (iii) it tends to its asymptotic value at $t \to \infty$ [20], which coincides with the bath temperature.

To conclude this Section, and to explain the essence and the importance of the dynamical correlations in more detail we would like to note the following. The dynamical correlations are incorporated in the master Equation (27) by means of the second term of (26), which involves the quasi-temperature $1/\beta^*(t)$. First, the quasi-temperature is defined as the state parameter conjugated to the interaction energy, see definition (14) of the relevant statistical operator. On the other hand, the dynamic equation (41) for the quasi-temperature involves both the generalized heat capacity (40) (which is expressed in terms of the "energy-energy" non-equilibrium correlation functions), and collision integrals (36) (which also bring the information about the dynamical correlations between the system and environment arising from the conservation law (32)).

Moreover, the second term in Equation (26) gives rise to additional contributions to the collision integrals $I_S(t)$ and $I_E(t)$ by taking the non-equilibrium correlations into account. These terms are even called "correlational" ones [3,15,21], and they determine an additional relaxation timescale [20], which turns out to be much shorter than that of the (S) subsystem dynamics.

5. Conclusions and Outlook

Equation (41) for the quasi-temperature and the master Equation (27) for the reduced statistical operator provide us with a complete description of open quantum dynamics in the weak coupling limit. It must be emphasized that both equations are non-local in time due to the structure of the nonequilibrium correction $\Delta\varrho(t)$ to the statistical operator (see Equation (25)).

Note that the interplay between memory effects and correlations may strongly affect kinetic processes [15,21]. First of all, a transition to the Markovian regime (when the memory effects become negligible) occurs due to the energy conservation and the long-living dynamical correlations, accompanying this phenomenon. It is known [3] that the Levinson equation (non-Markovian one) does not have an equilibrium solution, while the local in time Uehling-Uhlenbeck equation does. The correlational term eliminates this bottleneck of the quantum kinetic theory by providing a proper Markovization of the system and tending of the distribution functions to their (quasi)equilibrium limits. At this stage of the system evolution, the quasi-temperature $1/\beta^*(t)$ tends to its equilibrium value $1/\beta$, both correlational parts of the collision integrals (36) and Equation (41) become identically equal to zero, and the non-Markovian quantum kinetic equation converts to its Uehling-Uhlenbeck form.

From a strictly mathematical point of view, the time non-locality (non-Markovian effects) appears at the stage of integral presentation of the von Neuman equation regardless of taking the dynamical correlations into account. It means that the master Equation (27) turns out to be non-Markovian even if one neglects the second term in (26). Though the Markovian approximation is widely believed [16] to be justified if the time scale τ_S, over which the state of the system varies appreciably, is large compared to the time scale τ_E, over which the environment correlation functions decay, in the case of a particular open quantum system the situation can be more diverse. One can formally solve the (Heisenberg) equations of motions for the environment variables and insert the obtained results into the dynamic equations for the (S) subsystem variables. The obtained Langevin-type equations are found to be non-Markovian. However, if the dynamics of the environment variables is not strongly interconnected with that of the (S) subsystem, and the time behaviour of the bath variables can be calculated explicitly, one comes to the Markovian kinetic equations without any suggestions about relaxation times hierarchy. This is exactly the case of the dephasing model [22], where the dynamic equation for the system coherency does not involve the memory effects.

Secondly, memory effects are most pronounced at the initial stage of the system dynamics. In particular, their consideration turns out to be indispensable in the presence of ultra-short external fields [20]. Similar situations in which memory effects and correlations play an important role can emerge in open quantum systems. For instance, the period between switching of quantum registers can be comparable or even less than the dephasing time [22].

Finally, there exist various approaches [23–25] to the quantification of memory effects in quantum open systems, and even to the definition (or redefinition) of the non-Markovianity itself. Usually, they are based upon a conception of the trace distance between two quantum states, and the obtained results are expressed in terms of the rate of change of the above mentioned distance. In this context, one can propose another look at this issue, which is based, say, on the concept of the generalized thermodynamics. In particular, one can investigate the transition times from the essentially non-Markovian regimes to the local in time dynamics (which would manifest itself in tending of the quasi-temperature to its equilibrium limit) and compare them with other typical timescales for open quantum systems (e.g., the dephasing time or the thermalization time [22]). The ratio between the above mentioned times can be treated as a generalized measure of the non-Markovianity. In our opinion, such an approach would be most promising for small-sized systems, when the environment can hardly be treated as a thermal bath. It should be noted that our scheme can be directly applied to this case, when the environment has not been equilibrated yet and is characterized by the non-equilibrium temperature $1/\beta(t)$ which, in general, is not equal to the "correlational" quasi-temperature $1/\beta^*(t)$.

Definitely, the consistency and the robustness of our scheme should be verified on particular models of the open quantum systems. We believe these studies to be very perspective, and we are going to carry them out in our further researches using some exactly solvable models.

Author Contributions: Conceptualization, V.M.; Methodology, V.M.; Investigation, V.M., V.I.; Writing—Original Draft Preparation, V.M., V.I.; Writing—Review & Editing, V.M., V.I.

Funding: This research received no external funding.

Conflicts of Interest: The authors declare no conflict of interest.

References

1. Morozov, V.G. Memory effects and nonequilibrium correlations in the dynamics of open quantum systems. *Theor. Math. Phys.* **2018**, *194*, 105–113. [CrossRef]
2. Zubarev, D.N. *Nonequilibrium Statistical Thermodynamics*; Consultants Bureau: New York, NY, USA; London, UK, 1974.
3. Zubarev, D.; Morozov, V.G.; Röpke, G. *Statistical Mechanics of Nonequilibrium Processes, Vol. 1, Basic Concepts, Kinetic Theory*; Akademy Verlag: Berlin, Germany, 1996.
4. Zubarev, D.; Morozov, V.G.; Röpke, G. *Statistical Mechanics of Nonequilibrium Processes, Vol. 2, Relaxation and Hydrodynamic Processes*; Akademy Verlag: Berlin, Germany, 1996.
5. Luzzi, R.; Vasconcellos, Á.R.; Ramos, J.G. *Predictive Statistical Mechanics. A Nonequilibrium Ensemble Formalism*; Ser. Fundamental Theories of Physics; Kluwer: Dordrecht, The Netherlands, 2002; Volume 122.
6. Omelyan, I.P.; Mryglod, I.M. Generalized collective modes of a Lennard-Jones fluid. High mode approximation. *Condens. Matter Phys.* **1994**, *4*, 128–160. [CrossRef]
7. Mryglod, I.M.; Omelyan, I.P.; Tokarchuk, M.V. Generalized collective modes for the Lennard-Jones fluid. *Mol. Phys.* **1995**, *84*, 235–259. [CrossRef]
8. Mryglod, I.M.; Folk, R. On the hydrodynamic theory of a magnetic liquid II. Hydrodynamic modes in the Heisenberg fluid. *Physica A* **1996**, *234*, 129–150. [CrossRef]
9. Omelyan, I.P.; Tokarchuk, M.V. The modified collective-mode approach: Dielectric relaxation in water. *J. Phys. Condens. Matter* **2000**, *12*, L505. [CrossRef]
10. Omelyan, I.P; Mryglod, I.M.; Tokarchuk, M.V. Wavevector- and frequency-dependent shear viscosity of water: The modified collective mode approach and molecular dynamics calculations. *Condens. Matter Phys.* **2005**, *8*, 25–46. [CrossRef]
11. Bryk, T.; Mryglod, I. Concentration fluctuations and boson peak in a binary metallic glass: A generalized collective modes study. *Phys. Rev. B* **2010**, *82*, 174205. [CrossRef]
12. Bryk, T.; Mryglod, I. Structural relaxation in pure liquids: Analysis of wavenumber dependence within the approach of generalized collective modes. *Condens. Matter Phys.* **2008**, *11*, 139–154. [CrossRef]
13. Hubbard, J. Electron correlations in narrow energy bands. IV. The atomic representation. *Proc. R. Soc. Lond. Ser. A* **1965**, *285*, 542–560. [CrossRef]
14. Chaudhry, A.Z.; Gong, J. Role of initial system-environment correlations: A master equation approach. *Phys. Rev. A* **2013**, *88*, 052107. [CrossRef]

15. Morozov, V.G.; Röpke, G. Non-Markovian quantum kinetics and conservation laws. *J. Stat. Phys.* **2001**, *102*, 285–313. [CrossRef]
16. Breuer, H.-P.; Petruccione, F. *The Theory of Open Quantum Systems*; Oxford Univ. Press: Oxford, UK, 2002.
17. Purcell, E.M.; Pound, R.V. A nuclear spin system at negative temperature. *Phys. Rev.* **1951**, *81*, 279–280. [CrossRef]
18. Zelevinsky, V. *Quantum Physics. Volume 2: From Time-Dependent Dynamics to Many-Body Physics and Quantum Chaos*; John Wiley & Sons: Weinheim, Germany, 2011.
19. Fayngold, M.; Fayngold, V. *Quantum Mechanics and Quantum Information: A Guide through the Quantum World*; John Wiley & Sons: Weinheim, Germany, 2013.
20. Ignatyuk, V.V.; Morozov, V.M. Ultrafast dynamics of laser-pulse excited semiconductors: Non-Markovian quantum kinetic equations with nonequilibrium correlations. *Condens. Matter Phys.* **2004**, *7*, 579–602. [CrossRef]
21. Morozov, V.G. Non-Markovian electron-phonon relaxation. *Condens. Matter Phys.* **2000**, *3*, 577–595. [CrossRef]
22. Morozov, V.G.; Mathey, S.; Röpke, G. Decoherence in an exactly solvable qubit model with initial qubit-environment correlations. *Phys. Rev. A* **2012**, *85*, 022101. [CrossRef]
23. Clos, G.; Breuer, H.-P. Quantification of memory effects in the spin-boson model. *Phys. Rev. A* **2012**, *86*, 012115. [CrossRef]
24. Rivas, A.; Huelga, S.F.; Plenio, M.B. Quantum non-Markovianity: Characterization, quantification and detection. *Rep. Prog. Phys.* **2014**, *77*, 094001. [CrossRef] [PubMed]
25. Breuer, H.-P.; Laine, E.-M.; Piilo, J.; Vacchini, B. Colloquium: Non-Markovian dynamics in open quantum systems. *Rev. Mod. Phys.* **2016**, *88*, 021002. [CrossRef]

particles

MDPI

Communication

The Source Term of the Non-Equilibrium Statistical Operator

Gerd Röpke [1,2]

1 Institute of Physics, University of Rostock, D-18051 Rostock, Germany; gerd.roepke@uni-rostock.de
2 Department of Theoretical Nuclear Physics, National Research Nuclear University (MEPhI), 115409 Moscow, Russia

Received: 8 May 2019; Accepted: 4 June 2019; Published: 6 June 2019

Abstract: The method of Zubarev allows one to construct a statistical operator for the nonequilibrium. The von Neumann equation is modified introducing a source term that is considered as an infinitesimal small correction. This approach provides us with a very general and unified treatment of nonequilibrium processes. Considering as an example the electrical conductivity, we discuss the modification of the von Neumann equation to describe a stationary nonequilibrium process. The Zubarev approach has to be generalized to open quantum systems. The interaction of the system with the irrelevant degrees of freedom of the bath is globally described by the von Neumann equation with a finite source term. This is interpreted as a relaxation process to an appropriate relevant statistical operator. As an alternative, a quantum master equation can be worked out where the coupling to the bath is described by a dissipator. The production of entropy is analyzed.

Keywords: irreversibility; entropy; linear response theory; electrical conductivity

1. Electrical Conductivity-Phenomenology

Transport processes. The method of the nonequilibrium statistical operator (NSO) invented by D. N. Zubarev [1] is an important step working out a general approach to the statistical mechanics of nonequilibrium processes. It covers different fields of nonequilibrium theory, in particular the thermodynamics of irreversible processes, kinetic theory, linear response theory, open quantum systems, quantum master equations, and hydrodynamics; see [2,3]. The method of NSO provides us with a consistent and coherent approach to nonequilibrium statistics. However, it gives also a view of the sensible points, deriving equations of evolution for irreversible phenomena (e.g., transport processes and reaction rates) from the reversible basic equations of motion such as Hamilton equations, Maxwell theory, and quantum field theory.

Let us start with a simple example for a transport process, friction. Friction transforms mechanical work into heat. It is one of the fundamental processes that are considered to introduce irreversibility and the production of entropy according to the second law of thermodynamics.

A particular case is electrical conductivity. We consider a system containing two species of charged particles, the ions (charge $Z_i e$) and the electrons (charge $-e$), for instance a hydrogen plasma consisting of electrons and protons, or a piece of copper as a system of ions, fixed on lattice sites, and quasi-free electrons. The system is assumed to be charge neutral, so that the densities are related as $Z_i n_i = n_e$, where $n_c = \langle N_c \rangle / \Omega_0$ is the average of the particle number N_c per volume Ω_0. Without loss of generality, we assume in this work $Z_i = 1$. Under the influence of a constant external electrical field $\mathbf{E}_{\rm ext}$, an electrical current with density $\mathbf{j}$ is induced. As an empirical fact, below a critical value of $|\mathbf{E}_{\rm ext}|$, the current is proportional to the field. For isotropic systems, we have:

$$\mathbf{j} = \sigma \mathbf{E}_{\rm ext}, \tag{1}$$

with the transport coefficient σ being the electrical conductivity. Note that the electrical conductivity is defined with the screened, intrinsic electrical field, $\boldsymbol{j} = \sigma \boldsymbol{E}_{\rm int}$. In the case considered here, the intrinsic electrical field $\boldsymbol{E}_{\rm int}$ coincides with the external field.

To have an irreversible process, the mechanical work $\Omega_0 \boldsymbol{j} \cdot \boldsymbol{E}_{\rm ext}\, {\rm d}t$ must be transformed to heat Q,

$$\frac{1}{\Omega_0} \frac{\delta Q}{{\rm d}t} = \boldsymbol{j} \cdot \boldsymbol{E}_{\rm ext} = \frac{1}{\sigma} j^2, \tag{2}$$

if no other forms of work are performed by the system. The increase of heat is related to the production of entropy, ${\rm d}S = \delta Q / T_{\rm eq}$, if the system remains near thermodynamic equilibrium with temperature $T_{\rm eq}$.

We consider a quasi-stationary situation where the electrical field, in general $\boldsymbol{E}_{\rm ext}(\boldsymbol{r}, t)$, and the current density, in general $\boldsymbol{j}(\boldsymbol{r}, t)$, are constant with respect to time. Furthermore, we consider the homogeneous case where both quantities are not depending on position. In addition, the densities n_c of charged particles and the temperature T are considered as constant, also not depending on position. We denote this as the external conditions that we demand from the experiment.

Open systems. These quasi-stationary, homogeneous conditions with constant electrical current density, particle number density, and temperature are only possible for open systems. We characterize them by the finite volume, here a cylinder Ω_R^h with the axis parallel to $\boldsymbol{j}$ taken as the z axis, between $z = 0$ and $z = h$, and with radius R. The electrical field $\boldsymbol{E}_{\rm ext} = E_{\rm ext} \boldsymbol{e}_z$ is also directed along the z axis. To sustain the constant electrical current, particles must be introduced through the surface at $z = h$ (with high potential energy $V_{\rm ext}(h)$) and extracted through the opposite surface at $z = 0$ (with lower potential energy $V_{\rm ext}(0)$). The difference of the potential energy of an electron is $V_{\rm ext}(h) - V_{\rm ext}(0) = ehE_{\rm ext}$. Without loss of generality, we omit the current of ions.

The particles injected in the open system at high potential energy gain kinetic energy according to the conservation law in mechanics, before they leave the open system at low potential energy. However, because of the demand of homogeneity in space, the electron current that leaves the system transports the same amount of kinetic energy as the incoming electron current. According to the first law of thermodynamics, mechanical work is transformed to thermal energy. Heat is produced at the rate per volume (power density) according to Equation (2).

More precisely, to stay in quasi-equilibrium, this amount of energy must be extracted from the system to a bath. Instead of an isolated, closed system as frequently considered in physics, described by well-defined dynamical degrees of freedom, we have to consider an open system for the stationary transport process. The contact with the surroundings (the "bath", or additional degrees of freedom) is necessary not only to sustain the current of electrons, but also for the export of heat to sustain a constant temperature. We assume for the bath thermodynamic equilibrium at the external (bath) temperature $T_{\rm ext}$. Below, in Section 8, we consider it as a local property $T_{\rm ext}(\boldsymbol{r}, t)$. In the case that the open system is in contact with a material bath, we have thermal conductivity, e.g., by phonon transport. In a vacuum, the transport of energy is performed by radiation. In particular, the bremsstrahlung may be the primary process to transform mechanical energy into the energy of radiation. Temperature and heat for radiation are defined after absorption by a hohlraum, where the Planck spectrum of radiation is established in equilibrium.

The concept of heat is introduced as a process to export energy to a bath. According to the second law of thermodynamics, the density of entropy production results as:

$$\frac{1}{\Omega_R^h} \frac{{\rm d}S}{{\rm d}t} = \frac{1}{T_{\rm ext} \sigma} j^2. \tag{3}$$

The second law of thermodynamics implies $\sigma > 0$ (the flow of a river is never up-hill).

As a more general case, periodic dependence in time and space can be considered, and the optical conductivity or AC conductivity $\sigma(\boldsymbol{q}, \omega)$ depending on the wave vector $\boldsymbol{q}$ and the frequency ω is introduced. Because of linearity, a general dependence on space and time, such as the switch-on situation where the field $\boldsymbol{E}_{\rm ext}(t)$ is proportional to the step function, is treated via Fourier decomposition and superposition of the solution for the components. This general case can also be treated with our approach [4–6], but is not considered in this work, where we focus on the coupling to a bath.

2. Electrical Conductivity-Microscopic Approach

Microscopic model. We construct a microscopic approach to friction and electrical conductivity, which are typical irreversible processes. This means we start from the well-known equations of motion for the particles and fields according to quantum mechanics and quantum electrodynamics. These equations, as well as their classical limits (Newton's or Maxwell's equations) describe reversible motion. We consider a simple microscopic model: Electrons move in a system of heavy ions (at positions $\boldsymbol{R}_i$) under the influence of an external field $\boldsymbol{E}_{\rm ext}$. Within the Lorentz model, the electron–electron interaction is replaced by a mean field to ensure charge neutrality. The given electron–ion interaction $V_{\rm ei}(\boldsymbol{r})$ defines the Hamiltonian that characterizes the model system:

$$\mathrm{H_S} = \sum_p E_p \mathrm{a}_p^\dagger \mathrm{a}_p + \sum_{p,q} V(\boldsymbol{q}) \mathrm{a}_{p+q}^\dagger \mathrm{a}_p. \tag{4}$$

where $p = \{\boldsymbol{p}, \hat{\sigma}\}$ is the single-electron state with wave vector $\boldsymbol{p}$. The spin $\hat{\sigma}$ is treated implicitly. $E_p = \hbar^2 p^2/2m_e$ is the kinetic energy, and $V(\boldsymbol{q}) = \Omega_0^{-1} \sum_i^{N_i} \int d^3r\, e^{i\boldsymbol{q}\cdot\boldsymbol{r}} V_{\rm ei}(\boldsymbol{r} - \boldsymbol{R}_i)$ is the Fourier transform of the interaction with all ions at positions $\boldsymbol{R}_i$.

In addition, the influence of the external field $\boldsymbol{E}_{\rm ext}(t)$ (which in general may depend on time and space) is described by the contribution (electron charge $-e$):

$$\mathrm{H_F^t} = e\mathbf{R} \cdot \boldsymbol{E}_{\rm ext}(t) \tag{5}$$

with the electron position operator $\mathbf{R} = \sum_i^{N_e} \boldsymbol{r}_i$. This is the sum of the potential energies of all electrons in the system. The total Hamiltonian $\mathrm{H}^t = \mathrm{H_S} + \mathrm{H_F^t}$ determines the motion of the electrons in the microscopic approach, i.e., the dynamics of the system.

Without electron–ion interaction, the solution of the equation of motion for the electrons is simple. The momentum $\hbar\mathbf{p} = m_e\dot{\mathbf{r}}$ of each electron is changed with time according to $\hbar\dot{\mathbf{p}}_i = -e\boldsymbol{E}_{\rm ext}$. We consider the cylindrical volume $\Omega_R^{\rm dz}$ with height $h = {\rm d}z$. An electron incoming at dz with momentum $\hbar\boldsymbol{p}, p_z < 0$ and leaving the volume at $z = 0$ after ${\rm d}t = (-m_e/\hbar p_z){\rm d}z$ will have the z component of momentum $\hbar p_z + eE_{\rm ext}(m_e/\hbar p_z){\rm d}z$. This corresponds to an increase of kinetic energy by:

$${\rm d}E_{\rm kin} = \frac{1}{2m_e} 2eE_{\rm ext} m_e {\rm d}z + \mathcal{O}({\rm d}z^2) \tag{6}$$

equal to the loss $eE_{\rm ext}{\rm d}z$ of potential energy, as given by Equation (5). The acceleration of all incoming electrons to outgoing electrons makes the average momentum and the corresponding electrical current dependent on the position, which is in contradiction with the requested homogeneity.

The electron–ion interaction, Equation (4), destroys the increase of the average momentum in the z direction by scattering, which changes the direction of the momentum. In the adiabatic limit $M_i/m_e \to \infty$, we have elastic scattering. The average momentum of the electron system gained by the electrical field is transferred to the ion system (and is compensated by the ion system because of charge neutrality). The loss of average momentum of the electron subsystem defines the stationary current and the conductivity, as calculated below for a given $V_{\rm ei}(\boldsymbol{q})$. Nevertheless, the Hamiltonian $\mathrm{H}^t = \mathrm{H_S} + \mathrm{H_F^t}$ is not sufficient to describe the process of stationary conductivity because it does not describe the contact with the bath, in particular how the electrons enter and leave the open system and how energy is dissipated.

Contact with the bath. The conservation of particle number leads to the balance equation for the particle current and is described by the incoming and outgoing currents of the open system Ω_0. It is assumed that the process of injection and extraction of electrons to sustain the current in the open system is not relevant for the calculation of the conductivity. We can circumvent this problem considering a larger system $\bar{\Omega}$ where the particle number is conserved. This may be a circuit consisting of a capacitor, an inductor, and a resistor, driven by periodic external electromagnetic fields, so that a quasi-stationary state with forced oscillations with ω_0 is obtained. Examples are absorbed radiation by an antenna or the second circuit of a transformer.

Let us consider the induction of electrical fields by the change of magnetic field with time, expressed via the vector potential $\boldsymbol{A}_{\rm ext}(\boldsymbol{r},t)$ (Coulomb gauge), so that:

$$\boldsymbol{E}_{\rm ext}(\boldsymbol{r},t) = -\frac{\partial}{c\,\partial t}\boldsymbol{A}_{\rm ext}(\boldsymbol{r},t). \tag{7}$$

The coupling to the external field $\boldsymbol{A}_{\rm ext}(\boldsymbol{r},t)$ is given by the expression $(e\hbar/c)\mathbf{p}\cdot\boldsymbol{A}_{\rm ext}$, so that the average absorbed power density is $-\boldsymbol{j}\cdot\dot{\boldsymbol{A}}_{\rm ext}/c = \boldsymbol{j}\cdot\boldsymbol{E}_{\rm ext}$. The expression:

$$\mathrm{H}_{\rm F}^t = \frac{e\hbar}{c}\sum_p \boldsymbol{p}\cdot\boldsymbol{A}_{\rm ext}(t)\mathrm{a}_p^\dagger \mathrm{a}_p \tag{8}$$

has the advantage that it is expressed in second quantization with respect to momentum states, and the average current density:

$$j = \frac{-e\hbar}{m_e\Omega_0}\mathrm{Tr}\left\{\rho\sum_i^{N_e}\mathbf{p}_i\right\} = \frac{-e\hbar}{m_e\Omega_0}\sum_p \boldsymbol{p}\langle \mathrm{a}_p^\dagger \mathrm{a}_p\rangle \tag{9}$$

does not depend on position as demanded for the homogeneous situation. Now, we can relax the problem of particle exchange with the bath because there is particle conservation for the closed circuit.

However, we cannot eliminate the bath with respect to the absorption of the heat, which is produced by the electrical current flowing across the resistor. The motion of the electrons in the external field gives an average increase of kinetic energy. The transfer of electrical energy to mechanical energy per volume and time is given by $\boldsymbol{j}\cdot\boldsymbol{E}_{\rm ext}$. However, the external conditions are given so that not only the current density, but also the temperature is constant. This is in conflict with energy conservation. For the condition that in the stationary case, the electron system is homogeneous, i.e., the averages are not varying with position, the export of energy cannot be done by the electron system across the surface of the system, but needs other mechanisms, denoted as coupling to a thermal bath.

A standard device is the export of energy by coupling to a material thermal bath consisting of matter, which is characterized by the average kinetic energy according to a temperature $T_{\rm ext}$. The coupling is mediated by collisions between the ions and can be expressed by phonons. As a characteristic of the bath, back-reaction is excluded, and coherence and correlations are destructed. This refers, in particular, to the phase of the phonons. The phase is defined in a coherent state, also in the classical description of the electron–ion interaction, but not in quantum-statistical thermal equilibrium, which is described by occupation numbers of the phonon states.

More general, without the need for a material bath, is the radiation field, which is always present. The emission of photons is a well-known effect for the export of energy, but this is not the solution of the problem of irreversibility. A photon has a definite energy, and a radio wave a definite phase. Neither are thermalized. Only the Planck hohlraum radiation is thermalized and is characterized by the equilibrium temperature $T_{\rm eq}$. This black-body radiation is given by the Bose occupation numbers for the single-photon states:

$$n_{\rm B}(\omega,T_{\rm eq}) = \frac{1}{e^{\hbar\omega/k_{\rm B}T_{\rm eq}}-1}, \qquad \varrho(\omega,T_{\rm eq}) = \frac{\hbar\omega^3}{4\pi^3c^2}n_{\rm B}(\omega,T_{\rm eq}) \tag{10}$$

is the spectral radiance of blackbodies, i.e., the power emitted from the emitting surface, per unit projected area of emitting surface, per unit solid angle, per angular frequency unit. We use in this work the Planck hohlraum radiation to define heat and $T_{\rm eq}$. Other degrees of freedom, in particular the kinetic energy of the plasma constituents, may be in thermal equilibrium with the black-body radiation, which defines the bath. Then, the average energy per classical degree of freedom is $k_B T_{eq}/2$.

Flow of energy. Coming back to the DC conductivity, we discuss the flow of energy. The stationary current with density $\boldsymbol{j}$ induces a magnetic field, and with the constant electrical field $\boldsymbol{E}_{ext}$, the Poynting vector is obtained, which describes the flow density of electromagnetic energy from outer space into the material. The energy current density of the electromagnetic field is given by the Poynting vector $\boldsymbol{S}_{ext} = \boldsymbol{E}_{ext} \times \boldsymbol{B}_{ext}$. For the cylindrical configuration considered here, this is a radial vector perpendicular to the z axis. For the current density j, at radius R, the value $B_{ext} = \pi R^2 j / 2\pi R$ results, so that the energy current of the electromagnetic field into the volume $\Omega_R^h = \pi R^2 h$ comes out as the surface integral $\int \mathrm{d}\boldsymbol{O} \cdot \boldsymbol{S}_{ext} = j E_{ext} R/2 \times 2\pi R h = j E_{ext} \Omega_R^h$. This verifies the energy conservation: the power density $j\, E_{ext}$ absorbed by the electrons moving in the electrical field is imported via the electromagnetic energy density current $\boldsymbol{S}_{ext}$. There, it is transformed into mechanical energy, according to the reversible Maxwell equations of motion for the electromagnetic fields. In the stationary case, the amount of imported power has to be exported.

We consider the energy export from the system by thermal conduction and thermal radiation. In both cases, the formation of a Planck spectrum with a definite temperature T_{ext} and the corresponding black-body radiation describes the distribution of the energy with respect to the quantum states, and this energy can be addressed as heat. The export of energy is also possible in different forms, such as performing work by evaporating particles with high kinetic energy, phonons that are not thermalized, or emitting photons out of thermal equilibrium. Thermal conduction can be realized via the ion system by individual collisions with ions or collective excitations (phonons). The bottleneck is the transfer of kinetic energy from the light electrons, mass m_e, to the heavy ions, mass M_i, owing to collisions. Here, the ratio m_e/M_i determines the transfer of energy. In the second case of photon emission, radiation transport does not need contact with a material bath, but the omnipresent vacuum.

Entropy production. In addition, the production of entropy is of interest, which is related to the production of heat. We introduced heat as a property of the electromagnetic field, the black-body radiation. The transfer from external field energy to mechanical energy gives no change in the entropy. Similarly, the export of energy out of thermal equilibrium is not connected with the entropy production. Only the transformation to heat gives an increase of entropy. The formation of a Planck spectrum and the corresponding black-body radiation can be addressed as heat. We need a discussion of the bath, as well as the coupling of the system to the bath. We focus on the Maxwell field as the bath, but many relations can also be discussed for a phonon bath.

Bremsstrahlung radiation. We consider in this work radiation transport. The free-free transitions of electrons moving under the influence of an interaction potential, here the ion potential, lead to the emission or absorption of the bremsstrahlung. The emission of radiation by a plasma is characterized by the emission coefficient $j(\omega)$, which gives the rate of radiation energy per unit volume, frequency ω, and solid angle. For a system in thermal equilibrium, the emission coefficient is related to the absorption coefficient $\alpha(\omega)$ by Kirchhoff's law:

$$j_{em}(\omega) = \frac{\hbar\omega^3}{4\pi^3 c^2} \frac{1}{e^{\hbar\omega/k_B T_{eq}} - 1} \alpha(\omega) \tag{11}$$

where the spectral power density of blackbody radiation appears, and c is the speed of light. This expression can be obtained from the Larmor formula for the radiated power of an accelerated single electron,

$$P = -\frac{\mathrm{d}E}{\mathrm{d}t} = \frac{e^2}{6\pi\epsilon_0 c^3} (\ddot{\boldsymbol{r}})^2. \tag{12}$$

The thermally-averaged emission coefficient for a non-relativistic plasma considering free-free transitions without particle correlations reads according to Kramers [7]:

$$j_{\rm em}(\omega) = \frac{e^6 Z_i^2 n_e n_i}{24\pi^3\sqrt{6\pi}\epsilon_0^3 c^3 m_e^{3/2}} \frac{e^{-\hbar\omega/k_B T_{\rm eq}}}{\sqrt{k_B T_{\rm eq}}} \bar{g}_{\rm ff}(\omega) \tag{13}$$

with $\bar{g}_{\rm ff}(\omega) \approx 1$. The Gaunt factor $\bar{g}_{\rm ff}(\omega)$ was introduced by Gaunt [8] in order to account for quantum-mechanical modifications; see also Section 6 below.

However, the bremsstrahlung radiation emitted during the electron–ion collision has to be transported across the plasma where self-absorption may occur. If self-absorption can be neglected, the plasma is optically thin, and the radiation can escape. If the plasma becomes optically thick, radiation propagates only a short distance before it will be absorbed. At frequencies ω below the plasma frequency, $\omega < \omega_{\rm pl} = \sqrt{e^2 n_e/\epsilon_0 m_e}$, radiation cannot freely propagate. In the optically-thick plasma, the upper limit for the emitted radiation is determined by the Planck Formula (10), see also Section 8. The low-frequency part of the radiation spectrum follows the Raleigh–Jeans law $\varrho(\omega, T_{\rm eq}) \approx \omega^2 k_B T_{\rm eq}/4\pi^3 c^2$. It defines the temperature $T_{\rm eq}$ and, via the Planck formula, the heat deposited in the radiation field.

3. Semiempirical Calculation of the Conductivity of the Adiabatic Lorentz Plasma

Boltzmann equation. In the next step, after discussing microscopic properties of the system and the bath, we come back to the calculation of the conductivity of the adiabatic Lorentz plasma in the low-density limit. A semiempirical approach, the Boltzmann equation, considers the transfer of the ordered, directed motion of electrons to disordered motion owing to collisions. We consider the single-particle distribution function $f_1(\mathbf{p}, t)$. Because of homogeneity in space, in the classical case, there is no dependence on position $\mathbf{r}$. In the quantum case, we have the diagonal elements $f_1(\mathbf{p}, t) = \langle a_p^\dagger a_p \rangle^t$ of the density matrix; the spin $\hat{\sigma}$ in $p = \{\mathbf{p}, \hat{\sigma}\}$ is not treated explicitly. The average is performed with the statistical operator $\rho(t)$. In the inhomogeneous case, the non-diagonal elements of the density matrix lead to the $\mathbf{r}$ dependence of the Wigner function. In equilibrium, neglecting interaction in the low-density limit, the electron distribution is given by the ideal Fermi gas:

$$f_1^0(E_p) = \frac{1}{e^{\beta(E_p-\mu_e)}+1}, \qquad E_p = \frac{\hbar^2 p^2}{2m_e}, \qquad \beta = \frac{1}{k_B T_{\rm eq}}. \tag{14}$$

The electron chemical potential μ_e is calculated from the electron density $n_e(t) = \Omega_0^{-1}\sum_p f_1(\mathbf{p}, t)$. The electrical current density of electrons, charge $-e$,

$$\mathbf{j}(t) = \frac{-e\hbar}{m_e \Omega_0}\sum_p \mathbf{p} f_1(\mathbf{p}, t) \tag{15}$$

is zero in equilibrium.

Owing to external fields and collisions among particles, the distribution function changes with time. According to Boltzmann [9], we have:

$$\frac{\partial}{\partial t} f_1 = \left(\frac{\partial}{\partial t} f_1\right)_{\rm D} + \left(\frac{\partial}{\partial t} f_1\right)_{\rm St} \tag{16}$$

which becomes zero for the stationary state. The drift term contains the external force, with $\mathbf{v} = \hbar\mathbf{p}/m_e$ following:

$$\left(\frac{\partial}{\partial t} f_1\right)_{\rm D} = -\mathbf{v}\frac{\partial}{\partial \mathbf{r}} f_1(\mathbf{p}) - \mathbf{F}_{\rm ext}\frac{\partial}{\hbar\partial \mathbf{p}} f_1(\mathbf{p}) = e\mathbf{E}_{\rm ext}\frac{\partial}{\hbar\partial \mathbf{p}} f_1(\mathbf{p}) \tag{17}$$

for the homogeneous case. Note that a mean-field term can be added to the external force. The internal interactions are contained in the collision term $(\partial f_1/\partial t)_{\rm St}$ for which, from the BBGKYhierarchy, an exact expression can be given containing the two-particle distribution function [10]. As an approximation, we assume a balance between gain and loss, $(\partial f_1/\partial t)_{\rm St} = G - L$. With some phenomenological considerations, we find in the quantum case the collision term as:

$$\left(\frac{\partial}{\partial t} f_1\right)_{\rm St} = \int \frac{\mathrm{d}^3 \boldsymbol{p}' \Omega_0}{(2\pi)^3} \left\{ f_1(\boldsymbol{p}') w_{\boldsymbol{p}\boldsymbol{p}'} (1 - f_1(\boldsymbol{p})) - f_1(\boldsymbol{p}) w_{\boldsymbol{p}'\boldsymbol{p}} (1 - f_1(\boldsymbol{p}')) \right\}, \tag{18}$$

where $w_{\boldsymbol{p}\boldsymbol{p}'}$ is the transition rate from the momentum state $\boldsymbol{p}'$ to the state $\boldsymbol{p}$. The quantum behavior of the collisions is taken into account via the Pauli blocking factors $(1 - f_1(\boldsymbol{p}))$.

In the adiabatic limit, the interaction part of the Hamiltonian (4), matrix elements $H'_{\boldsymbol{p}'\boldsymbol{p}} = V(\boldsymbol{p}' - \boldsymbol{p})$ describe elastic collisions. In Born approximation, the transition rate is given by Fermi's golden rule,

$$w_{\boldsymbol{p}'\boldsymbol{p}} = \frac{2\pi}{\hbar} |H'_{\boldsymbol{p}'\boldsymbol{p}}|^2 \delta(E_p - E_{p'}) = w_{\boldsymbol{p}\boldsymbol{p}'}. \tag{19}$$

Relaxation time method. To calculate the electrical conductivity, we make the ansatz that for small electrical fields, also the deviation of $f_1(\boldsymbol{p})$ from the equilibrium distribution $f_1^0(E_p)$ is small, and we assume a linear relation. The deviation from equilibrium is described by the function $\Phi(\boldsymbol{p})$ defined as (see also [4]):

$$f_1(\boldsymbol{p}) = f_1^0(E_p) - \Phi(\boldsymbol{p}) \frac{\mathrm{d} f_1^0(E_p)}{\mathrm{d} E_p} k_{\rm B} T_{\rm eq} = f_1^0(E_p)\{1 + \Phi(\boldsymbol{p})(1 - f_1^0(E_p))\}. \tag{20}$$

For the equilibrium distribution $f_1^0(E_p)$, we have the detailed balance condition $w_{\boldsymbol{p}\boldsymbol{p}'} f_1^0(E_{p'})(1 - f_1^0(E_p)) = w_{\boldsymbol{p}'\boldsymbol{p}} f_1^0(E_p)(1 - f_1^0(E_{p'}))$. Insertion of Equation (20) into the Boltzmann Equation (16) yields with (18):

$$\frac{e\hbar}{m_e k_{\rm B} T_{\rm eq}} \boldsymbol{E}_{\rm ext} \cdot \boldsymbol{p} f_1^0(E_p)(1 - f_1^0(E_p)) \quad = \quad \int \frac{\mathrm{d}^3 \boldsymbol{p}' \Omega_0}{(2\pi)^3} w_{\boldsymbol{p}\boldsymbol{p}'} f_1^0(E_{p'})(1 - f_1^0(E_p))(\Phi(\boldsymbol{p}') - \Phi(\boldsymbol{p})),$$

where we have used the assumption that $\Phi(\boldsymbol{p}) \propto E_{\rm ext}$ and neglected terms with a higher order of $E_{\rm ext}$ (linearized Boltzmann equation). With the definition of the *relaxation time tensor:* $\hat{\tau}(\boldsymbol{p})$

$$\Phi(\boldsymbol{p}) = \frac{e\hbar}{m_e k_{\rm B} T_{\rm eq}} \boldsymbol{E}_{\rm ext} \cdot \hat{\tau}(\boldsymbol{p}) \cdot \boldsymbol{p} \tag{21}$$

the equation reads with $\boldsymbol{e}_E = \boldsymbol{E}_{\rm ext}/|\boldsymbol{E}_{\rm ext}|$:

$$\boldsymbol{e}_E \cdot \boldsymbol{p} = \int \frac{\mathrm{d}^3 \boldsymbol{p}' \Omega_0}{(2\pi)^3} w_{\boldsymbol{p}\boldsymbol{p}'} \frac{f_1^0(E_{p'})}{f_1^0(E_p)} \boldsymbol{e}_E \cdot [\hat{\tau}(\boldsymbol{p}') \cdot \boldsymbol{p}' - \hat{\tau}(\boldsymbol{p}) \cdot \boldsymbol{p}], \tag{22}$$

which is an equation for $\hat{\tau}(\boldsymbol{p})$, where $\boldsymbol{e}_E$ is the unity vector in the direction of the external electric field $\boldsymbol{e}_E = \boldsymbol{E}_{\rm ext}/E_{\rm ext}$. The electric current density Equation (15) depends only on the deviation of the distribution function since $f_1^0(E_p)$ is an even function in $\boldsymbol{p}$ (isotropy). We obtain by insertion of Equation (20) into Equation (15):

$$\boldsymbol{j} = \frac{-e\hbar}{m_e} 2 \int \frac{\mathrm{d}^3 \boldsymbol{p}}{(2\pi)^3} \boldsymbol{p} \Phi(\boldsymbol{p}) f_1^0(E_p)(1 - f_1^0(E_p)). \tag{23}$$

For isotropic systems, we have $\hat{\tau}(\boldsymbol{p}) = \tau^{\rm transp}(E_p)$, so that the solution of Equation (22) is:

$$\tau^{\rm transp}(E_p) = \left\{ \int \frac{d^3p'\Omega_0}{(2\pi)^3} w_{pp'}(1-\cos\vartheta) \right\}^{-1} \tag{24}$$

as can be verified by insertion, ϑ is the angle between $\boldsymbol{p}$ and $\boldsymbol{p}'$. The transport relaxation time follows from $\hbar/\tau^{\rm transp}(E_p) = \pi n_i/(2p^2)\sum_q q^2 V_{\rm ei}^2(q)\delta(E_{p+q}-E_p)$; see [6] and the result below (35).

Now, the conductivity reads with Equation (19):

$$\sigma = \frac{e^2\hbar^2}{m_e^2 k_{\rm B}T_{\rm eq}} 2\int \frac{d^3\boldsymbol{p}}{(2\pi)^3} p_z^2\, \tau^{\rm transp}(E_p) f_1^0(E_p)[1-f_1^0(E_p)]. \tag{25}$$

With (24), we have derived an analytic expression for the conductivity of the Lorentz model solving the Boltzmann equation.

Screened Coulomb interaction. To give explicit expressions, we specify the electron–ion interaction by the screened Coulomb (Debye) interaction:

$$V_{\rm ei}^{\rm D}(\boldsymbol{r}) = \frac{e^2}{4\pi\epsilon_0|\boldsymbol{r}|}{\rm e}^{-\kappa|\boldsymbol{r}|}, \quad \text{with } \kappa^2 = \frac{e^2 n_e}{\epsilon_0 k_{\rm B}T_{\rm eq}}.$$

The interaction Hamiltonian H$'$ in the momentum representation is obtained from Fourier transformation with $\boldsymbol{q} = \boldsymbol{p}' - \boldsymbol{p}$. It has the matrix elements:

$$H'_{p'p} = \frac{1}{\Omega_0}\int d^3\boldsymbol{r}\, {\rm e}^{{\rm i}\boldsymbol{q}\cdot\boldsymbol{r}} \sum_i^{N_i} V_{\rm ei}^{\rm D}(\boldsymbol{r}-\boldsymbol{R}_i) = -\frac{1}{\Omega_0}\sum_i^{N_i} {\rm e}^{{\rm i}\boldsymbol{q}\cdot\boldsymbol{R}_i}\frac{e^2}{\epsilon_0(q^2+\kappa^2)} \tag{26}$$

so that $|H'_{p'p}|^2 = S_{\rm ion}(\boldsymbol{q})n_i/\Omega_0\left[e^2/\epsilon_0(q^2+\kappa^2)\right]^2$, with the ion structure factor $S_{\rm ion}(\boldsymbol{q}) = \frac{1}{N_i}\sum_i^{N_i}\sum_j^{N_i}{\rm e}^{{\rm i}\boldsymbol{q}\cdot(\boldsymbol{R}_i-\boldsymbol{R}_j)}$. The inverse relaxation time (24) follows as:

$$\tau^{-1}(E_p) = n_i \frac{1}{4\pi}\frac{e^4}{\epsilon_0^2}\frac{m_e}{\hbar^3 p^3}\Lambda(p), \tag{27}$$

with the Coulomb logarithm $\Lambda(p) = \int_0^{2p}\frac{1}{(q^2+\kappa^2)^2}q^3 dq = \ln\sqrt{1+b} - \frac{1}{2}\frac{b}{1+b}$, $b = 4p^2 k_{\rm B}T_{\rm eq}\epsilon_0/(e^2 n_e)$, where an uncorrelated ion distribution $S_{\rm ion}(\boldsymbol{q}) = 1$ is assumed. In the low-density limit at fixed temperature considered here, the Fermi distribution function is replaced by the Boltzmann distribution function. For the conductivity, we finally obtain:

$$\sigma = \frac{2^{5/2}}{\pi^{3/2}}\frac{(k_{\rm B}T_{\rm eq})^{3/2}(4\pi\epsilon_0)^2}{m_e^{1/2}e^2}\frac{1}{\Lambda(p_{\rm therm})} = \frac{n_e e^2}{m_e}\bar{\tau}^{\rm transp}, \tag{28}$$

where the Coulomb logarithm is approximated by the value of the average p, with $\hbar^2 p_{\rm therm}^2/2m_e = 3k_{\rm B}T_{\rm eq}/2$; see also [6].

Virial expansion. In the more general case where electron-electron collisions are included, we find for the hydrogen plasma ($Z = 1$) the following low-density (virial) expansion [11,12]:

$$\sigma^{-1}(T,n) = A(T)\ln n + B(T) + C(T)\,n^{1/2}\ln n \pm \ldots \tag{29}$$

with:

$$A(T) = -\frac{1}{s}\frac{e^2 m_e^{1/2}}{(4\pi\epsilon_0)^2(k_{\rm B}T)^{3/2}}. \tag{30}$$

For the Lorentz plasma, the value $s = 2^{5/2}/\pi^{3/2}$ is an *exact* result. It is changed if electron-electron collisions are included, $s = 0.591$; see [4,11–15]. At low temperatures, the plasma is degenerate, and the Fermi function for the distribution of the electrons cannot be approximated by the Boltzmann distribution function. The value of s is changed and becomes $s = 3/(4\sqrt{2\pi})$ for the limit of strong degeneracy. The values of the higher virial coefficients $B(T), C(T)$ are determined by many-body effects and the short-range behavior of the effective interaction. Expressions are given, e.g., in [11], but their exact values are under discussion.

Boltzmann entropy. The Stosszahlansatz of the Boltzmann equation is a semi-empirical assumption, which was highly and controversially discussed for a long time. It makes the Boltzmann equation an irreversible equation of evolution, which is able to describe non-equilibrium processes. It can be shown, see, e.g., [4], that a particular quantity, the Boltzmann entropy:

$$S^{\text{Boltzmann}}(t) = -k_B \sum_p f_1(\boldsymbol{p},t) \ln f_1(\boldsymbol{p},t) \approx -2\,k_B \int \frac{d^3p\,\Omega_0}{(2\pi)^3} f_1(\boldsymbol{p},t) \ln f_1(\boldsymbol{p},t) \tag{31}$$

(classical case), can increase with time and remains constant in thermodynamic equilibrium. It is a main puzzle of nonequilibrium statistical physics how this property can arise on the basis of the reversible equations of motion that define the microscopic approach in physics. It was the merits of Bogoliubov, Zubarev, and others, to give a bridge between both positions, which is presented in Section 4.

It is obvious that the Boltzmann entropy (31) is not the thermodynamic entropy defined by the second law. The evaluation in thermodynamic equilibrium yields in the classical case, where $f_1^0(E_p) \approx (n_e/2)(2\pi\hbar^2/m_e k_B T)^{3/2} \exp(-\hbar^2 p^2/2m_e k_B T)$ (see Equation (14)), the well-known relation:

$$S^{\text{Boltzmann}} = S_{\text{eq,class}}(T,\Omega_0,N_e) = \frac{3}{2} k_B n_e \Omega_0 - n_e \Omega_0 \frac{\mu_e}{T} = \frac{U_{\text{class}}}{T} - \mu_e \frac{N_e}{T} \tag{32}$$

with $U^{\text{id}}_{\text{class}} = (3/2) N_e k_B T$ valid for the ideal, noninteracting gas, neglecting the contribution of two-particle correlations, etc. The relation between the Boltzmann entropy and the correct thermodynamic entropy, which takes the correlations in the system into account, becomes clear after introducing the relevant entropy in the subsequent section.

Let us come back to the increase of the Boltzmann entropy. Owing to energy conservation, we have in the external field $\boldsymbol{E}_{\text{ext}} = E_{\text{ext}} \boldsymbol{e}_z$ the increase of internal energy of the electron system $dU_{\text{class}}/dz = eN_e E_{\text{ext}}$ if we shift all electrons by dz. The Boltzmann entropy changes as $dS^{\text{Boltzmann}}/dt = eN_e E_{\text{ext}} v/T$ where $\boldsymbol{v}$ is the mean velocity of the electron system. This value coincides with the imported power $dU_{\text{class}}/dt = \Omega_0 \boldsymbol{j} \cdot \boldsymbol{E}_{\text{ext}}$. The chemical potential μ_e, which is connected with the electron density, remains constant. If we assume that by reason of any unknown strong relaxation process, the electron system remains near the thermodynamic equilibrium, and the change of internal energy U_{class} is described by the temperature T. Then, the change of the temperature would be:

$$\frac{dT}{dt} = \frac{2}{3k_B n_e} \boldsymbol{j} \cdot \boldsymbol{E}_{\text{ext}} = \frac{2}{3k_B n_e} \sigma E_{\text{ext}}^2. \tag{33}$$

However, the properties of the open system are not time dependent in the stationary case. Because the energy balance is of second order in $\boldsymbol{E}_{\text{ext}}$, it is neglected in linear response theory. Nevertheless, it is not clear whether the kinetic energy of moving bodies can be denoted as heat and interpreted as entropy, for instance considering the motion of celestial bodies.

Energy export to ions. To have a stationary state, the gain of internal energy must be transferred to the bath. We mentioned already the emission and absorption of photons; see Equation (11) and Section 8 below. Another microscopic model for the energy transfer is the collision with ions. Kinetic theory describes not only the dissipation of the total electron momentum, but also the transfer of the kinetic energy of electrons to the ion subsystem. We consider ions with finite mass M_i so that recoil effects are possible at collisions, which are no longer elastic. A second model is the excitation of collective modes of the ion system, the phonons, which may give a different picture.

Considering the energy transfer to the ions, we have a two-temperature situation with $T_e > T_i$. According to Landau and Spitzer [15], the energy density $e_{\rm kin} = (3/2)n_e k_{\rm B} T_e$ is decreased as:

$$\frac{\mathrm{d}}{\mathrm{d}t} e_{\rm kin} = \frac{3}{2} n_e k_{\rm B}(T_e - T_i) \frac{m_e}{M_i \bar{\tau}} \tag{34}$$

with the relaxation time (slightly different from the transport relaxation time (24)),

$$\bar{\tau} = \frac{\beta \hbar^2}{6 n_e \Omega_0} \sum_p p^2 \tau(E_p) f_1^0(E_p)[1 - f_1^0(E_p)], \tag{35}$$

with $\hbar/\tau(E_p) = 2\pi n_i \sum_q V_{\rm ei}^2(q)\delta(E_{p+q} - E_p)$; see [6]. This compensates the gain $n_e e^2 E_{\rm ext}^2 \bar{\tau}/m_e$ so that:

$$k_{\rm B}(T_e - T_i) = \frac{2M_i}{3m_e^2} \bar{\tau}^2 e^2 E_{\rm ext}^2. \tag{36}$$

As already mentioned, the difference is of second order in $E_{\rm ext}$ and may be neglected in linear response theory, but it becomes large in the adiabatic limit $m_e/M_i \to 0$. The exact value of the energy current may be changed within a more detailed description, but these arguments remain. Furthermore, the correlations in the ion system given by the pair distribution function, as well as collective modes in the excitation spectrum leading to dressed states will change the magnitude of the energy transfer to the (ionic) bath.

4. The Zubarev Method of Nonequilibrium Statistical Operator

The von Neumann equation. Whereas the Boltzmann equation used the semiempirical "Stosszahlansatz", the systematic derivation of the kinetic equation for $f_1(\boldsymbol{p}, t)$ from a microscopic description was intended by Bogoliubov [10] using the principle of weakening of initial correlations. A more general formulation of this important step to work out the theory of non-equilibrium processes was given by Zubarev [1–3]. To calculate averages $\langle A \rangle^t = \mathrm{Tr}\{\rho(t) A\}$, we need the statistical operator $\rho(t) = \sum_n |\psi_n(t)\rangle\, w_n\, \langle \psi_n(t)|$, which describes the probability distribution w_n of microstates $|\psi_n(t)\rangle$ in the thermodynamic macrostate. Let us assume that the equation of motion of each realization, quantum state $|\psi_n(t)\rangle$, is given by the reversible Schrödinger equation $\mathrm{i}\hbar\partial|\psi(t)\rangle/\partial t = \mathrm{H}^t|\psi(t)\rangle$. The Hamiltonian H^t may contain time-dependent external fields (for an isolated system in equilibrium, usually, the energy eigenfunctions are identified with the eigenstates of ρ, and the time evolution refers only to the phase of $|\psi_n(t)\rangle$). Then, the von Neumann equation follows as the equation of motion for the statistical operator,

$$\frac{\partial}{\partial t}\rho(t) + \frac{\mathrm{i}}{\hbar}\left[\mathrm{H}^t, \rho(t)\right] = 0. \tag{37}$$

Despite its character as a fundamental equation of motion in statistical physics, the von Neumann equation has two shortcomings:

(i) To determine $\rho(t)$, the initial value problem has to be solved.
(ii) As a reversible equation of motion, it cannot describe irreversible processes.

The solution of (i) is known for thermodynamic equilibrium, where $\rho(t) = \rho_{\rm eq}$ does not depend on time. We need an additional principle to determine $\rho_{\rm eq}$, the maximum of information entropy:

$$S_{\rm inf}[\rho] = -\mathrm{Tr}\{\rho \ln \rho\} \tag{38}$$

for arbitrary ρ that are consistent with the given conditions $\mathrm{Tr}\{\rho\} = 1$ (normalization) and the given constants of motion C_n:

$$\mathrm{Tr}\{\rho C_n\} = \langle C_n \rangle. \tag{39}$$

These are external conditions that describe how we influence the system, for instance preparing the volume and particle number and coupling this to a thermal bath. These self-consistency conditions can be implemented in the variational principle using the method of Lagrange multipliers; see [1]. The corresponding maximum value for $S_{\mathrm{inf}}[\rho]$:

$$S_{\mathrm{eq}}[\rho_{\mathrm{eq}}] = -k_{\mathrm{B}} \mathrm{Tr}\{\rho_{\mathrm{eq}} \ln \rho_{\mathrm{eq}}\} \tag{40}$$

is the equilibrium entropy of the system at given constraints $\langle C_n \rangle$, and k_{B} is the Boltzmann constant.

Well-known solutions of this variational principle are the Gibbs ensembles for thermodynamic equilibrium. For instance, in the grand canonical ensemble, the average value of energy is realized by a Lagrange multiplier, which is identified as temperature T, and the average value of particle numbers N_c is realized by Lagrange multipliers, which are identified as chemical potentials μ_c. The Lagrange multipliers are eliminated by solving Equation (39). The corresponding relations are known as the equations of state.

With respect to Item (ii), the expression $\mathrm{Tr}\{\rho(t) \ln \rho(t)\}$ cannot be used to define the entropy in non-equilibrium, because it cannot increase with time. Using the von Neumann equation,

$$\frac{\mathrm{d}}{\mathrm{d}t} \left[\mathrm{Tr}\{\rho(t) \ln \rho(t)\}\right] = 0 \tag{41}$$

follows. The discrepancy with the second law of thermodynamics that entropy may increase with time for a system in nonequilibrium can be solved according to Zubarev by a modification of the von Neumann equation.

The relevant statistical operator. Zubarev [1] proposed to extend the concept of information theory also to construct a relevant statistical operator $\rho_{\mathrm{rel}}(t)$ for given averages of relevant observables $\{B_n\}$ that are not constants of motion, but may change with time. Now, at each time step t, we find the maximum of information entropy solving:

$$-\,\delta\left[\mathrm{Tr}\{\rho_{\mathrm{rel}}(t) \ln \rho_{\mathrm{rel}}(t)\}\right] = 0 \tag{42}$$

with the self-consistency conditions:

$$\mathrm{Tr}\,\{\rho_{\mathrm{rel}}(t) B_n\} \equiv \langle B_n \rangle^t_{\mathrm{rel}} = \langle B_n \rangle^t. \tag{43}$$

and $\mathrm{Tr}\{\rho_{\mathrm{rel}}(t)\} = 1$. We use time-dependent Lagrange multipliers $\lambda_n(t)$ to account for the self-consistency conditions (43). The solution of the variational problem is the generalized Gibbs distribution:

$$\rho_{\mathrm{rel}}(t) = \mathrm{e}^{-\Phi(t) - \sum\limits_n \lambda_n(t) B_n}, \qquad \Phi(t) = \ln\, \mathrm{Tr}\left\{\mathrm{e}^{-\sum\limits_n \lambda_n(t) B_n}\right\}, \tag{44}$$

where, as in the equilibrium case, the Lagrange multipliers $\lambda_n(t)$ (thermodynamic parameters) are determined by the self-consistency conditions (43) and have to be eliminated. With the thermodynamic potential $\Phi(t)$ (Massieux–Planck function), the normalization condition is realized.

In the generalization of the equilibrium cases, the maximum of information entropy can be considered as the *relevant entropy in nonequilibrium*:

$$S_{\mathrm{rel}}(t) = -k_{\mathrm{B}}\, \mathrm{Tr}\,\{\rho_{\mathrm{rel}}(t)\ \ln \rho_{\mathrm{rel}}(t)\}\,. \tag{45}$$

Maxwell relations similar to the relations known from equilibrium thermodynamics can be derived [1]. In addition, we find for the production of relevant entropy (see also [4]),

$$\frac{\mathrm{d}S_{\mathrm{rel}}(t)}{\mathrm{d}t} = \sum_n \lambda_n(t) \frac{\mathrm{i}}{\hbar} \langle [\mathrm{H}^t, \mathrm{B}_n] \rangle^t = \sum_n \lambda_n(t) \langle \dot{\mathrm{B}}_n \rangle^t. \tag{46}$$

This relation is well known from the thermodynamics of irreversible processes. In contrast to Equation (41), this expression can have a positive value so that $S_{\mathrm{rel}}(t)$ can increase with time.

Coming back to the electrical conductivity as an example for an irreversible process, the nonequilibrium state is characterized by the current density $\boldsymbol{j}$, and with the density of heat production $\boldsymbol{j} \cdot \boldsymbol{E}_{\mathrm{ext}} = \sigma \boldsymbol{E}_{\mathrm{ext}}^2$, Equation (2), the density of entropy production is given by:

$$\frac{\mathrm{d}S_{\mathrm{rel}}(t)}{\mathrm{d}t} = \frac{\Omega_0}{T} \boldsymbol{j} \cdot \boldsymbol{E}_{\mathrm{ext}} = \frac{\Omega_0}{T} \sigma \boldsymbol{E}_{\mathrm{ext}}^2. \tag{47}$$

This result is obtained if the position $\mathbf{R}$ of the electrons, which couples to the external field, is considered as a relevant observable, so that $\langle \dot{\mathbf{R}} \rangle = (\hbar / m_e) \langle \mathbf{P} \rangle = -(\Omega_0 / e) \boldsymbol{j}$. The Hamiltonian contains also the external field $\boldsymbol{E}_{\mathrm{ext}}$, which must be compensated to obtain the stationary, homogeneous case. For this, the value $\vec{\lambda} = \beta \boldsymbol{E}_{\mathrm{ext}}$ is needed. It acts like a position-dependent chemical potential $\mu_{\mathrm{rel}}(\boldsymbol{r})$, which couples to the local electron density. Other choices of relevant observables are given below in Section 5.

A well-known example is the Boltzmann entropy (31). This expression is the relevant entropy in nonequilibrium if the single-particle distribution function $f_1(\boldsymbol{p}, t)$ is considered as a relevant observable. It can increase with time, as proven by the famous H-theorem. However, it is not the correct thermodynamic entropy, because in thermodynamic equilibrium, the contribution of correlations to the potential energy is missing.

The introduction of the relevant statistical operator does not solve the problem of nonequilibrium statistical physics. It is a semiempirical approach, and the selection of the set of relevant observables $\{\mathrm{B}_n\}$ is arbitrary, but determines the result for the relevant entropy. $S_{\mathrm{rel}}(t)$ is not the thermodynamic entropy because it is based on the arbitrary choice of the set $\{\mathrm{B}_n\}$ of relevant observables, and not all possible variables are correctly reproduced. The possible increase of the relevant entropy with time (47) is the effect of coarse graining introducing the reduced set of relevant observables. A main deficit is that it does not respect the equations of motion; it does not obey the Liouville-von Neumann equation. The dependence on time is parametric, but not dynamic. An important step to solve the problem of dynamics is given by the Zubarev method of the Nonequilibrium Statistical Operator (NSO).

The Zubarev solution of the initial value problem. The formal solution of the von Neumann Equation (37) is easily found,

$$\rho(t) = \mathrm{U}(t, t_0) \rho(t_0) \mathrm{U}^\dagger(t, t_0). \tag{48}$$

The unitary time evolution operator $\mathrm{U}(t, t_0)$ is the solution of the differential equation:

$$\mathrm{i}\hbar \frac{\partial}{\partial t} \mathrm{U}(t, t_0) = \mathrm{H}^t \mathrm{U}(t, t_0), \tag{49}$$

with the initial condition $\mathrm{U}(t_0, t_0) = 1$. If the Hamiltonian is not time dependent, we have:

$$\mathrm{U}(t, t_0) = \mathrm{e}^{-\frac{\mathrm{i}}{\hbar} \mathrm{H}(t - t_0)}. \tag{50}$$

If the Hamiltonian H^t is time dependent, the solution is given by a time-ordered exponent.

However, we do not know the initial state $\rho(t_0)$. An answer was given by Zubarev [1]. In the first step, we can take instead $\rho(t_0)$ the relevant statistical operator $\rho_{\mathrm{rel}}(t_0)$ at some initial time t_0,

$$\rho_{t_0}(t) = \mathrm{U}(t, t_0) \rho_{\mathrm{rel}}(t_0) \mathrm{U}^\dagger(t, t_0). \tag{51}$$

According to the Bogoliubov principle of the weakening of initial correlations [10], the missing correlations that are not correctly implemented in $\rho_{\rm rel}(t_0)$ are produced by the dynamical evolution of the system. This procedure is well known from molecular dynamics simulations where, starting from an artificial initial configuration, the stationary distribution is approximated after an initial relaxation time (synchronization). The crucial point is that one should consider the limit $t_0 \to -\infty$ so that enough time is available to establish all missing correlations. As known from ergodic theory, at least the conserved observables have to be correctly implemented in $\rho_{\rm rel}(t_0)$ because they cannot be produced dynamically. The more observables $\{B_n\}$ are correctly described by $\rho_{\rm rel}(t_0)$, the less time is necessary to produce the remaining correlations. Notice that the self-consistency conditions (43) valid at t_0 are not automatically valid also at t averaging with $\rho_{t_0}(t)$, if the time evolution according to Equation (51) is taken. Below, we discuss the case of incomplete dynamics if the open system is in contact with a bath.

In the second step, instead of selecting a special instant of time t_0, the average over the past is performed. According to Abel's theorem (see [1–3]), the limit $t_0 \to -\infty$ can be replaced by the limit $\epsilon \to +0$ in the expression:

$$\rho_\epsilon(t) = \epsilon \int_{-\infty}^{t} e^{\epsilon(t_1-t)} U(t,t_1)\rho_{\rm rel}(t_1)U^\dagger(t,t_1)dt_1. \tag{52}$$

This averaging over different initial time instants means a mixing of phases so that long-living oscillations are damped out. Finally, we obtain the nonequilibrium statistical operator as:

$$\rho_{\rm NSO}(t) = \lim_{\epsilon\to 0} \rho_\epsilon(t) \, . \tag{53}$$

This way, $\rho_{\rm rel}(t_1)$ for all times $-\infty < t_1 < t$ serves as the initial condition to solve the Liouville–von Neumann equation according to the Bogoliubov principle of weakening of initial correlations. The past that is of relevance, given by the relaxation time τ, becomes shorter, if the relevant (long-living) correlations are already correctly implemented. The limit $\epsilon \to +0$ is to be considered as $\epsilon \ll 1/\tau$. The limit $\epsilon \to +0$ has to be performed after the thermodynamic limit.

Selection of the set of relevant observables. An open issue is the appropriate selection of the set of relevant observables $\{B_n\}$ to characterize the nonequilibrium state of the system. The method of the nonequilibrium statistical operator allows one to extend the set of relevant observables arbitrarily so that the choice of the set of relevant observables seems to be irrelevant. All missing correlations are produced dynamically. As a minimum, the constants of motion C_n have to be included because their relaxation time is infinite, and their averages cannot be produced dynamically. The resulting $\rho_{\rm NSO}(t)$ (53) should not depend on the (arbitrary) choice of relevant observables $\{B_n\}$ if the limit $\epsilon \to 0$ is correctly performed. However, usually perturbation theory is applied, so that the result will depend on the selection of the set of relevant observables. The inclusion of long-living correlations into $\{B_n\}$ allows one to use lower order perturbation expansions to obtain acceptable results. In the context with the electrical conductivity, the selection of different sets of relevant observables has been extensively discussed; see, e.g., [4–6,11–14,16].

Entropy in the Zubarev NSO approach. An intricate problem is the definition of entropy for the nonequilibrium state. In nonequilibrium, entropy is produced, as investigated in the phenomenological approach to the thermodynamics of irreversible processes, considering currents induced by the generalized forces. Such a behavior occurs for the relevant entropy defined by the relevant distribution (45). A famous example that shows the increase of the relevant entropy (31) with time is the Boltzmann H (capital eta) theorem, where the relevant observables to define the nonequilibrium state is the single particle distribution function.

Note that the entropy puzzle cannot be solved by the relevant entropy. Not only the well-defined thermodynamic entropy in equilibrium is not reproduced. A so-called coarse graining has been performed. The information about the state is reduced because the degrees of freedom to describe the system are reduced. This may be an averaging in phase space over small cells. Furthermore, the average over different phases of the quantum state, the destruction of quantum interference (dephasing), and other projection techniques will destroy information. The loss of information then gives the increase of entropy. This procedure is artificial, depending on our way of describing the details of a process, or anthropomorphic, related to our technical possibilities to prepare and measure the state of a system and control the dynamics. In certain situations, such as quantum master equations (see [17,18]), kinetic theory (see [16]), and linear response theory (see [19]), the choice of relevant observables becomes quite natural (see also [4]). In general, there is no first principle approach that gives the decision about how the relevant degrees of freedom have to be selected out. From a fundamental point of view, this situation is unsatisfactory.

A possible definition of the entropy would be:

$$S_{\rm NSO}(t) = -k_{\rm B} {\rm Tr}\left\{\rho_{\rm NSO}(t) \ln \rho_{\rm NSO}(t)\right\} . \tag{54}$$

It is an open question whether the entropy $S_{\rm NSO}(t)$ will increase also in the limit $\epsilon \to +0$. Coming back to our example of DC conductivity, the stationary state means that $\rho_{\rm NSO}(t)$ should not depend on time t. The entropy in the open system is constant, but there is also a constant production of entropy, which is not derived from (54).

The extended Liouville–von Neumann equation. We consider a closed system with known dynamics H^t. The nonequilibrium statistical operator $\rho_\epsilon(t)$, Equation (52), obeys the extended von Neumann equation:

$$\frac{\partial \rho_\epsilon(t)}{\partial t} + \frac{\rm i}{\hbar}[\mathrm{H}^t, \rho_\epsilon(t)] = -\epsilon(\rho_\epsilon(t) - \rho_{\rm rel}(t)). \tag{55}$$

as can be seen after simple derivation with respect to time. In contrast to the von Neumann Equation (37), a source term arises on the right-hand side that becomes infinitesimally small in the limit $\epsilon \to +0$. This source term breaks the time inversion symmetry so that, for any finite value of ϵ, the solution $\rho_\epsilon(t)$ describes in general an irreversible evolution with time.

The source term implements the "initial condition" in the equation of motion as expressed by $\rho_{\rm rel}(t)$. Formally, the source term looks like a relaxation process. In addition to the internal dynamics, the system evolves towards the relevant distribution.

The construction of the source term is such that the time evolution of the relevant variables is not affected by the source term (we use the invariance of the trace with respect to cyclic permutations),

$$\frac{\rm d}{{\rm d}t}\langle \mathrm{B}_n\rangle^t = {\rm Tr}\left\{\frac{\partial \rho_\epsilon(t)}{\partial t}\mathrm{B}_n\right\} = -{\rm Tr}\left\{\frac{\rm i}{\hbar}[\mathrm{H}^t, \rho_\epsilon(t)]\mathrm{B}_n\right\} - \epsilon\left[\langle \mathrm{B}_n\rangle^t - \langle \mathrm{B}_n\rangle^t_{\rm rel}\right] = \left\langle \frac{\rm i}{\hbar}[\mathrm{H}^t, \mathrm{B}_n]\right\rangle^t = \langle \dot{\mathrm{B}}_n\rangle^t . \tag{56}$$

The source term cancels because of the self-consistency conditions (43). Thus, the time evolution of the relevant observables satisfies the dynamical equations of motion according to the Hamiltonian H^t.

Any real system is in contact with the surroundings. The intrinsic dynamics described by the Hamiltonian H^t is modified owing to the coupling of the open system to the bath. Within the quantum master equation approach (see Section 6 below), we can approximate the influence term describing the coupling to the bath by a relaxation term similar to the source term. However, at present, we consider the source term as a purely mathematical tool to select the retarded solution of the Liouville–von Neumann equation, and physical results are obtained only after performing the limit $\epsilon \to 0$.

5. Generalized Linear Response Theory

Linearization of the NSO. We use the Zubarev NSO method to calculate the electrical conductivity. It unifies kinetic theory and linear response theory. An extended discussion of this generalized linear response theory can be found in the literature [4,6,11,13,14,16], which will not be repeated here.

The main idea is to consider small fluctuations near the thermodynamic equilibrium. In the relevant statistical operator (44) containing the observables B_n with the Lagrange parameters $\lambda_n(t)$, we extract the conserved observables C_n with the Lagrange parameters β, μ_e, which determine the thermodynamic equilibrium. The remaining observables with Lagrange parameters $\beta F_n(t)$ are considered as small fluctuations, so that we can expand with respect to $F_n(t)$. In first order, we have:

$$\rho_{\rm rel}(t) = \rho_{\rm eq} + \beta \int_0^1 d\lambda \sum_n F_n(t)\, B_n(i\hbar\beta\lambda)\, \rho_{\rm eq}. \tag{57}$$

Here, we made use of the modified Heisenberg picture $O(\tau) = \exp(i\mathcal{H}\tau/\hbar) O \exp(-i\mathcal{H}\tau/\hbar)$ with $\tau \to i\hbar\beta\lambda$ and replacing in the exponents H_S by $\mathcal{H} = H_S - \mu_e N_e$. Note that $\mathcal{H}$ does not contain the external field H_F^t. Because of homogeneity, in $\rho_{\rm rel}$, any position-dependent external field has to be compensated by a position-dependent chemical potential.

After integration by parts, the NSO (52) with $H^t = H_S + H_F^t$ has the form:

$$\rho_\epsilon(t) = \rho_{\rm rel}(t) - \int_{-\infty}^{t} dt_1 e^{\epsilon(t_1-t)} U(t,t_1) \left\{ \frac{i}{\hbar} \left[(H_S + H_F^{t_1}), \rho_{\rm rel}(t_1) \right] + \frac{\partial}{\partial t_1} \rho_{\rm rel}(t_1) \right\} U^\dagger(t,t_1). \tag{58}$$

In our case of DC conductivity, where $H_F^t = e\boldsymbol{E}_{\rm ext} \cdot \mathbf{R}$ (5), we expand up to first order in $E_{\rm ext}$ and assume $F_n \propto E_{\rm ext}$. Since H_S commutes with the equilibrium $\rho_{\rm eq}$, the curly bracket is of order $\mathcal{O}(E_{\rm ext})$. In the stationary state, the statistical operators are not depending on t. With $(i/\hbar)[H_S, \mathbf{R}] = \mathbf{P}/m_e$, we arrive at (in this section, we use the notation $\mathbf{P} = \sum_i^{N_e} \hbar \mathbf{p}_i$ for the total momentum):

$$\rho_\epsilon = \rho_{\rm rel} - \beta \int_{-\infty}^{0} dt_1\, e^{\epsilon t_1} \int_0^1 d\lambda \left[-\frac{e}{m_e} \boldsymbol{E}_{\rm ext} \cdot \mathbf{P}(i\lambda\beta\hbar + t_1)\, \rho_{\rm eq} + \sum_n F_n\, \dot{B}_n(i\lambda\beta\hbar + t_1)\, \rho_{\rm eq} \right]. \tag{59}$$

In the stationary case considered here, there is no dependence of $\boldsymbol{E}_{\rm ext}(t), \rho_\epsilon(t), \rho_{\rm rel}(t), F_n(t)$ on time t. After fully linearizing the statistical operator (59) with (57), we have for the electrical current density:

$$j = \frac{e}{m_e\Omega_0} \langle \mathbf{P} \rangle = \frac{e\beta}{m_e\Omega_0} \left\{ \sum_n \left[(\mathbf{P}|B_n) - \langle \mathbf{P}; \dot{B}_n \rangle_{i\epsilon} \right] F_n + \langle \mathbf{P}; \mathbf{P} \rangle_{i\epsilon} \cdot \frac{e}{m_e} \boldsymbol{E}_{\rm ext} \right\} = \sigma \boldsymbol{E}_{\rm ext}. \tag{60}$$

Here, we introduced the Kubo scalar product (the particle number commutes with the observables):

$$(A\,|\,B) = \int_0^1 d\lambda {\rm Tr} \left\{ A\, e^{-\lambda\beta\mathcal{H}}\, B\, e^{\lambda\beta\mathcal{H}}\, \rho_{\rm eq} \right\} = \int_0^1 d\lambda\, {\rm Tr} \left\{ A\, B(i\lambda\beta\hbar)\, \rho_{\rm eq} \right\}, \tag{61}$$

and its Laplace transform, the thermodynamic correlation function:

$$\langle A; B \rangle_z = \int_{-\infty}^{0} dt\, e^{-izt} (A\,|\,B(t)) = \int_0^\infty dt\, e^{izt} (A(t)\,|\,B). \tag{62}$$

Note that similar expressions can be given for time-dependent (periodic) fields [4,16]. In the classical limit where the variables commute, additional integrals expanding the exponential are avoided.

Kubo formula. In particular, for the empty set of relevant fluctuations $\{B_n\}$ so that $\rho_{\rm rel} = \rho_{\rm eq}$, we obtain the Kubo formula (we choose $\boldsymbol{j}, \boldsymbol{E}_{\rm ext}$ parallel to the z axis so that $P = \mathbf{P} \cdot \boldsymbol{e}_z$ is the z component of $\mathbf{P}$):

$$\sigma_{\rm DC}^{\rm Kubo} = \frac{e^2\beta}{m_e^2\Omega_0} \langle P; P \rangle_{i\epsilon}. \tag{63}$$

A similar expression can also be given for the dynamical, wave-number vector-dependent conductivity $\sigma(\boldsymbol{q},\omega)$, which is related to other quantities such as the response function, the dielectric function, or the polarization function (see [4,14,16,20]). The relation (63) is a special form of the Fluctuation-Dissipation Theorem (FDT), which connects the time evolution of equilibrium fluctuations, here the current, with transport coefficients, here the conductivity.

In the lowest order of perturbation theory, we have the result:

$$\sigma_{\rm DC}^{\rm Kubo,0} = \frac{n_e e^2}{m_e}\frac{1}{\epsilon} \tag{64}$$

which diverges in the limit $\epsilon \to 0$. Perturbation theory cannot be applied immediately to evaluate the DC conductivity for interacting charged particles. The use of perturbation theory for the Kubo formula and performing partial summations are discussed in [6]. To avoid perturbation theory, the Kubo formula can be evaluated numerically, e.g., Molecular Dynamics (MD) simulations. Most recent approaches use the Kubo–Greenwood formula [6] and treat the electron system via Density-Functional Theory (DFT). In this approach also, an ϵ-broadening of the δ-like contributions is needed.

Elimination of the Lagrange parameters F_n. The Lagrange parameters F_n must be eliminated with Equation (43). After linearization (59), we find the response equations:

$$\langle {\rm B}_m\rangle - \langle {\rm B}_m\rangle_{\rm rel} = -\sum_n \langle {\rm B}_m; \dot{\rm B}_n\rangle_{i\epsilon} F_n + \langle {\rm B}_m; {\rm P}\rangle_{i\epsilon}\frac{e}{m_e}E_{\rm ext} = 0 \tag{65}$$

to determine the response parameters F_n, and the number of equations coincides with the number of variables to be determined. The coefficients of this linear system:

$$\sum_n P_{mn}F_n = D_m E_{\rm ext} \tag{66}$$

of equations are given by equilibrium correlation functions. Using Cramer's rule, the response parameters F_n are found to be proportional to the external field $\boldsymbol{E}_{\rm ext}$ with coefficients that are ratios of two determinants. The evaluation of the matrix elements that are equilibrium correlation functions can be performed using different methods such as numerical simulations, quantum statistical perturbation theories such as thermodynamic Green functions and Feynman diagrams, path integral methods, etc. Simple expressions for the conductivity are obtained if **P** is included in the set of relevant observables $\{{\rm B}_n\}$.

Force-force correlation function. The nonequilibrium state is characterized by the electrical current density $j = e/(m_e\Omega_0)\langle {\rm P}\rangle$, which is related to the total momentum ${\rm P} = \hbar\sum_i {\rm p}_{i,z}$. This motivates selecting it as the relevant observable ${\rm B}_n \to {\rm P}$. After the solution of the response equation and performing partial integrations [4,16], the resistance R in the static limit follows as [21]:

$$R = \frac{1}{\sigma} = \frac{\Omega_0\beta}{e^2N_e^2}\frac{\langle\dot{\rm P};\dot{\rm P}\rangle_{i\epsilon}}{1+\dfrac{\beta}{m_eN_e}\langle{\rm P};\dot{\rm P}\rangle_{i\epsilon}} = \frac{\Omega_0\beta}{e^2N_e^2}\langle\dot{\rm P}_{\rm st};\dot{\rm P}_{\rm st}\rangle_{i\epsilon}, \tag{67}$$

where $\dot{\rm P}_{\rm st} = \dot{\rm P} - \frac{\langle\dot{\rm P};{\rm P}\rangle_{i\epsilon}}{\langle{\rm P};{\rm P}\rangle_{i\epsilon}}{\rm P}$ is the stochastic part of the force, which is orthogonal (independent) on P (cf. the Langevin approach to Brownian motion), $\langle\dot{\rm P}_{\rm st};{\rm P}\rangle_{i\epsilon} = 0$. According to the so-called *second fluctuation-dissipation theorem*, the resistivity is given by the equilibrium correlation function of stochastic forces.

Now, perturbation theory can be applied, and in Born approximation, the Ziman formula, a standard result of transport theory, is obtained. We conclude that the use of relevant observables gives a better starting point for perturbation theory. In contrast to the Kubo formula that starts from thermal equilibrium as the initial state, the correct current is already reproduced in the initial state and must not be created by the dynamical evolution.

We give the result for the force-force correlation function in Born approximation:

$$\begin{aligned}\langle \dot{\mathrm{P}};\dot{\mathrm{P}}\rangle_{\mathrm{i}\epsilon} &= -\sum_{p,p',q,q'}\int_{-\infty}^{0} dt\, e^{\epsilon t}\int_0^1 d\lambda\, e^{\frac{i}{\hbar}(E_p-E_{p+q})(t-i\hbar\beta\lambda)} V_q V_{q'} q_z q'_z \langle a^\dagger_{p+q} a_p a^\dagger_{p'+q'} a_{p'}\rangle_{\mathrm{eq}} \\ &= \sum_{p,q}|V_q|^2\delta(E_p-E_{p+q}) f_p(1-f_p)\pi\hbar\frac{q^2}{3}. \end{aligned} \tag{68}$$

For the Debye potential, we obtain the result (28), but with the prefactor $s = 3/(4\sqrt{2\pi})$.

Despite the excellent results using the Ziman formula in solid and liquid metals where the electrons are strongly degenerate, we cannot conclude that the result (67) with (68) for the conductivity is already correct for low-density plasmas (the non-degenerate limit if T remains constant) in the lowest order of perturbation theory considered here. The prefactor $s = 3/(4\sqrt{2\pi})$ is wrong. If we go to the next order of interaction, divergent contributions arise. These divergences can be avoided by performing a partial summation, which will also change the coefficients in Equation (29), which are obtained in the lowest order of the perturbation expansion. The divergent contributions can also be avoided extending the set of relevant observables $\{\mathrm{B}_n\}$ (see Ref. [11]).

Higher moments of the single-particle distribution function. Besides the electrical current, also other deviations from thermal equilibrium can occur in the stationary nonequilibrium state such as a thermal current. In general, for homogeneous systems, we can consider arbitrary moments of the single-particle distribution function:

$$\mathrm{P}_n = \sum_p \hbar p_z (\beta E_p)^{n/2} a^\dagger_p a_p \tag{69}$$

as set of relevant observables $\{\mathrm{B}_n\}$. It can be shown that with increasing the number of moments, the result:

$$\sigma = s\frac{(k_\mathrm{B})^{3/2}(4\pi\epsilon_0))^2}{m_e^{1/2}e^2}\frac{1}{\Lambda(p_{\mathrm{therm}})} \tag{70}$$

(cf. Equation (29)) is improved, as can be shown with the Kohler variational principle; see [13,16]. The value $s = 3/(4\sqrt{2\pi})$ obtained from the single-moment approach is increasing to the limiting value $s = 2^{5/2}/\pi^{3/2}$. For details, see [4,13,14], where also other thermoelectric effects in plasmas are considered.

Single-particle distribution function and the general form of the linearized Boltzmann equation. Kinetic equations are obtained if the occupation numbers n_p of single-(quasi-) particle states $|p\rangle$ are taken as the set of relevant observables $\{\mathrm{B}_n\}$. In thermal equilibrium, neglecting interactions, the averaged occupation numbers of the single-electron states are given by the Fermi distribution function (14), $\langle \mathrm{n}_p\rangle_{\mathrm{eq}} = \mathrm{Tr}\{\rho_{\mathrm{eq}}\mathrm{n}_p\} = f_1^0(E_p)$. We consider the fluctuations of the occupation numbers $\Delta \mathrm{n}_p = \mathrm{n}_p - f_1^0(E_p)$ as relevant observables. The response equations, which eliminate the corresponding response parameters $F_p(t)$, have the structure of a linear system of coupled Boltzmann equations for the quasiparticles (see [16]):

$$\frac{e}{m_e}\boldsymbol{E}_{\mathrm{ext}}\cdot[(\mathbf{P}|\mathrm{n}_p) + \langle \mathbf{P};\dot{\mathrm{n}}_p\rangle_{i\epsilon}] = \sum_{p'} F_{p'} P_{p'p}\,, \tag{71}$$

with $P_{p'p} = (\dot{\mathrm{n}}_{p'}|\Delta\mathrm{n}_p) + \langle\dot{\mathrm{n}}_{p'};\dot{\mathrm{n}}_p\rangle_{\mathrm{i}\epsilon}$. The response parameters $F_p(t)$ are related to the averaged occupation numbers as:

$$f_1(p) = \mathrm{Tr}\{\rho(t)\mathrm{n}_p\} = f_1^0(E_p) + \beta\sum_{p'} F_{p'}(\Delta\mathrm{n}_{p'}|\Delta\mathrm{n}_p)\,. \tag{72}$$

The general form of the linear Boltzmann equation (71) can be compared with the expression obtained from kinetic theory. The left-hand side can be interpreted as the drift term, where self-energy effects are included in the correlation function $\langle \mathbf{P}; \dot{\mathrm{n}}_p \rangle_{\mathrm{i}\epsilon}$. The collision operator is given by $\langle \dot{\mathrm{n}}_{p'}; \dot{\mathrm{n}}_p \rangle_{\mathrm{i}\epsilon}$. Because the operators n_p are commuting, from the Kubo identity, it follows $(\dot{\mathrm{n}}_{p'}|\mathrm{n}_p) = (1/\hbar\beta)\langle[\mathrm{n}_{p'}, \mathrm{n}_p]\rangle = 0$. More precisely, the collision operator can be expressed in terms of the correlation function of the stochastic part of fluctuations; cf. Equation (67). The further evaluation of the conductivity is according to the kinetic approach in Section 3.

Two-particle distribution function, bound states. The question arises whether the conductivity, in particular the virial coefficient $A(T)$ (29) for the Lorentz plasma, is modified if the set of relevant observables is further extended. In the next step, we can consider the non-equilibrium two-particle distributions; see [4,11]. However, the corresponding corrections appear only in higher orders of the virial expansion (29). It seems that the virial coefficient $A(T)$ is an exact result. However, it is not clear whether in higher orders of density, singularities appear that can modify this result after partial summation of singular terms.

Another interesting quantum phenomenon is the formation of bound states. Such two-particle correlations can also be used to extend the set of relevant observables [22,23]. In particular, in low-density plasmas, such correlations are difficult to form dynamically and need a long relaxation time because a third particle is needed to fulfill the conservation laws. However, at fixed T, the concentration of bound states becomes small in the low density limit according to the mass action law.

We considered the interaction with uncorrelated ions, with structure factor $S(\boldsymbol{q}) = 1$. Multiple scattering by ordered ions with structure factor $S(\boldsymbol{q}) \neq 1$ will modify the result (27). In particular, for a perfect lattice, the electron system is described by Bloch states forming a band structure, and scattering disappears so that the conductivity becomes infinite (64).

Here, a main problem emerges. The electron Hamiltonian of the adiabatic Lorentz model (4) is bilinear and can, in principle, be diagonalized. We obtain stationary states as the exact solution, and the question arises from where dissipation in the system is coming. If an initial state is prepared with definite momentum by superposition of such exact solutions, the scattering into different directions of momentum is similar to the spreading out of a wave packet, and dissipation is only possible if the coherence is destroyed. The scattering by ions changes the total momentum of the electron system, but this cannot be considered as a dissipative process. In addition, for a closed circuit discussed above, we do not have asymptotically-free momentum states. Nevertheless, dissipation happens in real systems.

6. Open Systems

Flow of energy. We presented a nice and consistent approach to the electrical conductivity. The generalized linear response theory reproduces not only the low-density limit, which is also correctly described by kinetic theory, but gives the opportunity to treat also dense charged particle systems. However, the flow of energy is not correctly described. Because this is of second order in the external field, which determines the deviation from equilibrium, the account of the energy flow will not modify the results obtained in linear response theory.

Let us consider the system energy $\mathrm{H_S}$ (4). The dynamics is described by the Hamiltonian $\mathrm{H}^t = \mathrm{H_S} + \mathrm{H}^t_{\mathrm{F}}$, which includes the field $\boldsymbol{E}_{\mathrm{ext}}(t)$. Using the extended von Neumann equation, we calculate the change of the energy of the electron system:

$$\frac{\mathrm{d}}{\mathrm{d}t}\mathrm{Tr}\left\{\rho(t)\mathrm{H_S}\right\} = \mathrm{Tr}\left\{\rho(t)\frac{\mathrm{i}}{\hbar}[\mathrm{H}^t_{\mathrm{F}}, \mathrm{H_S}]\right\} - \epsilon\mathrm{Tr}\left\{[\rho(t) - \rho_{\mathrm{rel}}(t)]\mathrm{H_S}\right\}. \tag{73}$$

We immediately see the import of electrical power $\Omega_0 \boldsymbol{j} \cdot \boldsymbol{E}_{\mathrm{ext}}$ from the first term on the right-hand side. The second term becomes zero for $\epsilon \to 0$. Consequently, the average system energy is increasing with time.

This is in contradiction to the demand of a stationary, homogeneous solution with constant current density j. Electrons that enter the open system have the same properties (average particle density, average current density, average energy density, temperature) as electrons that leave the system, as demanded by homogeneity. As discussed earlier, this contradiction is solved if the coupling to a bath is taken into account. Then, the dynamical evolution of the system according to $\mathrm{H}^t = \mathrm{H_S} + \mathrm{H_F^t}$ is not complete, and the influence of the bath is missing. We have to treat an open system where energy can be exported by coupling to a bath. We expect that the details of this coupling are not relevant for the calculation of the conductivity. However, the bath coupling is of relevance for the production of entropy. We discuss here the coupling to a system of harmonic oscillators as realized by phonons or photons. In the subsequent section, we show how the Zubarev method of the NSO may be modified to include the effects of the bath.

Harmonic-oscillator bath. The system of harmonic oscillators describing the excitations with wave vector $\boldsymbol{q}$ and polarization $\boldsymbol{e}_q$ is given by the Hamiltonian:

$$\mathrm{H_{h.o.}} = \sum_q \omega_q \mathrm{b}_q^\dagger \mathrm{b}_q. \tag{74}$$

As the dispersion relation, we take $\omega_q = c|\boldsymbol{q}|$ with c as the velocity of light for the photon system or as the velocity of sound for acoustic phonons. For the interaction of the electron system with the phonon bath, the standard Froehlich expression:

$$\mathrm{H_{int}} = \frac{\mathrm{i}c_{\mathrm{ep}}}{\Omega_0^{1/2}} \sum_{p,q} \sqrt{q}\, \mathrm{a}_{p+q}^\dagger \mathrm{a}_p (\mathrm{b}_q - \mathrm{b}_q^\dagger) \tag{75}$$

can be taken, with the electron-phonon coupling parameter $c_{\mathrm{ep}} \propto M_i^{-1/2}$. Note that we can also treat the electron–phonon interaction as a process to produce electrical conductivity [19].

Photon bath. In this work, we focus on the electron–photon interaction $\mathrm{H_{int}} = e\sum_i^{N_e} \mathbf{r_i} \cdot \mathbf{E}$. In contrast to Equation (5) where $\boldsymbol{E}_{\mathrm{ext}}(\boldsymbol{r},t)$ denotes an external field, $\mathbf{E}(\boldsymbol{r},t)$ is the operator of the fluctuating Maxwell field. In Fourier space, in the long-wavelength limit, we have the dipole approximation, $\mathrm{H_{int}} = e\mathbf{R} \cdot \mathbf{E}(q=0)$. The system of harmonic oscillators is strongly coupled to a thermal bath so that the temperature T_{ext} is fixed. The NSO can be investigated [4] with the selection of relevant observables as degrees of freedom of the system, and the remaining (irrelevant) degrees of freedom define the bath. The relevant statistical operator is chosen as the direct product of the thermodynamic equilibrium for the phonon/photon system, ρ_{bath}, fixed by the external temperature T_{ext}, and the reduced system statistical operator obtained after tracing out the irrelevant degrees of freedom. Performing the Born–Markov and rotating-wave approximation, the quantum master equation is obtained,

$$\begin{aligned}\frac{\partial \rho_\epsilon(t)}{\partial t} + \frac{\mathrm{i}}{\hbar}[\mathrm{H}^t, \rho_\epsilon(t)] = -\frac{1}{\hbar^2} \int_{-\infty}^0 \mathrm{d}\tau \mathrm{e}^{-\epsilon\tau}\ & [\langle \mathrm{H_{int}} \mathrm{H_{int}}(\tau)\rangle_{\mathrm{bath}} \rho_\epsilon(t) + \rho_\epsilon(t) \langle \mathrm{H_{int}}(\tau) \mathrm{H_{int}} \rangle_{\mathrm{bath}} \\ & - \mathrm{Tr_{bath}} \{ \mathrm{H_{int}} \rho_\epsilon(t) \rho_{\mathrm{bath}} \mathrm{H_{int}}(\tau) + \mathrm{H_{int}}(\tau) \rho_\epsilon(t) \rho_{\mathrm{bath}} \mathrm{H_{int}} \}] .\end{aligned} \tag{76}$$

The notation $\langle \dots \rangle_{\mathrm{bath}}$ means average with respect to the phonon/photon bath, $\rho_{\mathrm{bath}} = Z_{\mathrm{bath}}^{-1} \mathrm{e}^{-\mathrm{H_{h.o.}}/k_B T_{\mathrm{ext}}}$. A further thermostat is needed to ensure thermodynamic equilibrium with temperature T_{ext} [4]. The evaluation of the right-hand side is given below, Equation (82).

Electromagnetic field. The evaluation of the field averages with the harmonic-oscillator bath ρ_{bath} can be performed. Finally, we give the result for the blackbody radiation [4,24] with the field $\mathbf{E}(\boldsymbol{r},t)$:

$$\Gamma_{ij}(\omega) = \int_0^\infty \mathrm{d}\tau\, \mathrm{e}^{\mathrm{i}(\omega+\mathrm{i}\varepsilon)\tau} \langle E_i(\tau) E_j(0) \rangle_{\mathrm{bath}} = \delta_{ij} \left(\frac{1}{2}\gamma(\omega) + \mathrm{i}S(\omega) \right) \tag{77}$$

with $\gamma(\omega) = 4\omega^3 [1 + n_B(\omega)] / (3\hbar c^3)$, and the principal value expression and:

$$S(\omega) = \frac{2}{3\pi\hbar c^3} \mathcal{P} \int_0^\infty d\omega_q \omega_q^3 \left[\frac{1 + n_B(\omega_q)}{\omega - \omega_q} + \frac{n_B(\omega_q)}{\omega + \omega_q} \right] . \tag{78}$$

Note that the Planck distribution (10) satisfies $n_B(-\omega) = -[1 + n_B(\omega)]$ such that $\gamma(\omega) = 4\omega^3[1 + n_B(\omega)]/(3\hbar c^3)$ for $\omega > 0$ and $\gamma(\omega) = 4|\omega|^3 n_B(|\omega|)/(3\hbar c^3)$ for $\omega < 0$.

The resulting quantum master equation describing the coupling such as atoms to the radiation field in dipole approximation, $H_{int} = -e\mathbf{R} \cdot \mathbf{E}$,

$$\frac{\partial}{\partial t}\rho_\epsilon(t) - \frac{1}{i\hbar}[H_S, \rho_\epsilon(t)] - \frac{1}{i\hbar}[H_{infl}, \rho_\epsilon(t)] = \mathcal{D}'[\rho_\epsilon(t)]. \tag{79}$$

has the Lindblad form. We perform the spectral decomposition with respect to the (discrete) eigenstates $|\phi_n\rangle$ of H_S,

$$\begin{aligned} \mathbf{R}(\omega) &= \int_{-\infty}^\infty dt\, e^{i\omega(t-t_0)}\, e^{iH_S(t-t_0)/\hbar} \mathbf{R} e^{-iH_S(t-t_0)/\hbar} = \mathbf{R}^\dagger(-\omega) \\ &= 2\pi\hbar \sum_{n,m} \delta(E_{S,n} - E_{S,m} + \hbar\omega) |\phi_n\rangle\langle\phi_n|\mathbf{R}|\phi_m\rangle\langle\phi_m| . \end{aligned} \tag{80}$$

The influence Hamiltonian:

$$H_{infl} = e^2\hbar \int d\omega\, S(\omega)\mathbf{R}^\dagger(\omega) \cdot \mathbf{R}(\omega) \tag{81}$$

leads to a renormalization of the system Hamiltonian H_S that is induced by the vacuum fluctuations of the radiation field (Lamb shift) and by the thermally-induced processes (Stark shift). The dissipator of the quantum master equation reads:

$$\begin{aligned} \mathcal{D}'[\rho_\epsilon(t)] &= \int_0^\infty d\omega \frac{4e^2\omega^3}{3\hbar c^3} [1 + n_B(\omega)] \left[\mathbf{R}(\omega)\rho_\epsilon(t)\mathbf{R}^\dagger(\omega) - \frac{1}{2}\{\mathbf{R}^\dagger(\omega)\mathbf{R}(\omega), \rho_\epsilon(t)\} \right] \\ &+ \int_0^\infty d\omega \frac{4e^2\omega^3}{3\hbar c^3} n_B(\omega) \left[\mathbf{R}^\dagger(\omega)\rho_\epsilon(t)\mathbf{R}(\omega) - \frac{1}{2}\{\mathbf{R}(\omega)\mathbf{R}^\dagger(\omega), \rho_\epsilon(t)\} \right] \end{aligned} \tag{82}$$

where the integral over the negative frequencies has been transformed into positive frequencies. The influence term (81) is used to dress the electrons. Only the dissipator (82) is considered for the export of energy.

This result can be interpreted in a simple way. The application of the destruction operator $\mathbf{R}(\omega)$ on a state of the system lowers its energy by the amount $\hbar\omega$ and describes the emission of a photon. The transition rate $\frac{4\omega^3}{3\hbar c^3} [1 + n_B(\omega)]$ contains the spontaneous emission, as well as the thermal emission of photons. The term $\mathbf{R}^\dagger(\omega)$ gives the creation of photons with transition rate $\frac{4\omega^3}{3\hbar c^3} n_B(\omega)$ describing the absorption of photons.

7. The Relaxation Term

Dissipator and relaxation. We can introduce the coupling to the thermal bath in different ways. After we described it by a Lindblad operator (79), based on a detailed description of interaction processes and performing some approximations, we now discuss whether we can also describe the influence of the bath by a relaxation term that describes the influence of a bath in a global, macroscopic way. The use of a relaxation time is very common in nonequilibrium statistical physics; see Section 3. We introduce the relaxation time as a characteristic, semiempirical quantity, which may be derived from a microscopic consideration. We analyze the von Neumann equation with a relaxation term similar to the source term (55),

$$\frac{\partial}{\partial t}\rho_\eta(t) - \frac{1}{i\hbar}[(H_S + H_F^t), \rho_\eta(t)] = -\eta[\rho_\eta(t) - \rho_{rel}(t)]. \tag{83}$$

Now, the relaxation parameter (superoperator) η is finite and models the influence of the bath. The relevant statistical operator $\rho_{rel}(t)$ is considered no longer as the memory of the known averages in the past, to realize the initial, causal conditions. It describes the goal to which the evolution goes, a teleological distribution. It is determined by the external conditions as discussed below.

The idea is that the irrelevant degrees of freedom are strongly relaxed to a quasi-equilibrium, similar to the Enskog approach to solve the Boltzmann equation. The influence on the average motion of the relevant observables is replaced by a transport coefficient similar to the friction force in the Langevin equation. A more detailed description will relate this macroscopic friction force to the correlation function of stochastic forces, as known from the Brownian motion.

Ideal gas with friction. Let us consider a simple example for illustration. We have relevant (the electron variables) and irrelevant (ionic) observables. As discussed above, the relevant part of the dynamics is described explicitly, whereas the irrelevant one is described globally, e.g., by a relaxation term. In our simple example, the relevant part of the dynamics is $H_{S,id} = \sum_i \hbar^2 p_i^2/2m_e$. We disregard the e–i interaction, but introduce a friction term η_{ei}, of course not as $\frac{\partial}{\partial t}\rho_\eta(t) = -\eta_{ei}\rho_\eta(t)$, but, to conserve normalization, energy, and particle number, we can consider the relaxation term:

$$\frac{\partial}{\partial t}\rho_\eta(t) - \frac{1}{i\hbar}[(H_{S,id} + H_F^t), \rho_\eta(t)] = -\eta_{ei}[\rho_\eta(t) - \rho_{eq,id}], \tag{84}$$

with the equilibrium distribution $\rho_{eq,id} = \exp[-\beta H_{S,id} + \beta\mu_e N_e]/Z_{eq,id}$ defined by temperature, chemical potential, zero mean velocity, and the ideal gas Hamiltonian $H_{S,id} = \sum_p E_p a_p^\dagger a_p$ (Note that H_F^t is not included. We demand a homogeneous distribution, and the external field would be compensated by a position-dependent chemical potential.). The norm and particle number are conserved, and for the average momentum, we have:

$$\frac{d}{dt}\langle P\rangle_\eta^t = \mathrm{Tr}\left\{\frac{\partial}{\partial t}\rho_\eta(t)P\right\} = -eE_{ext}N_e - \eta_{ei}\langle P\rangle_\eta^t \tag{85}$$

with the stationary result $j = \frac{-e}{m_e\Omega_0}\langle P\rangle_{stat} = \frac{e^2 n_e}{m_e\eta_{ei}}E_{ext}$ so that $\sigma = n_e e^2/(m_e\eta_{ei})$ results; see Equation (64). Comparing to the microscopic calculation (28), we identify $\eta_{ei} = 1/\bar{\tau}^{transp}$.

Dynamical collision frequency. We have shown that the phenomenological relaxation time $1/\eta_{ei}$ is related to the microscopic e–i interaction solved in Section 3. We know from the Langevin equation that transport (friction) coefficients are related to the correlation function of stochastic forces. We have to consider a stochastic process, and stochastic forces are needed to maintain thermal irregular motion, cf. Equation (67). We demonstrate this relation for the ideal gas with friction to describe the collisions with ions.

Within the Zubarev NSO approach, we derive the response of the system to a time-dependent external field; see [14,20]. Medium modifications of electromagnetic fields in an isotropic plasma are described by the dielectric permittivity tensor $\hat{\varepsilon}(q,\omega)$. In the long-wavelength limit $q \to 0$ (relevant for the emission and absorption of visible light considered here), the transverse and longitudinal dielectric function are identical. The dielectric function is written in the generalized Drude-like form with $\omega_{pl}^2 = n_e e^2/(\epsilon_0 m_e)$,

$$\varepsilon(q \to 0, \omega) = 1 = 1 + \frac{i}{\epsilon_0\omega}\sigma(q \to 0, \omega) = 1 - \frac{\omega_{pl}^2}{\omega[\omega + i\nu(\omega)]}. \tag{86}$$

The dynamical collision frequency $\nu(\omega)$ is obtained from the frequency-dependent force-force correlation function; see [25] and Equations (67) and (68).

$$\nu(\omega) = \frac{\beta}{N_e m_e} \langle \dot{\mathrm{P}}; \dot{\mathrm{P}} \rangle_{\omega + i\epsilon} \,. \tag{87}$$

For the DC conductivity follows $\sigma = \epsilon_0 \omega_{\rm pl}^2 / \nu(0) = n_e e^2 / [m_e \nu(0)]$, so that we identify $\eta_{\rm ei} = \nu(0)$.

Note that this global description of the effect of e–i interaction by a relaxation term is very crude, but was successfully applied to derive the Mermin dielectric function $\varepsilon^{\rm Mermin}(q,\omega)$ [26]. The contribution of e–i interaction for $q = 0$ is described by the dynamical collision frequency $\nu(\omega)$. The extension to finite q was possible taking the conservation laws for particle number, etc., into account.

Relaxation of internal energy, ideal gas. The relaxation of the electron momentum owing to e-i collisions is correctly described. The conservation of the norm and particle number is realized by construction. For the internal energy $U_{\rm S,id}(t) = \langle \mathrm{H}_{\rm S,id} \rangle_\eta^t$, we have with Equation (84):

$$\frac{\mathrm{d}}{\mathrm{d}t} U_{\rm S,id}(t) = j E_{\rm ext} \Omega_0 - \eta_{\rm bath} \left[U_{\rm S,id}(t) - \frac{3}{2} k_{\rm B} T_{\rm ext} N_e \right] \tag{88}$$

with the stationary result $U_{\rm stat} = \frac{3}{2} k_{\rm B} T_{\rm ext} N_e + j E_{\rm ext} \Omega_0 / \eta_{\rm bath}$. The values $j_{\rm eq} = 0$ and $U_{\rm eq} = \frac{3}{2} k_{\rm B} T_{\rm ext} N_e$ as demanded by the bath are not reached in the stationary state.

The relaxation coefficient $\eta_{\rm bath}$ is different from $\eta_{\rm ei}$ because elastic e-i collisions, which are relevant for the relaxation of momentum, will not contribute to the relaxation of internal energy. Other phenomena like bremsstrahlung emission (see Section 8) give the microscopic process for this relaxation term. The relaxation parameter η should be considered as the superoperator in the space of the dynamical variables $\{\mathrm{B}_n\}$ of the system, similar to the relaxation time $1/\tau^{\rm transp}(E_p)$ (24) acting on states $|p\rangle$.

Global energy relaxation. As a simple example for energy relaxation, we discuss temperature relaxation for a system in local thermodynamic equilibrium. For the ideal classical gas of electrons, we have the equilibrium distribution (see Equation (14)):

$$f_1^0(E_p) = \frac{n_e}{2} \left(\frac{2\pi\hbar^2}{m_e k_{\rm B} T} \right)^{3/2} \mathrm{e}^{-\frac{\hbar^2 p^2}{2 m_e k_{\rm B} T}} \,. \tag{89}$$

The change $T \to T_{\rm ext}$ where $T_{\rm ext}$ is the temperature of the bath can be described by the map:

$$f_1^0(E_p) = f_1^0 \left(\frac{\hbar^2 p^2}{2 m_e} \right) \to \left(\frac{T}{T_{\rm ext}} \right)^{3/2} f_1^0 \left(\frac{\hbar^2 p^2 T_{\rm ext}}{2 m_e T} \right) . \tag{90}$$

The equation of evolution for $T(t)$ is obtained from:

$$\frac{\partial}{\partial t} f_1^0(E_p; T(t)) = -\eta_{\rm bath} \left[f_1^0(E_p; T(t)) - f_1^0(E_p; T_{\rm ext}) \right] \tag{91}$$

so that near $T \approx T_{\rm ext}$, we find $\dot{T}(t) = -\eta_{\rm bath}[T(t) - T_{\rm ext}]$. This global relaxation of T scales all momenta in the same way and can be replaced by a more detailed description within a microscopic approach.

Hamiltonian dynamics. Now, we discuss the NSO method presented in Section 4. The dynamical evolution owing to the e–i interaction, given by $\mathrm{H}_{\rm S}$, is treated microscopically so that it must be taken off the relaxation term. However, this microscopic description is not complete because the interaction with a bath is not included. We obtain from Equation (56):

$$\frac{\mathrm{d}}{\mathrm{d}t}\langle \mathrm{B}_n\rangle^t = \frac{\mathrm{i}}{\hbar}\mathrm{Tr}\{[\mathrm{H}^t, \mathrm{B}_n]\rho_\eta(t)]\} - \eta_{\mathrm{bath}}\left[\mathrm{Tr}\{\rho_\eta(t)\mathrm{B}_n\} - \mathrm{Tr}\{\rho_{\mathrm{rel}}(t)\mathrm{B}_n\}\right]. \tag{92}$$

Now, the relaxation coefficient η_{bath} only describes the interaction with the bath. It is clearly seen that this relation becomes wrong for lim $\eta_{\mathrm{bath}} \to 0$ if the dynamics $\mathrm{H}^t = \mathrm{H}_\mathrm{S} + \mathrm{H}_\mathrm{F}^t$ is incomplete, i.e., not containing the coupling to the bath, and $\langle \mathrm{B}_n\rangle^t$ is a prescribed time evolution, which respects the influence of the bath. In particular, in a stationary state, the averages of the dynamical observables of the system, including the internal energy $\langle \mathrm{H}_\mathrm{S}\rangle^t$, should not depend on time. The appropriate choice of the source term, in particular the relevant operator $\rho_{\mathrm{rel}}(t)$, can be performed so that double counting of the Hamiltonian dynamics H^t is avoided.

As discussed above for an isolated, closed system, the source term can be constructed such that the dynamical evolution is projected out. The condition (43):

$$\langle \mathrm{B}_n\rangle^t = \langle \mathrm{B}_n\rangle^t_{\mathrm{rel}} \tag{93}$$

makes the time evolution (56) of the relevant observables B_n purely dynamical, i.e., according to H^t, and independent of the value of ϵ. However, in open systems, the dynamical observables of the system may also be influenced by the bath, so that the Hamiltonian time evolution, neglecting the influence of the bath, is incomplete, and therefore, it is in conflict with the demanded self-consistency condition (93).

Maximum production of entropy. We propose another definition of the relevant statistical operator for open systems in the stationary state. Given properties are only a small number of control observables. In our case, the relevant operator is characterized by the density n_e, the current density j controlled by the external field E_{ext}, and the internal energy density controlled by the bath temperature T_{ext}. The mean values of further observables are not measured, so that Equation (93) is meaningless. Instead, an arbitrary number of dynamical observables $\{\mathrm{B}_n\}$ of the system may be considered, and their averages are determined by the Kohler variational principle [16], where the arbitrary time dependence of the external field is considered. It can be related to the principle of the extremum of entropy production given by Prigogine and Glansdorff [1]. The static case $\omega = 0$ has been considered in [4,14].

Coming back to our example of DC conductivity, some control parameters are known in the past $t_1 < t$: the volume Ω_0, the particle density n_e, the temperature T_{ext}, and the external field $\mathbf{E}_{\mathrm{ext}}$, which, in general, may depend on time t_1. A Gibbs ensemble ρ_{eq} with H_S (remember that H_F^t is compensated by the chemical potential to have homogeneous solution), and the external conditions $\Omega_0, n_e, T_{\mathrm{ext}}$ are compatible with the demanded properties, but not very appropriate to describe the stationary state; see the discussion of the Kubo formula (63). At least, we expect to have a stationary distribution with a finite average momentum current density $j = (-e\hbar/m_e\Omega_0)\langle \mathbf{P}\rangle$, which characterizes the relevant distribution. We can add further moments or the detailed single-particle distribution function $f_1(\boldsymbol{p}, t)$ as the set $\{\mathrm{B}_n\}$ of relevant observables. The averages of these relevant observables are not prescribed by the self-consistency relations (93), but by the maximum production of information entropy, as shown, e.g., by the Kohler variational principle. The principle of maximum information entropy fixes all remaining (irrelevant) observables, such as missing moments if only a finite number of moments is taken, or two-particle correlation functions. The construction of the relevant statistical operator $\rho_{\mathrm{rel}}(t)$ has to be considered as a variational problem. According to the Kohler variational principle of the maximum production of relevant entropy at a given external field $\boldsymbol{E}_{\mathrm{ext}}$, we find that the more relevant observables $\{\mathrm{B}_n\}$ are included, the better (larger) being the result for the conductivity; see the examples in Section 5.

The approach presented here is known as synchronization or the sequence of different stages of non-equilibrium. Similar to the Enskog equation, we assume strong equilibration of the higher correlation functions (collision time scale), followed by the equilibration of the single-particle distribution function (free flight time scale) and the position-dependent hydrodynamic scale (transport and diffusion). The higher correlations are already equilibrated. For the conductivity in the low-density limit, the single-particle distribution function is sufficient. Higher order distribution functions relax quickly. An important example is the dressing of free particles to become quasiparticles with self-energy according to local thermodynamic equilibrium. We can discuss this as a fast synchronization of the irrelevant observables to the quasi-equilibrium, relevant distribution.

Dynamics and relaxation. It is our main issue to construct the equation of evolution with a relaxation term avoiding double counting of the dynamical part H^t of the interaction. For our open system, the time evolution operator $\mathrm{U}(t, t_0)$, Equation (49), has to be completed to contain also the interaction with the bath. In the expressions (58) and (59), the interaction with the bath has to be added. Within a microscopic approach, $\mathrm{d}\langle \mathrm{B}_n\rangle^t/\mathrm{d}t$ should also have the contribution of interaction with the bath. As is well known, a dissipator (76) can be derived so that $\rho(t)$ follows from a quantum master equation. Because of this additional interaction with the bath, the self-consistency condition (43) and (93) becomes obsolete for the averages of the relevant observables. Instead, only the external conditions $E_{\rm ext}$, $T_{\rm ext}$ are given, and the averages of the relevant observables $\{\mathrm{B}_n\}$ are determined from the maximum production of the relevant entropy.

As before, we approximately introduce a relevant statistical operator $\rho_{\rm rel}$, which is optimized with respect to the given dynamics $\mathrm{H_S}$ of the system, i.e., the maximum of production of the relevant entropy according to the Kohler variational principle. For this, we select out a set of relevant observables $\{\mathrm{B}_n\}$ and find the corresponding Lagrange parameters F_n solving the linear system $\sum_n P_{mn} F_n = D_m E_{\rm ext}$ of Equation (65). This approximation can be improved taking into account the influence of the bath, for instance replacing ϵ by $\eta_{\rm bath}$ calculating the correlation functions. Now, we solve the problem of the intrinsic energy $\langle \mathrm{H_S}\rangle^t$, which should be constant in the stationary state. The von Neumann equation with the friction term (83) gives for the time derivative:

$$0 = jE_{\rm ext} - \frac{3}{2} n_e \eta_{\rm bath} k_{\rm B} (T - T_{\rm ext}) \tag{94}$$

so that the temperature in the system is $T = T_{\rm ext} + \dfrac{2}{3\eta_{\rm bath} k_{\rm B}} \sigma E^2_{\rm ext}$, cf. Equation (36). In linear response, the temperature difference $\Delta T = T - T_{\rm ext} \propto E^2_{\rm ext}$ can be neglected. To estimate ΔT, we need a microscopic description of the bath coupling as discussed in Section 8.

8. Microscopic Description of the Bath Coupling

Dynamical collision frequency and bremsstrahlung emission. Bremsstrahlung emission has been considered as a possible process to export the energy from the system to the bath. It is related to absorption, which is obtained from classical field theory. Quantum field theory is needed to obtain spontaneous emission, cf. Equations (11)–(13). The dielectric function $\varepsilon(\omega)$ is connected to the index of refraction $n(\omega)$ and the absorption coefficient $\alpha(\omega)$ by $n(\omega) + (\mathrm{i}c/2\omega)\alpha(\omega) = \sqrt{\varepsilon(\omega)}$. The absorption coefficient is related to the bremsstrahlung radiation. In Born approximation, we obtain [14]:

$$\mathrm{Re}\, \nu(\omega) = \frac{e^4 n_i}{12\pi^2 \varepsilon_0^2 m_e} \left(\frac{2\pi m_e}{k_{\rm B} T}\right)^{1/2} \frac{1}{\hbar\omega} \left[e^{\beta\hbar\omega/2} - e^{-\beta\hbar\omega/2}\right] K_0\left(\frac{\hbar\omega}{2k_{\rm B}T}\right). \tag{95}$$

where $K_0(z) = \int_0^\infty \mathrm{d}t \cos(z \sinh t)$ is a modified Bessel function. The static ion structure factor is approximated as $S_i(q) \approx 1$. Comparing with the Kramers formula (13), the corresponding result for the Gaunt factor has been obtained. Further changes of Kramers' expression are obtained from the account of many-body effects.

As in the case of momentum relaxation described by the relaxation parameter $\eta_{\rm ei}$, we estimate the relaxation parameter $\eta_{\rm bath}$ which describes the relaxation of internal energy (94). We consider the loss of energy of the electrons owing to bremsstrahlung emission, Equation (13). Integrating over ω, the total emission power density is [27]:

$$P[\mathrm{W/m^3}] = -\frac{1}{\Omega_0}\frac{\mathrm{d}}{\mathrm{d}t}\langle \mathrm{H_S}\rangle = 1.69 \times 10^{-38} Z_i^2 n_e[\mathrm{m^{-3}}] n_i[\mathrm{m^{-3}}] \left(k_\mathrm{B}T[\mathrm{eV}]\right)^{1/2}. \quad (96)$$

This expression gives already the result in the corresponding SI units. For instance, typical experiments to measure the DC conductivity in dense plasmas [28] are performed at $k_\mathrm{B}T \approx 2$ eV and free electron density $n_e \approx 3 \times 10^{25}$ m^{-3}. At electrical fields, $E_\mathrm{ext} \approx 100$ V/m linear behavior $j = \sigma E_\mathrm{ext}$ has been observed, with $\sigma \approx 2 \times 10^4$ $[\Omega\,\mathrm{m}]^{-1}$. Comparison with our results (29) has been performed in [11]. According to (96), the total emission power density is $P \approx 2 \times 10^{13}$ W/m^3. This loss of energy owing to bremsstrahlung radiation determines the cooling rate of the plasma and the temperature of the stationary state according to Equation (94). With $jE_\mathrm{ext} = \sigma E_\mathrm{ext}^2 \approx 2 \times 10^8$ W/m^3, the temperature difference $\Delta T < 1$ K between the emitting system and the emitting bath is relatively small in the stationary case.

However, this estimation is valid only for a plasma that is optically thin, i.e., the radiation emitted by the electrons can escape from the plasma without reabsorption. In an optically-thick plasma, emitted radiation is reabsorbed (self-absorption) after a short distance compared to the size of the plasma. The balance of both emission and absorption processes in the stationary state leads to a lower efficiency of the energy transfer from the electrons to the radiation field and a corresponding higher plasma temperature in the stationary state. Then, the energy spectrum is constrained to the Planck spectrum (10). In particular, below the plasma frequency, electromagnetic radiation cannot propagate in the plasma. Radiation transport determines the export of energy, and the temperature of the radiation field $T_\mathrm{ext}(\boldsymbol{r}, t)$ becomes dependent on the position. The constraining Planck spectrum in the low-frequency limit (Raleigh–Jeans law) can be used to define the temperature. According to the Stefan–Boltzmann law, the heat is related to temperature as a property of the Planck spectrum (10), which gives the occupation numbers of photon states, not showing the phase of the electromagnetic wave.

Quantum structure of electromagnetic fields. As in the case of momentum relaxation η_ei, the energy relaxation η_bath is related to a microscopic process, the interaction of the electrons with the radiation field. As known from the Brownian motion, behind the relaxation term, which describes the average motion, there is a stochastic process. This allows one to calculate the relaxation parameter η_bath from the correlation function of stochastic forces (fluctuation-dissipation theorem); see Equation (67). Whereas for η_ei, the collision frequency $\nu(0)$ was considered, which describes the fluctuations of the Coulomb forces in the charged-particle system, we consider for η_bath the vacuum fluctuations of the electromagnetic field. In particular, a quantum field theory is needed to describe spontaneous emission of radiation; for details, see, e.g., [4,24].

Let us consider the quantum fluctuations $\mathbf{E}(\boldsymbol{r}, t)$, $\mathbf{B}(\boldsymbol{r}, t)$ in thermal equilibrium. The fluctuation properties of the electrical field are obtained from the Maxwell equations in free space. The vector potential in the Coulomb gauge leads to wave equations for the transverse vector potential, which may be solved by a plane wave decomposition with photon creation and annihilation operators $\mathrm{b}_\lambda(\boldsymbol{q})$, satisfying bosonic commutation relations. The commutator (where $[\mathrm{A}, \mathrm{B}] = \mathrm{AB} - \mathrm{BA}$) and the anticommutator (where $\{\mathrm{A}, \mathrm{B}\} = \mathrm{AB} + \mathrm{BA}$) function can be calculated; see [24]. As a result, for the anticommutator correlation function of the transverse electric field, averaged over the radiation field in thermal equilibrium at T, one obtains for the vector components with $x = \{c\Delta t, \Delta \boldsymbol{r}\}$:

$$\langle \{E_i(x), E_j(0)\}\rangle = -(\delta_{ij} - \frac{x_i x_j}{r^2})\frac{1}{2\pi^2 \tau_T^3 r} \times \left[\frac{\cosh[(r/c - t)/\tau_T]}{\sinh^3[(r/c - t)/\tau_T]} + \frac{\cosh[(r/c + t)/\tau_T]}{\sinh^3[(r/c + t)/\tau_T]}\right] \quad (97)$$

with $r = |\Delta \mathbf{r}|, t = \Delta t$, and $\tau_T = \hbar/(\pi k_B T)$ is the thermal correlation time. For $r \to 0$ follows, summing over i, j, the expression $\langle\{\mathbf{E}(0,t), \mathbf{E}(0)\}\rangle \approx \frac{6}{\pi^2 t^4}$ for $|t| \ll \tau_T$. This corresponds to vacuum contribution $(T = 0)$ and diverges near $t = 0$.

The thermal contribution is:

$$\langle\{\mathbf{E}(0,t), \mathbf{E}(0)\}\rangle_{\text{th}} = \frac{1}{\pi^2 \tau_T^4}\left[\frac{6 + 4\sinh^2(t/\tau_T)}{\sinh^4(t/\tau_T)} - \frac{6}{\pi^2 (t/\tau_T)^4}\right]. \tag{98}$$

Performing $t \to 0$, we get the energy density of the field in thermal equilibrium as $u_{\text{th}} = \langle\{\mathbf{E}(0), \mathbf{E}(0)\}\rangle_{\text{th}}/2 = 1/(15\pi^2\tau_T^4)$, which is the Stephan–Boltzmann law of black-body radiation. The long-time behavior $t \gg \tau_T$ results as $\langle\{\mathbf{E}(0,t), \mathbf{E}(0)\}\rangle_{\text{th}} \approx 16/(\pi^2\tau_T^4)\exp(-2|t|/\tau_T)$. We can consider the local, but low-frequency limit of the spectral density (see, e.g., [4]):

$$S_{EE}^{\text{therm}}(r = 0, \omega) = \int \mathrm{d}t e^{-\mathrm{i}\omega t}\langle\{\mathbf{E}(0,t), \mathbf{E}(0)\}\rangle_{\text{th}} \approx \frac{4}{\pi^2\tau_T^3}\frac{1}{1 + \omega^2\tau_T^2/4}. \tag{99}$$

We also have:

$$\Gamma(\omega) = 1/\hbar^2 \int_0^\infty \mathrm{d}t e^{-\mathrm{i}(\omega + \mathrm{i}\epsilon)t}\langle\{\mathbf{E}(0,t), \mathbf{E}(0)\}\rangle = \gamma(\omega)/2 + iS(\omega). \tag{100}$$

The thermal contribution has the low-frequency limit $\lim_{\omega\to 0} S_{EE}^{\text{therm}}(r = 0, \omega) = 4/(\pi^2\tau_T^3)$, and the results give:

$$\gamma \approx 4\omega^2 k_B T/(3\hbar c^3), \qquad \lim_{\omega\to 0} S_{EE}^{\text{therm}}(\omega) = \frac{4\zeta[3]}{3\pi\hbar c^3 \tau_T^3}, \tag{101}$$

with Apery's constant $\zeta[3] = 1.20205$, cf. Equation (77). In addition to the vacuum fluctuations, we have thermal fluctuations of the electrical field proportional T^3. Considering this low-frequency limit, we can introduce a local $(r = 0)$ temperature from the fluctuation spectrum of the electromagnetic fields.

Radiation damping. We cannot give here a detailed discussion of quantum electrodynamic processes. An interesting process is radiation damping. From classical electrodynamics, it is known that charged particles emit radiation if they are accelerated. Using the Larmor formula (12), the equation of motion for an electron that contains the interaction with the radiation field is the Abraham–Lorentz equation:

$$m_e\dot{\boldsymbol{v}}(t) - \boldsymbol{F}_{\text{ext}}(t) = \boldsymbol{F}_{\text{rad}}(t) = \frac{e^2}{6\pi\epsilon_0 c^3}\ddot{\boldsymbol{v}}(t) = m_e\tau_{\text{rad}}\ddot{\boldsymbol{v}}(t), \tag{102}$$

where $\boldsymbol{F}_{\text{ext}}(t)$ denotes an external force. The radiation damping term is determined by the characteristic time $\tau_{\text{rad}} = e^2/(6\pi\epsilon_0 m_e c^3) = 6.3 \times 10^{-24}$s.

The Abraham–Lorentz Equation (102) can also be derived if the radiation degrees of freedom are eliminated, as discussed above in Section 6; see [24]. Different problems such as runaway solutions arise; see [4]. The interaction with the radiation field, in particular bremsstrahlung processes, leads to a loss of quantum coherence, to localization, and to the transition to classical behavior [24]. The bremsstrahlung is emitted during the collision of charged particles. Emission of photons can be considered as a measuring process to localize the charged particle during the collision process. A more detailed discussion of the suppression of quantum coherence can be found in [29]. The balance of emitted and absorbed power in the classical limit is (12):

$$\frac{\mathrm{d}}{\mathrm{d}t}\langle \mathrm{H_S}\rangle = -\frac{2e^2}{3\epsilon_0 c^3}\sum_i^{N_e}\left(\frac{\mathrm{d}^2\boldsymbol{r}_i}{\mathrm{d}t^2}\right)^2 + e\sum_i^{N_e}\dot{\boldsymbol{r}}_i \cdot \boldsymbol{E}_{\text{ext}}(\boldsymbol{r}_i, t), \tag{103}$$

if reabsorption and coherence effects given by the ionic structure factor are discarded. The emission and absorption of radiation, as described by a quantum master equation, are some of the possibilities to solve the problem of the export of entropy.

9. Conclusions

von Neumann equation with the relaxation term. According to the Zubarev NSO method, a source term $-\epsilon[\rho(t) - \rho_{\rm rel}(t)]$ was introduced into the von Neumann Equation (55), with $\lim \epsilon \to 0$ after the thermodynamic limit. This source term is not a physical process, but rather a mathematical trick to select out the retarded solution of the equation of motion. Infinitesimal source terms to break a symmetry are known from other fields in physics such as phase transitions, for instance the direction of magnetization in the Heisenberg model or a phase in the superfluid phase, but also the Planck "Staubkorn" to establish the blackbody radiation spectrum in a "hohlraum". For a *closed system* with a known Hamiltonian, this source term has a remarkable property. We can select out an arbitrary set of relevant observables and construct the source term with the corresponding relevant statistical operator $\rho_{\rm rel}(t)$. As a consequence of the self-consistency conditions (43) and (93), the dynamics of the relevant observables (56) obeys the Hamiltonian dynamics also for finite ϵ. The invariance of the dynamics of the relevant observables with respect to the source term with arbitrary ϵ is a remarkable property of the extended von Neumann equation.

Open systems and relaxation term. We discussed open systems, in particular diabatic contact (exchange of energy, but not particles) with a thermal bath. The system is defined by the dynamical degrees of freedom and a Hamiltonian $\mathrm{H}^t = \mathrm{H_S} + \mathrm{H_F^t}$, which determines the equations of motion of the system, including the action of external fields $\boldsymbol{E}_{\rm ext}(t)$. In addition to the Hamiltonian dynamics, instead of the infinitesimal source term, a relaxation term with finite η is introduced in Equation (83) to model the influence of the bath, e.g., prescribing the temperature $T_{\rm ext}$. This finite source term is no longer interpreted as the initial conditions in the past to construct a solution of the von Neumann equation with time evolution H^t, but to give a final state to which the distribution relaxes, at each time instant in the past. More generally, a final state is given by the external conditions, and the influence on the system, the coupling to a bath, is globally described by a relaxation term. The form of the relaxation term, in our case the relevant statistical operator $\rho_{\rm rel}(t)$ and the phenomenological relaxation coefficient η, which, in general, is an operator, has to be chosen in an appropriate way. Note that alternative expressions for the relaxation term are possible. For instance, also for $\ln \rho(t)$, a von Neumann equation can be given, and a source term $-\epsilon[\ln \rho(t) - \ln \rho_{\rm rel}(t)]$ and a corresponding relaxation term with $\epsilon \to \eta$ can be proposed.

The Bogoliubov principle of the weakening of initial correlations. According to the Bogoliubov principle of weakening of initial correlations, the missing correlations to get $\rho(t)$ are produced dynamically. However, this argument is not valid in the case of an open system considered here, if, in addition to the Hamiltonian dynamics, the coupling to the bath is taken into account. In contrast to the system described by a Hamiltonian, the dynamical evolution of the bath is not exactly known. The average with the NSO (53) will not give the empirical averages even if the relevant statistical operator $\rho_{\rm rel}(t_1)$ is replaced by the exact $\rho(t_1)$. Only for a closed system with a known Hamiltonian, the Bogoliubov principle of the weakening of initial correlations is valid. For an open system, the missing correlations are not only produced by the Hamiltonian dynamics within the system, but are also influenced by the external, in general time-dependent conditions, which characterize the surroundings, the bath.

The self-consistency conditions. Let us consider an arbitrary, dynamical observable B_n of the system. If we know the history, i.e., $\langle \mathrm{B}_n \rangle^{t_1}$ in the past $t_1 < t$, the correct time evolution from t_1 to t should also contain the coupling to the bath. For example, this can be expressed in some approximation by a dissipator term (79). In this work, we propose to use a relaxation time approach to describe the external influence on the system. The time evolution of the average $\langle \mathrm{B}_n \rangle^t = \mathrm{Tr}\left\{\rho_\eta(t)\mathrm{B}_n\right\}$ is given by Equation (56) replacing $\epsilon \to \eta$. In general, the observables of the system are influenced by the bath; as an example, we considered the internal energy. Therefore, the relevant statistical operator $\rho_{\rm rel}(t)$ is not determined by the self-consistency conditions (43) and (93), because then the influence of the bath on the time evolution of the average $\langle B_n \rangle^t$ disappears. We have:

$$\langle B_n \rangle^t = \mathrm{Tr}\{\rho_\eta(t) B_n\} \neq \mathrm{Tr}\{\rho_{\mathrm{rel}}(t) B_n\} = \langle B_n \rangle^t_{\mathrm{rel}} \tag{104}$$

so that another prescription is needed to construct $\rho_{\mathrm{rel}}(t)$, different from the consideration of closed systems in Section 4.

The relevant statistical operator. The principle of maximum information entropy at given mean values of a set of relevant observables $\{B_n\}$ was used to construct $\rho_{\mathrm{rel}}(t)$, Equation (44), in Section 4. We applied this condition also in the case of open systems where some parameter values $\lambda_{n,\mathrm{ext}}$ corresponding to $\{B_{n,\mathrm{ext}}\}$ are prescribed by the external conditions. Other dynamical observables $\{B_{n,\mathrm{resp}}\}$ will show a response to the external conditions. Averages $\langle B_{n,\mathrm{resp}} \rangle^t$ of further observables are not measured. The self-consistency conditions to eliminate the corresponding response parameters $\lambda_{n,\mathrm{resp}}(t)$ become unfounded. In Section 5, the self-consistency conditions have been replaced by the condition of stationarity, where the time evolution of $\langle B_n \rangle^t$ is determined only by H^t. We propose another prescription. The response parameters $\lambda_{n,\mathrm{resp}}(t)$ of a given set $\{B_{n,\mathrm{resp}}\}$ of relevant observables are determined by the principle of maximum entropy production. As discussed in Section 5, in the case of linear response, the corresponding Kohler variational principle is equivalent to the solution of the stationarity conditions with (43) and (93). The selection of a set $\{B_{n,\mathrm{resp}}\}$ of relevant observables is a variational ansatz to determine an optimal relevant statistical operator $\rho_{\mathrm{rel}}(t)$ to which the system tends to evolve, as a response to the external influences. It is not dependent on the initial conditions and may be discussed in the context with the experimental evidence of universal dynamics far from equilibrium during the relaxation process observed recently [30].

Relaxation time. The source term to describe the influence of the bath on the time evolution of $\rho(t)$, Equation (83), contains the parameter η, which may be interpreted as inverse relaxation time and is, in general, a superoperator acting in the space of observables $\{B_n\}$ of the system. As an example, the electrical DC conductivity $\sigma(n_e, T)$ of the Lorentz model plasma was discussed. Different values $\eta_{\mathrm{ei}}, \eta_{\mathrm{bath}}$ were considered for the relaxation of the electron current and the internal energy, respectively. The values were determined from the calculation of the corresponding microscopical processes, the *e*–*i* interaction, and the bremsstrahlung emission, respectively. For comparison, in kinetic theory, a relaxation time tensor (21) was introduced, which depends on the wave number p. As known from a variational principle, a larger set $\{\hat{B}_n\}$ of relevant observables will improve the result for the calculation of σ using perturbation theory, so that the value of σ increases; see Section 5.

Stochastic processes. In Brownian motion, the friction term is connected with a stochastic process. As a famous relation, the friction coefficient is related to the fluctuation strength of the stochastic forces. Therefore, we expect that the von Neumann equation with the relaxation term has to be replaced by some stochastic process; see [4]. In the case of the relaxation of the electron current, we have considered the dynamical collision frequency, which is related to the correlation function of stochastic forces from the *e*–*i* interaction. The fluctuations of the electromagnetic fields (vacuum, as well as thermal) are related to the transition rates for photon emission, in particular the bremsstrahlung emission describing the export of energy.

Energy flow. The incoming power density is given by the classical electromagnetic fields, in particular the Poynting vector, which couple to the electrons. We do not need any information about how these fields are produced. The export of energy, described by the relaxation term, is realized by the interaction with the bath. Details about the interaction with the bath are not of relevance. The electron-ion system acts via the force-force correlation function. It mediates and limits the flow of energy, but does not produce entropy. Mechanical energy is transferred to radiation to be described by quantum electrodynamics. Reabsorption transforms the radiation spectrum to the Planck distribution as thermal equilibrium with a fixed temperature T_{ext}. The corresponding excitation energy in addition to the vacuum part, the thermal part, may be denoted as heat. The limiting value $\omega \to 0$ of the spectral density of the radiation field, the Rayleigh–Jeans law $B(\omega, T) = \omega^2 k_B T / 2\pi^2 c^2$, can be used to define a local temperature.

Heat production and entropy. Electrical conductivity describes a non-equilibrium process. Directed motion that is obtained from the external field is converted into isotropic, undirected motion after the interaction with ions. This interaction is a reversible motion, so that it is not connected with the production of thermodynamic entropy $S_{\rm th}$. Irreversibility is connected with the production of entropy. This means that in the case of electrical conductivity, heat is produced. An interesting process to transfer energy from the system to the bath is radiation, in particular the bremsstrahlung emission. The formation of a Planck spectrum can be identified as the production of heat. In equilibrium, heat cannot be transformed back to work, which means irreversible evolution.

Outlook. The results presented here are only a step toward a more fundamental approach to describe nonequilibrium processes. The stochastic properties of the electromagnetic fields should be analyzed more in detail to obtain a solution of the problem of irreversible evolution, including the electrical conductivity of a plasma. Using the Zubarev NSO method, exact results can be given for the DC conductivity in the low-density limit similar to a virial expansion, as discussed in the present work. This approach is extended to describe open systems, in particular the coupling to the radiation field.

Funding: This research received no external funding.

Acknowledgments: The author thanks V. G.Morozov, D. Blaschke, R. Redmer, and H. Reinholz for valuable comments and discussions. Work was initiated by the Symposium on "Nonequilibrium Phenomena in Strongly Correlated Systems" in Dubna, 16 April 2018.

Conflicts of Interest: The authors declare no conflict of interest.

References

1. Zubarev, D.N. *Nonequilibrium Statistical Thermodynamics*; Plenum Press: New York, NY, USA, 1974.
2. Zubarev, D.; Morozov, V.; Röpke, G. *Statistical Mechanics of Nonequilibrium Processes*; Akademie-Verlag: Berlin, Germany, 1996; Volume 1.
3. Zubarev, D.; Morozov, V.; Röpke, G. *Statistical Mechanics of Nonequilibrium Processes*; Akademie-Verlag: Berlin, Germany, 1997; Volume 2.
4. Röpke, G. *Nonequilibrium Statistical Physics*; Wiley-VCH: Weinheim, Germany, 2013.
5. Röpke, G. Nonequilibrium Statistical Operator. In *Non-Equilibrium Particle Dynamics*; Kim, A.S., Ed.; IntechOpen: London, UK, 2019; ISBN 978-1-83968-079-3, doi:10.5772/intechopen.84707.
6. Röpke, G. Electrical Conductivity of Charged Particle Systems and Zubarev's Nonequilibrium Statistical Operator Method. *Theor. Math. Phys.* **2018**, *194*, 74. [CrossRef]
7. Kramers, H. On the theory of X-ray absorption and of the continuous X-ray spectrum. *Philos. Mag.* **1923**, *46*, 836. [CrossRef]
8. Gaunt, J. Continuous absorption. *Proc. R. Soc. Lond. A* **1930**, *126*, 654. [CrossRef]
9. Boltzmann, L. *Vorlesungen über Gastheorie, II Theil*; Verlag J. A. Barth: Leipzig, Germany, 1898.
10. Bogoliubov, N.N. *Problems of Dynamic Theory in Statistical Physics*; Gostekhizdat: Moscow-Leningrad, Russia, 1946. (In Russian)
11. Röpke, G. Quantum-statistical approach to the electrical conductivity of dense, high-temperature plasmas. *Phys. Rev. A* **1988**, *38*, 3001. [CrossRef]
12. Röpke, G.; Redmer, R. Electrical conductivity of nondegenerate, fully ionized plasmas. *Phys. Rev. A* **1989**, *39*, 907. [CrossRef]
13. Redmer, R. Physical properties of dense, low-temperature plasmas. *Phys. Rep.* **1997**, *282*, 36. [CrossRef]
14. Reinholz, H. Dielectric and optical properties of dense plasmas. *Ann. Phys. (Paris)* **2005**, *30*, 1. [CrossRef]
15. Spitzer, J.L.; Härm, R. Transport Phenomena in a Completely Ionized Gas. *Phys. Rev.* **1953**, *89*, 977. [CrossRef]
16. Reinholz, H.; Röpke, G. Dielectric function beyond the random-phase approximation: Kinetic theory versus linear response theory. *Phys. Rev. E* **2012**, *85*, 036401. [CrossRef]
17. Gocke, C.; Röpke, G. Master equation of the reduced statistical operator of an atom in a plasma. *Theor. Math. Phys.* **2008**, *154*, 26. [CrossRef]

18. Lin, C.; Gocke, C.; Röpke, G.; Reinholz, H. Transition rates for a Rydberg atom surrounded by a plasma. *Phys. Rev. A* **2016**, *93*, 042711. [CrossRef]
19. Christoph, V.; Röpke, G. Theory of Inverse Linear Response Coefficients. *Phys. Status Solidi (b)* **1985**, *131*, 11. [CrossRef]
20. Röpke, G. Dielectric function and electrical DC conductivity of nonideal plasmas. *Phys. Rev. E* **1998**, *57*, 4673. [CrossRef]
21. Kalashnikov, V.P. Linear relaxation equations in the nonequilibrium statistical operator method. *Theor. Math. Phys.* **1978**, *34*, 412. [CrossRef]
22. Röpke, G. Electrical conductivity of a system of localized and delocalized electrons. *Theor. Math. Phys.* **1981**, *46*, 184. [CrossRef]
23. Adams, J.R.; Shilkin, N.S.; Fortov, V.E.; Gryaznov, V.K.; Mintsev, V.B.; Redmer, R.; Reinholz, H.; Röpke, G. Coulomb contribution to the direct current electrical conductivity of dense partially ionized plasmas. *Phys. Plasmas* **2007**, *14*, 062303. [CrossRef]
24. Breuer, H.P.; Petruccione, F. *The Theory of Open Quantum Systems*; Oxford University Press: Oxford, UK, 2006.
25. Reinholz, H.; Redmer, R.; Röpke, G.; Wierling, A. Long-wavelength limit of the dynamical local-field factor and dynamical conductivity of a two-component plasma. *Phys. Rev. E* **2000**, *62*, 5648. [CrossRef]
26. Röpke, G.; Selchow, A.; Wierling, A.; Reinholz, H. Lindhard dielectric function in the relaxation-time approximation and generalized linear response theory. *Phys. Lett. A* **1999**, *260*, 365. [CrossRef]
27. Huba, J.D. 2013 NRL Plasma Formulary, 2013 Revision, p. 58. Available online: https://library.psfc.mit.edu/catalog/online_pubs/NRL_FORMULARY_13.pdf (accessed on 6 June 2019)
28. Ivanov, Y.V.; Mintsev, V.B.; Fortov, V.E.; Dremin, A.N. Electric conductivity of a non-ideal plasma. *ZhETF* **1976**, *71*, 216; English translation: *JETP* **1976**, *44*, 112.
29. Joos, E.; Zeh, H.D.; Kiefer, C.; Giulini, D.; Kupsch, J.; Stamatescu, I.O. *Decoherence and the Appearance of a Classical World in Quantum Theory*, 2nd ed.; Springer: Berlin/Heidelberg, Germany, 2003.
30. Erne, S.; Bücker, R.; Gasenzer, T.; Berges, J.; Schmiedmayer, J. Observation of universal dynamics in an isolated one-dimensional Bose gas far from equilibrium. *Nature* **2018**, *253*, 225. [CrossRef] [PubMed]

particles

MDPI

Article

Reworking Zubarev's Approach to Nonequilibrium Quantum Statistical Mechanics

Francesco Becattini [1,*], Matteo Buzzegoli [1] and Eduardo Grossi [2]

1 Università di Firenze and INFN Sezione di Firenze, 50019 Firenze, Italy; matteo.buzzegoli@fi.infn.it
2 Institut für Theoretische Physik, University of Heidelberg, 69120 Heidelberg, Germany; grossi@thphys.uni-heidelberg.de
* Correspondence: becattini@fi.infn.it; Tel.: +39-055-457-2264

Received: 3 February 2019; Accepted: 19 March 2019; Published: 8 April 2019

Abstract: In this work, the nonequilibrium density operator approach introduced by Zubarev more than 50 years ago to describe quantum systems at a local thermodynamic equilibrium is revisited. This method, which was used to obtain the first "Kubo" formula of shear viscosity, is especially suitable to describe quantum effects in fluids. This feature makes it a viable tool to describe the physics of Quark–Gluon Plasma in relativistic nuclear collisions.

Keywords: non-equilibrium statistical operator; quantum statistical mechanics; relativistic hydrodynamics; Kubo formulae

1. Introduction

One of the authors (F.B.) would like to start this paper with a personal recollection. I first ran across Zubarev's papers when I was studying the derivation by A. Hosoya et al. [1] of the shear viscosity in quantum-field theory, a result widely known as "Kubo formula", like many of the same sort. This derivation was overtly based on Zubarev's method of nonequilibrium density (or statistical) operator, and I surmised that this method must have been a very important and renowned tool in quantum statistical mechanics. In fact, surprisingly, it could hardly be found in textbooks and in the recent literature, and I did not quite understand why the founding method of such an important formula was that overlooked. After some more self-education, I realized that, perhaps part of the problem was that Zubarev himself did not put the right emphasis on the crucial feature that his proposed operator should possess: to be stationary, hence well-suited to be used in relativistic quantum-field theory as a density operator in the Heisenberg representation. A nonequilibrium stationary density operator sounds somewhat contradictory, but this is not the case if we deal with a system that, at some time, is known to be in local thermodynamic equilibrium, as we see in more detail in Section 3.

In this work, we would like to not just summarize Zubarev's method [2–4], but also to make a critical appraisal and to provide a reformulation thereof that highlights the important features of this approach in a hopefully clear fashion. I also hope that this work could do justice to Zubarev and his remarkable achievement.

Notation

In this paper we use natural units, with $\hbar = c = K = 1$.

The Minkowskian metric tensor is $\mathrm{diag}(1,-1,-1,-1)$; for the Levi-Civita symbol, we use convention $\epsilon^{0123} = 1$.

Operators in the Hilbert space are denoted by a large upper hat, e.g., $\widehat{T}$, while unit vectors with a small upper hat, e.g., $\hat{v}$. Scalar products and contractions are sometimes denoted with a dot, e.g., $A_\mu B^\mu = A \cdot B$.

2. Local Thermodynamic Equilibrium

Zubarev formalism can be used in nonrelativistic as well as in relativistic quantum statistical mechanics. We can then start from the latter, more general case, which is applicable to relativistic fluids out of equilibrium [5]. The relativistic version of the nonequilibrium density operator was first put forward by Zubarev himself and his collaborators in 1979 [6], and later reworked by Van Weert in Reference [7].

The starting point is the definition of the local equilibrium density operator. In relativity, this notion needs the specification of a one-parameter family of 3D spacelike hypersurfaces $\Sigma(\tau)$ (see Figure 1), also known as foliation of spacetime [6–9]. "Time" τ does not necessarily coincide with the proper time marked by comoving clocks. Local equilibrium density operator $\widehat{\rho}_{\rm LE}$ is obtained by maximizing the total entropy:

$$S = -\mathrm{tr}(\widehat{\rho}\log(\widehat{\rho})) \tag{1}$$

with constrained values of energy–momentum and charge density, which should be equal to the actual values. In a covariant formulation, these densities are obtained by projecting the mean values of the stress–energy tensor and current onto the normalized vector perpendicular to Σ:

$$n_\mu \mathrm{tr}\left(\widehat{\rho}\,\widehat{T}^{\mu\nu}\right) = n_\mu T^{\mu\nu}, \qquad n_\mu \mathrm{tr}\left(\widehat{\rho}\,\widehat{j}^{\mu}\right) = n_\mu j^{\mu}. \tag{2}$$

where $T^{\mu\nu}$ and j^μ are the true values of the stress–energy and current fields. The operators in Equation (2) are in the Heisenberg representation. In addition to the energy, momentum, and charge densities, one should include the angular momentum density, but if the stress–energy tensor is the Belinfante [10], this further constraint is redundant and can be disregarded.

The resulting operator is the Local Equilibrium Density Operator (LEDO):

$$\widehat{\rho}_{\rm LE} = \frac{1}{Z_{\rm LE}} \exp\left[-\int_{\Sigma(\tau)} \mathrm{d}\Sigma\, n_\mu \left(\widehat{T}^{\mu\nu}(x)\beta_\nu(x) - \zeta(x)\widehat{j}^{\mu}(x)\right)\right] \tag{3}$$

where β and ζ are the relevant Lagrange multiplier functions for this problem, whose meaning is the four-temperature vector and the ratio between local chemical potential and temperature, respectively [8], $\mathrm{d}\Sigma$ is the measure of the hypersurface induced by the Minkowskian metric, and fields β and ζ are the solution of Constraints (2) with $\widehat{\rho} = \widehat{\rho}_{\rm LE}$, namely:

$$n_\mu \mathrm{tr}\left(\widehat{\rho}_{\rm LE}\,\widehat{T}^{\mu\nu}\right) = n_\mu T^{\mu\nu}_{\rm LE}[\beta,\zeta,n] = n_\mu T^{\mu\nu}, \qquad n_\mu \mathrm{tr}\left(\widehat{\rho}_{\rm LE}\,\widehat{j}^{\mu}\right) = n_\mu j^{\mu}_{\rm LE}[\beta,\zeta,n] = n_\mu j^{\mu}. \tag{4}$$

These equations indeed define a vector field β, which, in turn, can be used as a hydrodynamic frame, β [8] or thermodynamic frame [11], by identifying the four-velocity with

$$u = \frac{\beta}{\sqrt{\beta^2}} = T\beta, \tag{5}$$

which somehow inverts the usual definition.

It is important to stress that the LEDO in Equation (3) is not stationary because operators are generally time-dependent. The sufficient condition for stationarity is that β is a killing vector field, and ζ a constant; in this case, the LEDO becomes the general global thermodynamic equilibrium operator [12].

3. Nonequilibrium Density Operator Revisited

The true density operator in the Heisenberg representation must be stationary by definition, whereas the LEDO is not. The solution of how to work it out (which is an amendment of Zubarev's original idea) is overly simple: if, at some initial time τ_0, the system is known to be in local thermodynamic equilibrium, the actual, stationary, nonequilibrium density operator (NEDO) is $\widehat{\rho}_{\rm LE}(\tau_0)$. Therefore, the true mean values of quantum operators should be calculated as:

$$\langle \widehat{O} \rangle \equiv {\rm tr}(\widehat{\rho}\widehat{O}) = {\rm tr}(\widehat{\rho}_{\rm LE}(\tau_0)\widehat{O})$$

One can rewrite $\widehat{\rho}_{\rm LE}(\tau_0)$ in terms of the operators at present "time" τ by means of Gauss' theorem, taking into account that $\widehat{T}$ and $\widehat{j}$ are conserved. Defining

$$\mathrm{d}\Sigma_\mu = \mathrm{d}\Sigma\, n_\mu,$$

and $\mathrm{d}\Omega$ being the measure of a 4D region in spacetime, we have

$$-\int_{\Sigma(\tau_0)} \mathrm{d}\Sigma_\mu \left(\widehat{T}^{\mu\nu}\beta_\nu - \widehat{j}^\mu\zeta\right) = -\int_{\Sigma(\tau')} \mathrm{d}\Sigma_\mu \left(\widehat{T}^{\mu\nu}\beta_\nu - \widehat{j}^\mu\zeta\right) + \int_\Omega \mathrm{d}\Omega \left(\widehat{T}^{\mu\nu}\nabla_\mu\beta_\nu - \widehat{j}^\mu\nabla_\mu\zeta\right), \qquad (6)$$

where ∇ is the covariant derivative. Region Ω is the portion of spacetime enclosed by two hypersurfaces $\Sigma(\tau_0)$ and $\Sigma(\tau)$ and the timelike hypersurface at their boundaries, where the flux of $(\widehat{T}^{\mu\nu}\beta_\nu(x) - \widehat{j}^\mu\zeta(x))$ is supposed to vanish (see Figure 1). Consequently, the stationary NEDO reads:

$$\widehat{\rho} = \frac{1}{Z}\exp\left[-\int_{\Sigma(\tau_0)} \mathrm{d}\Sigma_\mu \left(\widehat{T}^{\mu\nu}\beta_\nu - \widehat{j}^\mu\zeta\right)\right] = \frac{1}{Z}\exp\left[-\int_{\Sigma(\tau)} \mathrm{d}\Sigma_\mu \left(\widehat{T}^{\mu\nu}\beta_\nu - \widehat{j}^\mu\zeta\right) + \int_\Omega \mathrm{d}\Omega \left(\widehat{T}^{\mu\nu}\nabla_\mu\beta_\nu - \widehat{j}^\mu\nabla_\mu\zeta\right)\right] \quad (7)$$

This expression is the generally covariant form of the one used in Reference [1] (Equation (2.9) therein), with the only difference that factor $\exp[\varepsilon(t-\tau)]$ does not appear in the second term. In Section 5, we see that such a factor is not necessary to obtain the correct "Kubo" formulae.

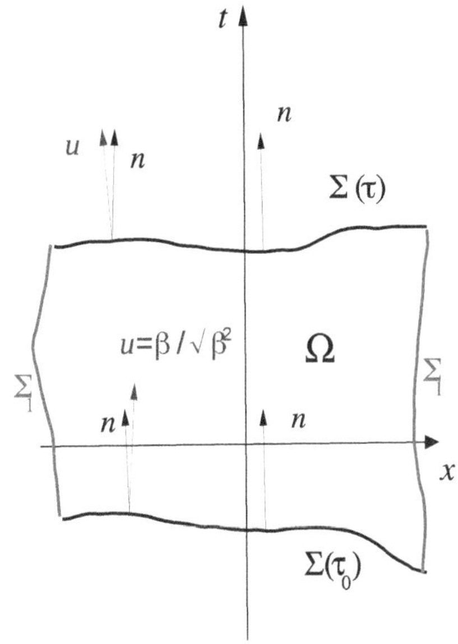

Figure 1. Spacelike hypersurfaces $\Sigma(\tau)$, $\Sigma(\tau_0)$ and their normal unit vector n defining local thermodynamical equilibrium for a relativistic fluid in Minkwoski spacetime. At timelike boundary Σ_l, the flux is supposed to vanish.

The NEDO can be worked out perturbatively by identifying the two terms in the exponent of Equation (7):

$$\widehat{A} = -\int_{\Sigma(\tau)} \mathrm{d}\Sigma_\mu \left(\widehat{T}^{\mu\nu}\beta_\nu - \widehat{j}^\mu\zeta\right) \qquad (8)$$

and

$$\widehat{B} = \int_\Omega \mathrm{d}\Omega \, \left(\widehat{T}^{\mu\nu}\nabla_\mu\beta_\nu - \widehat{j}^\mu\nabla_\mu\zeta\right), \tag{9}$$

and assuming that $\widehat{B}$ is small compared to $\widehat{A}$; this happens if the system has small correlation length, and if the gradients in Equation (9) are small, which is the hydrodynamic limit. We can then use identity

$$\exp[\widehat{A}+\widehat{B}] = \exp[\widehat{A}] + \int_0^1 \mathrm{d}z \, \exp[z(\widehat{A}+\widehat{B})]\widehat{B}\exp[-z\widehat{A}]\exp[\widehat{A}]$$

The expansion of $\exp[\widehat{A}+\widehat{B}]$ can be iterated in the integrand, and one obtains an operator expansion in $\widehat{B}$. Taking into account that

$$Z = \mathrm{tr}(\exp[\widehat{A}+\widehat{B}])$$

at the lowest order in $\widehat{B}$ (linear response):

$$\widehat{\rho} \simeq \widehat{\rho}_{\mathrm{LE}} + \int_0^1 \mathrm{d}z \, \exp[z\widehat{A}]\widehat{B}\exp[-z\widehat{A}]\widehat{\rho}_{\mathrm{LE}} - \langle\widehat{B}\rangle_{\mathrm{LE}}\widehat{\rho}_{\mathrm{LE}} \tag{10}$$

which is the starting point to obtain the "Kubo" formulae.

It should be pointed out that the original Zubarev formulae were somewhat different [6]. We work it out by using Cartesian coordinates and hyperplanes as hypersurfaces. Zubarev modified the equation for the NEDO in Heisenberg representation

$$\frac{\mathrm{d}\widehat{\rho}}{\mathrm{d}t} = -\varepsilon(\widehat{\rho} - \widehat{\rho}_{\mathrm{LE}}) \tag{11}$$

$\varepsilon > 0$ being a real parameter whose limit $\varepsilon \to 0$ is to be taken *after* the thermodynamic limit. The solution of the above equation at the present time, which can be chosen to be $t = 0$, reads:

$$\widehat{\rho}(0) = \widehat{\rho}_{\mathrm{LE}} - \int_{-\infty}^0 \mathrm{d}t \, \mathrm{e}^{\varepsilon t}\frac{\mathrm{d}\widehat{\rho}_{\mathrm{LE}}}{\mathrm{d}t} \tag{12}$$

One can now use the general expression for the derivative of an exponential to calculate:

$$\frac{\mathrm{d}\mathrm{e}^{\widehat{A}}}{\mathrm{d}t} = \int_0^1 \mathrm{d}z \, \mathrm{e}^{z\widehat{A}}\frac{\mathrm{d}\widehat{A}}{\mathrm{d}t}\mathrm{e}^{(1-z)\widehat{A}}$$

with $\widehat{A}$ given by Equation (8). This implies

$$\frac{\mathrm{d}Z_{\mathrm{LE}}}{\mathrm{d}t} = \frac{\mathrm{d}}{\mathrm{d}t}\mathrm{tr}(\mathrm{e}^{\widehat{A}}) = \mathrm{tr}\left(\frac{\mathrm{d}\widehat{A}}{\mathrm{d}t}\mathrm{e}^{\widehat{A}}\right) = Z_{\mathrm{LE}}\langle\frac{\mathrm{d}\widehat{A}}{\mathrm{d}t}\rangle_{\mathrm{LE}}$$

so that

$$\frac{\mathrm{d}\widehat{\rho}_{\mathrm{LE}}}{\mathrm{d}t} = \int_0^1 \mathrm{d}z \, \mathrm{e}^{z\widehat{A}}\frac{\mathrm{d}\widehat{A}}{\mathrm{d}t}\mathrm{e}^{-z\widehat{A}}\widehat{\rho}_{\mathrm{LE}} - \langle\frac{\mathrm{d}\widehat{A}}{\mathrm{d}t}\rangle_{\mathrm{LE}}\widehat{\rho}_{\mathrm{LE}} \tag{13}$$

If the surface boundary terms vanish, we have

$$\frac{\mathrm{d}\widehat{A}}{\mathrm{d}t} = -\int \mathrm{d}^3\mathrm{x} \, \frac{\partial}{\partial t}(\widehat{T}^{0\nu}\beta_\nu) = -\int \mathrm{d}^3\mathrm{x} \, \partial_\mu(\widehat{T}^{\mu\nu}\beta_\nu) = -\int \mathrm{d}^3\mathrm{x} \, \widehat{T}^{\mu\nu}\partial_\mu\beta_\nu \tag{14}$$

By plugging Equations (13) and (14) into Equation (12), we have:

$$\widehat{\rho}(0) - \widehat{\rho}_{\mathrm{LE}} = \int_0^1 \mathrm{d}z \, \mathrm{e}^{z\widehat{A}} \int_{-\infty}^0 \mathrm{d}^4x \;\; \mathrm{e}^{\varepsilon t}\widehat{T}^{\mu\nu}\partial_\mu\beta_\nu\mathrm{e}^{-z\widehat{A}} \, \widehat{\rho}_{\mathrm{LE}} - \int_{-\infty}^0 \mathrm{d}^4x \;\; \mathrm{e}^{\varepsilon t}\langle\widehat{T}^{\mu\nu}\rangle_{\mathrm{LE}}\partial_\mu\beta_\nu \, \widehat{\rho}_{\mathrm{LE}}$$

Taking Equation (9) into account, the above equation is basically linear Approximation (10) with an extra factor $\exp(\varepsilon t)$ in the integrand. In a sense, Zubarev Assumption (11) of a small source term in the density operator evolution equation in the Heisenberg representation leads to the linear approximation of the fully stationary density operator operator (7). However, it should be emphasized that such an extra factor is not necessary. The Heisenberg equation for the true density operator is $\mathrm{d}\widehat{\rho}/\mathrm{d}t = 0$ does not need any modification for the derivation of the Kubo formulae or any other result depending on local thermodynamic equilibrium, as we will show in Section 5. A fully relativistic viewpoint with the application of the Gauss theorem makes the derivation of the NEDO expression (7) straightforward, transparent and simple.

4. Entropy Production

A remarkable consequence of this approach is the derivation of a general equation for the entropy production rate, which was reported in References [6,7]. Let us start with the assumption that S is an integral of entropy current s^μ:

$$S(\tau) = -\mathrm{tr}(\widehat{\rho}_{\mathrm{LE}}(\tau)\log\widehat{\rho}_{\mathrm{LE}}(\tau)) = \int_{\Sigma(\tau)} \mathrm{d}\Sigma_\mu\, s^\mu$$

On the other hand, entropy can be expanded by using Equation (3):

$$\begin{aligned} S(\tau) = -\mathrm{tr}(\widehat{\rho}_{\mathrm{LE}}(\tau)\log\widehat{\rho}_{\mathrm{LE}}(\tau)) &= \log Z_{\mathrm{LE}} + \int_{\Sigma(\tau)} \mathrm{d}\Sigma_\mu\, \langle \widehat{T}^{\mu\nu}\rangle_{\mathrm{LE}}\beta_\nu - \zeta\langle \widehat{j}^\mu\rangle_{\mathrm{LE}} \\ &= \log Z_{\mathrm{LE}} + \int_{\Sigma(\tau)} \mathrm{d}\Sigma_\mu\, (T^{\mu\nu}\beta_\nu - \zeta j^\mu) \end{aligned} \tag{15}$$

where we have used Constraints (2), taking into account that $\mathrm{d}\Sigma_\mu = \mathrm{d}\Sigma\, n_\mu$.

The derivative with respect to τ can be computed by taking advantage of a general expression for the variation of an integral between two infinitesimally closed hypersurfaces:

$$\frac{\mathrm{d}S}{\mathrm{d}\tau} = \int_{\Sigma(\tau)} \mathrm{d}\Sigma(n\cdot U)\nabla\cdot s + \frac{1}{2}\int_{\partial\Sigma(\tau)} \mathrm{d}\tilde{S}_{\mu\nu}(s^\mu U^\nu - s^\nu U^\mu) \tag{16}$$

where $\partial\Sigma$ is the 2D boundary of Σ and $U^\mu = \partial x^\mu/\partial\tau$; $\tilde{S}$ is the dual of the surface element. Now, assume that the boundary term does not contribute, and calculate the same derivative by using Expression (15):

$$\begin{aligned} \frac{\mathrm{d}S}{\mathrm{d}\tau} &= \frac{\mathrm{d}\log Z_{\mathrm{LE}}}{\mathrm{d}\tau} + \int_{\Sigma(\tau)} \mathrm{d}\Sigma(n\cdot U)\nabla_\mu\,(T^{\mu\nu}\beta_\nu - \zeta j^\mu) \\ &= \frac{\mathrm{d}\log Z_{\mathrm{LE}}}{\mathrm{d}\tau} + \int_{\Sigma(\tau)} \mathrm{d}\Sigma(n\cdot U)T^{\mu\nu}\nabla_\mu\beta_\nu - j^\mu\nabla_\mu\zeta \end{aligned} \tag{17}$$

where we have taken advantage of the conservation of the *exact* values $T^{\mu\nu}$ and j^μ. The remaining task is to calculate the derivative of $\log Z_{\mathrm{LE}}$, which can be done by using its definition

$$\frac{\mathrm{d}\log Z_{\mathrm{LE}}}{\mathrm{d}\tau} = \frac{1}{Z_{\mathrm{LE}}}\frac{\mathrm{d}}{\mathrm{d}\tau}\mathrm{tr}(\exp[\widehat{A}])$$

with $\widehat{A}$ in Equation (8). By using the same formula as the derivative of a τ-dependent integral in Equation (17), and assuming that the boundary term vanishes:

$$\tfrac{1}{Z_{\mathrm{LE}}}\tfrac{\mathrm{d}}{\mathrm{d}\tau}\mathrm{tr}(\exp[\widehat{A}]) = \tfrac{1}{Z_{\mathrm{LE}}}\mathrm{tr}\left(\tfrac{\mathrm{d}\widehat{A}}{\mathrm{d}\tau}\exp[\widehat{A}]\right) = \langle\tfrac{\mathrm{d}\widehat{A}}{\mathrm{d}\tau}\rangle_{\mathrm{LE}} = -\int_{\Sigma(\tau)}\mathrm{d}\Sigma(n\cdot U)\left(T^{\mu\nu}_{\mathrm{LE}}\nabla_\mu\beta_\nu - j^\mu_{\mathrm{LE}}\nabla_\mu\zeta\right) \tag{18}$$

By plugging Equation (18) into Equation (17) and comparing with Equation (16), taking into account that the equation should hold for any τ, we have

$$\nabla \cdot s = (T^{\mu\nu} - T^{\mu\nu}_{\rm LE})\nabla_\mu \beta_\nu - (j^\mu - j^\mu_{\rm LE})\nabla_\mu \zeta, \tag{19}$$

which was found in Reference [6], and tells us that the deviations of the conserved currents actual values from those at the local thermodynamic equilibrium are responsible for entropy production.

5. Kubo Formulae

Let us now apply the expansion of the NEDO (10) to calculate the mean value of a local operator $\widehat{O}$ at present time t:

$$\langle \widehat{O}(x) \rangle \simeq \langle \widehat{O}(x) \rangle_{\rm LE} - \langle \widehat{O}(x) \rangle_{\rm LE} \langle \widehat{B} \rangle_{\rm LE} + \int_0^1 {\rm d}z \; \langle \widehat{O}(x) {\rm e}^{z\widehat{A}} \widehat{B} {\rm e}^{-z\widehat{A}} \rangle_{\rm LE} \tag{20}$$

where $\widehat{A}$ and $\widehat{B}$ are in Equations (8) and (9), respectively. To work out Formula (20), it is customary to approximate the $\widehat{A}$ in the z integral on the right-hand side with the global equilibrium expression. In a covariant fashion, this means making a zero-order approximation of the Taylor expansion of the thermodynamic fields from point x, where operator $\widehat{O}$ is to be calculated:

$$\widehat{A} = -\int_{\Sigma(\tau)} {\rm d}\Sigma_\mu \left(\widehat{T}^{\mu\nu} \beta_\nu - \widehat{j}^\mu \zeta \right) \simeq -\beta_\nu(\tau, \sigma) \int_{\Sigma(\tau)} {\rm d}\Sigma_\mu \, \widehat{T}^{\mu\nu} + \zeta(\tau, \sigma) \int_{\Sigma(t)} {\rm d}\Sigma_\mu \, \widehat{j}^\mu = -\beta_\nu(x) \widehat{P}^\nu + \zeta(x) \widehat{Q} \tag{21}$$

where $\widehat{P}$ is the total four-momentum and $\widehat{Q}$ the total charge. Hence,

$$\widehat{\rho}_{\rm LE} \simeq \frac{1}{Z_{\rm LE}} \exp[\,\widehat{A}\,] \simeq \frac{1}{Z} \exp[-\beta(x) \cdot \widehat{P} + \zeta(x) \widehat{Q}] \equiv \widehat{\rho}_{{\rm eq}(x)} \tag{22}$$

that is, $\widehat{\rho}_{{\rm eq}(x)}$ is the global equilibrium density operator having the same vector at point x and similarly for ζ as constant inverse temperature four-vector.

Furthermore, we replace the integration region enclosed by the two LTE hypersurfaces at t and t_0 with the spacelike tangent hyperplanes at points $x = (\tau, \sigma)$ and $x_0 = (\tau_0, \sigma)$, respectively, whose normal versor is n. This allows to carry out the integration over Minkowski spacetime by using Cartesian coordinates, that is, time t marked by an observer moving with velocity n, and a vector of coordinates $\mathbf{x}$ for the hyperplanes. These approximations make it possible to replace covariant derivatives with usual partial derivatives in Cartesian coordinates:

$$\int_\Omega {\rm d}\Omega \, \left(\widehat{T}^{\mu\nu} \nabla_\mu \beta_\nu - \widehat{j}^\mu \nabla_\mu \zeta \right) \to \int_{T\Omega} {\rm d}^4x \, \left(\widehat{T}^{\mu\nu} \partial_\mu \beta_\nu - \widehat{j}^\mu \partial_\mu \zeta \right) \tag{23}$$

where $T\Omega$ is the region encompassed by the two hyperplanes. Thereby, and provided that $n(x) = \hat{\beta}(x)$, that is, that the local equilibrium hypersurface is locally normal to the flow velocity defined by the four-temperature vector [8], Formula (20) can be turned into a more manageable one (see Appendix A for a summary of the derivation) involving the commutators of operator $\widehat{O}$, with the stress–energy tensor and current operators

$$\langle \widehat{O}(x) \rangle - \langle \widehat{O}(x) \rangle_{\rm LE} \simeq iT \int_{t_0}^{t} {\rm d}^4x' \int_{t_0}^{t'} {\rm d}\theta \, \left(\langle [\widehat{O}(x), \widehat{T}^{\mu\nu}(\theta, \mathbf{x}')] \rangle_{\beta(x)} \partial_\mu \beta_\nu(x') - \langle [\widehat{O}(x), \widehat{j}^\mu(\theta, \mathbf{x}')] \rangle_{\beta(x)} \partial_\mu \zeta(x') \right) \tag{24}$$

where $T = 1/\sqrt{\beta^2}$, and subscript $\beta(x)$ stands for averaging with the density operator in Equation (22). It is important to stress the different time arguments for the operators and the thermodynamic fields in Equation (24).

From Equation (24), it turns out that the deviation from LTE of the mean value of $\widehat{O}$ at any time depends on the whole history of thermodynamic fields β and ζ. However, the correlation length between $\widehat{O}(x)$ and both $\widehat{T}(x')$, $\widehat{j}(x')$ is typically much smaller than the distance over which the gradients of β and ζ have significant variations. This statement amounts to assuming a separation between the typical microscopic interaction scale and the macroscopic hydrodynamical scale. One would then be tempted to take the gradients out of the integral in Equation (24). However, much care should be taken in this because the derivation of Formula (24), more precisely nonequilibrium density operator (7), required the vanishing of the flux of $\widehat{T}^{\mu\nu}\beta_\nu - \widehat{j}^\mu\zeta$ at the boundary timelike hypersurface. If one expands the perturbation of the thermodynamic fields with respect to their equilibrium value, by definition those at point x, that is,

$$\delta\beta \equiv \beta - \beta_{\rm eq} = \beta - \beta(x) \qquad \delta\zeta \equiv \zeta - \zeta_{\rm eq} = \zeta - \zeta(x)$$

in a Fourier series, the only relevant components in the hydrodynamical limit for Integral (24) are those with very small frequency ω and wave vector $\mathbf{k}$. At the same time, the vanishing of the flux can be achieved by enforcing periodicity of the perturbations in $\mathbf{x} - \mathbf{x}'$. Taking these requirements into account, perturbations only include smallest wave four-vector K:

$$\delta\beta_\nu(x') \simeq A_\nu \frac{1}{2i}(\mathrm{e}^{iK\cdot(x'-x)} - \mathrm{e}^{-iK\cdot(x'-x)}) \tag{25}$$

with A_ν being a real constant, the amplitude of the smallest wave four-vector Fourier component. The above form fulfils $\delta\beta(x') = 0$ as well as the request of vanishing flux, provided that $K^i = \pi/L_i$, with L_i being the size of the compact domain in direction i. Hence, after the use of Equation (25), limit $K \to 0$ is to be taken, which is equivalent to the limit of infinite volume. The gradient of Equation (25) (keep in mind that, in Equation (24), $\partial_\mu = \partial/\partial x'^\mu$) can then be written as:

$$\partial_\mu\beta_\nu \simeq K_\mu A_\nu \frac{1}{2}(\mathrm{e}^{iK\cdot(x'-x)} + \mathrm{e}^{-iK\cdot(x'-x)}) = \partial_\mu\beta_\nu(x) \mathrm{Re}\, \mathrm{e}^{-iK\cdot(x'-x)} = \mathrm{Re}\, \partial_\mu\beta_\nu(x)\mathrm{e}^{-iK\cdot(x'-x)} \tag{26}$$

Plugging Equation (26) in Equation (24), in limit $K \to 0$, one obtains:

$$\begin{aligned} \langle\widehat{O}(x)\rangle - \langle\widehat{O}(x)\rangle_{\rm LE} \simeq \quad & \partial_\mu\beta_\nu(x) \lim_{K\to 0} \mathrm{Im}\, T \int_{t_0}^{t} \mathrm{d}^4x' \int_{t_0}^{t'} \mathrm{d}\theta\, \langle[\widehat{T}^{\mu\nu}(\theta,\mathbf{x}'),\widehat{O}(x)]\rangle_{\beta(x)}\mathrm{e}^{-iK\cdot(x'-x)} \\ & -\partial_\mu\zeta(x) \lim_{K\to 0} \mathrm{Im}\, T \int_{t_0}^{t} \mathrm{d}^4x' \int_{t_0}^{t'} \mathrm{d}\theta \langle[\widehat{j}^\mu(\theta,\mathbf{x}'),\widehat{O}(x)]\rangle_{\beta(x)}\mathrm{e}^{-iK\cdot(x'-x)} \end{aligned} \tag{27}$$

As the macroscopic time scale $t - t_0$ and the microscopic time scale inherent in the correlators are so different, one can take limit $t_0 \to -\infty$. If functions

$$\int \mathrm{d}^3x'\, \langle[\widehat{X}(\theta,\mathbf{x}'),\widehat{O}(x)]\rangle_{\beta(x)}$$

with $\widehat{X} = \widehat{T},\widehat{j}$ remain finite for $\theta \to -\infty$, then Equation (27), after integration by parts in t', can be turned into:

$$\begin{aligned} \langle\widehat{O}(x)\rangle - \langle\widehat{O}(x)\rangle_{\rm LE} \simeq \quad & \partial_\mu\beta_\nu(x) n^\alpha \frac{\partial}{\partial K^\alpha}\Big|_{n\cdot K=0} \lim_{K_T\to 0} \mathrm{Im}\, iT \int_{-\infty}^{t} \mathrm{d}^4x'\, \langle[\widehat{O}(x),\widehat{T}^{\mu\nu}(x')]\rangle_{\beta(x)}\mathrm{e}^{-iK\cdot(x'-x)} \\ & -\partial_\mu\zeta(x) n^\alpha \frac{\partial}{\partial K^\alpha}\Big|_{n\cdot K=0} \mathrm{Im}\, iT \int_{-\infty}^{t} \mathrm{d}^4x'\, \langle[\widehat{O}(x),\widehat{j}^\mu(x')]\rangle_{\beta(x)}\mathrm{e}^{-iK\cdot(x'-x)} \end{aligned} \tag{28}$$

where K_T is the projection of K orthogonal to n. This, as it becomes clear later, is the covariant form of the same formula obtained in Reference [1], with the (important) addition of the current term. In other words, it is the well-known formula expressing the transport coefficients as derivatives with respect to the frequency of the retarded correlators of stress–energy components, the so-called Kubo formula. Defining:

$$
\begin{aligned}
(\widehat{X},\widehat{Y}) \equiv & \quad n^\alpha \frac{\partial}{\partial K^\alpha}\Big|_{n\cdot k=0} \lim_{k_T\to 0} \mathrm{Im}\, iT \int_{-\infty}^{t} \mathrm{d}^4x' \, \langle [\widehat{X}(x),\widehat{Y}(x')]\rangle_{\beta(x)} \mathrm{e}^{-iK\cdot(x'-x)} \\
= & \quad n^\alpha \frac{\partial}{\partial K^\alpha}\Big|_{n\cdot k=0} \lim_{k_T\to 0} \mathrm{Im}\, iT \int_{-\infty}^{0} \mathrm{d}^4x' \, \langle [\widehat{X}(0),\widehat{Y}(x')]\rangle_{\beta(x)} \mathrm{e}^{-iK\cdot x'},
\end{aligned} \tag{29}
$$

which is bilinear in $\widehat{X}$ and $\widehat{Y}$, one can write the deviations of the stress–energy tensor from its LTE value as:

$$
\langle \widehat{T}^{\mu\nu}(x)\rangle - \langle \widehat{T}^{\mu\nu}(x)\rangle_{\mathrm{LE}} \equiv \delta T^{\mu\nu}(x) \simeq (\widehat{T}^{\mu\nu},\widehat{T}^{\rho\sigma})\,\partial_\rho\beta_\sigma(x) - (\widehat{T}^{\mu\nu},\widehat{j}^\rho)\,\partial_\rho\zeta(x). \tag{30}
$$

Similarly, the deviation of the current with respect to its value at LTE reads:

$$
\langle \widehat{j}^{\mu}(x)\rangle - \langle \widehat{j}^{\mu}(x)\rangle_{\mathrm{LE}} \equiv \delta j^{\mu}(x) = (\widehat{j}^{\mu},\widehat{T}^{\rho\sigma})\,\partial_\rho\beta_\sigma(x) - (\widehat{j}^{\mu},\widehat{j}^\rho)\,\partial_\rho\zeta(x). \tag{31}
$$

The next step is to decompose the correlators and the gradients of the relativistic fields into irreducible components under rotations, a procedure leading to the identification of familiar transport coefficients: shear and bulk viscosities, thermal conductivities, etc. We are not going to show how this is accomplished, but we would just like to point out, for the purpose of identifying the transport coefficients, that the gradients of β can be turned into gradients of velocity field u by using Equation (5). Having defined

$$
\Delta_{\mu\nu} = g_{\mu\nu} - u_\mu u_\nu
$$

and

$$
D = u\cdot\partial \qquad\qquad \nabla_T^\mu = \partial^\mu - u^\mu D,
$$

the transverse gradients of velocity field $\nabla_T^\mu u^\nu$ can be written as follows:

$$
\begin{aligned}
\nabla_{T\mu}u^\nu & = \nabla_{T\mu}\frac{\beta^\nu}{\sqrt{\beta^2}} = -\frac{1}{2}\beta^\nu(\beta^2)^{-3/2}\nabla_{T\mu}\beta^2 + \frac{1}{\sqrt{\beta^2}}\nabla_{T\mu}\beta^\nu \\
& = \frac{1}{\sqrt{\beta^2}}\left(-\frac{\beta^\nu\beta^\rho}{\beta^2}\nabla_{T\mu}\beta_\rho + \nabla_{T\mu}\beta^\nu\right) = \frac{1}{\sqrt{\beta^2}}\Delta^{\rho\nu}\nabla_{T\mu}\beta_\rho,
\end{aligned} \tag{32}
$$

where we have used Relation (5). Thereby, the Navier–Stokes shear term can be fully expressed in terms of inverse temperature four-vector β and its gradients. The same transformation can be proven for the other terms [8].

6. Outlook

The nonequilibrium statistical operator method introduced by D. Zubarev more than 50 years ago has been a very important achievement in statistical physics and has not received deserved attention. It can be used in all physical problems where a local thermodynamic equilibrium is reached, and it can be quite straightforwardly extended to relativistic statistical mechanics. In this work, we presented an amendment of its original formulation that reproduces known results and makes its application easier to relativistic hydrodynamics problems. Since it is a fully fledged quantum framework, this approach is especially suitable for the calculation of quantum effects. Among various applications, recent evidence of nonvanishing polarization in quark–gluon plasma [13] makes it the ideal tool to deal with this newly found phenomenon.

Author Contributions: Conceptualization, F.B.; Methodology, F.B., M.B., E.G.; Investigation, F.B., M.B. and E.G.; Writing–original draft preparation, F.B.; Writing–review & editing, F.B. and M.B.

Funding: This research was funded by INFN under the grant SIM.

Conflicts of Interest: The authors declare no conflict of interest.

Appendix A. Supplementary Notes on the Derivation of the Kubo Formula

Working out Equation (20) requires Equations (8) and (9). By also using Approximations (21) and (23), Equation (20) turns into:

$$\begin{aligned}\langle\widehat{O}(x)\rangle - \langle\widehat{O}(x)\rangle_{\rm LE} &\simeq -\int_{t_0}^{t} {\rm d}t' \int {\rm d}^3{\rm x}' \, \langle\widehat{O}(x)\rangle_{\rm LE} \left(\langle\widehat{T}^{\mu\nu}(t',\mathbf{x}')\rangle_{\rm LE}\partial_\mu\beta_\nu - \langle\widehat{j}^\mu(t',\mathbf{x}')\rangle_{\rm LE}\partial_\mu\zeta\right) \\ &+ \int_0^1 {\rm d}z \int_{t_0}^{t} {\rm d}t' \int {\rm d}^3{\rm x}' \left(\langle\widehat{O}(x){\rm e}^{-z(\beta(x)\cdot\widehat{P}-\zeta(x)\widehat{Q})}\widehat{T}^{\mu\nu}(t',\mathbf{x}'){\rm e}^{z(\beta(x)\cdot\widehat{P}-\zeta(x)\widehat{Q})}\rangle_{\rm LE}\partial_\mu\beta_\nu\right. \\ &- \left.\langle\widehat{O}(x){\rm e}^{-z(\beta(x)\cdot\widehat{P}-\zeta(x)\widehat{Q})}\widehat{j}^\mu(t',\mathbf{x}'){\rm e}^{z(\beta(x)\cdot\widehat{P}-\zeta(x)\widehat{Q})}\rangle_{\rm LE}\partial_\mu\zeta\right) \end{aligned} \tag{A1}$$

With $[\widehat{Q},\widehat{T}(x)] = 0$ and $[\widehat{Q},\widehat{j}(x)] = 0$, one can also write

$${\rm e}^{-z(\beta(x)\cdot P-\zeta(x)\widehat{Q})}\,\widehat{X}(t',\mathbf{x}')\,{\rm e}^{z(\beta(x)\cdot P-\zeta(x)\widehat{Q})} = \widehat{X}(t'+iz\sqrt{\beta^2},\mathbf{x}')$$

with $\widehat{X} = \widehat{T},\widehat{j}$, where, in the last expression, we tacitly assumed that $n = \hat{\beta}$, i.e., that the local equilibrium hypersurface coincides, locally around x, with the hypersurface normal to β [8]. Hence, the last term in the right-hand side of Equation (A1) can be rewritten as:

$$\int_0^1 {\rm d}z \int_{t_0}^{t} {\rm d}t' \int {\rm d}^3{\rm x}' \left(\langle\widehat{O}(x)\widehat{T}^{\mu\nu}(t'+iz\sqrt{\beta^2},\mathbf{x}')\rangle_{\rm LE}\partial_\mu\beta_\nu - \langle\widehat{O}(x)\widehat{j}^\mu(t'+iz\sqrt{\beta^2},\mathbf{x}')\rangle_{\rm LE}\partial_\mu\zeta\right)$$

provided that $n = \hat{\beta}$, that is, if the local equilibrium hypersurface locally coincides with the hypersurface normal to β [8]. Operator $\widehat{X} = \widehat{T},\widehat{j}$, can be rewritten as

$$\begin{aligned}\widehat{X}(t'+iz\sqrt{\beta^2},\mathbf{x}') &= \widehat{X}(t_0+iz\sqrt{\beta^2},\mathbf{x}') + \int_{t_0}^{t'} {\rm d}\theta \, \frac{\partial}{\partial\theta}\widehat{X}(\theta+iz\sqrt{\beta^2},\mathbf{x}') \\ &= \widehat{X}(t_0+iz\sqrt{\beta^2},\mathbf{x}') + \int_{t_0}^{t'} {\rm d}\theta \, \frac{1}{i\sqrt{\beta^2}}\frac{\partial}{\partial z}\widehat{X}(\theta+iz\sqrt{\beta^2},\mathbf{x}') \end{aligned} \tag{A2}$$

and integrating in z:

$$\begin{aligned}\int_0^1 {\rm d}z\langle\widehat{O}(x)\widehat{X}(t'+iz\sqrt{\beta^2},\mathbf{x}')\rangle_{\rm LE} &= \int_0^1 {\rm d}z\, \langle\widehat{O}(x)\widehat{X}(t_0+iz\sqrt{\beta^2},\mathbf{x}')\rangle_{\rm LE} \\ +\int_{t_0}^{t'} {\rm d}\theta\, \frac{1}{i\sqrt{\beta^2}} &\left(\langle\widehat{O}(x)\widehat{X}(\theta+i\sqrt{\beta^2},\mathbf{x}')\rangle_{\rm LE} - \langle\widehat{O}(x)\widehat{X}(\theta,\mathbf{x}')\rangle_{\rm LE}\right). \end{aligned} \tag{A3}$$

Now, we use the same approximation of $\widehat{A}$ as in Equation (21), and LTE mean values are calculated at equilibrium, with density Operator (22). Thus,

$$\begin{aligned}&\langle\widehat{O}(x)\widehat{X}(\theta+i\sqrt{\beta^2},\mathbf{x}')\rangle_{\rm LE} - \langle\widehat{O}(x)\widehat{X}(\theta,\mathbf{x}')\rangle_{\rm LE} \simeq \langle\widehat{O}(x)\widehat{X}(\theta+i\sqrt{\beta^2},\mathbf{x}')\rangle_{\beta(x)} - \langle\widehat{O}(x)\widehat{X}(\theta,\mathbf{x}')\rangle_{\beta(x)} \\ &= \langle\widehat{O}(x){\rm e}^{-\beta(x)\cdot\widehat{P}+\zeta(x)\widehat{Q}}\widehat{X}(\theta,\mathbf{x}'){\rm e}^{\beta(x)\cdot\widehat{P}-\zeta(x)\widehat{Q}}\rangle_{\beta(x)} - \langle\widehat{O}(x)\widehat{X}(\theta,\mathbf{x}')\rangle_{\beta(x)} \\ &= \langle\widehat{X}(\theta,\mathbf{x}')\widehat{O}(x)\rangle_{\beta(x)} - \langle\widehat{O}(x)\widehat{X}(\theta,\mathbf{x}')\rangle_{\beta(x)} = \langle[\widehat{X}(\theta,\mathbf{x}'),\widehat{O}(x)]\rangle_{\beta(x)}\end{aligned}$$

Substitution into Equation (A3) yields:

$$\int_0^1 {\rm d}z\langle\widehat{O}(x)\widehat{X}(t+iz\sqrt{\beta^2},\mathbf{x}')\rangle_{\rm LE} \simeq \int_0^1 {\rm d}z\,\langle\widehat{O}(x)\widehat{X}(t_0+iz\sqrt{\beta^2},\mathbf{x}')\rangle_{\beta(x)} + \frac{1}{i\sqrt{\beta^2}}\int_{t_0}^{t'} {\rm d}\theta\,\langle[\widehat{X}(\theta,\mathbf{x}'),\widehat{O}(x)]\rangle_{\beta(x)}. \tag{A4}$$

Using this result for $\widehat{X} = \widehat{T}, \widehat{j}$ allows to turn Equation (A1) into:

$$\begin{aligned}\langle\widehat{O}(x)\rangle - \langle\widehat{O}(x)\rangle_{\rm LE} \simeq & \int_{t_0}^{t} \mathrm{d}t' \int \mathrm{d}^3\mathrm{x}' \int_0^1 \mathrm{d}z \left[\left(\langle\widehat{O}(x)\widehat{T}^{\mu\nu}(t_0+iz\sqrt{\beta^2},\mathbf{x}')\rangle_{\beta(x)} - \langle\widehat{O}(x)\rangle_{\beta(x)}\langle\widehat{T}^{\mu\nu}(t',\mathbf{x}')\rangle_{\beta(x)}\right)\partial_\mu\beta_\nu\right. \\ & \left.\left(\langle\widehat{O}(x)\widehat{j}^{\mu}(t_0+iz\sqrt{\beta^2},\mathbf{x}')\rangle_{\beta(x)} - \langle\widehat{O}(x)\rangle_{\beta(x)}\langle\widehat{j}^{\mu}(t',\mathbf{x}')\rangle_{\beta(x)}\right)\partial_\mu\zeta\right] \\ + & \; iT\int_{t_0}^{t} \mathrm{d}t' \int_{t_0}^{t'} \mathrm{d}\theta \int \mathrm{d}^3\mathrm{x}' \left(\langle[\widehat{O}(x),\widehat{T}^{\mu\nu}(\theta,\mathbf{x}')]\rangle_{\beta(x)}\partial_\mu\beta_\nu(x') - \langle[\widehat{O}(x),\widehat{j}^{\mu}(\theta,\mathbf{x}')]\rangle_{\beta(x)}\partial_\mu\zeta(x')\right).\end{aligned} \tag{A5}$$

In the paper by A. Hosoya et al. [1], in limit $t_0 \to -\infty$, the first of the two integral terms is shown to be vanishing, based on the idea that $\lim_{t_0\to-\infty}\widehat{X}(t_0+iz\sqrt{\beta^2},\mathbf{x}') \simeq \lim_{t_0\to-\infty}\widehat{X}(t_0,\mathbf{x}')$ and that correlation between operator $\widehat{O}$ at time t and $\widehat{X}$ at an infinitely remote past is 0, that is,

$$\lim_{t_0\to-\infty}\langle\widehat{O}(x)\widehat{T}^{\mu\nu}(t_0,\mathbf{x}')\rangle_{\beta(x)} \simeq \lim_{t_0\to-\infty}\langle\widehat{O}(x)\rangle_{\beta(x)}\langle\widehat{T}^{\mu\nu}(t_0,\mathbf{x}')\rangle_{\beta(x)} = \langle\widehat{O}(x)\rangle_{\beta(x)}\langle\widehat{T}^{\mu\nu}(t',\mathbf{x}')\rangle_{\beta(x)}$$

where, in the last equality, we took advantage of the fact that the mean value of any operator is constant at equilibrium. Therefore, the first integral on the right-hand side of Equation (A5) vanishes, and we are left only with the second integration, that is, Equation (24).

Let us now define the λ-dependent partition function:

$$Z_{\rm LE}(\lambda) = \mathrm{tr}\left(\exp\left[-\lambda \mathrm{d}\Sigma\, n_\mu\left(\widehat{T}^{\mu\nu}\beta_\nu - \widehat{j}^{\mu}\zeta\right)\right]\right)$$

If we take the derivative with regard to λ, we have

$$\frac{\partial}{\partial\lambda}\log Z_{\rm LE}(\lambda) = \int \mathrm{d}\Sigma\, n_\mu\left(\langle\widehat{T}^{\mu\nu}\rangle_{\rm LE}(\lambda)\beta_\nu - \zeta\langle\widehat{j}^{\mu}\rangle_{\rm LE}(\lambda)\right)$$

whence

$$\log Z_{\rm LE}(1) - \log Z_{\rm LE}(\lambda_0) = \int_{\lambda_0}^{1}\mathrm{d}\lambda\int \mathrm{d}\Sigma\, n_\mu\left(\langle\widehat{T}^{\mu\nu}\rangle_{\rm LE}(\lambda)\beta_\nu - \zeta\langle\widehat{j}^{\mu}\rangle_{\rm LE}(\lambda)\right)$$

If we find λ_0, such that $\log Z_{\rm LE}(\lambda_0) = 0$, which happens under some reasonable assumptions $\lambda_0 = +\infty$, and inverting the order of integrations:

$$\log Z_{\rm LE} = \int \mathrm{d}\Sigma\, n_\mu \int_{\lambda_0}^{1}\mathrm{d}\lambda\left(\langle\widehat{T}^{\mu\nu}\rangle_{\rm LE}(\lambda)\beta_\nu - \zeta\langle\widehat{j}^{\mu}\rangle_{\rm LE}(\lambda)\right) \equiv \int \mathrm{d}\Sigma_\mu\phi^\mu, \tag{A6}$$

which shows that $\log Z_{\rm LE}$ is extensive, i.e., it can be written as an integral over the 3D hypersurface of a current, the thermodynamic potential current. At the same time, the above equation provides a formula to calculate ϕ^μ as an integral in λ.

References

1. Hosoya, A.; Sakagami, M.; Takao, M. Nonequilibrium Thermodynamics in Field Theory: Transport Coefficients. *Ann. Phys.* **1984**, *154*, 229. [CrossRef]
2. Zubarev, D.N. A statistical operator for non stationary processes. *Sov. Phys. Doklady* **1966**, *10*, 850.
3. Zubarev, D.N.; Tokarchuk, M.V. Nonequilibrium Thermo Field Dynamics and the Method of the Nonequilibrium Statistical Operator. *Theor. Math. Phys.* **1992**, *88*, 876. [CrossRef]
4. Morozov, V.G.; Röpke, G. Zubarev's method of a nonequilibrium statistical operator and some challenges in the theory of irreversible processes. *Condens. Matter Phys.* **1998**, *1*, 673. [CrossRef]
5. Harutyunyan, A.; Sedrakian, A.; Rischke, D.H. Relativistic Dissipative Fluid Dynamics from the Non-Equilibrium Statistical Operator. *Particles* **2018**, *1*, 11. [CrossRef]
6. Zubarev, D.N.; Prozorkevich, A.V.; Smolyanskii, S.A. Derivation of nonlinear generalized equations of quantum relativistic hydrodynamics. *Theor. Math. Phys.* **1979**, *40*, 821. [CrossRef]
7. Van Weert, C.G. Maximum entropy principle and relativistic hydrodynamics. *Ann. Phys.* **1982**, *140*, 133. [CrossRef]

8. Becattini, F.; Bucciantini, L.; Grossi, E.; Tinti, L. Local thermodynamical equilibrium and the beta frame for a quantum relativistic fluid. *Eur. Phys. J. C* **2015**, *75*, 191. [CrossRef]
9. Hayata, T.; Hidaka, Y.; Noumi, T.; Hongo, M. Relativistic hydrodynamics from quantum field theory on the basis of the generalized Gibbs ensemble method. *Phys. Rev. D* **2015**, *92*, 065008. [CrossRef]
10. Becattini, F.; Florkowski, W.; Speranza, E. Spin tensor and its role in non-equilibrium thermodynamics. *Phys. Lett. B* **2019**, *789*, 419. [CrossRef]
11. Jensen, K.; Kaminski, M.; Kovtun, P.; Meyer, R.; Ritz, A.; Yarom, A. Towards hydrodynamics without an entropy current. *Phys. Rev. Lett.* **2012**, *109*, 101601. [CrossRef] [PubMed]
12. Becattini, F. Spin tensor and its role in non-equilibrium thermodynamics. *Phys. Rev. Lett.* **2012**, *108*, 244502. [CrossRef] [PubMed]
13. The STAR Collaboration. Global Λ hyperon polarization in nuclear collisions: Evidence for the most vortical fluid. *Nature* **2017**, *548*, 62. [CrossRef] [PubMed]

particles

MDPI

Article

Anomaly-Induced Transport Phenomena from Imaginary-Time Formalism

Masaru Hongo [1,2,*] and Yoshimasa Hidaka [1,3]

1 RIKEN iTHEMS, RIKEN, Wako, Saitama 351-0198, Japan; hidaka@riken.jp
2 Research and Education Center for Natural Sciences, Keio University, Yokohama, Kanagawa 223-8521, Japan
3 Quantum Hadron Physics Laboratory, RIKEN Nishina Center, RIKEN, Wako, Saitama 351-0198, Japan
* Correspondence: masaru.hongo@riken.jp; Tel.: +81-48-462-1226

Received: 25 February 2019; Accepted: 6 May 2019; Published: 16 May 2019

Abstract: A derivation of anomaly-induced transport phenomena—the chiral magnetic/vortical effect—is revisited based on the imaginary-time formalism of quantum field theory. Considering the simplest anomalous system composed of a single Weyl fermion, we provide two derivations: perturbative (one-loop) evaluation of the anomalous transport coefficient, and the anomaly matching for the local thermodynamic functional.

Keywords: finite temperature field theory; path integrals; quantum fields in curved spacetime; quantum statistical mechanics; symmetries; quantum anomalies; hydrodynamics

1. Introduction

Quantum anomaly is one of the most fundamental properties of quantum systems, which keeps staying in the low-energy regime once it appears in an underlying UV theory [1,2]. As a consequence, the low-energy dynamics is strongly influenced by the existence of the quantum anomaly. A well-known example is the chiral anomaly in QCD, which gives rise to the Wess-Zumino term in the low-energy effective theory of QCD (the chiral perturbation theory) describing the neutral pion decay into two photons ($\pi^0 \to \gamma\gamma$) [3–5]. The notion of anomaly can be generalized to discrete symmetries of systems such as time-reversal symmetry. The anomaly matching argument [6,7] is actively applied to restrict the possible nontrivial ground states (See Refs. [8–19] for recent applications).

It has been recently noticed that quantum anomaly also appears even in the effective theory describing the real-time dynamics of nonequilibrium systems, e.g., hydrodynamics and the kinetic theory, and it affects the macroscopic transport properties in the hydrodynamic regime [20–61] (See also pioneering works by Vilenkin [62,63]). For example, the simplest anomalous system composed of a single right-handed Weyl fermion coupled to a background electromagnetic field shows interesting transport . When this system is put into an environment with a temperature T and a chemical potential μ_R, the chiral anomaly induces the dissipationless current along the magnetic field B^i given by

$$\langle \hat{J}^i_R \rangle_{\text{ano}} = \sigma_B B^i + \sigma_\omega \omega^i \quad \text{with} \quad \sigma_B = \frac{\mu_R}{4\pi^2}, \quad \sigma_\omega = \frac{\mu_R^2}{4\pi^2} + \frac{T^2}{12}, \tag{1}$$

where $\langle \hat{J}^\mu_R \rangle_{\text{ano}}$ denotes the anomalous part of the expectation value of the right-handed current, and σ_B (σ_ω) is regarded as the chiral magnetic (vortical) conductivity. The first and second terms in Equation (1) are called the chiral magnetic effect (CME) and chiral vortical effect (CVE), respectively (See Figure 1). It is worth pointing out that even in the weak coupling limit, σ_B and σ_ω do not diverge unlike the usual conductivity because their existence is protected by the quantum anomaly.

These anomalous transports are believed to be universally present when the system under consideration contains the chiral anomaly. For example, they are expected to take place in the quark-gluon plasma created in high-energy heavy-ion collisions [64–74], astrophysical plasma including neutrino process [75–80], and Weyl semimetals realized in condensed matter physics [81–90]. While we have not observed clear experimental signal of the anomaly-induced transport in the first two systems, it has been recently reported that the experimental signals of the CME are achieved in the Weyl semimetal [91–93].

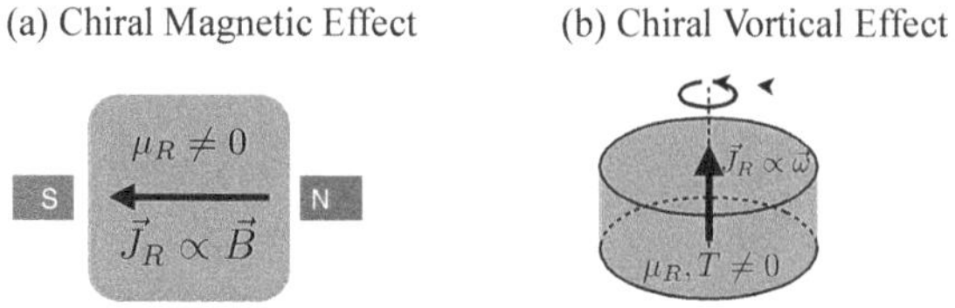

Figure 1. The schematic picture of the anomaly-induced transport phenomena: (**a**) Chiral magnetic effect. (**b**) Chiral vortical effect.

The theoretical derivation of the anomaly-induced transport phenomena has been remarkably developed in the past ten years, e.g., the direct field theoretical evaluation [20], the fluid/gravity correspondence [21–23,25], the phenomenological entropy-current analysis [24], the linear response theory [26,31,34,50,58], the kinetic theory [27,28,33,36,37,41,42,44,48,49,51–53,55,57,59–61], and the hydrostatic partition function method and extensions [29,30,32,35,38–40,43,45,46,54]. In this paper, we review the derivation of the anomaly-induced transport phenomena from the statistical mechanical viewpoint with the help of the imaginary-time (Matsubara) formalism of quantum field theory [94–97]. In particular, we demonstrate two derivations, which are basically on the same line as the last two derivations raised above. For that purpose, we consider the simplest anomalous system composed of a single Weyl fermion coupled to an external electromagnetic field. Although most results given in this paper has been already known, we give the clear rigorous justification of the hydrostatic partition function method for the anomalous system based on the statistical ensemble describing systems in general local thermal equilibrium. This shows that the hydrostatic partition function method is indeed not restricted to the real hydrostatic situation, but applicable to systems in general local thermal equilibrium.

The paper is organized as follows: In Section 2, we review the basic setup and formulation including the Zubarev's nonequilibrium statistical operator methods [98–100] (See also Refs. [101–104] for a recent sophisticated revival of a similar idea). In Section 3, we then provide the perturbative evaluation of the chiral magnetic/vortical conductivity with the help of the (equilibrium) linear response theory, from which we can read off the constitutive relation for the anomalous current. In Section 4, we give another nonperturbative derivation based on the anomaly matching for the local thermodynamic functional. Section 5 is devoted to the summary and discussion.

2. Preliminaries for the Anomaly-Induced Transport Phenomena

In this section, we briefly summarize the formulation to derive the anomaly-induced transport phenomena based on the imaginary-time formalism [98–104].

2.1. Anomalous (Non-)Conservation Laws for a Single Weyl Fermion

Let us consider the system consisting of a right-handed Weyl fermions ξ under an external $U(1)$ gauge field A_μ in a $(3+1)$ dimensional curved spacetime, whose action has the form:

$$\mathcal{S}[\xi,\xi^\dagger;A_\mu,e_\mu^a] = \int d^4x e\mathcal{L} \quad \text{with} \quad \mathcal{L} \equiv \frac{i}{2}\xi^\dagger \left(e_a^{\ \mu}\sigma^a \overrightarrow{D}_\mu - \overleftarrow{D}_\mu \sigma^a e_a^{\ \mu}\right)\xi, \quad e \equiv \det(e_\mu^a), \tag{2}$$

where we introduced $\sigma^a = (1, \sigma^i)$ with the Pauli matrices σ^i $(i = 1,2,3)$. Here $e_\mu^{\ a}(e^\mu_{\ a})$ denotes (inverse) vierbein satisfying $g_{\mu\nu} = e_\mu^{\ a} e_\nu^{\ b} \eta_{ab}$, $\eta^{ab} = e_\mu^{\ a} e_\nu^{\ b} g^{\mu\nu}$ with the spacetime curved metric $g_{\mu\nu}$ and Minkowski metric $\eta_{ab} = \mathrm{diag}(-1,+1,+1,+1)$. The left and right covariant derivatives are defined as

$$\overrightarrow{D}_\mu \xi \equiv \partial_\mu \xi - i(\mathcal{A}_\mu + A_\mu)\xi, \quad \xi^\dagger \overleftarrow{D}_\mu \equiv \partial_\mu \xi^\dagger + i\xi^\dagger(\mathcal{A}_\mu + A_\mu) \quad \text{with} \quad \mathcal{A}_\mu \equiv \frac{1}{2}\omega_\mu^{\ ab}\Sigma_{ab}, \tag{3}$$

where we introduced $\Sigma_{ab} \equiv i(\sigma^a\bar{\sigma}^b - \sigma^b\bar{\sigma}^a)/4$ with $\bar{\sigma}^a \equiv (-1, \sigma^i)$, which satisfies $\sigma^a\bar{\sigma}^b + \sigma^b\bar{\sigma}^a = 2\eta^{ab}$. Furthermore, employing the torsionless condition, we can express the spin connection $\omega_\mu^{\ ab} = -\omega_\mu^{\ ba}$ as

$$\omega_\mu^{\ ab} \equiv \frac{1}{2} e^{a\nu} e^{b\rho} (C_{\nu\rho\mu} - C_{\rho\nu\mu} - C_{\mu\nu\rho}) \quad \text{with} \quad C_{\mu\nu\rho} \equiv e_\mu^{\ c}(\partial_\nu e_{\rho c} - \partial_\rho e_{\nu c}). \tag{4}$$

Although the classical action (2) is invariant under a set of infinitesimal diffeomorphisms, local Lorentz, and $U(1)$ gauge transformations with parameters $\chi \equiv \{\zeta^\mu, \alpha_{ab}, \theta\}$:

$$\begin{cases} \delta_\chi e_\mu^{\ a} = \zeta^\nu \nabla_\nu e_\mu^{\ a} + e_\nu^{\ a} \nabla_\mu \zeta^\nu + \alpha^a_{\ b} e_\mu^{\ b}, \\ \delta_\chi A_\mu = \zeta^\nu \nabla_\nu A_\mu + A_\nu \nabla_\mu \zeta^\nu + \partial_\mu \theta, \\ \delta_\chi \xi = \zeta^\nu \partial_\nu \xi - \frac{i}{2}\alpha^{ab}\Sigma_{ab}\xi + i\theta\xi, \end{cases} \tag{5}$$

we encounter with the quantum anomaly attached to the Weyl fermion. As a consequence, the anomalous Ward-Takahashi identities results in the following operator identities corresponding to the (non-)conservation laws:

$$\begin{cases} \nabla_\mu \hat{T}^\mu_{\ \nu} = F_{\nu\mu} \hat{J}^\mu, \\ \nabla_\mu \hat{J}^\mu = -\frac{1}{8} C \varepsilon^{\mu\nu\rho\sigma} F_{\mu\nu} F_{\rho\sigma} - \lambda \varepsilon^{\mu\nu\rho\sigma} R^\alpha_{\ \beta\mu\nu} R^\beta_{\ \alpha\rho\sigma}, \end{cases} \tag{6}$$

where we introduced the energy-momentum tensor $\hat{T}^\mu_{\ \nu}$, $U(1)$ covariant charge current $\hat{J}^\mu$ defined as

$$\begin{aligned} \hat{T}^{\mu\nu} &= \frac{1}{e}\frac{\delta S}{\delta e_\mu^{\ a}} e^\nu_{\ a} = -\frac{i}{2}\xi^\dagger(\sigma^\mu \overrightarrow{D^\nu} - \overleftarrow{D^\nu}\sigma^\mu)\xi + \frac{1}{4}D_\rho(\eta^\dagger\{\sigma^\mu, \Sigma^{\nu\rho}\}\eta) + \mathcal{L} g^{\mu\nu}, \\ \hat{J}^\mu &= \frac{1}{e}\frac{\delta S}{\delta e_\mu^{\ a}} = \xi^\dagger \sigma^\mu \xi. \end{aligned} \tag{7}$$

The Lorentz invariance implies that the antisymmetric part of the energy tensor vanishes: $T^{\mu\nu} + T^{\nu\mu} = 0$; thus, $T^{\mu\nu}$ can be regarded as symmetric one. We also defined a field strength tensor for the background electromagnetic field $F_{\mu\nu} \equiv \partial_\mu A_\nu - \partial_\nu A_\mu$, and the Riemann curvature tensor $R^\mu_{\ \nu\rho\sigma}$ with the totally antisymmetric tensor $\varepsilon^{\mu\nu\rho\sigma}$ satisfying $\varepsilon^{0123} = 1/e$. For notational simplicity, we drop the subscript R for the $U(1)$ current. Here $C = 1/(4\pi^2)$ and $\lambda = 1/(768\pi^2)$ denote the anomaly coefficients coming from gauge and gravitational sectors, respectively. Since $\lambda\varepsilon^{\mu\nu\rho\sigma} R^\alpha_{\ \beta\mu\nu} R^\beta_{\ \alpha\rho\sigma}$ contains four derivatives, it does not contribute to the first-order hydrodynamics that we are interested in. Therefore, we will omit the gravitational part in the following discussion. Please note that while the gauge and diffeomorphism invariance provides two (non-)conservation laws, the local Lorentz invariance results in the symmetric property of the energy-momentum tensor operator. It is worth emphasizing that $\hat{J}^\mu$ in Equation (6) is the covariant current which can be related to the consistent current $\hat{J}^\mu_{\mathrm{con}}$ by

$$\hat{J}^\mu = \hat{J}^\mu_{\mathrm{con}} - \frac{1}{6} C \varepsilon^{\mu\nu\rho\sigma} A_\nu F_{\rho\sigma}. \tag{8}$$

An analogue of this relation in local thermal equilibrium will appear in Section 4, and it plays an important role to see how the anomaly matching is realized for the local thermodynamic functional.

2.2. Zubarev's Formula: Decomposing Dissipative and Nondissipative Transport

We then briefly review the Zubarev's nonequilibrium statistical operator method from the modern viewpoint (See e.g., Refs. [98–104] for recent discussions) and specify from where the anomaly-induced transport arises. Assuming that the system is initially in local thermal equilibrium, the Zubarev's formula provides us the expectation values of conserved current operators $\hat{\mathcal{J}}^{\mu}_{a} \equiv \{\hat{T}^{\mu}_{\ \nu}, \hat{J}^{\mu}\}$ over the initial density operator in the following compact form:

$$\langle \hat{\mathcal{J}}^{\mu}_{a}(t,\boldsymbol{x})\rangle = \langle \hat{\mathcal{J}}^{\mu}_{a}(t,\boldsymbol{x})\rangle^{\mathrm{LG}}_{t} + L^{\mu\nu}_{ab}(t,\boldsymbol{x})\nabla_{\nu}\lambda^{b}(t,\boldsymbol{x}) + O((\nabla\lambda)^2), \tag{9}$$

where we introduced the intensive local thermodynamic parameters $\lambda^{a} \equiv \{\beta^{\mu}, \nu\}$, which are related to the local fluid temperature $T = 1/\beta$, four-velocity u^{μ}, and the chemical potential μ through $\beta^{\mu} \equiv \beta u^{\mu}$, $\nu \equiv \beta\mu$. We also defined the average over the local Gibbs distribution $\hat{\rho}_{\mathrm{LG}}[\lambda;t]$, which describes systems in local thermal equilibrium, for an arbitrary operator $\hat{\mathcal{O}}$ as

$$\langle \hat{\mathcal{O}}\rangle^{\mathrm{LG}}_{t} \equiv \mathrm{Tr}\left(\hat{\rho}_{\mathrm{LG}}[\lambda;t]\hat{\mathcal{O}}\right) \quad \text{with} \quad \hat{\rho}_{\mathrm{LG}}[\lambda;t] \equiv \exp\left[-\hat{S}[\lambda;t]\right], \quad \hat{S}[\lambda;t] = \hat{K}[\lambda;t] + \Psi[\lambda;t], \tag{10}$$

where the entropy operator $\hat{S}[\lambda;t]$ is composed of the part including operators $\hat{\mathcal{J}}^{\mu}_{a}$ and normalization part for the density operator:

$$\hat{K}[\lambda;t] \equiv -\int d\Sigma_{t\mu}\left[\beta^{\nu}(t,\boldsymbol{x})\hat{T}^{\mu}_{\ \nu}(t,\boldsymbol{x}) + \nu(t,\boldsymbol{x})\hat{J}^{\mu}(t,\boldsymbol{x})\right], \tag{11}$$

$$\Psi[\lambda;t] \equiv \log \mathrm{Tr}\exp\left[-\hat{K}[\lambda;t]\right]. \tag{12}$$

We here employed the fully covariant notion by introducing the constant time (spacelike) hypersurface defined by its perpendicular surface vector $d\Sigma_{t\mu} \equiv -d^3x\sqrt{\gamma}n_{\mu}$. Choosing a certain globally defined time-coordinate function $\bar{t}(x)$, the unit normal vector n_{μ} can be expressed as

$$n_{\mu}(x) = -N(x)\partial_{\mu}\bar{t}(x) \quad \text{with} \quad N(x) \equiv \left(-\partial^{\mu}\bar{t}(x)\partial_{\mu}\bar{t}(x)\right)^{-1/2}, \tag{13}$$

where $N(x)$ is a so-called Lapse function. In addition, introducing the spatial coordinate on the $\bar{\boldsymbol{x}}$, we have the induced metric $\gamma_{\mu\nu} = g_{\mu\nu} + n_{\mu}n_{\nu}$ whose spatial part gives $\gamma \equiv \det\gamma_{\bar{i}\bar{j}}$ (See e.g., Refs. [102,103] for a detailed geometric setup). The introduction of the covariantized notion looks a little bit complicated, but one can always take the flat limit by setting $(\bar{t}(x), \bar{\boldsymbol{x}}(x)) = (t, \boldsymbol{x})$, which results in e. g. $d\Sigma_{t\mu}|_{\mathrm{flat}} = d^3x\delta^{0}_{\mu}$. Although it might be desirable to distinguish two coordinate systems defined by $(t,\boldsymbol{x})$ and $(\bar{t},\bar{\boldsymbol{x}})$, we will basically omit overline for the later one for notational simplicity since only $(\bar{t},\bar{\boldsymbol{x}})$-coordinate system is mainly used. The normalization part $\Psi[\lambda;t]$ is the local thermodynamic functional called the Massieu-Planck functional, and plays a central role in Section 4.

The crucial point here is that by construction, we can identify the first term in the right-hand-side of Equation (9) as the nondissipative transport taking place in locally thermalized system, whereas the second term as the dissipative correction coming from the deviation from local thermal equilibrium. In other words, the formula (9) gives a way to decompose the non-dissipative and dissipative transport at least in the leading-order derivative expansion. The second term is proportional to the (local) thermodynamic forces $\nabla_{\nu}\lambda^{b}$, and coefficients in front of them are indeed specified as transport coefficients such as the bulk/shear viscosity, and conductivity. They are expressed by the two-point (Kubo) correlation function, which is nothing but the Green-Kubo formula for the transport coefficient [98–104]. On the other hand, nondissipative part is often assumed to be simply given by the usual constitutive relation for a perfect fluid. This is the case for parity-invariant systems, since the nondissipative derivative corrections are accompanied with higher-order derivatives for parity-invariant systems. Nevertheless, if we consider a system without parity symmetry—like the Weyl fermion system given in Equation (2)—we generally encounter with first-order nondissipative derivative corrections in $\langle \hat{\mathcal{J}}^\mu_a(t,x)\rangle_t^{\mathrm{LG}}$. This is the origin of the anomaly-induced transport, and we will focus on how we can evaluate $\langle \hat{\mathcal{J}}^\mu_a(t,x)\rangle_t^{\mathrm{LG}}$ in the remaining part of this paper.

Before closing this section, we put a short comment on the absence of the anomalous contribution to the entropy production. To see this, using the conservation laws (6), we express the entropy production operator $\hat{\Sigma}[t,t_0;\lambda] \equiv \hat{S}[\lambda;t] - \hat{S}[\lambda;t_0]$ as

$$\hat{\Sigma}[t,t_0;\lambda] = \int_{t_0}^t d^4x e \nabla_\mu \hat{s}^\mu \quad \text{with} \quad \nabla_\mu \hat{s}^\mu \equiv -(\nabla_\nu \beta^\mu)\delta\hat{T}^\mu_\nu - (\nabla_\mu \nu + \beta^\nu F_{\mu\nu})\delta\hat{J}^\mu, \tag{14}$$

where we defined the local entropy production rate $\nabla_\mu \hat{s}^\mu$ with $\delta\hat{O}(t) \equiv \hat{O}(t) - \langle \hat{O}(t)\rangle_t^{\mathrm{LG}}$. We thus find that the local equilibrium part of the constitutive relation $\langle \hat{\mathcal{J}}^\mu_a\rangle_t^{\mathrm{LG}}$ which also contains the anomaly-induced transport as first-order derivative corrections, does not contribute to the local entropy production. This is perfectly consistent with the phenomenological derivation of the anomaly-induced transport based on the entropy-current analysis given in Ref. [24].

3. Perturbative Evaluation of Anomalous Transport Coefficients

In this section, we provide a simple perturbative derivation of the anomaly-induced transport given in Equation (1), and calculate anomalous transport coefficients σ_B and σ_ω at the one-loop level.

3.1. Derivative Expansion of the Local Gibbs Distribution

First of all, we note that the local equilibrium part of the constitutive relation, or $\langle \hat{\mathcal{J}}^\mu_a(t,x)\rangle_t^{\mathrm{LG}}$, is a functional of local thermodynamic parameters $\lambda^a = \{\beta^\mu, \nu\}$ and external fields $j \equiv \{A_\mu, e^a_\mu\}$ at a fixed constant time t since the local Gibbs distribution $\hat{\rho}_{\mathrm{LG}}[\lambda;t]$ depends on the configuration of them. Thus, $\langle \hat{\mathcal{J}}^\mu_a(t,x)\rangle_t^{\mathrm{LG}}$ inherently contains the derivative correction coming from the local Gibbs distribution itself.

Suppose that our system is described by the local Gibbs distribution slightly deviated from the global equilibrium (Gibbs) distribution only with the magnetic field and fluid vorticity. We also turn off the external fields and take the flat limit. In that situation, approximating the fluid velocity and the magnetic field as

$$\begin{cases} u_j(x) = (x^i - x^i_0)\partial_i u_j|_{x=x_0} = (x^i - x^i_0)\epsilon_{ijk}\omega^k, \\ A_j(x) = (x^i - x^i_0)\partial_i A_j|_{x=x_0} = \dfrac{1}{2}(x^i - x^i_0)\epsilon_{ijk}B^k, \end{cases} \tag{15}$$

we can expand the local Gibbs distribution on the top of the global Gibbs distribution as

$$\hat{\rho}_{\mathrm{LG}}[\lambda;t] = \tfrac{1}{Z}e^{-\beta(\hat{H}-\mu\hat{N})}\left[1 + T_\tau \textstyle\int_0^\beta d\tau \Delta\hat{S}(t-i\tau)\right] \quad \text{with} \quad \Delta\hat{S} \equiv \tfrac{1}{2}\textstyle\int d^3x \epsilon_{ijk}(x^i - x^i_0)\left(\hat{J}^j B^k + 2\hat{T}^{0j}\omega^k\right), \tag{16}$$

where we defined $\hat{O}(t - i\tau) \equiv e^{\tau(\hat{H}-\mu\hat{N})}\hat{O}(t)e^{-\tau(\hat{H}-\mu\hat{N})}$. Here $Z \equiv \mathrm{Tr}\, e^{-\beta(\hat{H}-\mu\hat{N})}$ denotes the partition function for the globally thermalized system, and we use $\langle\hat{O}\rangle_{\mathrm{eq}} \equiv \mathrm{Tr}(e^{-\beta(\hat{H}-\mu\hat{N})}\hat{O})/Z$. Then, noting that the averaged current in global thermal equilibrium vanishes $\langle \hat{J}^i(t,x_0)\rangle_{\mathrm{eq}} = 0$, we can evaluate $\langle \hat{J}^i(t,x_0)\rangle_t^{\mathrm{LG}}$ as

$$\begin{aligned} \langle \hat{J}^i(t,x_0)\rangle_t^{\mathrm{LG}} &= \frac{1}{2}\int_0^\beta d\tau \int d^3x \epsilon_{jkl}(x^j - x^j_0) \\ &\quad \times \left[\langle \hat{J}^k(t-i\tau,x)\hat{J}^i(t,x_0)\rangle_{\mathrm{eq}} B^l(t,x_0) + 2\langle \hat{T}^{0k}(t-i\tau,x)\hat{J}^i(t,x_0)\rangle_{\mathrm{eq}}\omega^l(t,x_0)\right] \\ &= \frac{i}{2}\epsilon_{jkl}\left[\partial_{q_j}\Delta_{J^kJ^i}(\omega_n,q)\big|_{\omega_n=0,\,q=0}B^l(t,x_0) + 2\partial_{q_j}\Delta_{T^{0k}J^i}(\omega_n,q)\big|_{\omega_n=0,\,q=0}\omega^l(t,x_0)\right], \end{aligned} \tag{17}$$

where we performed the Fourier transformation to proceed the second line. It is now clear that we only need to evaluate two-point imaginary-time—not real-time—correlation functions, namely $\langle \hat{J}^k(t-i\tau,x)\hat{J}^i(t,x_0)\rangle_{\mathrm{eq}}$ and $\langle \hat{T}^{0k}(t-i\tau,x)\hat{J}^i(t,x_0)\rangle_{\mathrm{eq}}$, or their low-frequency and wave-number in the Fourier space.

3.2. One-loop Evaluation of Anomalous Transport Coefficients

We then evaluate the anomalous transport coefficients with the help of the Matsubara formalism. Since we expand the local Gibbs distribution on the top of global Gibbs distribution, the Euclidean action $S_E[\xi, \xi^\dagger, \mu]$ for the right-handed Weyl fermion is simply given by

$$S_E[\xi,\xi^\dagger] = -\sum_P \xi_a^\dagger(P)\left(\mathcal{G}_0^{-1}(\tilde{P})\right)_{ab}\xi_b(P) \quad \text{with} \quad \mathcal{G}_0^{-1}(P) \equiv \sigma^\mu P_\mu, \quad \mathcal{G}_0(P) = \frac{\bar{\sigma}^\mu P_\mu}{P^2}, \tag{18}$$

where $a, b(= 1,2)$ denote the spinor indices, and $\mathcal{G}_0(P)$ the free propagator for the Weyl fermion. We also defined $\tilde{P}_\mu \equiv (-i\omega_n - \mu, \boldsymbol{p})$ with the Matsubara frequency $\omega_n \equiv (2n+1)\pi T$ and chemical potential μ. As usual, we introduced the Fourier transformation

$$\xi(\tau, \boldsymbol{x}) = T\sum_n \int \frac{d^3\boldsymbol{p}}{(2\pi)^3} e^{-i\omega_n \tau + i\boldsymbol{p}\cdot\boldsymbol{x}}\xi(\omega_n, \boldsymbol{p}), \tag{19}$$

with the temperature $T \equiv 1/\beta$. Please note that the argument of the propagator in Equation (18) is not P but $\tilde{P}$, and, thus, it represents the propagator fully dressed by the chemical potential μ. By using these, we need to evaluate the following diagrams:

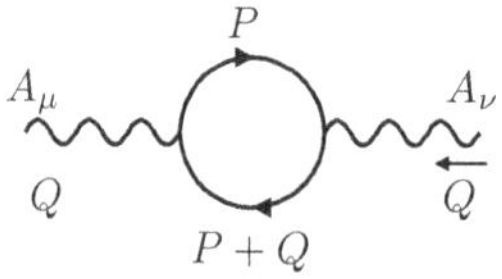

and

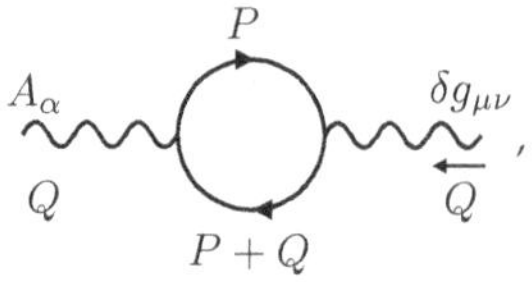

, (20)

where we will take the long-wave-length limit $Q \sim 0$.

First, let us evaluate the two-point current-current correlation function given by

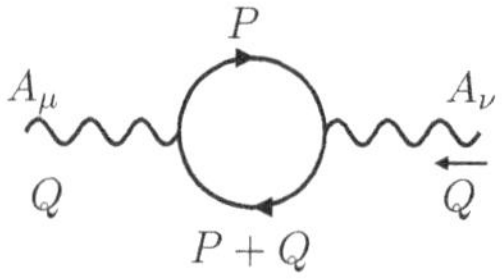

$$= -T_0 \sum_n \int \frac{d^3\boldsymbol{p}}{(2\pi)^3}\,\mathrm{tr}\left(\frac{(Q_\sigma + \tilde{P}_\sigma)\tilde{P}_\rho \bar{\sigma}^\rho \sigma^\mu \bar{\sigma}^\sigma \sigma^\nu}{(Q+\tilde{P})^2 \tilde{P}^2}\right), \tag{21}$$

where we used the free propagator defined in Equation (18). Here "tr" denotes the trace over the spinor indices. With the help of the trace formula for the Pauli matrices

$$\mathrm{tr}\,\bar{\sigma}^\mu \sigma^\nu \bar{\sigma}^\alpha \sigma^\beta = -2i\epsilon^{\mu\nu\alpha\beta} + 2\eta^{\mu\nu}\eta^{\alpha\beta} - 2\eta^{\mu\alpha}\eta^{\nu\beta} + 2\eta^{\mu\beta}\eta^{\nu\alpha}, \tag{22}$$

we can decompose the two-point functions into the antisymmetric part and other parts. Since we are interested in the anomalous term which results from the antisymmetric part, we only focus on that part:

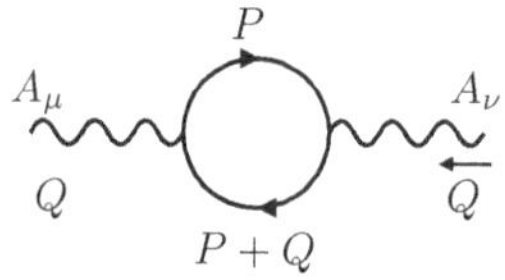

$$= -\frac{i\mu}{4\pi^2}\epsilon^{0\mu\nu\rho}Q_\rho + (\text{symmetric terms}) + O(Q^2), \tag{23}$$

Next, let us evaluate the two-point momentum-current correlation function. Then, the same calculus brings about the following result

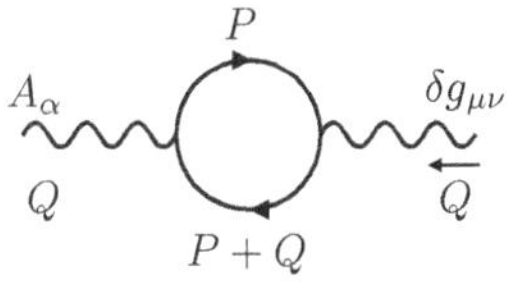

$$
= -\frac{1}{4}T_0\sum_n \int \frac{d^3p}{(2\pi)^3}(2\tilde{P}^\gamma + Q^\gamma)(\delta^\mu_\beta\delta^\nu_\gamma + \delta^\nu_\beta\delta^\mu_\gamma)\,\mathrm{tr}\left(\frac{(Q_\sigma+\tilde{P}_\sigma)\tilde{P}_\rho\bar{\sigma}^\rho\sigma^\beta\bar{\sigma}^\sigma\sigma^\alpha}{(Q+\tilde{P})^2\tilde{P}^2}\right)
$$

$$
= iQ_\rho\left(\eta^{\nu 0}\varepsilon^{\rho\mu 0\alpha} + \eta^{\mu 0}\varepsilon^{\rho\nu 0\alpha} + \delta^\nu_j\varepsilon^{\rho\mu j\alpha} + \delta^\mu_j\varepsilon^{\rho\nu j\alpha}\right)\left(\frac{\mu^2}{16\pi^2} + \frac{T_0^2}{48}\right)
+(\text{symmetric terms}) + \mathcal{O}(Q^2).
$$

Putting these results all together, Equation (17) results in

$$
\langle \hat{J}^i(t, \boldsymbol{x}_0)\rangle_t^{\mathrm{LG}} = \frac{\mu}{4\pi^2}B^i(t, \boldsymbol{x}_0) + \left(\frac{\mu^2}{4\pi^2} + \frac{T^2}{12}\right)\omega^i(t, \boldsymbol{x}_0), \tag{24}
$$

which is nothing but Equation (1). To summarize the above analysis, we have derived the anomaly-induced transport—chiral magnetic/vortical effect—for the Weyl fermion by expanding the local Gibbs distribution. This clearly shows that information on the anomaly-induced transport is fully contained in $\langle \hat{\mathcal{J}}^\mu_a(t, \boldsymbol{x})\rangle_t^{\mathrm{LG}}$. Although we performed the direct expansion of the local Gibbs distribution in this section, there is another way to systematically evaluate $\langle \hat{\mathcal{J}}^\mu_a(t, \boldsymbol{x})\rangle_t^{\mathrm{LG}}$ as we will see in the next section.

4. Anomaly Matching for Local Thermodynamic Functional

In the previous section, we have explicitly shown that the local equilibrium part of constitutive relations $\langle \hat{\mathcal{J}}^\mu_a(t, \boldsymbol{x})\rangle_t^{\mathrm{LG}}$ indeed contains the information on the anomaly-induced transport. Although it is the one-loop perturbative calculation, we expect the result, or the value of anomalous transport coefficients, is protected by the underlying chiral anomaly, and remain the same even if we take into account the effect of interactions nonperturbatively. In this section, we provide another way to see the anomaly-induced transport putting the emphasis on the nonperturbative aspect of the anomaly. The key quantity is the local thermodynamic functional $\Psi[\lambda, j; t]$ already defined in Equation (12).

4.1. Basic Properties of Local Thermodynamic Functional

We here summarize basic properties of the Massieu-Planck functional $\Psi[\lambda, j; t]$: the exact path-integral expression of $\Psi[\lambda, j; t]$ and resulting symmetry properties together with the variational formula.

4.1.1. Path-Integral Formula and Resulting Symmetry

We will first summarize the key result for the Massieu-Planck functional (See Refs. [102,103] for the derivation). Using the energy-momentum tensor operator $\hat{T}^\mu_{\ \nu}$ and covariant current operator $\hat{J}^\mu$ resulting from (2), we can express the Massieu-Planck functional by the imaginary-time path-integral in the same way with the usual Matsubara formalism for global thermal equilibrium. After a little bit tedious calculation (See Ref. [103]), we eventually obtain

$$
\Psi[\lambda, j; t] = \int \mathcal{D}\xi\mathcal{D}\xi^\dagger \exp\left(\widetilde{\mathcal{S}}[\xi, \xi^\dagger; \widetilde{A}, \widetilde{e}]\right), \tag{25}
$$

with the manifestly covariant action $\widetilde{\mathcal{S}}[\xi, \xi^\dagger; \widetilde{A}_\mu, \widetilde{e}^a_\mu]$ given by

$$
\widetilde{\mathcal{S}}[\xi, \xi^\dagger; \widetilde{A}_\mu, \widetilde{e}^a_\mu] = \int_0^{\beta_0} d\tau d^3x\widetilde{e}\left[\frac{i}{2}\xi^\dagger\left(\widetilde{e}^\mu_a\sigma^a\overrightarrow{\widetilde{D}}_\mu - \overleftarrow{\widetilde{D}}_\mu\sigma^a\widetilde{e}^\mu_a\right)\xi\right] \quad \text{with} \quad \widetilde{e} \equiv \det(\widetilde{e}^a_\mu). \tag{26}
$$

Here we introduced the thermal (inverse) vierbein $\tilde{e}_\mu^{\ a}$ ($\tilde{e}_a^{\ \mu}$) and the external $U(1)$ gauge field $\tilde{A}_\mu$ in thermally emergent curved spacetime as

$$\tilde{e}_0^{\ a} = e^\sigma u^a, \quad \tilde{e}_i^{\ a} = e_i^{\ a} \quad \text{and} \quad \tilde{A}_0 = e^\sigma \mu, \quad \tilde{A}_i = A_i, \tag{27}$$

where recalling $\beta^\mu(x) \equiv \beta(x) u^\mu(x)$ and $\nu(x) = \beta(x)\mu(x)$, we used

$$e^{\sigma(x)} \equiv \beta(x)/\beta_0, \quad \mu(x) \equiv \nu(x)/\beta(x), \quad \beta(x) \equiv \sqrt{-g_{\mu\nu}(x)\beta^\mu(x)\beta^\nu(x)}, \tag{28}$$

with a constant reference inverse temperature β_0. We also introduced $\tilde{e} \equiv \det \tilde{e}_\mu^{\ a}$ and the covariant derivative in thermal spacetime as

$$\begin{cases} \overrightarrow{D}_\mu \xi \equiv \tilde{\partial}_\mu \xi - i(\tilde{\mathcal{A}}_\mu + \tilde{A}_\mu)\xi, \\ \xi^\dagger \overleftarrow{D}_\mu \equiv \tilde{\partial}_\mu \xi^\dagger + i\xi^\dagger(\tilde{\mathcal{A}}_\mu + \tilde{A}_\mu), \end{cases} \quad \text{with} \quad \tilde{\partial}_\mu \equiv (i\partial_\tau, \partial_i), \quad \tilde{\mathcal{A}}_\mu \equiv \frac{1}{2}\tilde{\omega}_\mu^{\ ab}\Sigma_{ab}, \tag{29}$$

where the thermal spin connection is expressed by the thermal vierbein $\tilde{e}_\mu^{\ a}$ through the same relation in the original spacetime (4).

As is shown in these, we can say that the Massieu-Planck functional is expressed as the path-integral in the presence of the emergent background curved spacetime and $U(1)$ gauge field. Figure 2 shows a schematic picture to compare the imaginary-time formalism in global and local thermal equilibrium.

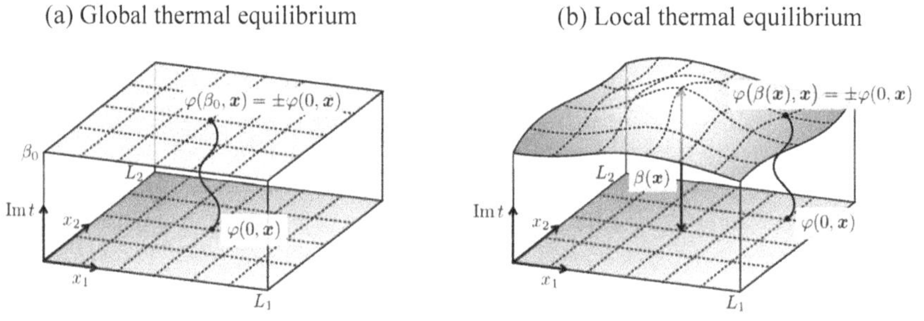

Figure 2. A comparison of the imaginary-time formalism (**a**) in global thermal equilibrium and (**b**) in local thermal equilibrium. Effects of inhomogeneous local thermodynamic parameters such as the local temperature is completely captured in terms of the emergent curved geometry. The boundary condition ± corresponds to the boson or the fermion.

Please note that this background structure is completely determined by configurations of the local thermodynamic variables λ^a (and external fields j) on the constant time hypersurface in the original spacetime. The crucial point here is that all these quantities do not depend on the imaginary-time coordinate τ, which leads to the Kaluza-Klein gauge symmetry. To see this clearly, we express the line element $d\tilde{s}^2 \equiv \tilde{e}_\mu^{\ a}\tilde{e}_\nu^{\ b}\eta_{ab} d\tilde{x}^\mu \otimes d\tilde{x}^\nu$ and $U(1)$ gauge connection $\tilde{A} \equiv \tilde{A}_\mu d\tilde{x}^\mu$ in thermal spacetime as

$$d\tilde{s}^2 = -e^{2\sigma}(d\tilde{t} + a_i dx^i)^2 + \gamma'_{ij} dx^i dx^j, \tag{30}$$

$$\tilde{A} = \tilde{A}_0(d\tilde{t} + a_i dx^i) + \tilde{A}'_i dx^i, \tag{31}$$

with $d\tilde{t} \equiv -id\tau$. Here we defined the following quantities

$$a_i \equiv -e^{-\sigma} u_i, \quad \gamma'_{ij} \equiv \gamma_{ij} + e^{2\sigma} a_i a_j, \quad \tilde{A}'_i \equiv= \tilde{A}_i - \tilde{A}_0 a_i. \tag{32}$$

Then, in addition to the spatial diffeomorphism invariance—invariance under spatial coordinate transformation $x \to x'(x)$— we now see the background (30) and (31) is invariant under the transformation given by

$$\begin{cases} \tilde{t} \to \tilde{t} + \chi(x), \\ x \to x, \\ a_i(x) \to a_i(x) - \partial_i \chi(x). \end{cases} \tag{33}$$

This is nothing but Kaluza-Klein gauge transformation, and a_i is identified as the Kaluza-Klein gauge field. Please note that γ_{ij} and $\tilde{A}_i = A_i$ do transform under the Kaluza-Klein gauge transformation so that γ'_{ij} and $\tilde{A}'_i$ do not. Therefore, it is useful to employ Kaluza-Klein gauge invariant quantities γ'_{ij} and $\tilde{A}'_i$ rather than γ_{ij} and $\tilde{A}_i$ as basic building blocks to construct the Massieu-Planck functional. Furthermore, since the system is composed of the Weyl fermion, the apparent $U(1)$ gauge invariance for $\tilde{A}'_i$ is anomalously broken. These spatial diffeomorphism, Kaluza-Klein gauge, and anomalous $U(1)$ gauge symmetries provide a basic restriction to the Massieu-Planck functional.

4.1.2. Variational Formula in the Presence of Quantum Anomaly

We then provide the variational formula for the Massieu-Planck functional $\Psi[\lambda, j; t]$, and show all information on $\langle \hat{\mathcal{J}}^{\mu}_a(t,x)\rangle^{\mathrm{LG}}_t$ is fully installed in it. To show this, let us consider the variation of $\hat{K}$ defined in Equation (11) under the infinitesimal general coordinate and gauge transformation with a set of parameters $\zeta^\mu = \epsilon\beta^\mu$ and $\theta = \epsilon(\nu - \beta \cdot A)$. ($\epsilon$ denotes an infinitesimal constant.) As a result, of the combination of diffeomorphism and $U(1)$ gauge transformations, the variation of the background $U(1)$ gauge field $\delta_\lambda A_\mu$ has the simple expression:

$$\delta_\lambda A_\mu = \pounds_\beta A_\mu + \nabla_\mu(\nu - \beta \cdot A) = \nabla_\mu \nu + \beta^\nu F_{\nu\mu}. \tag{34}$$

The crucial point here is that $\hat{K}$ remains invariant under the simultaneous transformation acting on both operators and external fields: $\delta_\lambda \hat{K} \equiv \delta^{\mathrm{para}}_\lambda \hat{K} + \delta^{\mathrm{ope}}_\lambda \hat{K} = 0$. This invariance can be shown by recalling all operators in $\hat{K}$ are $U(1)$ gauge invariant, and, furthermore, rewriting $\hat{K}$ as

$$\hat{K}[t, \lambda^a, e^a_\mu, A_\mu] = \int d^4x \sqrt{\gamma}\delta(t - t(x)) n_\mu(x) \lambda^a(x) \hat{\mathcal{J}}^\mu_a(x), \tag{35}$$

from which we can clearly see diffeomorphism (reparameterization) invariance. Moreover, $\delta^{\mathrm{ope}}_\lambda \hat{K}$ will also trivially vanish just because $\delta^{\mathrm{ope}}_\lambda \hat{K} = [i\hat{K}, \hat{K}] = 0$. As a result, we have the operator identity $\delta^{\mathrm{para}}_\lambda \hat{K} = 0$.

Then, let us investigate $\delta^{\mathrm{para}}_\lambda \hat{K}$ in detail, whose explicit definition is given by

$$\delta^{\mathrm{para}}_\lambda \hat{K} \equiv \int d^4x \left[\frac{\delta \hat{K}}{\delta t(x)} \pounds_\beta t(x) + \frac{\delta \hat{K}}{\delta \lambda^a(x)} \pounds_\beta \lambda^a(x) + \frac{\delta \hat{K}}{\delta e^a_\mu(x)} \pounds_\beta e^a_\mu(x) + \frac{\delta \hat{K}}{\delta A_\mu(x)} \delta_\lambda A_\mu(x) \right]. \tag{36}$$

To rewrite the first term of this equation, noting $\delta(t - t(x)) n_\mu = -N\delta(t - t(x))\partial_\mu t = N\partial_\mu \theta(t - t(x))$ following from the definition of n_μ, and performing the integration by parts, we rewrite $\hat{K}$ in Equation (35) as

$$\begin{aligned} \hat{K}[t, \lambda^a, e^a_\mu, A_\mu] &= -\int d^4x e\theta(t - t(x)) \nabla_\mu(\lambda^a(x) \hat{\mathcal{J}}^\mu_a(x)) \\ &= -\int d^4x e\theta(t - t(x)) \left(\hat{T}^\mu_\nu \nabla_\mu \beta^\nu + \hat{J}^\mu(\nabla_\mu \nu + \beta^\nu F_{\nu\mu}) - \frac{1}{8} C\nu \varepsilon^{\mu\nu\rho\sigma} F_{\mu\nu} F_{\rho\sigma} \right), \end{aligned} \tag{37}$$

where we used $e = N\sqrt{\gamma}$ and employed the operator identity for current operators (6) to proceed the second line. With the help of Equation (34) together with $\nabla_\mu \beta^\nu = e_a^{\ \nu} \pounds_\beta e_\mu^{\ a} + \beta^\rho \omega_{\rho\ \mu}^{\ \nu}$ followed from the so-called (torsionless) tetrad postulate $\nabla_\mu e_\nu^a + \omega_{\mu\ b}^{\ a} e_\nu^b = 0$, Equation (37) enables us to obtain

$$\int d^4x \frac{\delta \hat{K}}{\delta t(x)} \pounds_\beta t(x) = \int d^4x \sqrt{\gamma}\delta(t - t(x)) \left[\hat{T}^\mu_{\ a} \pounds_\beta e_\mu^{\ a} + \hat{J}^\mu \delta_\lambda A_\mu - \frac{1}{8} C v \varepsilon^{\mu\nu\rho\sigma} F_{\mu\nu} F_{\rho\sigma} \right] \beta', \tag{38}$$

where we defined $\beta' \equiv -\beta^\mu n_\mu$ and used the operator identity $\hat{T}^{ab} - \hat{T}^{ba} = 0$. By using the identity

$$n_\alpha \varepsilon^{\mu\nu\rho\sigma} F_{\mu\nu} F_{\rho\sigma} = -4\varepsilon^{\mu\nu\rho\sigma} n_\nu F_{\rho\sigma} F_{\alpha\mu}. \tag{39}$$

the last term in the second line of Equation (38) can be further simplified as

$$\begin{aligned} \int d^4x \sqrt{\gamma}\delta(t - t(x)) \left[\frac{1}{8} C v \beta^\alpha n_\alpha \varepsilon^{\mu\nu\rho\sigma} F_{\mu\nu} F_{\rho\sigma} \right] &= -\int d^4x \sqrt{\gamma}\delta(t - t(x)) \left[\frac{1}{2} C v \beta^\alpha n_\nu \varepsilon^{\mu\nu\rho\sigma} F_{\rho\sigma} F_{\alpha\mu} \right] \\ &= -\int d^4x \sqrt{\gamma}\delta(t - t(x)) C v B^\mu \delta_\lambda A_\mu. \end{aligned} \tag{40}$$

Here we defined the four-magnetic field as $B^\mu \equiv \widetilde{F}^{\mu\nu} n_\nu = \varepsilon^{\mu\nu\rho\sigma} n_\nu F_{\rho\sigma}/2$, and neglected the surface term accompanied by the integration by parts. We thus obtain the following compact result:

$$\int d^4x \frac{\delta \hat{K}}{\delta t(x)} \pounds_\beta t(x) = \int d^4x \beta' \sqrt{\gamma}\delta(t - t(x)) \left[\hat{T}^\mu_{\ a} \pounds_\beta e_\mu^{\ a} + (\hat{J}^\mu - C\beta'^{-1} v B^\mu)\delta_\lambda A_\mu \right]. \tag{41}$$

Equipped with this formula together with $\pounds_\beta \beta^\mu = 0$, and $\pounds_\beta v = \pounds_\beta (v - \beta \cdot A) + \beta^\mu \pounds_\beta A_\mu = \beta^\mu \delta_\lambda A_\mu$, we are now ready to express $\delta_\lambda^{\mathrm{para}} \hat{K}$ in Equation (36) by the use of the variation of the vierbein and gauge field:

$$\delta_\lambda^{\mathrm{para}} \hat{K} = \int d^3x \left[\left(\beta' \sqrt{\gamma} \hat{T}^\mu_{\ a} + \frac{\delta \hat{K}}{\delta e_\mu^{\ a}} \right) \pounds_\beta e_\mu^{\ a} + \left(\beta' \sqrt{\gamma} \left[\hat{J}^\mu - C\beta'^{-1} v B^\mu \right] + \frac{\delta \hat{K}}{\delta v} \beta^\mu + \frac{\delta \hat{K}}{\delta A_\mu} \right) \delta_\lambda A_\mu \right]. \tag{42}$$

Let us then take the average of this operator identity over the local Gibbs distribution $\hat{\rho}_{\mathrm{LG}}[\lambda; t]$. In the absence of the quantum anomaly, we can simply replace the averaged variation of $\hat{K}$ with the variation of the Massieu-Planck functional: $\langle \delta \hat{K}/\delta j \rangle_t^{\mathrm{LG}} = -\delta \Psi/\delta j$. Nevertheless, since we are considering the system with the chiral anomaly, we need to be careful when we take the variation of the charge density coupled to the local chemical potential. Using the relation $\partial(e\hat{J}^0)/\partial A_\mu = \sqrt{\gamma} C B^\mu$ resulting from the covariant anomaly, we can show

$$\frac{\delta \hat{K}}{\delta A_\mu} = e\hat{J}^0 \beta^\mu + \sqrt{\gamma} v C B^\mu - \beta' \sqrt{\gamma} \frac{\partial \hat{\mathcal{L}}}{\partial A_\mu}. \tag{43}$$

We can then identify the local Gibbs average of the last term in this equation as the covariant current in thermal spacetime, which results in the sum of the consistent current and the Bardeen-Zumino current composed of $\widetilde{A}_\mu$:

$$\beta' \sqrt{\gamma} \left\langle \frac{\partial \hat{\mathcal{L}}}{\partial A_\mu} \right\rangle_t^{\mathrm{LG}} = \mathcal{N} \int \mathcal{D}\xi \mathcal{D}\xi^\dagger e^{\widetilde{S}[\xi,\xi^\dagger;\widetilde{A},\widetilde{e}]} \frac{\delta \widetilde{S}}{\delta \widetilde{A}_\mu} = \frac{\delta \Psi}{\delta \widetilde{A}_\mu} - \frac{C}{6} \widetilde{\varepsilon}^{\mu\nu\rho\sigma} \widetilde{A}_\nu \mathcal{F}_{\rho\sigma}, \tag{44}$$

where $\mathcal{N}$ denotes a normalization constant, and we introduced a field strength tensor in thermal spacetime $\mathcal{F}_{\mu\nu} \equiv \widetilde{\partial}_\mu \widetilde{A}_\nu - \widetilde{\partial}_\nu \widetilde{A}_\mu$ together with the totally antisymmetric tensor $\widetilde{\varepsilon}^{\mu\nu\rho\sigma} \equiv N(\beta_0/\beta')\varepsilon^{\mu\nu\rho\sigma}$. Using this together with $\langle \delta \hat{K}/\delta e_\mu^{\ a} \rangle_t^{\mathrm{LG}} = -\delta \Psi/\delta e_\mu^{\ a}$, we eventually obtain the following identity:

$$\langle \delta_\lambda^{\text{para}} \hat{K} \rangle_t^{\text{LG}} = \int d^3x \left[\left(\beta' \sqrt{\gamma} \langle \hat{T}^\mu_{\ a} \rangle_t^{\text{LG}} - \frac{\delta \Psi}{\delta e_\mu^{\ a}} \right) \pounds_\beta e_\mu^{\ a} + \left(\beta' \sqrt{\gamma} \langle \hat{J}^\mu \rangle_t^{\text{LG}} - \frac{\delta \Psi}{\delta \tilde{A}_\mu} + \frac{C}{6} \tilde{\varepsilon}^{\mu\nu\rho\sigma} \tilde{A}_\nu \mathcal{F}_{\rho\sigma} \right) \delta_\lambda A_\mu \right]. \tag{45}$$

Therefore, noting that that this identity holds for an arbitrary variation of the background vierbein and gauge field, the identity $\langle \delta_\lambda^{\text{para}} \hat{K} \rangle_t^{\text{LG}} = 0$ provides the variational formula for the Masseiu-Planck functional

$$\langle \hat{T}^\mu_{\ a}(t, \boldsymbol{x}) \rangle_t^{\text{LG}} = \frac{1}{\beta' \sqrt{\gamma}} \frac{\delta \Psi[\lambda, j, t]}{\delta e_\mu^{\ a}(x)}, \tag{46}$$

$$\langle \hat{J}^\mu(t, \boldsymbol{x}) \rangle_t^{\text{LG}} = \frac{1}{\beta' \sqrt{\gamma}} \frac{\delta \Psi[\lambda, j, t]}{\delta \tilde{A}_\mu(x)} - \frac{C}{6} \tilde{\varepsilon}^{\mu\nu\rho\sigma} \tilde{A}_\nu \mathcal{F}_{\rho\sigma}. \tag{47}$$

We thus conclude that the average values of any conserved current operator over local thermal equilibrium is fully captured by the single (local thermodynamic) functional known as the Masseiu-Planck functional. It is worth pointing out that because we deal with the average of the covariant current $\langle \hat{J}(x) \rangle_t^{\text{LG}}$, we have the last term in Equation (47) analogous to the Bardeen-Zumino current [105] (See also Refs. [29,43,47]). In summary, we can identify the Massieu-Planck functional $\Psi[\lambda, j; t]$ as a generating functional for a (nondissipative) local equilibrium part of hydrodynamics, or $\langle \hat{\mathcal{J}}^\mu_{\ a}(t, \boldsymbol{x}) \rangle_t^{\text{LG}}$.

Before moving to the path-integral formula for the Massieu-Planck functional, we put a short comment on the useful "gauge and coordinate choice", which we call *hydrostatic gauge*. Since we have a freedom to choose the local time-direction and time-component of the external gauge field, we can employ the hydrostatic gauge fixing condition

$$t^\mu(x) = \beta^\mu(x)/\beta_0, \quad t^\mu(x) A_\mu(x) = \nu(x)/\beta_0, \tag{48}$$

with a constant reference temperature β_0. In this special choice of the gauge, the above transformation does not induce the gauge transformation because $\theta = \epsilon(\nu - \beta \cdot A) = 0$, and furthermore, thanks to the refined choice of our local time-direction, the fluid looks like entirely at rest. This is the origin of the name hydro*static*. Nevertheless, note that this does not means the system is in a stationary hydrostatic state since we do not assume β^μ is a killing vector: $\pounds_\beta g_{\mu\nu} \neq 0$. The main reason the hydrostatic gauge gives the most useful gauge is that we can equate the background field in original (real) spacetime with that in (imaginary) thermal spacetime: $e_\mu^{\ a}|_{\text{hs}} = \tilde{e}_\mu^{\ a}$ and $A_\mu|_{\text{hs}} = \tilde{A}_\mu$. As a result, the above variational formula results in (46) and (47) as

$$\langle \hat{T}^\mu_{\ a}(t, \boldsymbol{x}) \rangle_t^{\text{LG}} = \frac{1}{\beta_0 e} \frac{\delta \Psi[\lambda, j; t]}{\delta e_\mu^{\ a}(x)} \bigg|_{\text{hs}}, \tag{49}$$

$$\langle \hat{J}^\mu(t, \boldsymbol{x}) \rangle_t^{\text{LG}} = \frac{1}{\beta_0 e} \frac{\delta \Psi[\lambda, j; t]}{\delta A_\mu(x)} \bigg|_{\text{hs}} - \frac{C}{6} \varepsilon^{\mu\nu\rho\sigma} A_\nu F_{\rho\sigma} \big|_{\text{hs}}, \tag{50}$$

which enable us to regard the Massieu-Planck functional as a usual generating functional.

4.2. Anomaly Matching for Local Thermodynamic Functional

Based on the obtained formulae, we now discuss the anomaly-induced transport from the point of view of the anomaly matching for the Massieu-Planck functional.

Before moving to the anomaly-induced transport, let us briefly see how we can derive the constitutive relation for a perfect fluid. Employing the simplest power counting scheme $\lambda = O(\nabla^0)$, $j = O(\nabla^0)$, we perform the derivative expansion of the Massieu-Planck function as follows:

$$\Psi[\lambda, j; t] = \Psi^{(0)}[\lambda, j; t] + \Psi^{(1)}[\lambda, j; t] + O(\nabla^2), \tag{51}$$

where the superscript represents the number of spatial derivatives acting on parameters λ and j. Then, the symmetry argument reviewed in the previous subsection tells us that we cannot use the Kaluza-Klein and $U(1)$ gauge fields in the leading-order derivative expansion. As a result, the general form of the leading-order Massieu-Planck functional $\Psi^{(0)}[\lambda, j; t]$ is expressed as

$$\Psi^{(0)}[\lambda, j; t] = \int_0^{\beta_0} d\tau d^3x \tilde{e} p(\beta, \nu) = \int d^3x \beta' \sqrt{\gamma} p(\beta, \nu), \tag{52}$$

where $p(\beta, \nu)$ is a certain function depending on β and ν. By taking the variation with respect to the vierbein and gauge field, we are able to obtain the leading-order constitutive relation as

$$\langle \hat{T}^{\mu\nu}(t, \boldsymbol{x}) \rangle^{\mathrm{LG}}_{(0)} = (e + p) u^\mu u^\nu + p g^{\mu\nu} + O(\nabla^1), \quad \langle \hat{J}^\mu(t, \boldsymbol{x}) \rangle^{\mathrm{LG}}_{(0)} = n u^\mu + O(\nabla^1). \tag{53}$$

This is nothing but the constitutive relation for the perfect fluid with e, n, p being the energy density, charge density, and fluid pressure, respectively.

Then, the next problem is to specify the first-order derivative correction of the Massieu-Planck functional $\Psi^{(1)}[\lambda, j; t]$, which is present (absent) in the absence (presence) of the parity symmetry. Since our system is composed of the right-handed Weyl fermion, and thus, there is no parity symmetry, the first-order correction is not prohibited. In this case, two (anomalous) gauge symmetries again plays a central role to extract information on the anomaly-induced transport contained in $\Psi^{(1)}[\lambda, j; t]$. In the following, after giving a bottom up view relying on the one-loop result in the previous section, we switch to a top down view of the anomaly matching, from which we can derive the anomaly-induced transport beyond the one-loop level.

4.2.1. Chiral Anomaly in Thermal Spacetime

At one-loop level, we have already derived the anomaly-induced transport given in Equation (24). On the other hand, we also have the variational formula (47) in a general gauge, or (50) in the hydrostatic gauge. Let us take the hydrostatic gauge. Then, the combination of the above results enables us to obtain the following functional differential equation for $\Psi^{(1)}$:

$$\frac{1}{\beta_0} \frac{\delta \Psi^{(1)}_{\mathrm{ano}}[\lambda, j; t]}{\delta A_i(x)} \bigg|_{\mathrm{hs}} + \frac{\mu}{12\pi^2} B^i - \frac{1}{12\pi^2} \varepsilon^{0ijk} A_k \partial_j \mu = \frac{\mu}{4\pi^2} B^i + \left(\frac{\mu^2}{4\pi^2} + \frac{T^2}{12} \right) \omega^i, \tag{54}$$

where we take the flat limit and assume global thermal equilibrium with a constant temperature β_0 in the variational formula. This equation can be easily solved as

$$\begin{aligned} \Psi^{(1)}_{\mathrm{ano}}[\lambda, j; t] \bigg|^{\mathrm{eq}}_{\mathrm{hs}} &= \frac{\beta_0}{12\pi^2} \int d^3x \mu A_i B^i + \beta_0 \int d^3x \left(\frac{1}{4\pi^2} \mu^2 + \frac{1}{12} T^2 \right) A_i \omega^i \\ &= \frac{\beta_0}{12\pi^2} \int d^3x \varepsilon^{0ijk} \mu A_i \partial_j A_k + \frac{\beta_0}{2} \int d^3x \varepsilon^{0ijk} \left(\frac{1}{4\pi^2} \mu^2 + \frac{1}{12} T^2 \right) A_i \partial_j u_k \end{aligned} \tag{55}$$

up to irrelevant constants. On the other hand, we have already clarified that the Massieu-Planck functional need to respect both $U(1)$ and Kaluza-Klein gauge invariance. This constraint then enables us to guess the full result on $\Psi^{(1)}$ for general local thermal equilibrium though Equation (55) is obtained by matching with the one-loop result for linear perturbations on the top of global thermal equilibrium. By using the $U(1)$ and Kaluza-Klein gauge covariant quantities—$\widetilde{A}'_i$ and a_i, respectively—together with $\widetilde{A}_0 = e^\sigma \mu$, we specify the first-order derivative correction as

$$\Psi^{(1)}_{\mathrm{ano}}[\lambda, j; t] = \frac{C\beta_0}{3} \int d^3x e \varepsilon^{0ijk} \widetilde{A}_0 \widetilde{A}'_i \partial_j \widetilde{A}'_k + \frac{C\beta_0}{6} \int d^3x e \varepsilon^{0ijk} \widetilde{A}_0^2 \widetilde{A}'_i \partial_j a_k, - \frac{C_1}{2\beta_0} \int d^3x e \varepsilon^{0ijk} \widetilde{A}'_i \partial_j a_k, \tag{56}$$

with $C_1 \equiv 1/12$. Please note that $\widetilde{A}_0$ and $\widetilde{A}'_i$ defined in Equations (27) and (32) are manifestly Kaluza-Klein gauge invariant quantities.

Let us then confirm the consistency for this result based on the anomaly matching for the Massieu-Planck functional itself. For that purpose, we consider the time-independent gauge transformation given by $\delta_\theta \widetilde{A}_0 = 0,\ \delta_\theta \widetilde{A}_i = \partial_i \theta(x)$. Under this gauge transformation, the Fujikawa method [2] says that the anomalous shift of the Massieu-Planck functional is given by the consistent anomaly:

$$\delta_\theta \Psi[\lambda, j; t] = -\frac{C\beta_0}{3} \int d^3x \theta e \varepsilon^{0ijk} \partial_i \widetilde{A}_0 \partial_j \widetilde{A}_k. \tag{57}$$

On the other hand, one can directly show that the first two term of $\Psi^{(1)}_{\text{ano}}[\lambda, j; t]$ in Equation (56) correctly reproduces this anomalous shift as

$$\begin{aligned}
\delta_\theta \Psi^{(1)}_{\text{ano}}[\lambda, j; t] &= \frac{C\beta_0}{3} \int d^3x e \varepsilon^{0ijk} \widetilde{A}_0 \partial_i \theta \partial_j \widetilde{A}'_k + \frac{C\beta_0}{6} \int d^3x e \varepsilon^{0ijk} \widetilde{A}_0^2 \partial_i \theta \partial_j a_k \\
&= -\frac{C\beta_0}{3} \int d^3x \theta e \varepsilon^{0ijk} \partial_i \widetilde{A}_0 \partial_j (\widetilde{A}_k - \widetilde{A}_0 a_k) - \frac{C\beta_0}{3} \int d^3x \theta e \varepsilon^{0ijk} \widetilde{A}_0 \partial_i \widetilde{A}_0 \partial_j a_k + (\text{surface terms}) \\
&= -\frac{C\beta_0}{3} \int d^3x \theta \varepsilon^{0ijk} \partial_i \widetilde{A}_0 \partial_j \widetilde{A}_k + (\text{surface terms}).
\end{aligned} \tag{58}$$

Therefore, we see that the anomalous transport coefficients C proportional to the chemical potential μ is indeed related to the anomaly coefficient attached to the Weyl fermion.

Nevertheless, the last term in Equation (56), which brings about the CVE proportional to T^2, is not restricted by the chiral anomaly. From the symmetry point of view, this is just because the last term in Equation (56) remains *invariant* under the $U(1)$ gauge transformation. This corresponds the fact that the entropy production argument with chiral anomaly leads to the existence of both chiral magnetic and vortical effect [24], in which only the anomalous transport coefficients proportional to the chemical potential are determined. Then, the natural question is *"Does the CVE proportional to T^2 have any relation with the quantum anomaly?"*

4.2.2. Global Anomaly for Kaluza-Klein Gauge Transformation

It was pointed out the T^2 term of the chiral vortical coefficient is related to the gravitational contribution to the chiral anomaly [26,56]. However, unlike the chiral magnetic coefficient discussed in this section, it is not clear that how the CVE relates to the $\varepsilon^{\mu\nu\rho\sigma} R^\alpha{}_{\beta\mu\nu} R^\beta{}_{\alpha\rho\sigma}$, because the number of derivative in $\varepsilon^{\mu\nu\rho\sigma} R^\alpha{}_{\beta\mu\nu} R^\beta{}_{\alpha\rho\sigma}$ is higher than that in $\varepsilon^{\mu\nu\rho\sigma} F_{\mu\nu} F_{\rho\sigma}$. In other words, $\varepsilon^{\mu\nu\rho\sigma} R^\alpha{}_{\beta\mu\nu} R^\beta{}_{\alpha\rho\sigma}$ does not directly contribute to the first-order hydrodynamics. An alternative explanation of T^2 term is that the chiral vortical coefficient is related to a global anomaly [45,46,106]. Here, we show the relation between the global anomaly and chiral vortical effect.

As a warm up exercise, let us first consider the global anomaly attached to the Weyl fermion in $1+1$ dimensions, which possesses the chiral anomaly given by

$$\partial_\mu \hat{J}^\mu = -\frac{1}{2} C_{2D} \varepsilon^{\mu\nu} F_{\mu\nu} \quad \text{with} \quad C_{2D} \equiv \frac{1}{2\pi}, \tag{59}$$

where $\hat{J}^\mu$ again denotes the covariant current in $1+1$ dimensional system. In this case, there are no chiral magnetic and vortical effects because there is no transverse direction, and thus, no magnetic field and vorticity. However, there exist nonvanishing $\langle \hat{J}^z \rangle$ and $\langle \hat{T}^0_z \rangle$ caused by chiral and global anomalies. The direct calculation at equilibrium shows

$$\begin{aligned}\langle \hat{T}^0_z \rangle_{\text{eq}} &= \int_0^\infty \frac{dp_z}{2\pi} p_z \left[n_F(|p_z| - \mu) + n_F(|p_z| + \mu) \right] = \frac{\mu^2}{4\pi} + \frac{\pi}{12} T^2, \\ \langle \hat{J}^z \rangle_{\text{eq}} &= \int_0^\infty \frac{dp_z}{2\pi} \frac{p_z}{|p_z|} \left[n_F(|p_z| - \mu) - n_F(|p_z| + \mu) \right] = \frac{\mu}{2\pi}.\end{aligned} \tag{60}$$

On the other hand, the same procedure given above leads to the variational formula in $(1+1)$ dimensions:

$$\begin{aligned}\langle \hat{T}^\mu_{\ a} \rangle^{\text{LG}}_t &= \frac{1}{\beta' \sqrt{\gamma}} \frac{\delta \Psi[t;\lambda]}{\delta e_\mu^{\ a}(x)}, \\ \langle \hat{J}^\mu \rangle^{\text{LG}}_t &= \frac{1}{\beta' \sqrt{\gamma}} \frac{\delta \Psi[t;\lambda]}{\delta \widetilde{A}_\mu(x)} - \frac{1}{2} C_{2D} \widetilde{\varepsilon}^{\mu\nu} \widetilde{A}_\nu,\end{aligned} \tag{61}$$

where $\widetilde{\varepsilon}^{\mu\nu} = N(\beta_0/\beta')\varepsilon^{\mu\nu}$. Then, the matching condition for the momentum density and current results in

$$\frac{1}{\beta_0} \frac{\delta \Psi_{\text{ano}}}{\delta e_0^{\ z}} = -\frac{1}{\beta_0} \frac{\delta \Psi_{\text{ano}}}{\delta a_z} = \frac{C_{2D}}{2} \mu^2 + \pi C_1 T^2, \tag{62}$$

$$\frac{1}{\beta_0} \frac{\delta \Psi_{\text{ano}}}{\delta A_z} + \frac{C_{2D}}{2} \mu = C_{2D} \mu. \tag{63}$$

Solving Equations (62) and (63), we find

$$\Psi_{\text{ano}} = \frac{C_{2D} \beta_0}{2} \int dz \widetilde{A}_0 \widetilde{A}'_z - \pi \frac{C_1}{\beta_0} \int dz a_z. \tag{64}$$

This gives the anomalous part of the Masseiu-Planck functional. To detect anomalies, we compactify the spatial direction with the length L. Here we will show Ψ_{ano} has two types of anomalies. One is the chiral anomaly: Under $U(1)$ gauge transformation $\widetilde{A}_z \to \widetilde{A}_z + \partial_z \theta(z)$, the anomalous shift of Ψ arises:

$$\delta_\theta \Psi_{\text{ano}} = -\frac{C_{2D} \beta_0}{2} \int dz \theta \partial_z \widetilde{A}_0, \tag{65}$$

which correctly reproduces the consistent anomaly in thermal spacetime. The other is the global anomaly associated with the Kaluza-Klein gauge transformation:

$$\begin{cases} \widetilde{t} \to \widetilde{t} + \chi(z), \\ a_z \to a_z - \partial_z \chi(z), \end{cases} \tag{66}$$

where $\widetilde{A}'_z$ remains invariant. Under this transformation, Ψ_{ano} also acquires the anomalous shift given by

$$\delta_\chi \Psi_{\text{ano}} = \pi \frac{C_1}{\beta_0} \int dz \partial_z \chi(z), \tag{67}$$

which is just a boundary term, so that Ψ_{ano} is invariant under local transformation with $\chi(0) = \chi(L)$. However, if we consider global transformation, $\chi(z) = -2i\beta_0 z/L$, which corresponds to the imaginary-time shift $\tau \to \tau + 2z\beta_0/L$ that keep the boundary condition, we have an additional phase

$$\Psi_{\text{ano}} \to \Psi_{\text{ano}} - 2\pi i C_1, \tag{68}$$

which can be understood as the global anomaly associated with the large diffeomorphism. This anomalous phase is related to the three-dimensional gravitational Chern-Simons term through the anomaly inflow mechanism, which is also related to the gravitational contribution to chiral anomaly in $3+1$ dimensions [107,108].

This argument can be generalized to higher dimensions. In $(3+1)$ dimensions, Ψ_{ano} is given in Equation (56). To detect the global anomaly, we compactify the space to $S^1 \times S^2$, where we choose z as the coordinate on S^1. Under the large diffeomorphism, $\tau \to \tau + 2z\beta_0/L$, the term contributing to the T^2 part of CVE transforms as

$$\Psi_{\text{ano}} \to \Psi_{\text{ano}} - 2\pi i C_1 \int \frac{d^2x}{2\pi} e\varepsilon^{0ijz}\partial_i \widetilde{A}'_j. \tag{69}$$

This is the global mixed anomaly between $U(1)$ gauge and large diffeomorphism. Therefore, we see that the chiral vortical coefficient proportional to T^2, which is nothing but C_1, is related to the mixed global anomaly. Nevertheless, it should be noted that the mixed global anomaly only fixes a "fractional" part of T^2 term. This is because a shift $C_1 \to C_1 + n$ with $n \in \mathbb{Z}$ does not change the partition functional [54].

5. Summary and Discussion

In this paper, we have discussed two approaches to derive the anomaly-induced transport phenomena for the system composed of a Weyl fermion: perturbative evaluation of the chiral magnetic/vortical conductivity with the help of the (equilibrium) linear response theory, and the nonperturbative determination of anomalous parts of the local thermodynamic functional on the basis of the anomaly matching. Both derivations are based on the imaginary-time formalism of the quantum field theory, and we have seen that the obtained anomalous constitutive relations correctly describe the chiral magnetic/vortical effect. Although it is not so clear in the first derivation, the second derivation shows that the chiral magnetic/vortical effect results from the first-order derivative corrections of the local thermodynamic functional, and thus, they are clearly nondissipative in nature. This is perfectly consistent with the known result obtained from the hydrostatic partition function method [29–32,35,38–40,43,45,46], and we rigorously clarify why that method works well. This local equilibrium part of the constitutive relation also complete the application of Zubarev's nonequilibrium statistical operator method to derive the hydrodynamic equation for the parity-violating (anomalous) fluid.

There are several interesting questions related to the current work. It has been already pointed out that the coefficient in front of the T^2-term of the CVE will be renormalized in the presence of dynamical gauge fields such as the gluon in the QCD plasma [109]. It may be interesting to examine which part of the anomaly matching argument associated with the large diffeomorphism (Kaluza-Klein gauge) transformation should be modified due to the existence of the dynamical gauge field. Another important issue associated with the inclusion of dynamical electromagnetic field is its dynamics. When we consider the dynamics of the electromagnetic field rather than treating it as the background one, we encounter with several interesting phenomena such as the chiral plasma instability [110–114], and mixing of some hydrodynamic modes (chiral magnetic wave) to be the massive collective excitation (chiral plasmon) [48,65,115,116]. It is desirable to systematically describe them based on the generalization of magnetohydrodynamics for the chiral plasma by formulating chiral magnetohydrodynamics. Chiral magnetohydrodynamics is just recently formulated based on e.g., the phenomenological entropy-current analysis [117] (See also Refs. [118–124]), but less is clarified from the underlying quantum field theory. Combined with the recent development of the magnetohydrodynamics itself from the field theoretical viewpoint [125–130], it may be interesting to formulate chiral magnetohydrodynamics based on the Zubarev's nonequilibrium statistical operator method equipped with the path-integral formula for the local thermodynamic functional reviewed in this paper.

Author Contributions: All authors have substantially contributed to the research reported in this work and the writing of the manuscript.

Funding: This research was funded by Japan Society of Promotion of Science (JSPS) Grant-in-Aid for Scientific Research (KAKENHI) Grant Numbers JP16K17716, 17H06462, 18H01211, and 18H01217, and also supported by the Ministry of Education, Culture, Sports, Science, and Technology(MEXT)-Supported Program for the Strategic Research Foundation at Private Universities "Topological Science" (Grant No. S1511006).

Acknowledgments: M.H. was supported by the Special Postdoctoral Researchers Program at RIKEN. This work was partially supported by the RIKEN iTHES/iTHEMS Program, in particular, iTHEMS STAMP working group.

Conflicts of Interest: The authors declare no conflict of interest.

References

1. Bertlmann, R.A. *Anomalies in Quantum Field Theory*; Oxford University Press: Oxford, UK, 2000; Volume 91.
2. Fujikawa, K.; Suzuki, H. *Path Integrals and Quantum Anomalies*; Oxford University Press on Demand: Oxford, UK, 2004; Volume 122.
3. Fukuda, H.; Miyamoto, Y. On the γ-Decay of Neutral Meson. *Prog. Theor. Phys.* **1949**, *4*, 347–357. [CrossRef]
4. Adler, S.L. Axial vector vertex in spinor electrodynamics. *Phys. Rev.* **1969**, *177*, 2426–2438. [CrossRef]
5. Bell, J.S.; Jackiw, R. A PCAC puzzle: $\pi^0 \to \gamma\gamma$ in the σ model. *Nuovo Cim.* **1969**, *A60*, 47–61. [CrossRef]
6. 't Hooft, G. Naturalness, chiral symmetry, and spontaneous chiral symmetry breaking. In *Recent Developments in Gauge Theories. NATO Advanced Study Institutes Series (Series B. Physics)*; Springer: Boston, MA, USA, 1979; Volume 59. [CrossRef]
7. Frishman, Y.; Schwimmer, A.; Banks, T.; Yankielowicz, S. The Axial Anomaly and the Bound State Spectrum in Confining Theories. *Nucl. Phys.* **1981**, *B177*, 157–171. [CrossRef]
8. Wen, X.G. Classifying gauge anomalies through symmetry-protected trivial orders and classifying gravitational anomalies through topological orders. *Phys. Rev.* **2013**, *D88*, 045013. [CrossRef]
9. Tachikawa, Y.; Yonekura, K. On time-reversal anomaly of 2+1d topological phases. *PTEP* **2017**, *2017*, 033B04. [CrossRef]
10. Gaiotto, D.; Kapustin, A.; Komargodski, Z.; Seiberg, N. Theta, Time Reversal, and Temperature. *J. High Energy Phys.* **2017**, *5*, 091. [CrossRef]
11. Tanizaki, Y.; Kikuchi, Y. Vacuum structure of bifundamental gauge theories at finite topological angles. *J. High Energy Phys.* **2017**, *6*, 102. [CrossRef]
12. Shimizu, H.; Yonekura, K. Anomaly constraints on deconfinement and chiral phase transition. *Phys. Rev.* **2018**, *D97*, 105011. [CrossRef]
13. Tanizaki, Y.; Misumi, T.; Sakai, N. Circle compactification and 't Hooft anomaly. *J. High Energy Phys.* **2017**, *12*, 56. [CrossRef]
14. Tanizaki, Y.; Kikuchi, Y.; Misumi, T.; Sakai, N. Anomaly matching for phase diagram of massless $\mathbb{Z}_N$-QCD. *Phys. Rev.* **2018**, *D97*, 054012. [CrossRef]
15. Sulejmanpasic, T.; Tanizaki, Y. C-P-T anomaly matching in bosonic quantum field theory and spin chains. *Phys. Rev.* **2018**, *B97*, 144201. [CrossRef]
16. Yao, Y.; Hsieh, C.T.; Oshikawa, M. Anomaly matching and symmetry-protected critical phases in $SU(N)$ spin systems in 1 + 1 dimensions. *arXiv* **2018**, arXiv:1805.06885.
17. Tanizaki, Y.; Sulejmanpasic, T. Anomaly and global inconsistency matching: θ-angles, $SU(3)/U(1)^2$ nonlinear sigma model, $SU(3)$ chains and its generalizations. *Phys. Rev.* **2018**, *B98*, 115126. [CrossRef]
18. Tanizaki, Y. Anomaly constraint on massless QCD and the role of Skyrmions in chiral symmetry breaking. *J. High Energy Phys.* **2018**, *8*, 171. [CrossRef]
19. Yonekura, K. Anomaly matching in QCD thermal phase transition. *arXiv* **2019**, arXiv:1901.08188.
20. Fukushima, K.; Kharzeev, D.E.; Warringa, H.J. The Chiral Magnetic Effect. *Phys. Rev.* **2008**, *D78*, 074033. [CrossRef]
21. Erdmenger, J.; Haack, M.; Kaminski, M.; Yarom, A. Fluid dynamics of R-charged black holes. *J. High Energy Phys.* **2009**, *1*, 55. [CrossRef]
22. Banerjee, N.; Bhattacharya, J.; Bhattacharyya, S.; Dutta, S.; Loganayagam, R.; Surowka, P. Hydrodynamics from charged black branes. *J. High Energy Phys.* **2011**, *1*, 094. [CrossRef]

23. Torabian, M.; Yee, H.U. Holographic nonlinear hydrodynamics from AdS/CFT with multiple/non-Abelian symmetries. *J. High Energy Phys.* **2009**, *8*, 20. [CrossRef]
24. Son, D.T.; Surowka, P. Hydrodynamics with Triangle Anomalies. *Phys. Rev. Lett.* **2009**, *103*, 191601. [CrossRef] [PubMed]
25. Amado, I.; Landsteiner, K.; Pena-Benitez, F. Anomalous transport coefficients from Kubo formulas in Holography. *J. High Energy Phys.* **2011**, *5*, 081. [CrossRef]
26. Landsteiner, K.; Megias, E.; Pena-Benitez, F. Gravitational Anomaly and Transport. *Phys. Rev. Lett.* **2011**, *107*, 021601. [CrossRef]
27. Gao, J.H.; Liang, Z.T.; Pu, S.; Wang, Q.; Wang, X.N. Chiral Anomaly and Local Polarization Effect from Quantum Kinetic Approach. *Phys. Rev. Lett.* **2012**, *109*, 232301. [CrossRef]
28. Son, D.T.; Yamamoto, N. Berry Curvature, Triangle Anomalies, and the Chiral Magnetic Effect in Fermi Liquids. *Phys. Rev. Lett.* **2012**, *109*, 181602. [CrossRef]
29. Banerjee, N.; Bhattacharya, J.; Bhattacharyya, S.; Jain, S.; Minwalla, S.; Sharma, T. Constraints on Fluid Dynamics from Equilibrium Partition Functions. *J. High Energy Phys.* **2012**, *9*, 46. [CrossRef]
30. Jensen, K.; Kaminski, M.; Kovtun, P.; Meyer, R.; Ritz, A.; Yarom, A. Towards hydrodynamics without an entropy current. *Phys. Rev. Lett.* **2012**, *109*, 101601. [CrossRef]
31. Jensen, K. Triangle Anomalies, Thermodynamics, and Hydrodynamics. *Phys. Rev.* **2012**, *D85*, 125017. [CrossRef]
32. Banerjee, N.; Dutta, S.; Jain, S.; Loganayagam, R.; Sharma, T. Constraints on Anomalous Fluid in Arbitrary Dimensions. *J. High Energy Phys.* **2013**, *3*, 48. [CrossRef]
33. Stephanov, M.A.; Yin, Y. Chiral Kinetic Theory. *Phys. Rev. Lett.* **2012**, *109*, 162001. [CrossRef] [PubMed]
34. Landsteiner, K.; Megias, E.; Pena-Benitez, F. Anomalous Transport from Kubo Formulae. *Lect. Notes Phys.* **2013**, *871*, 433–468. [CrossRef]
35. Jensen, K.; Loganayagam, R.; Yarom, A. Thermodynamics, gravitational anomalies and cones. *J. High Energy Phys.* **2013**, *2*, 88. [CrossRef]
36. Son, D.T.; Yamamoto, N. Kinetic theory with Berry curvature from quantum field theories. *Phys. Rev.* **2013**, *D87*, 085016. [CrossRef]
37. Chen, J.W.; Pu, S.; Wang, Q.; Wang, X.N. Berry Curvature and Four-Dimensional Monopoles in the Relativistic Chiral Kinetic Equation. *Phys. Rev. Lett.* **2013**, *110*, 262301. [CrossRef]
38. Jensen, K.; Kovtun, P.; Ritz, A. Chiral conductivities and effective field theory. *J. High Energy Phys.* **2013**, *10*, 186. [CrossRef]
39. Jensen, K.; Loganayagam, R.; Yarom, A. Anomaly inflow and thermal equilibrium. *J. High Energy Phys.* **2014**, *5*, 134. [CrossRef]
40. Jensen, K.; Loganayagam, R.; Yarom, A. Chern-Simons terms from thermal circles and anomalies. *J. High Energy Phys.* **2014**, *5*, 110. [CrossRef]
41. Manuel, C.; Torres-Rincon, J.M. Kinetic theory of chiral relativistic plasmas and energy density of their gauge collective excitations. *Phys. Rev.* **2014**, *D89*, 096002. [CrossRef]
42. Chen, J.Y.; Son, D.T.; Stephanov, M.A.; Yee, H.U.; Yin, Y. Lorentz Invariance in Chiral Kinetic Theory. *Phys. Rev. Lett.* **2014**, *113*, 182302. [CrossRef] [PubMed]
43. Haehl, F.M.; Loganayagam, R.; Rangamani, M. Adiabatic hydrodynamics: The eightfold way to dissipation. *J. High Energy Phys.* **2015**, *5*, 060. [CrossRef]
44. Chen, J.Y.; Son, D.T.; Stephanov, M.A. Collisions in Chiral Kinetic Theory. *Phys. Rev. Lett.* **2015**, *115*, 021601. [CrossRef] [PubMed]
45. Golkar, S.; Sethi, S. Global Anomalies and Effective Field Theory. *J. High Energy Phys.* **2016**, *5*, 105. [CrossRef]
46. Chowdhury, S.D.; David, J.R. Global gravitational anomalies and transport. *J. High Energy Phys.* **2016**, *12*, 116. [CrossRef]
47. Landsteiner, K. Notes on Anomaly Induced Transport. *Acta Phys. Polon.* **2016**, *B47*, 2617. [CrossRef]
48. Gorbar, E.V.; Miransky, V.A.; Shovkovy, I.A.; Sukhachov, P.O. Consistent Chiral Kinetic Theory in Weyl Materials: Chiral Magnetic Plasmons. *Phys. Rev. Lett.* **2017**, *118*, 127601. [CrossRef] [PubMed]
49. Hidaka, Y.; Pu, S.; Yang, D.L. Relativistic Chiral Kinetic Theory from Quantum Field Theories. *Phys. Rev.* **2017**, *D95*, 091901. [CrossRef]
50. Buzzegoli, M.; Grossi, E.; Becattini, F. General equilibrium second-order hydrodynamic coefficients for free quantum fields. *J. High Energy Phys.* **2017**, *10*, 091. [CrossRef]

51. Hidaka, Y.; Pu, S.; Yang, D.L. Nonlinear Responses of Chiral Fluids from Kinetic Theory. *Phys. Rev.* **2018**, *D97*, 016004. [CrossRef]
52. Mueller, N.; Venugopalan, R. The chiral anomaly, Berry's phase and chiral kinetic theory, from world-lines in quantum field theory. *Phys. Rev.* **2018**, *D97*, 051901. [CrossRef]
53. Mueller, N.; Venugopalan, R. Worldline construction of a covariant chiral kinetic theory. *Phys. Rev.* **2017**, *D96*, 016023. [CrossRef]
54. Glorioso, P.; Liu, H.; Rajagopal, S. Global Anomalies, Discrete Symmetries, and Hydrodynamic Effective Actions. *J. High Energy Phys.* **2019**, *1*, 043. [CrossRef]
55. Hidaka, Y.; Yang, D.L. Nonequilibrium chiral magnetic/vortical effects in viscous fluids. *Phys. Rev.* **2018**, *D98*, 016012. [CrossRef]
56. Stone, M.; Kim, J. Mixed Anomalies: Chiral Vortical Effect and the Sommerfeld Expansion. *Phys. Rev.* **2018**, *D98*, 025012. [CrossRef]
57. Carignano, S.; Manuel, C.; Torres-Rincon, J.M. Consistent relativistic chiral kinetic theory: A derivation from on-shell effective field theory. *Phys. Rev.* **2018**, *D98*, 076005. [CrossRef]
58. Buzzegoli, M.; Becattini, F. General thermodynamic equilibrium with axial chemical potential for the free Dirac field. *J. High Energy Phys.* **2018**, *12*, 002. [CrossRef]
59. Dayi, O.F.; Kilinçarslan, E. Quantum Kinetic Equation in the Rotating Frame and Chiral Kinetic Theory. *Phys. Rev.* **2018**, *D98*, 081701. [CrossRef]
60. Liu, Y.C.; Gao, L.L.; Mameda, K.; Huang, X.G. Chiral kinetic theory in curved spacetime. *arXiv* **2018**, arXiv:1812.10127.
61. Mueller, N.; Venugopalan, R. Constructing phase space distributions with internal symmetries. *arXiv* **2019**, arXiv:1901.10492.
62. Vilenkin, A. Macroscopic parity violating effects: Neutrino fluxes from rotating black holes and in rotating thermal radiation. *Phys. Rev.* **1979**, *D20*, 1807–1812. [CrossRef]
63. Vilenkin, A. Equilibrium parity violating current in a magnetic field. *Phys. Rev.* **1980**, *D22*, 3080–3084. [CrossRef]
64. Kharzeev, D.E.; McLerran, L.D.; Warringa, H.J. The Effects of topological charge change in heavy ion collisions: 'Event by event P and CP violation'. *Nuclear Phys.* **2008**, *A803*, 227–253. [CrossRef]
65. Kharzeev, D.E.; Yee, H.U. Chiral Magnetic Wave. *Phys. Rev.* **2011**, *D83*, 085007. [CrossRef]
66. Burnier, Y.; Kharzeev, D.E.; Liao, J.; Yee, H.U. Chiral magnetic wave at finite baryon density and the electric quadrupole moment of quark-gluon plasma in heavy ion collisions. *Phys. Rev. Lett.* **2011**, *107*, 052303. [CrossRef]
67. Hongo, M.; Hirono, Y.; Hirano, T. Anomalous-hydrodynamic analysis of charge-dependent elliptic flow in heavy-ion collisions. *Phys. Lett.* **2017**, *B775*, 266–270. [CrossRef]
68. Yee, H.U.; Yin, Y. Realistic Implementation of Chiral Magnetic Wave in Heavy Ion Collisions. *Phys. Rev.* **2014**, *C89*, 044909. [CrossRef]
69. Hirono, Y.; Hirano, T.; Kharzeev, D.E. The chiral magnetic effect in heavy-ion collisions from event-by-event anomalous hydrodynamics. *arXiv* **2014**, arXiv:1412.0311.
70. Adamczyk, L.; Adkins, J.K.; Agakishiev, G.; Aggarwal, M.M. Observation of charge asymmetry dependence of pion elliptic flow and the possible chiral magnetic wave in heavy-ion collisions. *Phys. Rev. Lett.* **2015**, *114*, 252302. [CrossRef] [PubMed]
71. Yin, Y.; Liao, J. Hydrodynamics with chiral anomaly and charge separation in relativistic heavy ion collisions. *Phys. Lett.* **2016**, *B756*, 42–46. [CrossRef]
72. Huang, X.G. Electromagnetic fields and anomalous transports in heavy-ion collisions—A pedagogical review. *Rept. Prog. Phys.* **2016**, *79*, 076302. [CrossRef]
73. Kharzeev, D.E.; Liao, J.; Voloshin, S.A.; Wang, G. Chiral magnetic and vortical effects in high-energy nuclear collisions—A status report. *Prog. Part. Nuclear Phys.* **2016**, *88*, 1–28. [CrossRef]
74. Shi, S.; Jiang, Y.; Lilleskov, E.; Liao, J. Anomalous Chiral Transport in Heavy Ion Collisions from Anomalous-Viscous Fluid Dynamics. *Ann. Phys.* **2018**, *394*, 50–72. [CrossRef]
75. Charbonneau, J.; Zhitnitsky, A. Topological Currents in Neutron Stars: Kicks, Precession, Toroidal Fields, and Magnetic Helicity. *J. Cosmol. Astropart. Phys.* **2010**, *1008*, 010. [CrossRef]
76. Grabowska, D.; Kaplan, D.B.; Reddy, S. Role of the electron mass in damping chiral plasma instability in Supernovae and neutron stars. *Phys. Rev.* **2015**, *D91*, 085035. [CrossRef]

77. Kaminski, M.; Uhlemann, C.F.; Bleicher, M.; Schaffner-Bielich, J. Anomalous hydrodynamics kicks neutron stars. *Phys. Lett.* **2016**, *B760*, 170–174. [CrossRef]
78. Sigl, G.; Leite, N. Chiral Magnetic Effect in Protoneutron Stars and Magnetic Field Spectral Evolution. *J. Cosmol. Astropart. Phys.* **2016**, *1601*, 025. [CrossRef]
79. Yamamoto, N. Chiral transport of neutrinos in supernovae: Neutrino-induced fluid helicity and helical plasma instability. *Phys. Rev.* **2016**, *D93*, 065017. [CrossRef]
80. Masada, Y.; Kotake, K.; Takiwaki, T.; Yamamoto, N. Chiral magnetohydrodynamic turbulence in core-collapse supernovae. *Phys. Rev.* **2018**, *D98*, 083018. [CrossRef]
81. Zyuzin, A.A.; Burkov, A.A. Topological response in Weyl semimetals and the chiral anomaly. *Phys. Rev.* **2012**, *B86*, 115133. [CrossRef]
82. Goswami, P.; Tewari, S. Axionic field theory of (3+1)-dimensional Weyl semimetals. *Phys. Rev.* **2013**, *B88*, 245107. [CrossRef]
83. Chen, Y.; Wu, S.; Burkov, A.A. Axion response in Weyl semimetals. *Phys. Rev.* **2013**, *B88*, 125105. [CrossRef]
84. Basar, G.; Kharzeev, D.E.; Yee, H.U. Triangle anomaly in Weyl semimetals. *Phys. Rev.* **2014**, *B89*, 035142. [CrossRef]
85. Hosur, P.; Qi, X. Recent developments in transport phenomena in Weyl semimetals. *Comptes Rendus Phys.* **2013**, *14*, 857–870. [CrossRef]
86. Landsteiner, K. Anomalous transport of Weyl fermions in Weyl semimetals. *Phys. Rev.* **2014**, *B89*, 075124. [CrossRef]
87. Chernodub, M.N.; Cortijo, A.; Grushin, A.G.; Landsteiner, K.; Vozmediano, M.A.H. Condensed matter realization of the axial magnetic effect. *Phys. Rev.* **2014**, *B89*, 081407. [CrossRef]
88. Gorbar, E.V.; Miransky, V.A.; Shovkovy, I.A. Chiral anomaly, dimensional reduction, and magnetoresistivity of Weyl and Dirac semimetals. *Phys. Rev.* **2014**, *B89*, 085126. [CrossRef]
89. Armitage, N.P.; Mele, E.J.; Vishwanath, A. Weyl and Dirac Semimetals in Three Dimensional Solids. *Rev. Mod. Phys.* **2018**, *90*, 015001. [CrossRef]
90. Gorbar, E.V.; Miransky, V.A.; Shovkovy, I.A.; Sukhachov, P.O. Anomalous transport properties of Dirac and Weyl semimetals (Review Article). *Low Temp. Phys.* **2018**, *44*, 487–505. [CrossRef]
91. Li, Q.; Kharzeev, D.E.; Zhang, C.; Huang, Y.; Pletikosic, I.; Fedorov, A.V.; Zhong, R.D.; Schneeloch, J.A.; Gu, G.D.; Valla, T. Observation of the chiral magnetic effect in ZrTe5. *Nat. Phys.* **2016**, *12*, 550–554. [CrossRef]
92. Lv, B.Q.; Weng, H.M.; Fu, B.B.; Wang, X.P.; Miao, H.; Ma, J. Experimental discovery of Weyl semimetal TaAs. *Phys. Rev.* **2015**, *X5*, 031013. [CrossRef]
93. Xu, S.Y.; Belopolski, I.; Alidoust, N.; Neupane, M.; Bian, G.; Zhang, C.; Sank, R. Discovery of a Weyl Fermion semimetal and topological Fermi arcs. *Science* **2015**, *349*, 613–617. [CrossRef]
94. Matsubara, T. A New Approach to Quantum-Statistical Mechanics. *Prog. Theor. Phys.* **1955**, *14*, 351–378. [CrossRef]
95. Abrikosov, A.A.; Gorkov, L.P.; Dzyaloshinskii, I.E. On the Application of Quantum-Field-Theory Methods to Problems of Quantum Statistics at Finite Temperatures. *Sov. Phys. JETP* **1959**, *9*, 636–641.
96. Le Bellac, M. *Thermal Field Theory*; Cambridge University Press: Cambridge, UK, 2000.
97. Kapusta, J.I.; Gale, C. *Finite-Temperature Field Theory: Principles and Applications*; Cambridge University Press: Cambridge, UK, 2006.
98. Zubarev, D.N.; Prozorkevich, A.V.; Smolyanskii, S.A. Derivation of nonlinear generalized equations of quantum relativistic hydrodynamics. *Theor. Math. Phys.* **1979**, *40*, 821–831. [CrossRef]
99. Zubarev, D.N.; Morozov, V.; Ropke, G. *Statistical Mechanics of Nonequilibrium Processes, Volume 1: Basic Concepts, Kinetic Theory*, 1st ed.; Wiley-VCH: Hoboken, NJ, USA, 1996.
100. Zubarev, D.N.; Morozov, V.; Ropke, G. *Statistical Mechanics of Nonequilibrium Processes, Volume 2: Relaxation and Hydrodynamic Processes*; Wiley-VCH: Hoboken, NJ, USA, 1997.
101. Becattini, F.; Bucciantini, L.; Grossi, E.; Tinti, L. Local thermodynamical equilibrium and the beta frame for a quantum relativistic fluid. *Eur. Phys. J.* **2015**, *C75*, 191. [CrossRef]
102. Hayata, T.; Hidaka, Y.; Noumi, T.; Hongo, M. Relativistic hydrodynamics from quantum field theory on the basis of the generalized Gibbs ensemble method. *Phys. Rev.* **2015**, *D92*, 065008. [CrossRef]
103. Hongo, M. Path-integral formula for local thermal equilibrium. *Ann. Phys.* **2017**, *383*, 1–32. [CrossRef]
104. Hongo, M. Nonrelativistic Hydrodynamics from Quantum Field Theory: (I) Normal Fluid Composed of Spinless Schrödinger Fields. *J. Stat. Phys.* **2019**. [CrossRef]

105. Bardeen, W.A.; Zumino, B. Consistent and Covariant Anomalies in Gauge and Gravitational Theories. *Nucl. Phys.* **1984**, *B244*, 421–453. [CrossRef]
106. Nakai, R.; Ryu, S.; Nomura, K. Laughlin's argument for the quantized thermal Hall effect. *Phys. Rev.* **2017**, *B95*, 165405. [CrossRef]
107. Witten, E. Global Aspects of Current Algebra. *Nucl. Phys.* **1983**, *B223*, 422–432. [CrossRef]
108. Witten, E. Global gravitational anomalies. *Commun. Math. Phys.* **1985**, *100*, 197. [CrossRef]
109. Golkar, S.; Son, D.T. (Non)-renormalization of the chiral vortical effect coefficient. *J. High Energy Phys.* **2015**, *2*, 169. [CrossRef]
110. Boyarsky, A.; Frohlich, J.; Ruchayskiy, O. Self-consistent evolution of magnetic fields and chiral asymmetry in the early Universe. *Phys. Rev. Lett.* **2012**, *108*, 031301. [CrossRef]
111. Tashiro, H.; Vachaspati, T.; Vilenkin, A. Chiral Effects and Cosmic Magnetic Fields. *Phys. Rev.* **2012**, *D86*, 105033. [CrossRef]
112. Akamatsu, Y.; Yamamoto, N. Chiral Plasma Instabilities. *Phys. Rev. Lett.* **2013**, *111*, 052002. [CrossRef]
113. Akamatsu, Y.; Yamamoto, N. Chiral Langevin theory for non-Abelian plasmas. *Phys. Rev.* **2014**, *D90*, 125031. [CrossRef]
114. Manuel, C.; Torres-Rincon, J.M. Dynamical evolution of the chiral magnetic effect: Applications to the quark-gluon plasma. *Phys. Rev.* **2015**, *D92*, 074018. [CrossRef]
115. Gorbar, E.V.; Miransky, V.A.; Shovkovy, I.A.; Sukhachov, P.O. Chiral magnetic plasmons in anomalous relativistic matter. *Phys. Rev.* **2017**, *B95*, 115202. [CrossRef]
116. Rybalka, D.; Gorbar, E.; Shovkovy, I. Hydrodynamic modes in a magnetized chiral plasma with vorticity. *Phys. Rev.* **2019**, *D99*, 016017. [CrossRef]
117. Hattori, K.; Hirono, Y.; Yee, H.U.; Yin, Y. MagnetoHydrodynamics with chiral anomaly: Phases of collective excitations and instabilities. *arXiv* **2017**, arXiv:1711.08450.
118. Giovannini, M.; Shaposhnikov, M.E. Primordial hypermagnetic fields and triangle anomaly. *Phys. Rev.* **1998** *D57*, 2186. [CrossRef]
119. Giovannini, M. Anomalous Magnetohydrodynamics. *Phys. Rev.* **2013**, *D88*, 063536. [CrossRef]
120. Boyarsky, A.; Frohlich, J.; Ruchayskiy, O. Magnetohydrodynamics of Chiral Relativistic Fluids. *Phys. Rev.* **2015**, *D92*, 043004. [CrossRef]
121. Gorbar, E.V.; Shovkovy, I.A.; Vilchinskii, S.; Rudenok, I.; Boyarsky, A.; Ruchayskiy, O. Anomalous Maxwell equations for inhomogeneous chiral plasma. *Phys. Rev.* **2016**, *D93*, 105028. [CrossRef]
122. Yamamoto, N. Scaling laws in chiral hydrodynamic turbulence. *Phys. Rev.* **2016**, *D93*, 125016. [CrossRef]
123. Giovannini, M. Anomalous magnetohydrodynamics in the extreme relativistic domain. *Phys. Rev.* **2016**, *D94*, 081301. [CrossRef]
124. Rogachevskii, I.; Ruchayskiy, O.; Boyarsky, A.; Fröhlich, J.; Kleeorin, N.; Brandenburg, A.; Schober, J. Laminar and turbulent dynamos in chiral magnetohydrodynamics-I: Theory. *Astrophys. J.* **2017**, *846*, 153. [CrossRef]
125. Huang, X.G.; Sedrakian, A.; Rischke, D.H. Kubo formulae for relativistic fluids in strong magnetic fields. *Ann. Phys.* **2011**, *326*, 3075–3094. [CrossRef]
126. Grozdanov, S.; Hofman, D.M.; Iqbal, N. Generalized global symmetries and dissipative magnetohydrodynamics. *Phys. Rev.* **2017**, *D95*, 096003. [CrossRef]
127. Hernandez, J.; Kovtun, P. Relativistic magnetohydrodynamics. *J. High Energy Phys.* **2017**, *5*, 001. [CrossRef]
128. Armas, J.; Jain, A. Magnetohydrodynamics as superfluidity. *arXiv* **2018**, arXiv:1808.01939.
129. Glorioso, P.; Son, D.T. Effective field theory of magnetohydrodynamics from generalized global symmetries. *arXiv* **2018**, arXiv:1811.04879.
130. Armas, J.; Jain, A. One-form superfluids & magnetohydrodynamics. *arXiv* **2018**, arXiv:1811.04913.

particles

MDPI

Article

Unification of Thermo Field Kinetic and Hydrodynamics Approaches in the Theory of Dense Quantum–Field Systems

Mykhailo Tokarchuk [1,2,*] and Petro Hlushak [1]

1 Institute for Condensed Matter Physics of the National Academy of Sciences of Ukraine, 1, Svientsitskii Str., 79011 Lviv, Ukraine; phl@icmp.lviv.ua
2 National University "Lvivska Politechnika", 12, S. Bandera Str., 79013 Lviv, Ukraine
* Correspondence: mtok@icmp.lviv.ua; Tel.: +38-032-276-1978

Received: 29 October 2018; Accepted: 13 December 2018; Published: 21 December 2018

Abstract: A formulation of nonequilibrium thermo-field dynamics has been performed using the nonequilibrium statistical operator method by D.N. Zubarev. Generalized transfer equations for a consistent description of the kinetics and hydrodynamics of the dense quantum field system with strongly-bound states are derived.

Keywords: nonequilibrium thermo-field dynamics; kinetics; hydrodynamics; kinetic equations; transport coefficients; bound states; quark-gluon plasma

1. Introduction

The problem of accounting for the bound states (clusters) [1,2] formed by particles is particularly important in the development of the theories of nonequilibrium processes of thermal quantum field systems, such as nuclear matter [3–16]. Kinetic and hydrodynamic processes in a hot, compressed nuclear matter, which appears after ultrarelativistic collisions of heavy nuclei [7,14,16–21], are mutually connected, and therefore, the bound states between nucleons should be considered. This is of great importance for the analysis and correlation of final reaction products. Obviously, a nucleon-nucleon interaction investigation based on a quark-gluon plasma is a sequential microscopic approach to the dynamical description of reactions in a nuclear matter. The problems of a dense quark-gluon matter were discussed in detail in [4,5,12,13,22–27].

In his recent works [1,2,19], G. Röpke noted the importance of constructing a nonequilibrium theory in which along with hydrodynamic parameters, a cluster distribution function is taken into account, similarly to the case of the classical theory of non-equilibrium processes of dense gases and liquids [28–31].

In modern theoretical studies of the nonequilibrium properties of quark-gluon plasma [12,13,23,24], which is one of the states of nuclear matter, one of the most widely-used statistical concepts is the entropy of Tsallis and Renyi [32–42]. This is due to the fact that the results of experimental data on the distribution of high-energy hadrons over transverse momentums [32] are described by the power distributions and are characterized by temperature oscillations and possible fractal structures [43]. At the same time, the important problem of the construction of kinetic and hydrodynamic equations for nuclear matter of high density and high temperature is not sufficiently addressed for these systems. However, within the framework of the Gibbs statistics, the equations of hydrodynamics and thermodynamics were already considered in many papers using the method of Zubarev's nonequilibrium statistical operator [44–53], the projection operator method [54,55], and kinetic equations [56–59]. Thus, we propose an approach to solve these problems based on the nonequilibrium thermo-field dynamics [60–62] in the formulation of the method of the nonequilibrium statistical operator [63–65]. We use the thermo-field formalism proposed by Umezawa, Matsumoto, and Tachiki [66,67], mainly because it accounts for the quantum field nature of the interaction of the particles in the synthesis with Gibbs statistics.

Below, in the Section 2 of this paper, we consider the nonequilibrium thermo-field dynamics in the formulation of the nonequilibrium statistical operator method [68–71] in Renyi statistics. We use the statistics of Renyi, which has the power distribution. When the Renyi parameter is $q = 1$, we obtain the results of Gibbs statistics. In addition, Renyi entropy is additive in contrast to the Tsallis entropy.

Next, in the Section 3, generalized equations for the consistent description of kinetic and hydrodynamic processes, which take into account the bound states that emerge in the thermal quantum field system, will be presented.

2. Nonequilibrium Statistical Operator in Thermo-Field Space

We use the nonequilibrium statistical operator method in the thermo-field formulation [63,64], where the mean values corresponding to the observables can be found using the nonequilibrium thermo-vacuum state vector $|\varrho(t)\rangle\rangle$:

$$\langle A\rangle^t = \langle\langle 1|A\varrho(t)\rangle\rangle = \langle\langle 1|\hat{A}|\varrho(t)\rangle\rangle, \tag{1}$$

where $\hat{A}$ is a superoperator acting on the state $|\varrho(t)\rangle\rangle$. The nonequilibrium thermo-vacuum state vector $|\varrho(t)\rangle\rangle$ satisfies the Schrödinger equation [63]:

$$\frac{\partial}{\partial t}|\varrho(t)\rangle\rangle - \left|\frac{1}{i\hbar}[H,\varrho(t)]\right\rangle\rangle = 0, \tag{2}$$

or:

$$\frac{\partial}{\partial t}|\varrho(t)\rangle\rangle - \frac{1}{i\hbar}\hat{H}|\varrho(t)\rangle\rangle = 0. \tag{3}$$

Here, the total Hamiltonian $\hat{H}$ takes the form:

$$\hat{H} = H - \tilde{H}, \tag{4}$$

where $\langle\langle 1|\hat{H} = 0$ and $H = H(\hat{a}^+,\hat{a})$, $\tilde{H} = H^{(*)}(\tilde{a}^+,\tilde{a})$ are superoperators constructed from the creation and annihilation of superoperators of the thermal Liouville space [63,66,67]. The superoperators H and $\tilde{H}$ are accordingly defined by the relations:

$$|H\varrho(t)\rangle\rangle = H|\varrho(t)\rangle\rangle, \qquad |\varrho(t)H\rangle\rangle = \tilde{H}|\varrho(t)\rangle\rangle. \tag{5}$$

The superoperators $\hat{a}_l^+$, $\hat{a}_j$, $\tilde{a}_l^+$ and $\tilde{a}_j$ satisfy the same commutation relations as the operators a_l^+, a_j of the corresponding statistics:

$$\begin{aligned} &[\hat{a}_l,\hat{a}_j^+]_\sigma = [\tilde{a}_l,\tilde{a}_j^+]_\sigma = \delta_{lj}, && [\hat{a}_l,\tilde{a}_j]_\sigma = [\hat{a}_l^+,\tilde{a}_j^+]_\sigma = 0,\\ &[\hat{a}_l,\hat{a}_j]_\sigma = [\hat{a}_l^+,\hat{a}_j^+]_\sigma = 0, && [\tilde{a}_l,\tilde{a}_j]_\sigma = [\tilde{a}_l^+,\tilde{a}_j^+]_\sigma = 0, \end{aligned} \tag{6}$$

where $[A,B]_\sigma = AB - \sigma BA$, $\sigma = +1$ for bosons and $\sigma = -1$ for fermions. The annihilation superoperators $\hat{a}_l$ and $\tilde{a}_l$ are defined by their action on the ground state, the supervacuum [60–62]:

$$\hat{a}_l|00\rangle\rangle = \tilde{a}_l|00\rangle\rangle = 0, \tag{7}$$

where $|00\rangle\rangle = |0\rangle\langle 0|\rangle\rangle$ is the supervacuum. In this case, we have the relations $\hat{a}_l|0\rangle = a_l|0\rangle = 0$ and $\langle 0|\tilde{a}_l = 0$. In other words, the supervacuum $|00\rangle\rangle$ is the orthogonalized state of two vacuum states $\langle 0|$ and $|0\rangle$. Taking commutation relations (6) and definitions (7) into account, we can represent the unit vectors $|1\rangle\rangle = |\sum_l |l\rangle\langle l|\rangle\rangle$ and $\langle\langle 1| = \langle\langle\sum_l |l\rangle\langle l||$ in the form

$$\begin{aligned} |1\rangle\rangle &= \exp\left\{\sum_l \hat{a}_l^+ \tilde{a}_l^+\right\}|00\rangle\rangle, \\ \langle\langle 1| &= \langle\langle 00|\exp\left\{\sum_l \tilde{a}_l \hat{a}_l\right\}. \end{aligned} \tag{8}$$

Using these vectors, we write the relations between the actions of the superoperators $\hat{a}_l^+$, $\hat{a}_j$, $\tilde{a}_l^+$, and $\tilde{a}_j$:

$$\begin{aligned} \hat{a}_l|1\rangle\rangle &= \tilde{a}_l^+|1\rangle\rangle, & \langle\langle 1|\hat{a}_l^+ &= \langle\langle 1|\tilde{a}_l, \\ \hat{a}_l^+|1\rangle\rangle &= \sigma\tilde{a}_l|1\rangle\rangle, & \langle\langle 1|\hat{a}_l &= \langle\langle 1|\tilde{a}_l^+\sigma. \end{aligned} \tag{9}$$

Hence, in the thermo-field dynamics formalism [60–62], the number of operators is doubled by introducing the operators $A(\hat{a}^+,\hat{a})$ and $\tilde{A}(\tilde{a}^+,\tilde{a})$, which satisfy the conditions:

$$\begin{aligned} \widetilde{A_1A_2} &= \tilde{A}_1\tilde{A}_2, \quad \tilde{\tilde{A}} = A, \\ \widetilde{c_1A_1+c_2A_2} &= c_1^*\tilde{A}_1 + c_2^*\tilde{A}_2, \\ |A\rangle\rangle &= \hat{A}|1\rangle\rangle, \\ |A_1A_2\rangle\rangle &= \hat{A}_1|A_2\rangle\rangle, \end{aligned} \tag{10}$$

where the asterisk denotes complex conjugation. A more detailed description of the properties of the superoperators $\hat{a}_l^+$, $\hat{a}_j$, $\tilde{a}_l^+$, and $\tilde{a}_j$ and the thermal Liouville space was presented in [60–62]. The nonequilibrium thermo vacuum state vector is normalized: $\langle\langle 1|\varrho(t)\rangle\rangle = \langle\langle 1|\hat{\varrho}(t)|1\rangle\rangle = 1$, where $\hat{\varrho}(t)$ is the nonequilibrium statistical superoperator, which depends on $\hat{a}_l^+$ and $\hat{a}_j$, $\hat{\varrho}(t) \equiv \varrho\,(\hat{a}^+,\hat{a};t)$. The superoperator $\tilde{\varrho}(t) \equiv \varrho^+(\tilde{a}^+,\tilde{a};t)$ depends on $\tilde{a}_l^+$, $\tilde{a}_j$.

In the nonequilibrium statistical operator method in the thermo-field formulation [63,64], the nonequilibrium thermo-vacuum state vector as a solution of the Schrödinger Equation (3) with a source $-\varepsilon\Big(|\varrho(t)\rangle\rangle - |\varrho_{\text{rel}}(t)\rangle\rangle\Big)$, with the projection taken into account, can be found in the form:

$$|\varrho(t)\rangle\rangle = |\varrho_{\text{rel}}(t)\rangle\rangle + \int_{-\infty}^{t} dt'\, e^{\varepsilon(t'-t)}T(t,t')\left[1-\mathcal{P}_{\text{rel}}(t')\right]\frac{1}{i\hbar}\hat{H}|\varrho_{\text{rel}}(t')\rangle\rangle. \tag{11}$$

Here, $T(t,t') = \exp_+\left\{\int_{t'}^{t} dt'\left[1-\mathcal{P}_{\text{rel}}(t')\right]\frac{1}{i\hbar}\hat{H}\right\}$ is the evolution operator with the projection taken into account, where $\exp_+$ is the ordered exponential, $\varepsilon \to +0$ after the thermodynamic limit transition.

$$\begin{aligned} \mathcal{P}_{\text{rel}}(t)(|\ldots\rangle\rangle) = |\varrho_{\text{rel}}(t)\rangle\rangle &+ \sum_n \frac{\delta|\varrho_{\text{rel}}(t)\rangle\rangle}{\delta\langle\langle 1|\hat{p}_n|\varrho(t)\rangle\rangle}\langle\langle 1|\hat{p}_n|\ldots\rangle\rangle \\ &- \sum_n \frac{\delta|\varrho_{\text{rel}}(t)\rangle\rangle}{\delta\langle\langle 1|\hat{p}_n|\varrho(t)\rangle\rangle}\langle\langle 1|\hat{p}_n|\ldots\rangle\rangle\langle\langle 1|\ldots\rangle\rangle \end{aligned} \tag{12}$$

is the Kawasaki–Ganton projection operator, which acts only on the state vectors $|\ldots\rangle\rangle$ and has the operator properties $\mathcal{P}_{\text{rel}}(t)|\varrho(t')\rangle\rangle = |\varrho_{\text{rel}}(t)\rangle\rangle$, $\mathcal{P}_{\text{rel}}(t)|\varrho_{\text{rel}}(t')\rangle\rangle = |\varrho_{\text{rel}}(t)\rangle\rangle$, $\mathcal{P}_{\text{rel}}(t)\mathcal{P}_{\text{rel}}(t') = \mathcal{P}_{\text{rel}}(t)$. The relevant thermo-vacuum state vector $|\varrho_{\text{rel}}(t)\rangle\rangle = \hat{\varrho}_{\text{rel}}(t)|1\rangle\rangle$, is normalized in accordance with the relation $\langle\langle 1|\varrho_{\text{rel}}(t)\rangle\rangle = \langle\langle 1|\hat{\varrho}_{\text{rel}}(t)|1\rangle\rangle = 1$, where $\hat{\varrho}_{\text{rel}}(t)$ is the relevant statistical superoperator. The relevant thermo-vacuum state vector of the system can be defined as follows. We assume that $\langle p_n\rangle^t = \langle\langle\langle 1|\hat{p}_n|\varrho(t)\rangle\rangle\rangle$ is the set of observed variables describing the nonequilibrium system state, where p_n are the operators constructed on the respective creation and annihilation operators a_l^+ and a_l. The relevant statistical operator $\varrho_{\text{rel}}(t)$ is determined from the extremum of the Renyi entropy functional:

$$L_R(t) = \frac{1}{1-q}\ln\langle\langle 1|(|\varrho'(t)\rangle\rangle)^q - \alpha\langle\langle 1|\varrho'(t)\rangle\rangle - \sum_n F_n^*(t)\langle\langle 1|\hat{p}_n|\varrho'(t)\rangle\rangle$$

under the additional condition that the mean values $\langle p_n \rangle^t$ are given with the normalization condition $\langle\langle 1|\hat{\varrho}(t)|1\rangle\rangle = 1$ preserved. The Lagrange parameters α and $F_n^*(t)$ are determined from the respective normalization condition and self-consistency conditions:

$$\langle \ldots \rangle^t_{\rm rel} = \langle\langle 1| \ldots |\varrho_{\rm rel}(t)\rangle\rangle, \qquad \langle p_n \rangle^t = \langle p_n \rangle^t_{\rm rel} = \langle\langle 1|\hat{p}_n|\varrho_{\rm rel}(t)\rangle\rangle. \tag{13}$$

The relevant statistical operator $\varrho_{\rm rel}(t)$ then becomes:

$$\varrho_{\rm rel}(t) = \frac{1}{Z_R(t)}\Big[1 - \frac{q-1}{q}\sum_n F_n^*(t)\delta\hat{p}_n(t)\Big]^{\frac{1}{q-1}}, \tag{14}$$

where q is the Renyi parameter, $\delta\hat{p}_n(t) = \hat{p} - \langle\langle 1|\hat{p}_n|\varrho(t)\rangle\rangle$, and:

$$Z_R(t) = \Big\langle\Big\langle 1\Big|\Big[1 - \frac{q-1}{q}\sum_n F_n^*(t)\delta\hat{p}_n(t)\Big]^{\frac{1}{q-1}}\Big\rangle\Big\rangle, \tag{15}$$

is the partition function. The sum over n can denote the summation over the wave vector $\mathbf{k}$, the kind of particles, and a whole series of quantum numbers, such as spin. From (14) at $q = 1$, we obtain the relevant statistical operator corresponding to Gibbs statistics [63]:

$$\varrho_{\rm rel}(t) = \exp\Big\{ - \Phi(t) - \sum_n F_n^*(t)p_n\Big\}, \tag{16}$$

where $\Phi(t) = \ln \mathrm{Sp} \exp\{-\sum_n F_n^*(t)p_n\}$ is the Massieu–Planck functional. Substituting (14) in (11), we now obtain the nonequilibrium thermo-vacuum vector:

$$|\varrho(t)\rangle\rangle = |\varrho_{\rm rel}(t)\rangle\rangle + \sum_n \int_{-\infty}^t dt' e^{\varepsilon(t'-t)}T(t,t')\Big|\int_0^1 d\tau \varrho^{\tau}_{\rm rel}(t')J_n(t')\varrho_{\rm rel}(t)^{1-\tau}(t')\Big\rangle\Big\rangle F_n^*(t'), \tag{17}$$

where $J_n(t) = [1 - \mathcal{P}(t)]\,\frac{1}{q}\psi^{-1}(t)\dot{\hat{p}}_n$ are the operators of the generalized flows describing the dissipative processes $\dot{\hat{p}}_n = -\frac{1}{i\hbar}\hat{H}\hat{p}_n$ in the system. The projection operator $\mathcal{P}(t)$ acts on operators and has the structure:

$$\begin{aligned}\mathcal{P}(t)(\ldots) = \langle\langle 1| \ldots |\varrho_{\rm rel}(t)\rangle\rangle + \sum_m \delta\Big[\int_0^1 d\tau \varrho^{\tau}_{\rm rel}(t)\psi^{-1}(t)\Big(F_m(t) \\ + \sum_n f^{-1}_{mn}(t)\delta\hat{p}_n\Big)\varrho^{-\tau}_{\rm rel}\Big]\Big\langle\Big\langle \ldots\Big|\int_0^1 d\tau\varrho^{\tau}_{\rm rel}(t)\delta\hat{p}_n\varrho^{-\tau}_{\rm rel}(t)\varrho_{\rm rel}(t)\Big\rangle\Big\rangle,\end{aligned} \tag{18}$$

where $\delta[\ldots] = [\ldots] - \langle\langle 1|[\ldots]|\varrho_{\rm rel}(t)\rangle\rangle$ and $f_{mn}(t) = \frac{\delta\langle\langle 1|\hat{p}_m|\varrho(t)\rangle\rangle}{\delta F_n(t)}$. The operator $\psi(t)$ has the form $\psi(t) = 1 - \frac{q-1}{q}\sum_n F_n^*(t)\delta\hat{p}_n(t)$. Using the nonequilibrium thermo-vacuum state vector $|\varrho(t)\rangle\rangle$ given by (17), we obtain the transport equations for the nonequilibrium means $\langle\langle 1|\hat{p}_n|\varrho(t)\rangle\rangle$ in the thermo-field representation. For this, we use the identity:

$$\frac{\partial}{\partial t}\langle\langle 1|\hat{p}_n|\varrho(t)\rangle\rangle = \langle\langle 1|\dot{\hat{p}}_n|\varrho(t)\rangle\rangle = \langle\langle 1|\dot{\hat{p}}_n|\varrho_{\rm rel}(t)\rangle\rangle + \langle\langle J_n(t)|\varrho(t)\rangle\rangle. \tag{19}$$

Averaging the last term on the right-hand side with $|\varrho(t)\rangle\rangle$ given by (17), we obtain the transport equations for the means $\langle\langle 1|\hat{p}_n|\varrho_{\rm rel}(t)\rangle\rangle$:

$$\begin{aligned}\frac{\partial}{\partial t}\langle\langle 1|\hat{p}_n|\varrho(t)\rangle\rangle &= \langle\langle 1|\dot{\hat{p}}_n|\varrho_{\rm rel}(t)\rangle\rangle \\ &+ \sum_{n'}\int_{-\infty}^t dt'\, e^{\varepsilon(t'-t)}\Big\langle\Big\langle \dot{\hat{p}}_n T(t,t')\Big|\int_0^1 d\tau\, \varrho^{\tau}_{\rm rel}(t')J_{n'}(t')\varrho^{1-\tau}_{\rm rel}(t')\Big\rangle\Big\rangle\, F^*_{n'}(t').\end{aligned} \tag{20}$$

Transport Equation (20) takes the memory effects into account and can be used to describe nonequilibrium processes in quantum Bose and Fermi systems in concrete cases in the framework of the nonequilibrium thermo-field dynamics of extensive statistics. In particular, a system of relativistic transport equations for a consistent description of the kinetic and hydrodynamic processes in a quark-gluon system was derived in [64] using the nonequilibrium statistical operator method in the thermo-field representation in Gibbs statistics. The advanced approach in terms of Renyi statistics can be generalized to the case of relativistic systems, and this observation is important [33,35–42]. This subject will be described in forthcoming works.

3. Thermo-Field Transport Equation Taking into Account Bound States

We will consider a quantum field system in which bound states can appear between the particles. Let us introduce annihilation and creation operators of a bound state $(A\alpha)$ with the A-particle:

$$\begin{aligned} a_{A\alpha}(\mathbf{p}) &= \sum_{1,\ldots,A} \Psi_{A\alpha\mathbf{p}}(1,\ldots,A)a(1)\ldots a(A), \\ a^+_{A\alpha}(\mathbf{p}) &= \sum_{1,\ldots,A} \Psi^*_{A\alpha\mathbf{p}}(1,\ldots,A)a^+(1)\ldots a^+(A), \end{aligned} \tag{21}$$

where $\Psi_{A\alpha\mathbf{p}}(1,\ldots,A)$ is a self-function of the A-particle bound state, α denotes internal quantum numbers (spin, etc.), $\mathbf{p}$ is a particle momentum, and the sum covers the particles. Annihilation and creation operators $a(j)$ and $a^+(j)$ satisfy the following commutation relations:

$$[a(l),a^+(j)]_\sigma = \delta_{l,j}, \qquad [a(l),a(j)]_\sigma = [a^+(l),a^+(j)]_\sigma = 0, \tag{22}$$

where the σ-commutator is determined by $[a,b]_\sigma = ab - \sigma ba$ with $\sigma = \pm 1$: $+1$ for bosons and -1 for fermions.

The Hamiltonian of such a system can be written in the form:

$$\begin{aligned} H = &\sum_{A,\alpha} \int \frac{d\mathbf{p}d\mathbf{q}}{(2\pi\hbar)^6} \frac{p^2}{2m_A} a^+_{A\alpha}\left(\mathbf{p}-\frac{\mathbf{q}}{2}\right) a_{A\alpha}\left(\mathbf{p}+\frac{\mathbf{q}}{2}\right) \\ &+\frac{1}{2}\sum_{A,B}\sum_{\alpha,\beta} \int \frac{d\mathbf{p}d\mathbf{p}'d\mathbf{q}}{(2\pi\hbar)^9} V_{AB}(\mathbf{q}) a^+_{A\alpha}\left(\mathbf{p}+\frac{\mathbf{q}-\mathbf{p}'}{2}\right) \hat{n}_{B\beta}(\mathbf{q}) a_{A\alpha}\left(\mathbf{p}-\frac{\mathbf{q}-\mathbf{p}'}{2}\right), \end{aligned} \tag{23}$$

where $V_{AB}(\mathbf{q})$ is interaction energy between A- and B-particle bound states and $\mathbf{q}$ is a wavevector. Annihilation and creation operators $a_{A\alpha}(\mathbf{p})$ and $a^+_{A\alpha}(\mathbf{p})$ satisfy the following commutation relations:

$$\begin{aligned} &[a_{A\alpha}(\mathbf{p}), a^+_{B\beta}(\mathbf{p}')]_\sigma = \delta_{A,B}\delta_{\alpha,\beta}\delta(\mathbf{p}-\mathbf{p}'), \\ &[a_{A\alpha}(\mathbf{p}), a_{B\beta}(\mathbf{p}')]_\sigma = [a^+_{A\alpha}(\mathbf{p}), a^+_{B\beta}(\mathbf{p}')]_\sigma = 0. \end{aligned} \tag{24}$$

$\hat{n}_{B\beta}(\mathbf{q})$ in (23) is a Fourier transform of the B-particle density operator:

$$\hat{n}_{B\beta}(\mathbf{q}) = \int \frac{d\mathbf{p}}{(2\pi\hbar)^3} a^+_{B\mathbf{p}-\frac{\mathbf{q}}{2}} a_{B\mathbf{p}+\frac{\mathbf{q}}{2}}.$$

As parameters of a reduced description for the consistent description of the kinetics and hydrodynamics of a system, where bound states between the particles can appear, let us choose nonequilibrium distribution functions of A-particle bound states in thermo-field representation:

$$\langle\langle 1|\hat{n}_{A\alpha}(\mathbf{r},\mathbf{p})|\varrho(t)\rangle\rangle = f_{A\alpha}(\mathbf{r},\mathbf{p};t) = f_{A\alpha}(x;t), \quad x = \{\mathbf{r},\mathbf{p}\}. \tag{25}$$

Here, $f_{A\alpha}(x;t)$ is a Wigner function of the A-particle bound state where:

$$\hat{n}_{A\alpha}(\mathbf{r},\mathbf{p}) \equiv \hat{n}_{A\alpha}(x) = \int \frac{d\mathbf{q}}{(2\pi\hbar)^3}\, e^{-\frac{1}{i\hbar}\mathbf{q}\cdot\mathbf{r}} \hat{a}^{+}_{A\alpha}\left(\mathbf{p}-\frac{\mathbf{q}}{2}\right)\hat{a}_{A\alpha}\left(\mathbf{p}+\frac{\mathbf{q}}{2}\right) \tag{26}$$

is the Klimontovich density operator; and the average value of the total energy density operator:

$$\langle\langle 1|\hat{H}(\mathbf{r})|\varrho(t)\rangle\rangle = \langle\langle 1|H(\mathbf{r})\varrho(t)\rangle\rangle. \tag{27}$$

By this $\int d\mathbf{r}\, H(\mathbf{r}) = H$, $\hat{H}(\mathbf{r})$ is a superoperator of the total energy density, which is constructed on annihilation and creation superoperators $\hat{a}_{A\alpha}(\mathbf{p})$ and $\hat{a}^{+}_{A\alpha}(\mathbf{p})$. The latter satisfy commutation relations (24). Following [63], one can rewrite relevant statistical operator $\hat{\varrho}_{rel}(t)$, $|\varrho_{rel}(t)\rangle\rangle = \hat{\varrho}_{rel}(t)|1\rangle\rangle$ and with (14) from $q = 1$ for the mentioned parameters of a reduced description in the form:

$$\hat{\varrho}_{rel}(t) = \exp\left\{-\Phi^*(t) - \int d\mathbf{r}\,\beta(\mathbf{r};t)\left(\hat{H}(\mathbf{r}) - \sum_{A,\alpha}\int \frac{d\mathbf{p}}{(2\pi\hbar)^3}\,\mu_{A\alpha}(x;t)\hat{n}_{A\alpha}(x)\right)\right\}, \tag{28}$$

where Lagrange multipliers $\beta(\mathbf{r};t)$ and $\mu_{A\alpha}(x;t)$ can be found from the self-consistency conditions, respectively:

$$\langle\langle 1|\hat{H}(\mathbf{r})|\varrho(t)\rangle\rangle = \langle\langle 1|\hat{H}(\mathbf{r})|\varrho_{rel}(t)\rangle\rangle, \tag{29}$$

$$\langle\langle 1|\hat{n}_{A\alpha}(x)|\varrho(t)\rangle\rangle = \langle\langle 1|\hat{n}_{A\alpha}(x)|\varrho_{rel}(t)\rangle\rangle, \tag{30}$$

$\Phi^*(t)$ is the Massieu–Planck functional, and it can be defined from the normalization condition:

$$\Phi^*(t) = \ln\left\langle\!\!\left\langle 1\left|\exp\left\{-\int d\mathbf{r}\,\beta(\mathbf{r};t)\left(\hat{H}(\mathbf{r}) - \sum_{A,\alpha}\int\frac{d\mathbf{p}}{(2\pi\hbar)^3}\mu_{A\alpha}(x;t)\hat{n}_{A\alpha}(x)\right)\right\}\right.\right\rangle\!\!\right\rangle. \tag{31}$$

Using now the general structure of nonequilibrium thermo-field dynamics (20), one can obtain a set of generalized transport equations for A-particle Wigner distribution functions and the average interaction energy:

$$\begin{aligned} \frac{\partial}{\partial t}\langle\langle 1|\hat{n}_{A\alpha}(x)|\varrho(t)\rangle\rangle &= \langle\langle 1|\dot{\hat{n}}_{A\alpha}(x)|\varrho_{q}(t)\rangle\rangle \\ &+ \int d\mathbf{r}'\int_{-\infty}^{t} dt'\, e^{\varepsilon(t'-t)}\varphi^{A\alpha}_{nH}(x,\mathbf{r}';t,t')\beta(\mathbf{r}';t') \\ + \sum_{B,\beta}\int dx' &\int_{-\infty}^{t} dt'\, e^{\varepsilon(t'-t)}\varphi^{A\alpha B\beta}_{nn}(x,x';t,t')\beta(\mathbf{r}';t')\mu_{B\beta}(x';t'), \end{aligned} \tag{32}$$

$$\begin{aligned} \frac{\partial}{\partial t}\langle\langle 1|\hat{H}(\mathbf{r})|\varrho(t)\rangle\rangle &= \langle\langle 1|\dot{\hat{H}}(\mathbf{r})|\varrho_{q}(t)\rangle\rangle \\ &+ \int d\mathbf{r}'\int_{-\infty}^{t} dt'\, e^{\varepsilon(t'-t)}\varphi_{HH}(\mathbf{r},\mathbf{r}';t,t')\beta(\mathbf{r}';t') \\ + \sum_{B,\beta}\int dx' &\int_{-\infty}^{t} dt'\, e^{\varepsilon(t'-t)}\varphi^{B\beta}_{Hn}(\mathbf{r},x';t,t')\beta(\mathbf{r}';t')\mu_{B\beta}(x';t'), \end{aligned} \tag{33}$$

where $x' = \{\mathbf{r}', \mathbf{p}'\}$, $dx' = (2\pi\hbar)^{-3} d\mathbf{r}'\, d\mathbf{p}'$. Here,

$$\varphi_{nn}^{\substack{A\alpha \\ B\beta}}(x, x'; t, t') = \left\langle\!\!\left\langle 1 \middle| \hat{J}_{n_{A\alpha}}(x,t) T(t,t') \middle| \int_0^1 d\tau\, \varrho_{rel}^{\tau}(t') J_{n_{B\beta}}(x';t') \varrho_{rel}^{1-\tau}(t') \right\rangle\!\!\right\rangle, \tag{34}$$

$$\varphi_{nH}^{A\alpha}(x, \mathbf{r}'; t, t') = \left\langle\!\!\left\langle 1 \middle| \hat{J}_{n_{A\alpha}}(x,t) T(t,t') \middle| \int_0^1 d\tau\, \varrho_{rel}^{\tau}(t') J_{H}(\mathbf{r}';t') \varrho_{rel}^{1-\tau}(t') \right\rangle\!\!\right\rangle, \tag{35}$$

$$\varphi_{Hn}^{B\beta}(\mathbf{r}', x'; t, t') = \left\langle\!\!\left\langle 1 \middle| \hat{J}_{H}(\mathbf{r},t) T(t,t') \middle| \int_0^1 d\tau\, \varrho_{rel}^{\tau}(t') J_{n_{B\beta}}(x';t') \varrho_{rel}^{1-\tau}(t') \right\rangle\!\!\right\rangle, \tag{36}$$

$$\varphi_{HH}(\mathbf{r}, \mathbf{r}'; t, t') = \left\langle\!\!\left\langle 1 \middle| \hat{J}_{H}(\mathbf{r},t) T(t,t') \middle| \int_0^1 d\tau\, \varrho_{rel}^{\tau}(t') J_{H}(\mathbf{r}';t') \varrho_{rel}^{1-\tau}(t') \right\rangle\!\!\right\rangle \tag{37}$$

are generalized transport cores, which describe dissipative processes. In these formulae:

$$\begin{aligned} J_H(\mathbf{r};t) &= \Big(1 - \mathrm{P}(t')\Big) \dot{H}(\mathbf{r}), \\ J_{n_{A\alpha}}(\mathbf{r},\mathbf{p};t) &= \Big(1 - \mathrm{P}(t')\Big) \dot{n}_{A\alpha}(x) \end{aligned} \tag{38}$$

are generalized flows, $\dot{H}(\mathbf{r}) = -\frac{1}{i\hbar}[H, H(\mathbf{r})]$, $\dot{n}_{A\alpha}(\mathbf{r},\mathbf{p}) = -\frac{1}{i\hbar}[H, n_{A\alpha}(x)]$, and $\mathrm{P}(t)$ is a generalized Mori projection operator in thermo-field representation. It acts on operators:

$$\begin{aligned} \mathrm{P}(t)P = \langle\langle|\hat{P}|\varrho_{rel}(t)\rangle\rangle + \int d\mathbf{r}\, \frac{\delta\langle\langle 1|\hat{P}|\varrho_{rel}(t)\rangle\rangle}{\delta\langle\langle 1|\hat{H}(\mathbf{r})|\varrho(t)\rangle\rangle} \Big(H(\mathbf{r}) - \langle\langle 1|\hat{H}(\mathbf{r})|\varrho(t)\rangle\rangle \Big) \\ + \sum_{A,\alpha} \int \frac{d\mathbf{r}\, d\mathbf{p}}{(2\pi\hbar)^3} \frac{\delta\langle\langle 1|\hat{P}|\varrho_{rel}(t)\rangle\rangle}{\delta\langle\langle 1|\hat{n}_{A\alpha}(x)|\varrho(t)\rangle\rangle} \Big(n_{A\alpha}(x) - \langle\langle 1|\hat{n}_{A\alpha}(x)|\varrho(t)\rangle\rangle \Big) \end{aligned} \tag{39}$$

and has all the properties of a projection operator:

$$\begin{aligned} \mathrm{P}(t)H(\mathbf{r}) = H(\mathbf{r}), \quad \mathrm{P}(t)\mathrm{P}(t') = \mathrm{P}(t), \\ \mathrm{P}(t)n_{A\alpha}(\mathbf{r},\mathbf{p}) = n_{A\alpha}(\mathbf{r},\mathbf{p}), \quad \Big(1 - \mathrm{P}(t)\Big)\mathrm{P}(t) = 0. \end{aligned}$$

The obtained transport equations have the general meaning and can describe both weak and strong nonequilibrium processes of a quantum system taking into consideration bound states. In the calculation of the transport cores (34)–(37) in each case, the problem arises due to the fact that the relevant thermo-vacuum state is not the ground state for the superoperators $\hat{a}_{A\alpha}(\mathbf{P})$, $\hat{a}^{+}_{A\alpha}(\mathbf{P})$ and $\tilde{a}_{A\alpha}(\mathbf{P})$, $\tilde{a}^{+}_{A\alpha}(\mathbf{P})$. The essence of this problem is to construct a dynamic mapping of superoperators $\hat{a}_{A\alpha}(\mathbf{P})$, $\hat{a}^{+}_{A\alpha}(\mathbf{P})$ and $\tilde{a}_{A\alpha}(\mathbf{P})$, $\tilde{a}^{+}_{A\alpha}(\mathbf{P})$ by some superoperators of "quasiparticles", for which the relevant thermo-vacuum state is the ground one.

In the next step, we will construct such annihilation and creation superoperators, for which the relevant thermo-vacuum state vector is a vacuum state. Analyzing the structure of relevant statistical superoperator (28), one can mark out some part that would correspond to the system of non-interacting quantum A-particles. Let us write $\hat{\varrho}_{rel}(t)$ in an evident form and separate terms that are connected with the interaction energy between the particles:

$$\begin{aligned} \hat{\varrho}_{rel}(t) = \exp\Bigg\{ -\Phi^*(t) - \int d\mathbf{r}\, \beta(\mathbf{r};t) \\ \times \sum_{A,\alpha} \int \frac{d\mathbf{p}}{(2\pi\hbar)^3} \left[\frac{\mathbf{p}^2}{2m_A} \hat{n}_{A\alpha}(x) - \mu_{A\alpha}(x;t) \hat{n}_{A\alpha}(x) \right] - \int d\mathbf{r} \beta(\mathbf{r};t) \hat{H}_{\mathrm{int}}(\mathbf{r}) \Bigg\}. \end{aligned} \tag{40}$$

Using operator equality (A and B are some operators):

$$\mathrm{e}^{A+B} = \left[1 + \int_0^1 d\tau\, \mathrm{e}^{\tau(A+B)}\, B\, \mathrm{e}^{-\tau A}\right] \mathrm{e}^{A},$$

the relation for $\hat{\varrho}_{rel}(t)$ can be rewritten in the following form:

$$\hat{\varrho}_{rel}(t) = \left[1 - \int d\mathbf{r}\, \beta(\mathbf{r};t) \int_0^1 d\tau\, \hat{\varrho}^{\tau}_{rel}(t) \hat{H}_{\rm int}(\mathbf{r}) \left(\hat{\varrho}^{0}_{rel}(t)\right)^{-\tau}\right] \hat{\varrho}^{0}_{rel}(t), \tag{41}$$

where:

$$\hat{\varrho}^{0}_{rel}(t) = \exp\left\{\Phi(t) - \int d\mathbf{r}\, \beta(\mathbf{r};t) \sum_{A,\alpha} \int \frac{d\mathbf{p}}{(2\pi\hbar)^3} \left[\frac{p^2}{2m_A} \hat{n}_{A\alpha}(x) - \mu_{A\alpha}(x;t) \hat{n}_{A\alpha}(x)\right]\right\}, \tag{42}$$

or:

$$\hat{\varrho}^{0}_{rel}(t) = \exp\left\{\Phi(t) - \int d\mathbf{r}\, \beta(\mathbf{r};t) \sum_{A,\alpha} \int \frac{d\mathbf{p}}{(2\pi\hbar)^3} b_{A\alpha}(x;t) \hat{n}_{A\alpha}(x)\right\}, \tag{43}$$

where $b_{A\alpha}(x;t) = \left[\frac{\mathbf{p}^2}{2m_A} - \mu_{A\alpha}(x;t)\right]$. Relevant statistical superoperator $\hat{\varrho}^{0}_{rel}(t)$ is bilinear on annihilation and creation superoperators $\hat{a}_{A\alpha}(\mathbf{P})$ and $\hat{a}^{+}_{A\alpha}(\mathbf{P})$, as well as on the non-perturbed part of Hamiltonian $\bar{H}_0$. One can write the total relevant superoperator as some non-perturbed part of $\hat{\varrho}^{0}_{rel}(t)$ and the part that describes the interaction of quantum particles in the relevant state. Further, we introduce the following designation:

$$\hat{\varrho}_{rel}(t) = \hat{\varrho}^{0}_{rel}(t) + \hat{\varrho}'_{rel}(t), \tag{44}$$

where:

$$\hat{\varrho}'_{rel}(t) = -\int d\mathbf{r}\, \beta(\mathbf{r};t) \int_0^1 d\tau\, \hat{\varrho}^{\tau}_{rel}(t) \hat{H}_{\rm int}(\mathbf{r}) \left(\hat{\varrho}^{0}_{rel}(t)\right)^{-\tau} \hat{\varrho}^{0}_{rel}(t). \tag{45}$$

Relevant thermo-vacuum states $|\hat{\varrho}_{rel}(t)\rangle\rangle$ and $|\hat{\varrho}^{0}_{rel}(t)\rangle\rangle$ are not vacuum states for annihilation and creation superoperators $\hat{a}_{A\alpha}(\mathbf{P})$, $\hat{a}^{+}_{A\alpha}(\mathbf{P})$, $\tilde{a}_{A\alpha}(\mathbf{P})$, $\tilde{a}^{+}_{A\alpha}(\mathbf{P})$. However, for $|\hat{\varrho}^{0}_{rel}(t)\rangle\rangle$, one can construct new superoperators $\hat{\gamma}_{A\alpha}(\mathbf{P})$, $\hat{\gamma}^{+}_{A\alpha}(\mathbf{P})$, $\tilde{\gamma}_{A\alpha}(\mathbf{P})$, $\tilde{\gamma}^{+}_{A\alpha}(\mathbf{P})$ as a linear combination of superoperators $\hat{a}_{A\alpha}(\mathbf{P})$, $\hat{a}^{+}_{A\alpha}(\mathbf{P})$ and $\tilde{a}_{A\alpha}(\mathbf{P})$, $\tilde{a}^{+}_{A\alpha}(\mathbf{P})$ in order to satisfy the conditions:

$$\begin{aligned} \hat{\gamma}_{A\alpha}(\mathbf{P};t)|\varrho^{0}_{rel}(t)\rangle\rangle &= 0, \qquad & \langle\langle 1|\hat{\gamma}^{+}_{A\alpha}(\mathbf{P};t) &= 0, \\ \tilde{\gamma}_{A\alpha}(\mathbf{P};t)|\varrho^{0}_{rel}(t)\rangle\rangle &= 0, \qquad & \langle\langle 1|\tilde{\gamma}^{+}_{A\alpha}(\mathbf{P};t) &= 0. \end{aligned} \tag{46}$$

To achieve this, let us consider an action of annihilation superoperators $\hat{a}_{A\alpha}(\mathbf{P};t)$, $\tilde{a}_{A\alpha}(\mathbf{P};t)$ on relevant state $|\varrho^{0}_{rel}(t_0)\rangle\rangle$:

$$\begin{aligned} \hat{a}_{A\alpha}(\mathbf{P};t)|\varrho^{0}_{rel}(t_0)\rangle\rangle &= f_{A\alpha}(\mathbf{P};t-t_0)\tilde{a}^{+}_{A\alpha}(\mathbf{P};t)|\varrho^{0}_{rel}(t_0)\rangle\rangle, \\ \tilde{a}_{A\alpha}(\mathbf{P};t)|\varrho^{0}_{rel}(t_0)\rangle\rangle &= \sigma f_{A\alpha}(\mathbf{P};t-t_0)\hat{a}^{+}_{A\alpha}(\mathbf{P};t)|\varrho^{0}_{rel}(t_0)\rangle\rangle, \end{aligned} \tag{47}$$

where superoperators $\hat{a}_{A\alpha}(\mathbf{p};t)$, $\hat{a}^{+}_{A\alpha}(\mathbf{p};t)$, $\tilde{a}_{A\alpha}(\mathbf{p};t)$, $\hat{a}^{+}_{A\alpha}(\mathbf{p};t)$ are in the Heisenberg representation:

$$\begin{aligned} \hat{a}_{A\alpha}(\mathbf{P};t) &= \mathrm{e}^{-\frac{1}{i\hbar}\bar{H}_0 t}\, \hat{a}_{A\alpha}(\mathbf{P})\, \mathrm{e}^{\frac{1}{i\hbar}\bar{H}_0 t}, \qquad & \tilde{a}_{A\alpha}(\mathbf{P};t) &= \mathrm{e}^{-\frac{1}{i\hbar}\bar{H}_0 t}\, \tilde{a}_{A\alpha}(\mathbf{P})\, \mathrm{e}^{\frac{1}{i\hbar}\bar{H}_0 t}, \\ \hat{a}^{+}_{A\alpha}(\mathbf{P};t) &= \mathrm{e}^{-\frac{1}{i\hbar}\bar{H}_0 t}\, \hat{a}^{+}_{A\alpha}(\mathbf{P})\, \mathrm{e}^{\frac{1}{i\hbar}\bar{H}_0 t}, \qquad & \tilde{a}^{+}_{A\alpha}(\mathbf{P};t) &= \mathrm{e}^{-\frac{1}{i\hbar}\bar{H}_0 t}\, \tilde{a}^{+}_{A\alpha}(\mathbf{P})\, \mathrm{e}^{\frac{1}{i\hbar}\bar{H}_0 t}, \end{aligned}$$

and satisfy commutation relations:

$$\begin{aligned}
\left[\hat{a}_{A\alpha}(\mathbf{P};t),\hat{a}^{+}_{B\beta}(\mathbf{P}';t)\right]_{\sigma} &= \delta_{A,B}\delta_{\alpha,\beta}\delta(\mathbf{P}-\mathbf{P}'),\\
\left[\tilde{a}_{A\alpha}(\mathbf{P};t),\tilde{a}^{+}_{B\beta}(\mathbf{P}';t)\right]_{\sigma} &= \delta_{A,B}\delta_{\alpha,\beta}\delta(\mathbf{P}-\mathbf{P}'),\\
\left[\hat{a}_{A\alpha}(\mathbf{P};t),\tilde{a}_{B\beta}(\mathbf{P}';t)\right]_{\sigma} = \left[\hat{a}^{+}_{A\alpha}(\mathbf{P};t),\tilde{a}^{+}_{B\beta}(\mathbf{P}';t)\right]_{\sigma} &= 0.
\end{aligned}$$

It is necessary to note that superoperators $\hat{H}(\mathbf{r})$, $\hat{n}_{A\alpha}(x)$ are built on superoperators $\hat{a}_{A\alpha}(\mathbf{p}+\frac{\mathbf{q}}{2})$, $\hat{a}^{+}_{A\alpha}(\mathbf{p}-\frac{\mathbf{q}}{2})$, $\tilde{a}_{A\alpha}(\mathbf{p}+\frac{\mathbf{q}}{2})$, $\tilde{a}^{+}_{A\alpha}(\mathbf{p}-\frac{\mathbf{q}}{2})$. Therefore, for convenience, here, a unit denotation was introduced for arguments like $\mathbf{P}=\mathbf{p}\pm\frac{\mathbf{q}}{2}$. This should be taken into account in further calculations where obvious expressions are needed.

According to the general relations of [63,64], we can introduce new operators $\hat{\gamma}_{A\alpha}(\mathbf{P};t)$, $\hat{\gamma}^{+}_{A\alpha}(\mathbf{P};t)$, $\tilde{\gamma}_{A\alpha}(\mathbf{P};t)$, $\tilde{\gamma}^{+}_{A\alpha}(\mathbf{P};t)$ via superoperators $\hat{a}_{A\alpha}(\mathbf{P};t)$, $\hat{a}^{+}_{A\alpha}(\mathbf{P};t)$, $\tilde{a}_{A\alpha}(\mathbf{P};t)$, $\tilde{a}^{+}_{A\alpha}(\mathbf{P};t)$:

$$\begin{aligned}
\hat{\gamma}_{A\alpha}(\mathbf{P};t) &= \sqrt{1+\sigma n_{A\alpha}(\mathbf{P};t,t_0)}\left[\hat{a}_{A\alpha}(\mathbf{P};t)-\frac{n_{A\alpha}(\mathbf{P};t,t_0)}{1+\sigma n_{A\alpha}(\mathbf{P};t,t_0)}\tilde{a}^{+}_{A\alpha}(\mathbf{P};t)\right],\\
\tilde{\gamma}^{+}_{A\alpha}(\mathbf{P};t) &= \sqrt{1+\sigma n_{A\alpha}(\mathbf{P};t,t_0)}\left[\tilde{a}^{+}_{A\alpha}(\mathbf{P};t)-\sigma\hat{a}_{A\alpha}(\mathbf{P};t)\right].
\end{aligned} \tag{48}$$

The relations (48) satisfy the conditions (46). Here:

$$\begin{aligned}
n_{A\alpha}(\mathbf{p},\mathbf{q};t,t_0) = n_{A\alpha}(\mathbf{P};t,t_0) &= \langle\langle 1|\tilde{a}^{+}_{A\alpha}(\mathbf{P};t)\tilde{a}_{A\alpha}(\mathbf{P};t)|\varrho^{0}_{rel}(t_0)\rangle\rangle\\
&= \langle\langle 1|\tilde{a}^{+}_{A\alpha}(\mathbf{p}-\frac{\mathbf{q}}{2};t)\tilde{a}_{A\alpha}(\mathbf{p}+\frac{\mathbf{q}}{2};t)|\varrho^{0}_{rel}(t_0)\rangle\rangle,
\end{aligned}$$

is a relevant distribution function of A-particle bound states in momentum space $\mathbf{p}$, $\mathbf{q}$, which is calculated with the help of relevant thermo-vacuum state vector $|\varrho^{0}_{rel}(t_0)\rangle\rangle$ (43). Function $f_{A\alpha}(\mathbf{P};t-t_0)$ in the formulae (47) is connected with $n_{A\alpha}(\mathbf{P};t,t_0)$ by the relation:

$$f_{A\alpha}(\mathbf{P};t-t_0) = \frac{n_{A\alpha}(\mathbf{P};t,t_0)}{1+\sigma n_{A\alpha}(\mathbf{P};t,t_0)}.$$

Superoperators $\hat{\gamma}_{A\alpha}(\mathbf{P};t)$, $\hat{\gamma}_{A\alpha}(\mathbf{P};t)$, $\tilde{\gamma}^{+}_{A\alpha}(\mathbf{P};t)$, and $\tilde{\gamma}^{+}_{A\alpha}(\mathbf{P};t)$ satisfy the "canonical" commutation relations:

$$\begin{aligned}
\left[\hat{\gamma}_{A\alpha}(\mathbf{P};t),\hat{\gamma}^{+}_{B\beta}(\mathbf{P}';t)\right]_{\sigma} &= \delta_{A,B}\delta_{\alpha,\beta}\delta(\mathbf{P}-\mathbf{P}'),\\
\left[\tilde{\gamma}_{A\alpha}(\mathbf{P};t),\tilde{\gamma}^{+}_{B\beta}(\mathbf{P}';t)\right]_{\sigma} &= \delta_{A,B}\delta_{\alpha,\beta}\delta(\mathbf{P}-\mathbf{P}'),\\
\left[\hat{\gamma}_{A\alpha}(\mathbf{P};t),\tilde{\gamma}_{B\beta}(\mathbf{P}';t)\right]_{\sigma} &= \left[\hat{\gamma}^{+}_{A\alpha}(\mathbf{P};t),\tilde{\gamma}^{+}_{B\beta}(\mathbf{P}';t)\right]_{\sigma} = 0.
\end{aligned} \tag{49}$$

Inversed transformations to superoperators $\hat{a}_{A\alpha}(\mathbf{P};t)$, $\tilde{a}^{+}_{A\alpha}(\mathbf{P};t)$ are easily obtained from (48):

$$\begin{aligned}
\hat{a}_{A\alpha}(\mathbf{P};t) &= \sqrt{1+\sigma n_{A\alpha}(\mathbf{P};t,t_0)}\left[\hat{\gamma}_{A\alpha}(\mathbf{P};t)+\frac{n_{A\alpha}(\mathbf{P};t,t_0)}{1+\sigma n_{A\alpha}(\mathbf{P};t,t_0)}\tilde{\gamma}^{+}_{A\alpha}(\mathbf{P};t)\right],\\
\tilde{a}^{+}_{A\alpha}(\mathbf{P};t) &= \sqrt{1+\sigma n_{A\alpha}(\mathbf{P};t,t_0)}\left[\tilde{\gamma}^{+}_{A\alpha}(\mathbf{P};t)+\sigma\hat{\gamma}_{A\alpha}(\mathbf{P};t)\right].
\end{aligned} \tag{50}$$

$\hat{\gamma}_{A\alpha}(\mathbf{P};t)$, $\hat{\gamma}^{+}_{A\alpha}(\mathbf{P};t)$, $\tilde{\gamma}_{A\alpha}(\mathbf{P};t)$, $\tilde{\gamma}^{+}_{A\alpha}(\mathbf{P};t)$ could be defined as some operators of annihilation and creation of A-quasiparticle bound states, for which relevant thermo-vacuum state $|\varrho^{0}_{rel}(t_0)\rangle\rangle$ (43) is a vacuum state. In such a way, we obtained relations of dynamical reflection of superoperators $\hat{a}_{A\alpha}(\mathbf{P};t)$, $\hat{a}^{+}_{A\alpha}(\mathbf{P};t)$, $\tilde{a}_{A\alpha}(\mathbf{P};t)$, $\tilde{a}^{+}_{A\alpha}(\mathbf{P};t)$ to new superoperators of "quasiparticles" $\hat{\gamma}_{A\alpha}(\mathbf{P};t)$, $\hat{\gamma}^{+}_{A\alpha}(\mathbf{P};t)$, $\tilde{\gamma}_{A\alpha}(\mathbf{P};t)$, $\tilde{\gamma}^{+}_{A\alpha}(\mathbf{P};t)$. Now, we can consider some particular strategy for the calculation of the transport cores by switching to the superoperators of "quasiparticles" $\hat{\gamma}_{A\alpha}(\mathbf{P};t)$, $\hat{\gamma}^{+}_{A\alpha}(\mathbf{P};t)$, $\tilde{\gamma}_{A\alpha}(\mathbf{P};t)$, $\tilde{\gamma}^{+}_{A\alpha}(\mathbf{P};t)$.

Here, we can use series expansions over the interaction of the relevant superoperator (44). These issues require a separate, detailed study.

A set of transport Equations (32) and (33) together with dynamical reflections (48) and (50) of superoperators in the thermo-field space constitute the basis for a consistent description of the kinetics and hydrodynamics of a dense quantum system with strongly-bound states. Both strong and weak nonequilibrium processes of a nuclear matter can be investigated using this approach, in which the particle interaction is characterized by strongly-bound states, taking into account their nuclear nature [3–6].

Weak nonequilibrium processes can be described when the fluctuations of the parameters $\delta\beta(\mathbf{r};t) = \beta(\mathbf{r};t) - \beta$, $\delta\mu_{A\alpha}(x;t) = \mu_{A\alpha}(x;t) - \mu_{A\alpha}$ are small, where β and $\mu_{A\alpha}$ are equilibrium values for temperature and chemical potential, respectively. In this case, the system of Equations (32) and (33) will have a similar structure, but is closed with respect to $\langle\langle 1|\delta\hat{n}_{A\alpha}(x)|\varrho(t)\rangle\rangle$, $\langle\langle 1|\delta\hat{H}(\mathbf{r})|\varrho(t)\rangle\rangle$, where $\delta\hat{n}_{A\alpha}(x) = \hat{n}_{A\alpha}(x) - \langle\langle 1|\hat{n}_{A\alpha}(x)|\varrho_0\rangle\rangle$, $\delta\hat{H}(\mathbf{r}) = \hat{H}(\mathbf{r}) - \langle\langle 1|\hat{H}(\mathbf{r})|\varrho_0\rangle\rangle$, $|\varrho_0\rangle\rangle$ is the equilibrium thermo vacuum state vector of the systems.

In addition, by designing a system of equations on moments 1, $\mathbf{P}$ of the distribution function, we obtain, respectively, the equation of the thermo-field hydrodynamic for the dense quantum-field systems. These questions require separate consideration and will be investigated in future work.

4. Conclusions

We generalized the nonequilibrium thermo-field dynamics in the framework of Zubarev's nonequilibrium statistical operator method [63] within the framework of Renyi statistics. The non-Markov transport equations in the thermo-field presentation in Renyi statistics are obtained, which can be used to describe the nonequilibrium processes in quantum Bose and Fermi systems. In the case of $q \to 1$ [72,73], when Renyi statistics are transformed into non-extensive Tsallis statistics, we obtain the corresponding generalized transport equations with non-additive entropy for the system. Based on this approach and Gibbs statistics, the generalized equations of the consistent description of kinetics and hydrodynamics for dense quantum field systems with strongly-bound states were obtained. We obtained the relations of the dynamic mapping of the superoperators $\hat{a}_{A\alpha}(\mathbf{P};t)$, $\hat{a}^{+}_{A\alpha}(\mathbf{P};t)$, $\tilde{a}_{A\alpha}(\mathbf{P};t)$, $\tilde{a}^{+}_{A\alpha}(\mathbf{P};t)$ with the new superoperators of "quasiparticles" $\hat{\gamma}_{A\alpha}(\mathbf{P};t)$, $\hat{\gamma}^{+}_{A\alpha}(\mathbf{P};t)$, $\tilde{\gamma}_{A\alpha}(\mathbf{P};t)$, $\tilde{\gamma}^{+}_{A\alpha}(\mathbf{P};t)$, for which the relevant thermo vacuum state of the non-interacting particles is the ground one. This is important for the calculation of the transport cores.

Using this approach, one can investigate both strong and weak nonequilibrium processes of nuclear matter, when the interaction between particles of the latter is characterized by strongly-bound states of an internucleon nature [4,5].

Author Contributions: Conceptualization, M.T.; Methodology, M.T.; Investigation, M.T., P.H.; Writing—Original Draft Preparation, M.T., P.H.; Writing—Review & Editing, M.T., P.H.

Funding: This research received no external funding.

Conflicts of Interest: The authors declare no conflict of interest.

References

1. Röpke, G. Nuclear matter EoS including few-nucleon correlations. *Nuovo Cimento C* **2016**, *39*, 392.
2. Röpke, G. Correlations and clustering in dilute matter. In *Nuclear Particle Correlations and Cluster Physics*; Schröder, W., Ed.; World Scientific: Singapore, 2017; Chapter 2, pp. 31–69.
3. Negele, J.W. The mean field theory of nuclear structure and dynamics. *Rev. Mod. Phys.* **1982**, *54*, 913–1015. [CrossRef]
4. Toneev, V.D.; Schulz, K.; Gudima,K.K.; Röpke, G. Towards study of hot and dense nuclear matter in heavy ion collisions. *Phys. Elem. Part. Nucl. (Part. Nucl.)* **1986**, *17*, 1093–1172. (In Russian)
5. Röpke, G.; Schulz, K.; Gudima, K.K.; Toneev, V.D. Dynamical approaches to heavy-ion collision in intermediate energy region. *Phys. Elem. Part. Nucl. (Part. Nucl.)* **1990**, *21*, 364–418. (In Russian)

6. McLerran, L. The physics of the quark-gluon plasma. *Rev. Mod. Phys.* **1986**, *58*, 1021–1064. [CrossRef]
7. Blättel, B.; Koch, V.; Mosel, U. Transport-theoretical analysis of relativistic heavy-ion collisions. *Rep. Prog. Phys.* **1993**, *56*. [CrossRef]
8. Mrówczy´nski, S. *Quark-Qluon Plasma*; World Scientific: Singapore, 1990.
9. Cleymans, J.; Gavai, R.V.; Suhonen, E. Quarks and gluons at high temperatures and densities. *Phys. Rep.* **1986**, *130*, 217–292. [CrossRef]
10. Jacob, M.; Satz, H. *Quark Matter Formation and Heavy Ion Collisions*; World Scientific: Singapore, 1982.
11. McLerran, L. Probes of the quark-gluon plasma as it might be produced in ultra-relativistic nuclear collisions. *Acta Phys. Pol. B* **1985**, *16*, 669–682.
12. Shuryak, E.V. What RHIC experiments and theory tell us about properties of quark-gluon plasma? *Nucl. Phys. A* **2005**, *750*, 64–83. [CrossRef]
13. Shuryak, E. Strongly coupled quark-gluon plasma in heavy ion collisions. *Rev. Mod. Phys.* **2017**, *89*, 035001. [CrossRef]
14. Jaiswal, A.; Roy, V. Relativistic hydrodynamics in heavy-ion collisions: General aspects and recent developments. *Adv. High Energy Phys.* **2016**, *2016*, 9623034. [CrossRef]
15. Florkowski, W.; Heller, M.P.; Spalinski, M. New theories of relativistic hydrodynamics in the LHC era. *Rep. Prog. Phys.* **2018**, *81*, 046001. [CrossRef] [PubMed]
16. Li, Y. A flow paradigm in heavy-ion collisions. *arXiv* **2018**, arXiv:1712.04580.
17. Hirino, T.; van der Kolk, N.; Bilandzic, A. Hydrodynamics and Flow. *Lect. Notes Phys.* **2010**, *785*, 139–178._4. [CrossRef]
18. Florkowski, W. Hydrodynamic description of ultrarelativistic heavy-ion collisions. *arXiv* **2017**, arXiv:1712.05162.
19. Röpke, G.; Shlomo, S.; Bonasera, A.; Natowitz, J.B.; Yennello, S.J.; McIntosh, A.B.; Mabiala, J.; Qin, L.; Kowalski, S.; Hagel, K.; et al. Density determinations in heavy ion collisions. *Phys. Rev. C* **2013**, *88*, 024609. [CrossRef]
20. Hempel, M.; Hagel, K.; Natowitz, J.; Röpke, G.; Typel, S. Constraining supernova equations of state with equilibrium constants from heavy-ion collisions. *Phys. Rev. C* **2015**, *91*, 045805. [CrossRef]
21. Bastian, N.-U.F.; Blaschke, D.; Fischer, T.; Röpke, G. Nowards a Unified Quark-Hadron-Matter Equation of State for Applications in Astrophysics and Heavy-Ion Collisions. *Universe* **2018**, *4*, 67. [CrossRef]
22. Elze, H.-T.; Heinz, U. Quark-gluon transport theory. *Phys. Rep.* **1989**, *183*, 81–135. [CrossRef]
23. Lee, T.D. The strongly interacting quark-gluon plasma and future physics. *Nucl. Phys. A* **2005**, *750*, 1–8. [CrossRef]
24. Gyulassy, M.; McLerran, I. New forms of QCD matter discovered at RHIC. *Nucl. Phys. A* **2005**, *750*, 30–63. [CrossRef]
25. Romatschke, P. Do nuclear collisions create a locally equilibrated quark-gluon plasma? *Eur. Phys. J.* **2017**, *77*, 21. [CrossRef]
26. Romatschke, P. Relativistic Fluid Dynamics Far From Local Equilibrium. *Phys. Rev. Lett.* **2018**, *120*, 012301. [CrossRef] [PubMed]
27. Baier, R.; Romatschke, P.; Son, D.T.; Starinets, A.O.; Stephanov, M.A. Relativistic viscous hydrodynamics, conformal invariance, and holography. *J. High Energy Phys.* **2008**, *4*, 100. [CrossRef]
28. Zubarev, D.N.; Morozov, V.G. Formulation of boundary conditions for the BBGRY hierarchy with allowance for local conservation laws. *Theor. Math. Phys.* **1984**, *60*, 814–820. [CrossRef]
29. Zubarev, D.N.; Morozov, V.G.; Omelyan, I.P.; Tokarchuk, M.V. Kinetic equations for dense gases and liquids. *Theor. Math. Phys.* **1991**, *87*, 412–424. [CrossRef]
30. Zubarev, D.N.; Morozov, V.G.; Omelyan, I.P.; Tokarchuk, M.V. Unification of the kinetic and hydrodynamics approaches in theory of dense gases and liquids. *Theor. Math. Phys.* **1993**, *96*, 997–1012. [CrossRef]
31. Markiv, B.; Omelyan, I.; Tokarchuk, M. Consistent Description of Kinetics and Hydrodynamics of Weakly Nonequilibrium Processes in Simple Liquids. *J. Stat. Phys.* **2014**, *155*, 843–866. [CrossRef]
32. Alberico, W.M.; Lavagno, A.; Quarati, P. Nonextensive statistics, fluctuations and correlations in high energy nuclear collisions. *Eur. Phys. J. C* **2000**, *12*, 499–506. [CrossRef]
33. Biro, T.S.; Molnar, E. Fluids dynamical equations and transport coefficients of relativistic gases with non-extensive statistics. *Phys. Rev. C* **2012**, *85*, 024905. [CrossRef]
34. Shen, K.-M.; Biro, T.S.; Wang, E.-K. Different non-extensive models for heavy-ion collisions. *Physica A* **2018**, *492*, 2353–2360. [CrossRef]

35. Osada, T.; Wilk, G. Nonextensive/Dissipative Correspondence in Relativistic Hydrodynamics. *Prog. Theor. Phys. Suppl.* **2008**, *174*, 168–172. [CrossRef]
36. Osada, T.; Wilk, G. Erratum: Nonextensive hydrodynamics for relativistic heavy-ion collisions. *Phys. Rev. C* **2008**, *77*, 044903. [CrossRef]
37. Osada, T.; Wilk, G. Nonextensive perfect hydrodynamics—A model of dissipative relativistic hydrodynamics? *Cent. Eur. J. Phys.* **2009**, *7*, 432–443. [CrossRef]
38. Osada, T. Relativistic hydrodynamical model in the presence of long-range correlations. *Phys. Rev. C* **2010**, *81*, 024907. [CrossRef]
39. Lavagno, A. Relativistic nonextensive thermodynamics. *Phys. Lett. A* **2002**, *301*, 13–18. [CrossRef]
40. Gianpiero,G.; Lavagno, A.; Pigato, D. Nonextensive statistical effects in the quark-gluon plasma formation at relativistic heavy-ion collisions energies. *Cent. Eur. J. Phys.* **2012**, *10*, 594–601. [CrossRef]
41. Lavagno, A.; Pigato, D. Nonextensive statistical effects and strangeness production in hot and dense nuclear matter. *J. Phys. G Nucl. Part.* **2012**, *39*, 125106. [CrossRef]
42. Lavagno, A.; Pigato, D. Nonextensive nuclear liquid-gas phase transition. *Physica A* **2013**, *392*, 5164–5171. [CrossRef]
43. Wilk, G.; Wlodarczyk, Z. Temperature oscillations and sound waves in hadronic matter. *Physica A* **2017**, *486*, 579–586. [CrossRef]
44. Zubarev, D.N.; Prozorkevich, A.V.; Smolyanskii, S.A. Derivation of nonlinear generalized equations of quantum relativistic hydrodynamics. *Theor. Math. Phys.* **1979**, *40*, 821–831. [CrossRef]
45. Prozorkevich, A.V.; Samorodov, V.L.; Smolyanskii, S.A. Quantum relativistic hydrodynamics of systems with broken symmetry. I. Local-equilibrium state. *Theor. Math. Phys.* **1982**, *52*, 920–926. [CrossRef]
46. Smolyanskii, S.A. Quantum relativistic hydrodynamics of systems with broken symmetry II. Nonequilibrium state. *Theor. Math. Phys.* **1982**, *52*, 809–814. [CrossRef]
47. Hosoya, A.; Sakagami, M.A.; Takao, M. Nonequilibrium thermodynamics in field theory: Transport coefficients. *Ann. Phys.* **1984**, *154*, 229–252. [CrossRef]
48. Becattini, F.; Tinti, L. Nonequilibrium thermodynamical inequivalence of quantum stress-energy and spin tensors. *Phys. Rev. D* **2013**, *87*, 025029. [CrossRef]
49. Tinti, L. *Progress in Mathematical Relativity, Gravitation and Cosmology*; Springer: Berlin/Heidelberg, Germany, 2014.
50. Becattini, F.; Bucciantini, L.; Grossi, E.; Tinti, L. Local thermodynamical equilibrium and the β frame for a quantum relativistic fluid. *Eur. Phys. J. C* **2015**, *75*, 191. [CrossRef]
51. Hayata, T.; Hidaka, Y.; Nomi, T.; Hongo, M. Relativistic hydrodynamics from quantum field theory on the basis of the generalized Gibbs ensemble method. *Phys. Rev. D* **2015**, *92*, 065008. [CrossRef]
52. Harutyunyan, A.; Sedrakian, A.; Rischke, D.H. Relativistic Dissipative Fluid Dynamics from the Non-Equilibrium Statistical Operator. *Particles* **2018**, *1*, 155–165. [CrossRef]
53. Harutyunyan, A.; Sedrakian, A. Bulk Viscosity of the Hot Quark Plasma from from the Non-Equilibrium Statistical Operator. *Particles* **2018**, *1*, 212–229. [CrossRef]
54. Koide, T.; Kodama, T. Transport coefficient of non-Newtonian fluid and causal dissipative hydrodynamis. *Phys. Rev. E* **2008**, *78*, 051107. [CrossRef]
55. Huang, X.-G.; Koide, T. Shear viscosity, bulk viscosity, and relaxation times of causal dissipative relativistic fluid-dynamics at finite temperature and chemical potential. *Nucl. Phys. A* **2013**, *889*, 73–92. [CrossRef]
56. Morozov, V.G.; Röpke, G.; Höll, A. Kinetic Theory of Quantum Electrodynamic Plasma in a Strong Electromagnetic Field: I. The Covariant Formalism. *Theor. Math. Phys.* **2002**, *131*, 812–831. [CrossRef]
57. Morozov, V.G.; Röpke, G.; Höll, A. Kinetic Theory of Quantum Electrodynamic Plasma in a Strong Electromagnetic Field: II. The Covariant Mean-Field Approximation. *Theor. Math. Phys.* **2002**, *132*, 1029–1042. [CrossRef]
58. Blaizot, J.-P.; Li, Y. Onset of hydrodynamics for a quark-gluon plasma from the evolution of momentsof distribution functions. *J. High Energy Phys.* **2017**, 161. [CrossRef]
59. Tinti, L.; Jaiswal, A.; Ryblewski, R. Quasiparticle second-order viscous hydrodynamics from kinetic theory. *Phys. Rev. D* **2017**, *95*, 054007. [CrossRef]
60. Arimitsu, T.; Umezawa, H. A General Formulation of Nonequilibrium Thermo Field Dynamics. *Progr. Theor. Phys.* **1985**, *74*, 429–432. [CrossRef]

61. Arimitsu, T.; Umezawa, H. Non-Equilibrium Thermo Field Dynamics. *Progr. Theor. Phys.* **1987**, *77*, 32–52. [CrossRef]
62. Arimitsu, T. A canonical formalism of dissipative quantum systems. Non-equilibrium thermofield dynamics. *Condens. Matter Phys.* **1994**, *4*, 26–88. [CrossRef]
63. Zubarev, D.N.; Tokarchuk, M.V. Nonequilibrium thermofield dynamics and the nonequilibrium statistical operator method I. Basic relations. *Theor. Math. Phys.* **1991**, *88*, 876–893. [CrossRef]
64. Tokarchuk, M.V.; Arimitsu, T.; Kobryn, A.E. Thermo field hydrodynamic and kinetic equations of dense quantum nuclear systems. *Condens. Matter Phys.* **1998**, *1*, 605–642. [CrossRef]
65. Glushak, P.A.; Markiv, B.B.; Tokarchuk, M.V. Zubarev's Nonequilibrium Statistical Operator Method in the Generalized Statistics of Multiparticle Systems. *Theor. Math. Phys.* **2018**, *194*, 57–73. [CrossRef]
66. Takahashi, Y.; Umezawa, H. Thermo field dynamics. *Collect. Phenom.* **1975**, *2*, 55–80; reprinted in *Int. J. Mod. Phys. B* **1996**, *10*, 1755–1805. [CrossRef]
67. Umezawa, H.; Matsumoto, H.; Tachiki, M. *Thermo Field Dynamics and Condensed States*; North-Holland: Amsterdam, The Netherlands, 1982.
68. Zubarev, D.N. *Nonequilibrium Statistical Thermodynamics*; Consultant Bureau: New York, NY, USA, 1974.
69. Zubarev, D.N.; Morozov, V.G.; Röpke, G. *Statistical Mechanics of Nonequilibrium Processes*; Akademie Verlag: Berlin, Germany, 1996; Volume 1.
70. Zubarev, D.N.; Morozov, V.G.; Röpke, G. *Statistical Mechanics of Nonequilibrium Processes*; Akademie Verlag: Berlin, Germany, 1997; Volume 2.
71. Markiv, B.B.; Tokarchuk, R.M.; Kostrobij, P.P.; Tokarchuk, M.V. Nonequilibrium statistical operator method in Renyi statistics. *Physica A* **2011**, *390*, 785–791. [CrossRef]
72. Rudoi, Y.G. Generalized Informational Entropy and Noncanonical Distribution in Equilibrium Statistical Mechanics. *Theor. Math. Phys.* **2003**, *135*, 451–496.
73. Bashkirov, A.G. On maximum entropy principle, superstatistics, power-law distribution and Renyi parameter. *Physica A* **2004**, *340*, 153–162. [CrossRef]

particles

MDPI

Article

Relativistic Dissipative Fluid Dynamics from the Non-Equilibrium Statistical Operator

Arus Harutyunyan [1,*], Armen Sedrakian [2] and Dirk H. Rischke [1,3]

1 Institute for Theoretical Physics, Goethe University, Max-von-Laue-Straße, 1, 60438 Frankfurt am Main, Germany; drischke@th.physik.uni-frankfurt.de
2 Frankfurt Institute for Advanced Studies, Ruth-Moufang-Straße, 1, 60438 Frankfurt am Main, Germany; sedrakian@fias.uni-frankfurt.de
3 Department of Modern Physics, University of Science and Technology of China, Hefei 230026, China
* Correspondence: arus@th.physik.uni-frankfurt.de

Received: 26 April 2018; Accepted: 19 June 2018; Published: 21 June 2018

Abstract: We present a new derivation of second-order relativistic dissipative fluid dynamics for quantum systems using Zubarev's formalism for the non-equilibrium statistical operator. In particular, we discuss the shear-stress tensor to second order in gradients and argue that the relaxation terms for the dissipative quantities arise from memory effects contained in the statistical operator. We also identify new transport coefficients which describe the relaxation of dissipative processes to second order and express them in terms of equilibrium correlation functions, thus establishing Kubo-type formulae for the second-order transport coefficients.

Keywords: relativistic fluid dynamics; statistical operator; non-equilibrium states; transport coefficients; correlation functions

1. Introduction

Fluid dynamics is a powerful tool to describe low-frequency and long-wavelength phenomena in statistical systems [1]. It finds numerous applications in astrophysics, cosmology, heavy-ion physics, and other areas. In particular, it has been successfully applied to describe the collective behavior of hot and dense strongly interacting matter created in heavy-ion collision experiments at Relativistic Heavy Ion Collider (RHIC) and Large Hadron Collider (LHC). In these experiments, a new state of matter, the quark-gluon plasma (QGP), was discovered, which behaves almost like a perfect fluid.

There are two main approaches which can be used to derive the equations of motion of fluid dynamics and the pertaining transport coefficients from the underlying microscopic theory. For weakly interacting systems, one commonly relies on kinetic theory based on the Boltzmann equation for the quasi-particle distribution function [2–5]. For strongly interacting quantum systems, where the quasi-particle picture breaks down and/or the quantum nature of the fields itself is important, kinetic theory is no longer applicable, and a full quantum-statistical approach based on the Liouville equation for the non-equilibrium statistical operator is required.

In this work, we adopt the method of the non-equilibrium statistical operator (NESO) [6,7] to obtain the relativistic fluid-dynamical equations of motion for strongly correlated matter, such as the QGP, in the non-perturbative regime. The method was applied to quantum fields [8] and has been since extended to treat systems in strong magnetic fields [9]. It is based on a generalization of the Gibbs canonical ensemble to non-equilibrium states, i.e., the statistical operator is promoted to a non-local functional of the thermodynamic parameters and their space-time derivatives. Assuming that the thermodynamic parameters are sufficiently smooth over the correlation lengths characterizing the system, the statistical operator is expanded into a series in gradients of these parameters to the desired order. The fluid-dynamical equations for the dissipative fluxes emerge then after statistically averaging the relevant quantum operators. An advantage of the NESO method is that the transport coefficients of the system are automatically obtained in the form of Kubo-type relations, i.e., they are related to certain correlation functions of the underlying field theory in the strong-coupling regime. There exist a number of formulations of relativistic fluid dynamics in terms of near-equilibrium quantities which are related to the NESO method employed by us; for recent work, see References [10–12].

This contribution provides a concise presentation of our recent work on the derivation of second-order dissipative fluid dynamics via the NESO method [13,14]. As is well known, relativistic fluid dynamics describes the state of a fluid in terms of its energy-momentum tensor and currents of conserved charges, which in the relevant low-frequency and long-wavelength limit can be expanded around their equilibrium values. The zeroth-order expansion corresponds to ideal (non-dissipative) fluid dynamics. At first order, dissipative relativistic fluid dynamics emerges from a truncation that keeps the terms of linear order in gradients [1,15]. Second-order relativistic theories have also been constructed [16,17] to avoid the acausality of the first-order theory and the resulting numerical instabilities. In second-order theories, the dissipative fluxes satisfy relaxation equations, which describe the process of their relaxation towards their Navier–Stokes values at asymptotically large times. While the general structure of second-order fluid dynamics is known, different results have been obtained for the coefficients entering these equations (see, e.g., References [18,19]). The various versions of second-order fluid dynamics and the pertaining relaxation equations are reviewed and compared to each other, e.g., in the review articles [2,4,5], to which we refer the reader for more detailed expositions.

This work is structured as follows. Section 2 gives a brief summary of Zubarev's formalism for the NESO [6,7]. Section 3 recapitulates Navier–Stokes theory and the Kubo formulae for the first-order transport coefficients. The second-order transport equations are discussed in Section 4 and a summary is given in Section 5. We work in flat space-time described by the metric tensor $g^{\mu\nu} = \mathrm{diag}(+,-,-,-)$.

2. Non-Equilibrium Statistical Operator and Correlation Functions

The fluid-dynamical state of a relativistic quantum system is described by the operators of the energy-momentum tensor $\hat{T}^{\mu\nu}(x)$ and the conserved particle current $\hat{N}^{\mu}(x)$. For example, in the case of Dirac fermions, the particle current is given by $\hat{N}^{\mu} = \hat{\bar{\psi}}\gamma^{\mu}\hat{\psi}$, where $\hat{\psi}$ is the Dirac field operator, and γ^{μ} are the Dirac matrices. The equations of relativistic fluid dynamics consist of the covariant conservation laws for these quantities

$$\partial_{\mu}\hat{T}^{\mu\nu}(x) = 0, \qquad \partial_{\mu}\hat{N}^{\mu}(x) = 0. \tag{1}$$

Here, we assume that the fluid consists of only one particle species. The generalization to the case of several conserved species is straightforward and is given elsewhere [13].

In general, the fluid-dynamical description is applicable, if the actual state of a given system does not deviate too much from local thermodynamic equilibrium. This allows one to introduce a fictitious local-equilibrium reference state, characterized by space-time dependent thermodynamic parameters, such as temperature $T(x) \equiv \beta^{-1}(x)$, chemical potential $\mu(x)$, and fluid 4-velocity $u^{\nu}(x)$. The deviation of the actual state from this fictitious reference state is then taken to be proportional to gradients of these fields. The assumption that the deviation from local equilibrium is small is equivalent to assuming that these fields are slowly varying functions of the space-time coordinates $x \equiv (\boldsymbol{x}, t)$. Note that, in this context, "slowly" means that the characteristic *macroscopic* scales over which the fluid-dynamical quantities change in space and time should be much larger than the characteristic *microscopic* scales of the system, e.g., for quasi-particles the mean free path between collisions. In terms of the thermodynamic parameters defined above, we define new auxiliary functions

$$\beta^{\nu}(x) = \beta(x)u^{\nu}(x), \qquad \alpha(x) = \beta(x)\mu(x). \tag{2}$$

Now, consider the NESO given by Huang et al. [9]:

$$\hat{\rho}(t) = Q^{-1}e^{-\hat{A}+\hat{B}}, \qquad Q = \mathrm{Tr}e^{-\hat{A}+\hat{B}}, \tag{3}$$

where

$$\begin{aligned} \hat{A}(t) &= \int d^3x \Big[\beta^{\nu}(x)\hat{T}_{0\nu}(x) - \alpha(x)\hat{N}^0(x)\Big], &(4)\\ \hat{B}(t) &= \int d^3x_1 \int_{-\infty}^{t} dt_1 e^{\varepsilon(t_1-t)}\hat{C}(x_1), &(5)\\ \hat{C}(x) &= \hat{T}_{\mu\nu}(x)\partial^{\mu}\beta^{\nu}(x) - \hat{N}^{\mu}(x)\partial_{\mu}\alpha(x), &(6) \end{aligned}$$

with $\varepsilon \to +0$ taken after the thermodynamic limit. The NESO satisfies the quantum Liouville equation with an infinitesimal source term ε, which for positive values selects the retarded solution [6,7]. The operators $\hat{A}(t)$ and $\hat{B}(t)$ correspond to the equilibrium and non-equilibrium parts of the statistical operator, where the operator $\hat{C}(x)$ stands for the thermodynamic "force" as it involves the gradients of the thermodynamic variables, i.e., temperature, chemical potential, and fluid 4-velocity. We also define the *local-equilibrium statistical operator* as

$$\hat{\rho}_l(t) = Q_l^{-1}e^{-\hat{A}}, \qquad Q_l = \mathrm{Tr}e^{-\hat{A}}, \tag{7}$$

which is the analog of the Gibbs distribution involving local thermodynamic parameters.

Before proceeding, we remark that the thermodynamic variables are well-defined quantities only in an equilibrium state, but not for a non-equilibrium state. The reason they appear at all in our discussion is the introduction of a fictitious local-equilibrium state, from which the actual non-equilibrium state should not deviate too much. The freedom in choosing this fictitious state can be exploited to determine the parameters $\alpha(x)$, $\beta(x)$, and the fluid 4-velocity $u^{\nu}(x)$ characterizing this state. For this purpose, we first define the operators of the energy and particle densities via $\hat{\epsilon}(x) = u_{\mu}(x)u_{\nu}(x)\hat{T}^{\mu\nu}(x)$ and $\hat{n}(x) = u_{\mu}(x)\hat{N}^{\mu}(x)$. These simply imply that $\hat{\epsilon}(x)$ and $\hat{n}(x)$ are the time-like eigenvalues of the energy-momentum tensor and the particle current, respectively, measured by a local observer comoving with a fluid element. The local values of the Lorentz-invariant thermodynamic parameters $\beta(x)$ and $\alpha(x)$ can now be fixed by requiring that the average values of the operators $\hat{\epsilon}(x)$ and $\hat{n}(x)$ match the local-equilibrium values of these quantities. These so-called *Landau matching conditions* [6,7] are then written as

$$\langle\hat{\epsilon}(x)\rangle = \langle\hat{\epsilon}(x)\rangle_l, \qquad \langle\hat{n}(x)\rangle = \langle\hat{n}(x)\rangle_l, \tag{8}$$

where for an arbitrary operator $\hat{X}(x)$ the non-equilibrium and local-equilibrium statistical averages are defined as

$$\langle\hat{X}(x)\rangle = \mathrm{Tr}[\hat{\rho}(t)\hat{X}(x)], \qquad \langle\hat{X}(x)\rangle_l = \mathrm{Tr}\big[\hat{\rho}_l(t)\hat{X}(x)\big]. \tag{9}$$

Finally, the fluid 4-velocity u^{μ} can be determined by relating it to a particular physical current. For example, in the Landau–Lifshitz frame, the 4-velocity is parallel to the fluid 4-momentum or, equivalently, to the energy flow, i.e., $u_{\mu}\langle\hat{T}^{\mu\nu}\rangle = \langle\hat{\epsilon}\rangle u^{\nu}$ [1]. In the Eckart frame, the fluid velocity is associated with the particle flow via $\langle\hat{N}^{\mu}\rangle = \langle\hat{n}\rangle u^{\mu}$ [15]. However, in the following, we keep the fluid velocity generic without specifying any particular reference frame.

The next step is to expand the NESO around the local-equilibrium value in Equation (7) treating the non-equilibrium part, which is described by the operator $\hat{B}$, as a perturbation

$$\hat{\rho} = \hat{\rho}_l + \hat{\rho}_1 + \hat{\rho}_2, \tag{10}$$

where the first-order term is given by

$$\hat{\rho}_1(t) = \int d^4x_1 \int_0^1 d\tau \left[\hat{C}_\tau(x_1) - \langle \hat{C}_\tau(x_1)\rangle_l\right] \hat{\rho}_l, \tag{11}$$

while the second-order term is

$$\begin{aligned}\hat{\rho}_2(t) = \frac{1}{2}\int d^4x_1 d^4x_2 \int_0^1 d\tau \int_0^1 d\lambda \Big[\tilde{T}\{\hat{C}_\lambda(x_1)\hat{C}_\tau(x_2)\} - \langle \tilde{T}\{\hat{C}_\lambda(x_1)\hat{C}_\tau(x_2)\}\rangle_l \\ -\langle \hat{C}_\lambda(x_1)\rangle_l \hat{C}_\tau(x_2) - \hat{C}_\lambda(x_1)\langle \hat{C}_\tau(x_2)\rangle_l + 2\langle \hat{C}_\lambda(x_1)\rangle_l \langle \hat{C}_\tau(x_2)\rangle_l\Big]\hat{\rho}_l.\end{aligned} \tag{12}$$

Here, $\tilde{T}$ is the anti-chronological operator acting on the variables τ and λ and we used the short-hand notations

$$\int d^4x_1 = \int d^3x_1 \int_{-\infty}^{t} dt_1 e^{\varepsilon(t_1-t)}, \qquad \hat{X}_\alpha = e^{-\alpha\hat{A}}\hat{X}e^{\alpha\hat{A}}, \qquad \alpha \in \tau, \lambda. \tag{13}$$

The expansion of Equation (10) implies that the statistical average of any operator $\hat{X}(x)$ can be decomposed into three terms

$$\langle \hat{X}(x)\rangle = \langle \hat{X}(x)\rangle_l + \langle \hat{X}(x)\rangle_1 + \langle \hat{X}(x)\rangle_2, \tag{14}$$

where the first-order term is given by

$$\langle \hat{X}(x)\rangle_1 = \int d^4x_1 \Big(\hat{X}(x), \hat{C}(x_1)\Big), \tag{15}$$

with

$$\Big(\hat{X}(x), \hat{Y}(x_1)\Big) = \int_0^1 d\tau \langle \hat{X}(x)\left[\hat{Y}_\tau(x_1) - \langle \hat{Y}_\tau(x_1)\rangle_l\right]\rangle_l \tag{16}$$

being the two-point correlation function between two arbitrary operators [8,9]. The second-order term in Equation (14) can be written as

$$\langle \hat{X}(x)\rangle_2 = \int d^4x_1 d^4x_2 \Big(\hat{X}(x), \hat{C}(x_1), \hat{C}(x_2)\Big), \tag{17}$$

where we introduced the three-point correlation function of the operators $\hat{X}$, $\hat{Y}$, and $\hat{Z}$ as

$$\begin{aligned}\Big(\hat{X}(x), \hat{Y}(x_1), \hat{Z}(x_2)\Big) &= \frac{1}{2}\int_0^1 d\tau \int_0^1 d\lambda \langle \tilde{T}\hat{X}(x)\Big[\hat{Y}_\lambda(x_1)\hat{Z}_\tau(x_2) - \langle \tilde{T}\hat{Y}_\lambda(x_1)\hat{Z}_\tau(x_2)\rangle_l \\ &- \langle \hat{Y}_\lambda(x_1)\rangle_l \hat{Z}_\tau(x_2) - \hat{Y}_\lambda(x_1)\langle \hat{Z}_\tau(x_2)\rangle_l + 2\langle \hat{Y}_\lambda(x_1)\rangle_l \langle \hat{Z}_\tau(x_2)\rangle_l\Big]\rangle_l.\end{aligned} \tag{18}$$

3. Relativistic Fluid Dynamics at First Order in Gradients

To examine specific dissipative processes, i.e., heat conduction, particle diffusion, and shear and bulk stresses, the energy-momentum tensor and the particle current are decomposed as

$$\hat{T}^{\mu\nu} = \hat{\epsilon}u^\mu u^\nu - \hat{p}\Delta^{\mu\nu} + \hat{q}^\mu u^\nu + \hat{q}^\nu u^\mu + \hat{\pi}^{\mu\nu}, \tag{19}$$

$$\hat{N}^\mu = \hat{n}u^\mu + \hat{j}^\mu, \tag{20}$$

where the fluid velocity u_μ is normalized as $u_\mu u^\mu = 1$, and $\Delta^{\mu\nu} = g^{\mu\nu} - u^\mu u^\nu$ is the projection operator onto the 3-space orthogonal to u_μ. The energy-momentum tensor in Equation (19) is assumed to be symmetric with respect to its indices. We remind that u^μ and $\Delta^{\mu\nu}$ appearing in these expressions are classical fields, i.e., c-numbers, whereas the rest of the quantities are (microscopic) quantum operators, the physical identification of which is as follows: $\hat{\epsilon}$ is the operator of the energy density; $\hat{n}$ is the operator of particle (number) density; $\hat{p}$ is the operator of the pressure; and the dissipative terms $\hat{\pi}^{\mu\nu}$, $\hat{q}^{\mu}$, and $\hat{j}^{\mu}$ are the shear-stress tensor, the energy-diffusion flux, and the particle-diffusion flux, respectively.

The tensor decompositions in Equations (19) and (20) have the most general form that can be constructed from the fluid velocity and the tensor $\Delta^{\mu\nu}$. The operators of the physical quantities on the right-hand sides of Equations (19) and (20) can be written as certain projections of the energy-momentum tensor and the particle current,

$$\hat{\epsilon} = u_\mu u_\nu \hat{T}^{\mu\nu}, \qquad \hat{n} = u_\mu \hat{N}^\mu, \qquad \hat{p} = -\frac{1}{3}\Delta_{\mu\nu}\hat{T}^{\mu\nu}, \tag{21}$$

$$\hat{\pi}^{\mu\nu} = \Delta^{\mu\nu}_{\alpha\beta}\hat{T}^{\alpha\beta}, \qquad \hat{q}^\mu = u_\alpha \Delta^{\mu}_{\beta}\hat{T}^{\alpha\beta}, \qquad \hat{j}^\nu = \Delta^{\nu}_{\mu}\hat{N}^\mu, \tag{22}$$

where

$$\Delta_{\mu\nu\rho\sigma} = \frac{1}{2}\left(\Delta_{\mu\rho}\Delta_{\nu\sigma} + \Delta_{\mu\sigma}\Delta_{\nu\rho}\right) - \frac{1}{3}\Delta_{\mu\nu}\Delta_{\rho\sigma} \tag{23}$$

is a traceless rank–four projector orthogonal to u^μ. The dissipative quantities satisfy the conditions

$$u_\nu \hat{q}^\nu = 0, \qquad u_\nu \hat{j}^\nu = 0, \qquad u_\nu \hat{\pi}^{\mu\nu} = 0, \qquad \hat{\pi}^\mu_\mu = 0. \tag{24}$$

In local equilibrium, the averages of these operators vanish [20]:

$$\langle \hat{q}^\mu \rangle_l = 0, \qquad \langle \hat{j}^\mu \rangle_l = 0, \qquad \langle \hat{\pi}^{\mu\nu} \rangle_l = 0, \tag{25}$$

and one recovers the limit of ideal fluid dynamics. The local-equilibrium pressure is given by the equation of state, i.e., $\langle \hat{p} \rangle_l \equiv p = p(\epsilon, n)$, which closes the set of ideal fluid-dynamical equations of motion.

Consider next fluid dynamics at first order in gradients. Quite generally, the fluid-dynamical quantities $\pi^{\mu\nu}$, q^μ, and j^μ are obtained as the statistical averages of the corresponding operators over the NESO according to Equations (14)–(18). Keeping only the first-order terms in Equation (14), we obtain the relativistic Navier–Stokes equations

$$\pi_{\mu\nu} = 2\eta\sigma_{\mu\nu}, \qquad \Pi = -\zeta\theta, \qquad \mathscr{J}_\mu = \kappa\left(\frac{nT}{h}\right)^2 \nabla_\mu \alpha, \tag{26}$$

where $\pi_{\mu\nu} \equiv \langle \hat{\pi}_{\mu\nu} \rangle$, the bulk viscous pressure $\Pi \equiv \langle \hat{p} \rangle - \langle \hat{p} \rangle_l$ is the difference between the first-order average of the pressure operator and the local-equilibrium value of pressure, $h = \epsilon + p$ is the enthalpy density, and

$$\mathscr{J}_\mu = j_\mu - \frac{n}{h} q_\mu \tag{27}$$

is the irreversible particle flow, i.e., the particle flow with respect to the energy flow [16,17]. On the right-hand sides of Equation (26), $\sigma_{\mu\nu} = \partial_{<\alpha} u_{\beta>}$ is the shear tensor, where angular brackets denote the projection with the projector in Equation (23), i.e., $A_{<\mu\nu>} = \Delta^{\alpha\beta}_{\mu\nu} A_{\alpha\beta}$, $\theta = \partial_\mu u^\mu$ is the expansion scalar, and $\nabla_\alpha = \Delta_{\alpha\beta}\partial^\beta$ is the covariant spatial derivative. The coefficients η, ζ, and κ are the transport coefficients of the shear and bulk viscosities, and the thermal conductivity, respectively.

These transport coefficients can be expressed through two-point correlation functions via the following Kubo formulae [8–10]

$$\eta = \frac{\beta}{10}\int d^4x_1\left(\hat{\pi}_{\mu\nu}(x),\hat{\pi}^{\mu\nu}(x_1)\right), \tag{28}$$

$$\zeta = \beta\int d^4x_1\left(\hat{p}^*(x),\hat{p}^*(x_1)\right), \tag{29}$$

$$\kappa = -\frac{\beta^2}{3}\int d^4x_1\left(\hat{h}_\mu(x),\hat{h}^\mu(x_1)\right), \tag{30}$$

where

$$\hat{p}^* = \hat{p} - \gamma\hat{\epsilon} - \delta\hat{n}, \qquad \hat{h}^\mu = \hat{q}^\mu - \frac{h}{n}\hat{j}^\mu, \tag{31}$$

and

$$\gamma = \left(\frac{\partial p}{\partial \epsilon}\right)_n, \qquad \delta = \left(\frac{\partial p}{\partial n}\right)_\epsilon. \tag{32}$$

The correlation functions in Equations (28)–(30) are evaluated in a uniform background, i.e., as if the system was in *global thermodynamical equilibrium*. They can be expressed in terms of the two-point retarded *equilibrium Green functions* as [8,9]

$$\eta = -\frac{1}{10}\frac{d}{d\omega}\mathrm{Im}G^R_{\hat{\pi}_{\mu\nu}\hat{\pi}^{\mu\nu}}(\omega)\bigg|_{\omega=0}, \tag{33}$$

$$\zeta = -\frac{d}{d\omega}\mathrm{Im}G^R_{\hat{p}^*\hat{p}^*}(\omega)\bigg|_{\omega=0}, \tag{34}$$

$$\kappa = \frac{1}{3T}\frac{d}{d\omega}\mathrm{Im}G^R_{\hat{h}_\mu\hat{h}^\mu}(\omega)\bigg|_{\omega=0}, \tag{35}$$

where, for any two operators $\hat{X}$ and $\hat{Y}$,

$$G^R_{\hat{X}\hat{Y}}(\omega) \equiv -i\int_0^\infty dt e^{i\omega t}\int d^3x \langle[\hat{X}(\boldsymbol{x},t),\hat{Y}(\boldsymbol{0},0)]\rangle_l. \tag{36}$$

Equations (33)–(35) represent a particularly suitable form for the Kubo formulae, which lends itself to evaluation using the methods of equilibrium finite-temperature field theory.

Before closing this section, it is useful to clarify the relation between the expansions in powers of the thermodynamic forces and in powers of the Knudsen number $K = l/L$, where l and L are typical microscopic and macroscopic length scales, respectively. To obtain the relations in Equation (26) from Equation (15), we used Curie's theorem. It states that, in an isotropic medium, the correlations between operators of different rank vanish [21]. The integrands in Equations (28)–(30) are mainly concentrated within the range $|x_1 - x| \lesssim l$, where l is the mean correlation length, which in the weak-coupling limit is of the order of the particle mean free path. The fluid-dynamical regime implies $l \ll L$, where L is the typical length scale over which the parameters β^ν and α vary in space. Therefore, the thermodynamic forces $\partial^\mu\beta^\nu$ and $\partial^\mu\alpha$ involved in Equation (6) can be factored out from the integral in Equation (15) with their average values at x, i.e., the *non-locality* of the thermodynamic forces can be neglected in this approximation. Because $|\sigma^{\rho\sigma}| \simeq |u^\rho|/L$, the relations in Equation (26) obtained from the gradient expansion in Equation (10) of the NESO are consistent with the expansion scheme in powers of the Knudsen number.

4. Relativistic Fluid Dynamics at Second Order in Gradients

We have computed systematically all second-order corrections to the dissipative quantities $\pi^{\mu\nu}$, Π, and $\mathscr{J}^{\mu}$ based on Equations (14)–(18) [13,14]. Before presenting the results, we note that the second-order contributions arise not only from Equation (17), which is quadratic in the thermodynamic force $\hat{C}$, but also from Equation (15), where the non-local nature of the thermodynamic forces in space and time should be carefully taken into account. The non-local effects generate finite relaxation terms in the fluid-dynamical equations, which are required for causality. To see that these corrections are of second order in the Knudsen number, note that they involve the differences of the thermodynamic forces, e.g., $\partial^{\mu}\beta^{\nu}$, at the points x_1 and x (see Equations (6) and (15)). Therefore, we can approximate $\partial^{\mu}\beta^{\nu}(x_1) - \partial^{\mu}\beta^{\nu}(x) \simeq \partial_{\lambda}\partial^{\mu}\beta^{\nu}(x)(x_1 - x)^{\lambda} \sim K\partial^{\mu}\beta^{\nu}(x)$, because $x_1 - x \sim l$ and $\partial \sim L^{-1}$, as already done in Section 3. Thus, these corrections contain an additional power of the Knudsen number K as compared to the first-order expressions in Equation (26) and, therefore, are of second order.

Here, we restrict ourselves to the second-order expression for the shear-stress tensor and compare it with the results of References [18,22].

4.1. Second-Order Corrections to the Shear-Stress Tensor

As explained above, we now keep the NESO at second order in small perturbations from local equilibrium and, in addition, we retain terms which are of second order in the gradients of thermodynamic forces. In this manner, we find the shear-stress tensor at second order as

$$\pi_{\mu\nu} = 2\eta\sigma_{\mu\nu} - 2\eta\tau_{\pi}(\dot{\sigma}_{\mu\nu} + \gamma\theta\sigma_{\mu\nu}) + \lambda_{\pi}\sigma_{\alpha<\mu}\sigma^{\alpha}_{\nu>} + 2\lambda_{\pi\Pi}\theta\sigma_{\mu\nu} + \lambda_{\pi\mathscr{J}}\nabla_{<\mu}\alpha\nabla_{\nu>}\alpha, \tag{37}$$

where $\dot{\sigma}_{\mu\nu} \equiv \Delta_{\mu\nu\rho\sigma}D\sigma^{\rho\sigma}$, with $D = u^{\mu}\partial_{\mu}$ being the comoving derivative, and τ_{π}, λ_{π}, $\lambda_{\pi\Pi}$, and $\lambda_{\pi\mathscr{J}}$ represent four new coefficients associated with the second-order corrections to the shear stress. The first term on the right-hand side of Equation (37) is easily recognized as the first-order (Navier–Stokes) contribution. The second-order terms collected in the parentheses (i.e., those $\propto \tau_{\pi}$) represent the non-local corrections to Equation (15), whereas the last three terms stand for the nonlinear corrections arising from the three-point correlation functions in Equation (17). The first non-local correction describes *memory effects* due to its non-locality in time. The relevant transport coefficient τ_{π}, which has the dimension of time, measures how long the information remains in the "memory" of the shear-stress tensor $\pi_{\mu\nu}$. Therefore, it is natural to associate it with the relaxation time of the shear stresses towards their asymptotic Navier–Stokes values. The second term involves a product of $\sigma_{\mu\nu}$ with $\theta = \partial_{\mu}u^{\mu}$ and can be regarded as a (scalar) measure of the spatial "non-locality" in the fluid-velocity field. This term describes how the shear-stress tensor is distorted by uniform expansion or contraction of the fluid.

We find that the relaxation time τ_{π} is related to the frequency derivative of the corresponding first-order transport coefficient, i.e., the shear viscosity, by a Kubo formula

$$\eta\tau_{\pi} = -i\frac{d}{d\omega}\eta(\omega)\bigg|_{\omega=0} = \frac{1}{10}\frac{d^2}{d\omega^2}\mathrm{Re}G^{R}_{\hat{\pi}_{\mu\nu}\hat{\pi}^{\mu\nu}}(\omega)\bigg|_{\omega=0}, \tag{38}$$

where $\eta \equiv \eta(0)$ is given by Equation (33), the retarded Green's function $G^{R}_{\hat{\pi}_{\mu\nu}\hat{\pi}^{\mu\nu}}$ is defined in Equation (36), and the frequency-dependent shear viscosity $\eta(\omega)$ is given by Equation (33) for non-vanishing ω. Similar expressions for the relaxation times were obtained previously in References [18,22–24].

The physical meaning of the Equation (38) for τ_{π} is easy to understand. As mentioned above, the relaxation terms originate from the non-local (memory) effects encoded in the non-equilibrium statistical operator. In the case where these memory effects are neglected (first-order theory), the proportionality between $\pi_{\mu\nu}$ and $\sigma_{\mu\nu}$ is given by the zero-frequency (static) limit of the shear viscosity, as seen from Equations (26) and (33). The memory effects imply a time delay, which translates into a frequency dependence of the shear viscosity [25]. At leading order, this is accounted for by the first-order frequency derivative of $\eta(\omega)$ as Equation (38) demonstrates.

The last three terms in Equation (37) contain all combinations of the thermodynamic forces $\sigma_{\mu\nu}$, θ, and $\nabla_\mu\alpha$ which are allowed by the symmetries to quadratic order. These are $\theta\sigma_{\mu\nu}$, $\sigma_{\rho<\mu}\sigma^\rho_{\nu>}$, and $\nabla_{<\mu}\alpha\nabla_{\nu>}\alpha$. The second-order transport coefficients associated with these terms can be expressed via three-point correlation functions according to

$$\lambda_\pi = \frac{12}{35}\beta^2\int d^4x_1 d^4x_2\Big(\hat{\pi}^\nu_\mu(x),\hat{\pi}^\lambda_\nu(x_1),\hat{\pi}^\mu_\lambda(x_2)\Big), \tag{39}$$

$$\lambda_{\pi\Pi} = -\frac{\beta^2}{5}\int d^4x_1 d^4x_2\Big(\hat{\pi}_{\mu\nu}(x),\hat{\pi}^{\mu\nu}(x_1),\hat{p}^*(x_2)\Big), \tag{40}$$

$$\lambda_{\pi\mathscr{J}} = \frac{1}{5}\int d^4x_1 d^4x_2\Big(\hat{\pi}_{\mu\nu}(x),\hat{\mathscr{J}}^\mu(x_1),\hat{\mathscr{J}}^\nu(x_2)\Big), \tag{41}$$

where $\hat{\mathscr{J}}^\mu$ is the operator corresponding to the 4-current (27). In analogy to the leading-order coefficient η, which is given by the two-point correlation of the shear-stress tensor, the second-order coefficient λ_π is given by the three-point correlation of the shear-stress tensor. The coefficient $\lambda_{\pi\Pi}$ describes the nonlinear coupling between shear- and bulk-viscous processes and is given by a three-point correlation function between two shear-stress tensors and the bulk viscous pressure. Finally, the coefficient $\lambda_{\pi\mathscr{J}}$ describes the nonlinear coupling between the shear and the diffusion processes. Similarly, this coefficient is given by a three-point correlation function between two diffusion currents and the shear-stress tensor. Note that, in Equation (37), the term $\propto\lambda_{\pi\Pi}$ and the second term in parenthesis have the same gradient structure, but they have different origins and physical interpretation. The term $\propto\tau_\pi$ originates from *non-local* effects in the statistical distribution, whereas the term $\propto\lambda_{\pi\Pi}$ stands purely for the *nonlinear* coupling between the bulk- and the shear-viscous effects. In this sense, it is natural to regard as nonlinear only the term $\propto\lambda_{\pi\Pi}$, but not the term $\propto\tau_\pi$. A similar classification of the second-order terms was suggested earlier in Reference [19].

4.2. Comparison with Previous Studies

For the sake of simplicity we consider here a fluid without conserved charges. In this case, Equation (32) implies $\gamma\equiv c_s^2$, where c_s is the speed of sound, and Equation (37) reduces to

$$\pi_{\mu\nu} = 2\eta\sigma_{\mu\nu} - 2\eta\tau_\pi(\dot{\sigma}_{\mu\nu} + c_s^2\theta\sigma_{\mu\nu}) + \lambda_\pi\sigma_{\alpha<\mu}\sigma^\alpha_{\nu>} + 2\lambda_{\pi\Pi}\theta\sigma_{\mu\nu}. \tag{42}$$

Baier et al. [18] found in this case and for conformal fluids

$$\pi^B_{\mu\nu} = 2\eta\sigma_{\mu\nu} - 2\eta\tau_\pi\left(\dot{\sigma}_{\mu\nu} + \frac{1}{3}\theta\sigma_{\mu\nu}\right) + \lambda_1\sigma_{\alpha<\mu}\sigma^\alpha_{\nu>}, \tag{43}$$

where we have neglected terms proportional to the vorticity tensor $w_{\alpha\beta} = (\nabla_\alpha u_\beta - \nabla_\beta u_\alpha)/2$. (Note that Baier et al. [18] and Romatschke [22] used a metric convention opposite to ours, and their definition of the shear viscosity differs from ours by a factor of 2). Because $c_s^2 = 1/3$ for a conformal fluid, we recover from Equation (42) the term proportional to τ_π in Equation (43). Furthermore, because conformal invariance implies a vanishing bulk viscous pressure, the correlations involving the operator $\hat{p}^*$ (see Equations (29) and (31)) vanish, i.e., $\lambda_{\pi\Pi} = 0$ in this case. Finally we see that $\lambda_1\equiv\lambda_\pi$.

In the case of non-conformal fluids, the second-order expression for the shear-stress tensor was found, e.g., in Reference [22] in the absence of conserved charges. Again, neglecting the vorticity tensor and assuming flat space-time,

$$\pi^R_{\mu\nu} = 2\eta\sigma_{\mu\nu} - 2\eta\tau_\pi\left(\dot{\sigma}_{\mu\nu} + \frac{1}{3}\theta\sigma_{\mu\nu}\right) + \lambda_1\sigma_{\alpha<\mu}\sigma^\alpha_{\nu>} - \frac{2}{3}\eta\tau^*_\pi\theta\sigma_{\mu\nu} + \lambda_4\nabla_{<\mu}\ln s\nabla_{\nu>}\ln s. \tag{44}$$

The term $\propto$ τ_π^* has the same gradient structure as the non-local term $-2\eta\tau_\pi\theta\sigma_{\mu\nu}/3$. Comparing Equation (44) with our expression in Equation (42), we identify $\tau_\pi^* = \tau_\pi(3c_s^2 - 1) - 3\lambda_{\pi\Pi}/\eta$, and $\lambda_4 = 0$.

We also note that Equation (37) does not contain terms proportional to the vorticity. To derive such terms, one needs to include an initial non-zero angular momentum in the local-equilibrium distribution [26].

4.3. Relaxation Equation for the Shear-Stress Tensor

A relaxation-type equation for $\pi_{\mu\nu}$ can now be derived from Equation (37). For this purpose, we replace the first-order expression $2\sigma^{\rho\sigma} \to \eta^{-1}\pi^{\rho\sigma}$ in the second term on the right-hand-side of Equation (37), as has also been done in References [18,27,28]. This substitution is justified up to second order in space-time gradients. We then obtain

$$-2\eta\tau_\pi\dot{\sigma}_{\mu\nu} \simeq -\tau_\pi\dot{\pi}_{\mu\nu} + \tau_\pi\beta\eta^{-1}\left(\gamma\frac{\partial\eta}{\partial\beta} - \delta\frac{\partial\eta}{\partial\alpha}\right)\theta\pi_{\mu\nu} \simeq -\tau_\pi\dot{\pi}_{\mu\nu} + 2\tau_\pi\beta\left(\gamma\frac{\partial\eta}{\partial\beta} - \delta\frac{\partial\eta}{\partial\alpha}\right)\theta\sigma_{\mu\nu}, \tag{45}$$

where $\dot{\pi}_{\mu\nu} = \Delta_{\mu\nu\rho\sigma}D\pi^{\rho\sigma}$. The terms in brackets contain the corresponding partial derivatives of η, which in general are not small and should not be neglected. In Equation (45), we employed the relations $D\beta = \beta\theta\gamma$ and $D\alpha = -\beta\theta\delta$ [9]. Combining Equations (37) and (45) and introducing the coefficient

$$\lambda = \lambda_{\pi\Pi} - \gamma\eta\tau_\pi + \tau_\pi\beta\left(\gamma\frac{\partial\eta}{\partial\beta} - \delta\frac{\partial\eta}{\partial\alpha}\right), \tag{46}$$

we finally obtain

$$\tau_\pi\dot{\pi}_{\mu\nu} + \pi_{\mu\nu} = 2\eta\sigma_{\mu\nu} + 2\lambda\theta\sigma_{\mu\nu} + \lambda_\pi\sigma_{\rho<\mu}\sigma^\rho_{\nu>} + \lambda_{\pi\mathscr{J}}\nabla_{<\mu}\alpha\nabla_{\nu>}\alpha. \tag{47}$$

The time-derivative term on the left-hand side describes the relaxation of the shear-stress tensor towards its Navier–Stokes value on the characteristic time scale τ_π. Indeed, for vanishing right-hand side the relaxation is exponential, $\pi_{\mu\nu} \propto \exp(-t/\tau_\pi)$, with a characteristic relaxation time scale τ_π. We would like to stress that the exponential relaxation over a time scale τ_π is a direct consequence of the substitution $2\sigma^{\rho\sigma} \to \eta^{-1}\pi^{\rho\sigma}$ made above; it is not a manifestation of a specific relaxation process on the microscopic level. However, a direct way to obtain such a relaxation term is via the method of moments applied to the Boltzmann equation [3]. In this case, the time scale τ_π is an intrinsic property of the collision kernel in the Boltzmann equation.

5. Summary

This work concisely presents the derivation of second-order relativistic dissipative fluid dynamics within Zubarev's NESO formalism – a method which is well-suited for treatments of strongly correlated systems. The simple case of a one-component fluid without electromagnetic fields or vorticity in flat space-time was considered here.

Our analysis shows that the second-order dissipative terms arise from: (i) the quadratic terms in the Taylor expansion of the statistical operator; and (ii) the linear terms of the same expansion which include memory and non-locality in space. In particular, we find that the type-(ii) terms describe the relaxation in time of the dissipative fluxes, which is essential for the causality of the fluid-dynamical theory.

Using the NESO method and the example of the shear-stress tensor, we demonstrated that the second-order transport coefficients can be expressed in terms of certain two- and three-point equilibrium correlation functions. A discussion of the transport coefficients associated with other thermodynamic fluxes can be found elsewhere [14]. Furthermore, we have shown that Kubo-type formulae for the relaxation times of the dissipative fluxes can be obtained within the NESO formalism (see Equation (38)). These are given by the zero-frequency limit of the derivatives of the corresponding first-order transport coefficients with respect to the frequency. These can be computed from the theory of quantum fields in equilibrium at non-zero temperature as, for example, was done by us for the QGP within the Nambu–Jona–Lasinio model [29,30].

Author Contributions: Conceptualization, A.H., A.S., D.H.R.; Methodology, A.H., A.S., D.H.R.; Investigation, A.H., A.S., D.H.R.; Writing—Original Draft Preparation, A.H., A.S., D.H.R.; Writing—Review & Editing, A.H., A.S., D.H.R.; Funding Acquisition, A.S., D.H.R.

Funding: This research was funded by HGS-HIRe graduate program at Goethe University, Deutsche Forschungsgemeinschaft (Germany) through grants SE 1836/4-1 and CRC-TR 211, the State Administration of Foreign Experts Affairs (China) through Expert project GDW20167100136.

Acknowledgments: We are grateful to Ulrich Heinz and Xu-Guang Huang for discussions. A.H. acknowledges support from the HGS-HIRe graduate program at Goethe University. A.S. was supported by the Deutsche Forschungsgemeinschaft (Grant No. SE 1836/4-1). D.H.R. acknowledges support by the High-End Visiting Expert project GDW20167100136 of the State Administration of Foreign Experts Affairs (SAFEA) of China and by the Deutsche Forschungsgemeinschaft (DFG) through the grant CRC-TR 211 "Strong-interaction matter under extreme conditions".

Conflicts of Interest: The authors declare no conflict of interest.

References

1. Landau, L.; Lifshitz, E. *Fluid Mechanics*; Butterworth-Heinemann: Oxford, UK, 1987.
2. Denicol, G.S. Kinetic foundations of relativistic dissipative fluid dynamics. *J. Phys. G Nucl. Phys.* **2014**, *41*, 124004.
3. Denicol, G.S.; Niemi, H.; Molnar, E.; Rischke, D.H. Derivation of transient relativistic fluid dynamics from the Boltzmann equation. *Phys. Rev. D* **2012**, *85*, 039902.
4. Florkowski, W.; Heller, M.P.; Spalinski, M. New theories of relativistic hydrodynamics in the LHC era. *Rep. Prog. Phys.* **2018**, *81*, 046001.
5. Romatschke, P. New Developments in Relativistic Viscous Hydrodynamics. *Int. J. Mod. Phys. E* **2010**, *19*, 1–53.
6. Zubarev, D. *Nonequilibrium Statistical Thermodynamics*; Studies in Soviet Science; Consultants Bureau: London, UK, 1974.
7. Zubarev, D.; Morozov, V.; Röpke, G. *Statistical Mechanics of Nonequilibrium Processes*; John Wiley & Sons: Hoboken, NJ, USA, 1997.
8. Hosoya, A.; Sakagami, M.A.; Takao, M. Nonequilibrium thermodynamics in field theory: Transport coefficients. *Ann. Phys.* **1984**, *154*, 229–252.
9. Huang, X.G.; Sedrakian, A.; Rischke, D.H. Kubo formulas for relativistic fluids in strong magnetic fields. *Ann. Phys.* **2011**, *326*, 3075–3094.
10. Hayata, T.; Hidaka, Y.; Noumi, T.; Hongo, M. Relativistic hydrodynamics from quantum field theory on the basis of the generalized Gibbs ensemble method. *Phys. Rev. D* **2015**, *92*, 065008.
11. Becattini, F.; Bucciantini, L.; Grossi, E.; Tinti, L. Local thermodynamical equilibrium and the frame for a quantum relativistic fluid. *Eur. Phys. J. C* **2015**, *75*, 191.
12. Hongo, M. Path-integral formula for local thermal equilibrium. *Ann. Phys.* **2017**, *383*, 1–32.
13. Harutyunyan, A.; Sedrakian, A.; Rischke, D.H. Second-order relativistic hydrodynamics from a non-equilibrium statistical operator. **2018**, in preparation.
14. Harutyunyan, A. Relativistic Hydrodynamics and Transport in Strongly Correlated Systems. Ph.D. Thesis, Goethe University, Frankfurt am Main, Germany, 2017.
15. Eckart, C. The Thermodynamics of Irreversible Processes. III. Relativistic theory of the simple fluid. *Phys. Rev.* **1940**, *58*, 919–924.
16. Israel, W. Nonstationary irreversible thermodynamics: A causal relativistic theory. *Ann. Phys.* **1976**, *100*, 310–331.
17. Israel, W.; Stewart, J.M. Transient relativistic thermodynamics and kinetic theory. *Ann. Phys.* **1979**, *118*, 341–372.
18. Baier, R.; Romatschke, P.; Thanh Son, D.; Starinets, A.O.; Stephanov, M.A. Relativistic viscous hydrodynamics, conformal invariance, and holography. *J. High Energy Phys.* **2008**, *4*, 100.

19. Moore, G.D.; Sohrabi, K.A. Thermodynamical second-order hydrodynamic coefficients. *J. High Energy Phys.* **2012**, *11*, 148.
20. Zubarev, D.N.; Prozorkevich, A.V.; Smolyanskii, S.A. Derivation of nonlinear generalized equations of quantum relativistic hydrodynamics. *Theor. Math. Phys.* **1979**, *40*, 821–831.
21. De Groot, S.; Mazur, P. *Non-Equilibrium Thermodynamics;* Interscience Publishers: Amsterdam, The Netherlands, 1969.
22. Romatschke, P. Relativistic viscous fluid dynamics and non-equilibrium entropy. *Class. Quantum Gravity* **2010**, *27*, 025006.
23. Moore, G.D.; Sohrabi, K.A. Kubo Formulas for Second-Order Hydrodynamic Coefficients. *Phys. Rev. Lett.* **2011**, *106*, 122302.
24. Czajka, A.; Jeon, S. Kubo formulas for the shear and bulk viscosity relaxation times and the scalar field theory shear τ_π calculation. *Phys. Rev. D* **2017**, *95*, 064906.
25. Lublinsky, M.; Shuryak, E. Improved Hydrodynamics from the AdS/CFT. *Phys. Rev. D* **2009**, *80*, 065026.
26. Buzzegoli, M.; Grossi, E.; Becattini, F. General equilibrium second-order hydrodynamic coefficients for free quantum fields. *J. High Energy Phys.* **2017**, *10*, 091.
27. Jaiswal, A. Relativistic dissipative hydrodynamics from kinetic theory with relaxation-time approximation. *Phys. Rev. D* **2013**, *87*, 051901.
28. Finazzo, S.I.; Rougemont, R.; Marrochio, H.; Noronha, J. Hydrodynamic transport coefficients for the non-conformal quark-gluon plasma from holography. *J. High Energy Phys.* **2015**, *2*, 51.
29. Harutyunyan, A.; Rischke, D.H.; Sedrakian, A. Transport coefficients of two-flavor quark matter from the Kubo formalism. *Phys. Rev. D* **2017**, *95*, 114021.
30. Harutyunyan, A.; Sedrakian, A. Bulk viscosity of two-flavor quark matter from the Kubo formalism. *Phys. Rev. D* **2017**, *96*, 034006.

particles

MDPI

Article

Application of the Non-Equilibrium Statistical Operator Method to the Dynamical Conductivity of Metallic and Classical Plasmas

Mikhail Veysman [1,*], Gerd Röpke [2,3] and Heidi Reinholz [2,4]

1 Joint Institute for High Temperatures (JIHT) RAS, Izhorskaya 13/19, 125412 Moscow, Russia
2 Institut für Physik, Universität Rostock, 18051 Rostock, Germany; gerd.roepke@uni-rostock.de (G.R.); heidi.reinholz@uni-rostock.de (H.R.)
3 National Research Nuclear University (MEPhI), 115409 Moscow, Russia
4 School of Physics, The University of Western Australia, Crawley, WA 6009, Australia
* Correspondence: bme@ihed.ras.ru; Tel.: +7-917-141-54-18

Received: 22 March 2019; Accepted: 23 April 2019; Published: 7 May 2019

Abstract: The fruitfulness of the method of a non-equilibrium statistical operator (NSO) and generalized linear response theory is demonstrated calculating the permittivity, dynamical conductivity, absorption coefficient, and dynamical collision frequency of plasmas in the degenerate, metallic state as well as classical plasmas. A wide range of plasma parameters is considered, and a wide range of frequencies of laser radiation acting on such plasmas is treated. New analytical expressions for the plasma response are obtained by this method, and several limiting cases are discussed.

Keywords: non-equilibrium statistical operator; linear response theory; permittivity, dynamical conductivity, absorption coefficient, dynamical collision frequency; ordered lattice, disordered lattice; Umklapp process; interband transitions

1. Introduction

The non-equilibrium quantum statistical operator (NSO) was proposed by D.N. Zubarev [1], and its 100-year anniversary was celebrated recently. The NSO method is an important step in working out a unified, general approach to nonequilibrium phenomena such as transport and relaxation processes. Different approaches to describe nonequilibrium processes, such as kinetic theory, linear response theory, and quantum master equations, are obtained within a very general approach, after specifying the relevant degrees of freedom that characterize the non-equilibrium state of the system. Recent reviews of the NSO method and its applications can be found, e.g., in [2–6].

The NSO method has been successfully applied to many problems related to the transport and optical properties of charged particle systems, such as warm dense matter (WDM). Reviews of the calculations of dynamical response of dense plasmas are found, e.g., in [7,8]. A main advantage of the approach is that special approaches, valid in limiting cases, can be generalized to describe more complex situations. For instance, kinetic theory has been worked out for low-density systems where the single-particle distribution function is relevant to describing the non-equilibrium state of the system, and correlations can be neglected. In contrast, linear response theory has been worked out to describe systems at arbitrary densities, but near thermodynamical equilibrium. A unified theory that covers both limiting cases has been worked out using the NSO method, see [9]. In particular, the correct frequency dependence of the response functions has been found, in contrast to conventional kinetic theory. A further advantage of the approach is that non-equilibrium properties of quantum as well as classical plasmas can be considered consistently on the same footing. Altogether, the NSO method allows one to study the transport and optical properties of plasmas at arbitrary densities and temperatures, including the region of WDM where correlations are strong, in particular between ions, and where the electrons become degenerate. The response to classical Maxwell fields, represented by a time-dependent external field in the Hamiltonian, can be investigated in a wide range of frequencies of the external field. This refers also to the response of WDM that is irradiated by laser fields, in particular the frequency-dependent absorption coefficient. To include a spontaneous emission of photons, a quantum description of the Maxwell fields is necessary.

In this paper, we present briefly the NSO method and its application to the permittivity of metallic plasmas, which is described by a Hamiltonian accounting for electron–phonon interactions and Umklapp processes, as well as the application to the permittivity of plasmas without a long-range order of ions, which is described by a Hamiltonian accounting for electron–ion and electron–electron interactions. We continue our previous investigations to work out a systematic quantum statistical approach to the response properties of WDM [10–14] with an application to aluminum, considering additional processes of interaction in the strongly coupled Coulomb system. We derive analytical expressions for the dynamical collision frequency and related quantities, in particular the absorption coefficient. The behavior of these response properties, such as temperature dependence and frequency dependence, is discussed in special limiting cases.

These results are of interest for the investigation of material at extremal conditions, e.g., high-particle and high-energy densities. If a solid metallic target is irradiated by powerful laser pulses, the electron component of such a target undergoes modifications of its properties, changing from the state of a metallic "plasma" to a state of a classical non-degenerate plasma. This transition of the electron system from a degenerate state to a classical behavior is consistently described in our approach. In addition, the ion system may change from a solid state, where the ion positions are strongly correlated forming a lattice, to a liquid or a plasma state, where the long-range order of ion positions is destructed. In the present work, we neglect the short-range order of the ion system in the liquid or plasma state, so that the electron–ion interaction is considered as independent scattering at the individual ions. For the electron–ion interaction in the solid state of matter, the coherent part of multiple scattering by the ionic lattice leads to the formation of electron band (Bloch) states. The deviation of ions from the lattice position is described as phonon excitation, and the electron–phonon interaction together with Umklapp processes is considered in this work as responsible for the dynamical conductivity of the solid metal, in addition to electron–electron collisions. Such transitions from collective electron–phonon interactions in a solid to individual electron–ion interactions in the disordered ion configuration directly opens up the question about the switching between the respective Hamiltonians. A more general approach is possible using the concept of the dynamical structure factor which reflects not only the configuration of the ions but also the dynamical behavior, including collective excitations, of the ion system. This problem, however, requires a separate investigation and is not considered in the present work.

With respect to the application to aluminum plasmas, recent experiments in the WDM region [15,16] to measure the dynamical conductivity are also treated by density-functional theory (DFT) for electrons combined with molecular dynamics (MD) calculations for the ions [17]. These calculations have the advantage that optimal single-electron orbitals are calculated, and these orbitals reflect the electron structure of the aluminum ion, improving our effective electron–ion ($e-i$) interaction potential. In addition, the static ionic structure factor is calculated so that a short-range order in the liquid or plasma phase is implemented in the calculation of the dynamical conductivity. However, the choice of the density functional for the correlation energy remains an open problem of these DFT-MD calculations. A shortcoming of the DFT-MD approach is that electron–electron ($e-e$) collisions are not properly included in this mean-field theory, in contrast to our generalized linear response approach, where the contribution of $e-e$ collisions is taken into account, see also [18].

A systematic improvement of our approach is the use of optimal single-electron orbits and $e-i$ interaction potentials. In addition, the dynamical ion structure factor that causes not only multiple scattering of the electrons, but also the excitation of the ion system, in particular phonons, should be considered in a systematic approach. These improvements in our calculations that establish a closer connection to DFT-MD simulations are a subject of future work.

2. A Brief Description of the Method

The plasma permittivity $\varepsilon(\omega)$ of an electromagnetic field with the frequency ω is directly related to the dynamical conductivity $\sigma(\omega)$ according to $\varepsilon(\omega) = 1 + i\sigma(\omega)/(\varepsilon_0\omega)$ or, using Gauss units instead of SI units, as follows:

$$\varepsilon(\omega) = 1 + 4\pi i\sigma(\omega)/\omega. \tag{1}$$

Here and below we consider isotropic media in the case of weak spacial dispersion or the long-wavelength (with respect to plasma perturbations) limit. In this case, the permittivity does not depend on the wave vector of perturbations. The longitudinal permittivity coincides with the transverse one: $\varepsilon_{\parallel} = \varepsilon_{\perp} = \varepsilon$ [19].

For the calculation of $\sigma(\omega)$, one should determine the (quantum) statistically averaged electric current, arising as the system's response to external electromagnetic fields. Such calculation can be done using the NSO $\hat{\rho} = \hat{\rho}_{\rm rel} + \hat{\rho}_{\rm irrel}$, which can be constructed as a sum of the so-called *relevant statistical operator* $\hat{\rho}_{\rm rel}$ describing the quasi-equilibrium and the *irrelevant statistical operator* $\hat{\rho}_{\rm irrel}$, which represents the nonequilibrium contribution.

The *relevant statistical operator* is introduced as a generalized Gibbs ensemble, derived from the principle of the maximum of entropy:

$$\begin{aligned} \hat{\rho}_{\rm rel}(t) &= Z_{\rm rel}(t)^{-1} \exp\left[-\beta(\hat{H} - \mu\hat{N}) + \textstyle\sum_n F_n(t)\hat{B}_n\right] \\ Z_{\rm rel}(t) &= \mathrm{Tr}\left[-\beta(\hat{H} - \mu\hat{N}) + \textstyle\sum_n F_n(t)\hat{B}_n\right] \end{aligned} \tag{2}$$

where $\hat{H}$ is the Hamiltonian of the system. $\hat{N} = \sum_p \hat{a}_p^\dagger \hat{a}_p$ is the particle number operator, where $\hat{a}_p^\dagger$ and $\hat{a}_p$ are the creation and annihilation operators of the electrons in state p. For the chosen set of relevant observables $\{\boldsymbol{B}_n\}, n = 1\ldots\mathcal{N}$, we request

$$\mathrm{Tr}\left\{\hat{B}_n\rho(t)\right\} = \langle\hat{B}_n\rangle^t = \mathrm{Tr}\left\{\hat{B}_n\hat{\rho}_{\rm rel}(t)\right\}, \tag{3}$$

meaning that the observed statistical averages $\langle\ldots\rangle^t$ at time t are correctly reproduced by the averages with the relevant statistical operator $\hat{\rho}_{\rm rel}(t)$. The Lagrange parameters $F_n(t)$ are then determined by the set of requested expressions (3) as response parameters. Similar conditions on $\langle\hat{N}\rangle$ and $\langle\hat{H}\rangle$ determine μ as chemical potential and $\beta = 1/T_e$, respectively, where T_e is the electron temperature. (We give the temperature in energy units, $k_{\rm B} = 1$, instead of SI units where $\beta = 1/k_{\rm B}T_e$.)

If $\mathcal{N} = 0$ (i.e., an empty set of relevant observables), the operator $\hat{\rho}_{\rm rel}$ (2) is identical with the statistical operator for the grand canonical ensemble [3]. In that case, the well-known Kubo formula [20] for the electrical conductivity follows immediately [4,5].

The choice of relevant observables can be arbitrary. Different choices lead to the same results if non-perturbative approaches such as infinite diagram summations or numerical calculations of correlation functions are used [5,8,21]. However, the account of only a finite number of terms within a perturbation expansion can lead to even divergent results. Therefore, it is necessary to choose the set of relevant observables in a way that the relevant statistical operator [5] already ensures a close approximation of the considered system.

According to [9] (see also [4,8,21]), the NSO $\hat{\rho}(t)$ is determined by the dynamical evolution of the system with Hamiltonian $\hat{H}_{\rm tot} = \hat{H} + \hat{H}_{\rm ext}(t)$:

$$\hat{\rho}(t) = \lim_{\eta \to +0} \eta \int_{-\infty}^{t} dt' e^{-\eta(t-t')} \hat{U}(t,t') \hat{\rho}_{\rm rel}(t') \hat{U}^{\dagger}(t,t') \tag{4}$$

where $\hat{U}(t,t')$ is the time evolution operator, which solves the equation

$$i\hbar \partial_t \hat{U}(t,t') = \hat{H}_{\rm tot} \hat{U}(t,t'), \quad \hat{U}(t',t') = 1 \tag{5}$$

with $\hat{H}_{\rm ext}(t)$ being the Hamiltonian of the external perturbation. Due to Equation (4), correlations from the initial state are further built up, which is determined by the relevant statistical operator $\hat{\rho}_{\rm rel}(t)$ (2).

For a high frequency electromagnetic field with an electric field strength $E(t)$ acting on matter, the external perturbation $\hat{H}_{\rm ext}(t)$ can be written in dipole approximation as

$$\hat{H}_{\rm ext}(t) = -e\hat{\boldsymbol{R}} \cdot \boldsymbol{E}(t), \ \hat{\boldsymbol{R}} = \sum\nolimits_a \hat{\boldsymbol{r}}_a, \ \dot{\hat{\boldsymbol{R}}} = \hat{\boldsymbol{P}}_{1\Sigma}/m \tag{6}$$

where m is the electron mass, and e is the electron charge. $\hat{\boldsymbol{P}}_{1\Sigma} = \sum_\nu \hat{\boldsymbol{P}}_{1,\nu}$ is the operator of the total momentum of electrons, which is the sum of momentums of electrons from different energy zones ν. It coincides with the first moment of the density matrix, see Equation (11) below.

In *linear response theory*, which we assume to be applicable, an expansion of the relevant $\hat{\rho}_{\rm rel}(t)$, Equation (2), and the irrelevant $\hat{\rho}_{\rm irrel}(t) = \hat{\rho}(t) - \hat{\rho}_{\rm rel}(t)$ statistical operators with respect to the external perturbation and the response parameters $F_n(t)$ are considered, see [5,9]. Together with Equation (3) and using the Kubo identity, this gives rise to the following system of equations:

$$\langle \delta \hat{B}_n \rangle = \sum\nolimits_m (\hat{B}_n; \delta \hat{B}_m) F_m \tag{7}$$

$$\sum_m \left[-i\omega \left\{ (\hat{B}_n; \hat{B}_m) + \langle \dot{\hat{B}}_m; \delta \hat{B}_m \rangle_z \right\} + (\hat{B}_n; \dot{\hat{B}}_m) + \langle \dot{\hat{B}}_n; \dot{\hat{B}}_m \rangle_z \right] F_m = \beta \frac{e}{m} \left\{ (\hat{B}_n; \hat{\boldsymbol{P}}_{1\Sigma}) + \langle \dot{\hat{B}}_m; \hat{\boldsymbol{P}}_{1\Sigma} \rangle_z \right\} \boldsymbol{E} \tag{8}$$

where $z = \omega + i\eta$; $\delta \hat{B}_n = \hat{B}_n - \langle \hat{B}_n \rangle_0$, and $\langle \hat{B}_n \rangle_0$ is the statistical average of $\hat{B}_n$ with the *equilibrium statistical operator* of the grand canonical ensemble $\hat{\rho}_0 = Z_0^{-1} \exp[-(\hat{H} - \mu \hat{N})/T_e]$ with $Z_0 = {\rm Tr}\{e^{-(\hat{H}-\mu\hat{N})/T_e}\}$.

In Equations (7) and (8), expressions such as $(\hat{A}; \hat{B})$ and $\langle \hat{A}; \hat{B} \rangle_z$ denote Kubo scalar products of operators $\hat{A}$ and $\hat{B}$ and the Laplace transform of the Kubo scalar product of these operators, respectively. The latter are called *equilibrium correlation functions*. They are defined by expressions

$$(\hat{A}; \hat{B}) = \int_0^\beta d\tau \, {\rm Tr} \left\{ \hat{A}(-i\hbar\tau) \hat{B}^+ \hat{\rho}_0 \right\} \tag{9}$$

$$\langle \hat{A}; \hat{B} \rangle_z = \int_0^\infty dt e^{izt} \left(\hat{A}(t); \hat{B} \right) \tag{10}$$

where the operator $\hat{A}$ is taken in Heisenberg representation $\hat{A}(t) = e^{i\hat{H}t/\hbar} \hat{A} e^{-i\hat{H}t}$.

For further treatment of Equations (7) and (8), it is necessary to define the set of relevant observables B_n. For the description of the permittivity of plasmas, it is convenient to choose the moments of the density matrix as the set of relevant observables:

$$\hat{\boldsymbol{B}}_{\mathfrak{n}} = \hat{\boldsymbol{P}}_{\mathfrak{n}} = \sum_{p_\nu} \hbar p_\nu \hat{n}_{p,\nu} (E_{p,\nu}/T_e)^{(L-1)/2}, \quad \mathfrak{n} \equiv \{L, \nu\} \tag{11}$$

where $\hat{n}_{p,\nu} = \hat{a}^+_{\boldsymbol{p},\nu} \hat{a}_{\boldsymbol{p},\nu}$, $\boldsymbol{p}_\nu = m\, \partial E_{p,\nu}/\partial p$, and

$$E_{p,\nu} = \boldsymbol{p}^2/(2m\, m_\nu) + E_{0,\nu} \tag{12}$$

where m_ν and $E_{0,\nu}$ are the effective electron mass (normalized to electron mass m) and the energy of the bottom of the ν-th zone, respectively. Here, for generality, we consider moments of the density matrix stipulated by different powers of electrons momentum $\boldsymbol{p}$ (labeled by the index "L") and by different energy zones (labeled by the index "ν"). The index "$\mathfrak{n}$" of observables comprises both L and ν; $\hat{a}^+_{\boldsymbol{p},\nu}$ and $\hat{a}_{\boldsymbol{p},\nu}$ are creation and annihilation operators for single-electron states with momentum $\boldsymbol{p}$ in the ν-th band.

The equilibrium correlation functions occurring in Equations (7) and (8) will be evaluated below. Here we only mention that $(\hat{B}_n; \hat{B}_m) = 0$ because the commutator $[\hat{B}_n, \hat{B}_m]$ vanishes. In the lowest order of interaction, which is proportional to e^2, one can show [22] that the terms in (8) containing only one operator $\dot{\hat{B}}_n$ can be omitted in comparison to the leading order. In an isotropic system, we take the electrical field as well as the current density in the z direction so that only the absolute value is of relevance. Equations (7) and (8) are rewritten as the following system of equations for the dimensionless response parameters $\mathcal{F}_{\mathfrak{m}}$ in terms of the dimensionless correlation functions $\mathfrak{N}_{\mathfrak{nm}}$ and $\mathfrak{C}_{\mathfrak{nm}}$:

$$\langle \hat{P}_{\mathfrak{n}} \rangle = \frac{enE}{\omega_{\mathrm{a.u.}}} \sum_{\mathfrak{m}} \mathfrak{N}_{\mathfrak{nm}} \mathcal{F}_{\mathfrak{m}} \tag{13}$$

$$\sum_{\mathfrak{m}} \left[\mathfrak{C}_{\mathfrak{nm}} - i\tilde{\omega} \mathfrak{N}_{\mathfrak{nm}} \right] \mathcal{F}_{\mathfrak{m}} = \sum_{\mu} \mathfrak{N}_{\mathfrak{n}\{1\mu\}} \tag{14}$$

where $\mathfrak{N}_{\mathfrak{n}\{1\mu\}}$ has the second index with $L = 1$ and band index μ,

$$\mathfrak{N}_{\mathfrak{nm}} = \frac{(\hat{\boldsymbol{P}}_{\mathfrak{n}}; \hat{\boldsymbol{P}}_{\mathfrak{m}})}{mnT_e}, \quad \mathfrak{C}_{\mathfrak{nm}}(\omega) = \frac{\langle \dot{\hat{\boldsymbol{P}}}_{\mathfrak{n}}; \dot{\hat{\boldsymbol{P}}}_{\mathfrak{m}} \rangle_{\omega + i\eta}}{mnT_e \omega_{\mathrm{a.u.}}},$$
$$F_{\mathfrak{m}} = \mathcal{F}_{\mathfrak{m}} \frac{e\,E}{mT_e}. \tag{15}$$

n is the particle number density of electrons in the conduction band (free electron density). $\omega_{\mathrm{a.u.}}$ is the atomic unit of the frequency, so that $\hbar\omega_{\mathrm{a.u.}} = E_H = me^4/\hbar^2 \approx 27.2$ eV is the Hartree energy unit, and $\tilde{\omega} = \omega/\omega_{\mathrm{a.u.}}$ is the dimensionless frequency. The indexes $\mathfrak{m}, \mathfrak{n} = \{L, \nu\}$ contain L, the power of the momentum, and ν, the number of the energy band.

The electrical current $\langle \hat{J} \rangle = \sigma E$ can be calculated using the relation $\hat{J} = e\hat{P}_{1\Sigma}/m$. Inserting expression (13), we derive the permittivity (1) as a Drude-like formula

$$\lim_{k \to 0} \varepsilon(\boldsymbol{k}, \omega) = \varepsilon(\omega) = 1 - \frac{\omega_{\mathrm{pl}}^2}{\omega\,[\omega + i\nu(\omega)]}, \tag{16}$$

with $\omega_{\rm pl}^2 = 4\pi ne^2/m$ and an *effective collision frequency* $\nu(\omega)$, which can be expressed in terms of dimensionless response parameters and correlation functions $\mathfrak{N}_{\rm nm}$ and $\mathfrak{C}_{\rm nm}$, as defined in (15), according to

$$\nu(\omega) = \nu_1(\omega) r_\omega(\omega) \tag{17}$$

$$\nu_1(\omega) = \omega_{\rm a.u.} \frac{\mathfrak{C}_{11}}{\mathfrak{N}_{11}}, \; r_\omega(\omega) = \frac{\mathfrak{N}_{11}}{\mathfrak{C}_{11}} \frac{1 + i\omega^* \sum\limits_{\rm m,\nu} \mathfrak{N}_{\{1,\nu\}\rm m} \mathcal{F}_{\rm m}}{\sum\limits_{\rm m,\nu} \mathfrak{N}_{\{1,\nu\}\rm m} \mathcal{F}_{\rm m}} \tag{18}$$

where the index "1" means $\mathfrak{n} = 1 = \{1,1\}$, i.e., $L = 1$ in Equation (11), and $\nu = 1$ is the conduction band. $\nu_1(\omega)$ is the complex *effective collision frequency* of electrons for Drude-like transitions (within the conduction band) and in single-moment approximation, while r_ω (18) is the so-called *renormalization factor*, which takes into account the influence of higher moments of the density operator [8,12,22] and, in the case considered here, the influence of transitions between different bands. Inserting the solution of the system of Equations (14) for $\mathcal{F}_{\rm m}$ into Expressions (18), we obtain the complex *effective collision frequency* in terms of the correlation functions $\mathfrak{N}_{\rm nm}$ and $\mathfrak{C}_{\rm nm}$.

In our further considerations we look at the two following cases:

(a) $L = 1, \nu = 1, 2 \ldots$, i.e., the case of different energy bands, but only the 1st moment of the density operator. Then $\mathfrak{n} = \{L, \nu\} = \{1, \nu\} = \nu$. Inserting the definition of moments (13) for $P_{\{1,\nu\}}$ into Expression (15) for $\mathfrak{N}_{\nu\mu}$, using the Kubo identity and expressing the electron momentum $\boldsymbol{p}$ via $\dot{\boldsymbol{r}}$, one can show [3] that

$$\mathfrak{N}_{\nu\mu} = \delta_{\nu,\mu} n_\nu / n \tag{19}$$

where n_ν is the number of electrons in the ν-th band.

(b) $L = 1, 2 \ldots, \nu = 1$, i.e., the case of a single conduction band and different moments of the density operator. Then $\mathfrak{n} = \{L, \nu\} = \{L, 1\} = L$.

Expressions for the correlation functions $\mathfrak{N}_{lm}$, $l, m \geq 1$ can be found elsewhere (see, e.g., [3,18]):

$$\mathfrak{N}_{lm} = \frac{\Gamma[(l+m+3)/2]}{\Gamma(5/2)} \frac{I_{(l+m-1)/2}(\epsilon_\mu)}{I_{1/2}(\epsilon_\mu)}, \; l, m \geq 1 \tag{20}$$

where $\epsilon_\mu = \mu/T_e$ is dimensionless chemical potential,

$$\epsilon_\mu = X_{1/2}\left(2\epsilon_{\rm F}^{3/2}/3\right), \tag{21}$$

with the Fermi integrals $I_\nu(y) = \Gamma(\nu+1) \int_0^\infty x^\nu [e^{x-y}+1]^{-1} dx$; $\epsilon_{\rm F} = E_F/T_e = \Theta^{-1}$, where Θ is the degeneracy parameter, and $E_{\rm F} = \hbar^2/(2m)(3\pi^2 n)^{2/3}$ is the Fermi energy; the dimensionless chemical potential ϵ_μ in (21) is expressed via the inverse Fermi integral $X_{1/2}(x)$, which refers to the Fermi integral $I_{1/2}(x)$. Particularly, from (20) one has

$$\mathfrak{N}_{11} = 1, \quad \mathfrak{N}_{31} = \frac{5}{2} \frac{I_{3/2}(\epsilon_\mu)}{I_{1/2}(\epsilon_\mu)}, \quad \mathfrak{N}_{33} = \frac{35}{4} \frac{I_{5/2}(\epsilon_\mu)}{I_{1/2}(\epsilon_\mu)}. \tag{22}$$

In the non-degenerate case, $I_\nu(\epsilon_\mu) = e^{\epsilon_\mu}$ for all ν and $\mathfrak{N}_{31} = 5/2$, $\mathfrak{N}_{33} = 35/4$, see [9].

In previous works [9,22], correlation functions with only the first and third moments of the density matrix (11) in the sum (18) were considered. It was shown that this leads to an accuracy of a few % for the calculation of the renormalization factor. Therefore, restricting our approximation to only two bands or two moments of the density matrix in Cases (a) and (b), respectively, and using the solution of Equation (14), the *renormalization factor* can be written in terms of respective correlation functions:

$$
\begin{aligned}
r(\omega) &= \frac{1}{\mathfrak{C}_{11}} \frac{1+i\tilde{\omega}Q_\omega}{Q_\omega} \\
Q_\omega &= \frac{\mathfrak{A}_{22}-2\mathfrak{N}_{22}\mathfrak{A}_{21}+\mathfrak{N}_{22}^2\mathfrak{A}_{11}}{\mathfrak{A}_{11}\mathfrak{A}_{22}-\mathfrak{A}_{21}^2} \quad \text{for Case (a)} \\
Q_\omega &= \frac{\mathfrak{A}_{33}-2\mathfrak{N}_{31}\mathfrak{A}_{31}+\mathfrak{N}_{31}^2\mathfrak{A}_{11}}{\mathfrak{A}_{11}\mathfrak{A}_{33}-\mathfrak{A}_{31}^2} \quad \text{for Case (b)} \\
\mathfrak{A}_{lm} &= \mathfrak{C}_{lm} - i\tilde{\omega}\mathfrak{N}_{lm},\ l,m \geq 1.
\end{aligned}
\tag{23}
$$

Here, Expressions (19) and (22), respectively, have been used.

According to the definitions (10), (11) and (15), the correlation functions $\mathfrak{C}_{nm}(\omega)$ can be expressed in terms of correlation functions of electron creation and annihilation operators as

$$
\mathfrak{C}_{\mathfrak{n}\mathfrak{m}}(\omega) = \frac{-\beta}{mn\omega_{\text{a.u.}}} \sum\nolimits_{p_\nu,p_\mu} p_{\nu,z} p_{\mu,z} \times (E_{p,\nu}/T_e)^{\frac{L-1}{2}} (E_{p,\mu}/T_e)^{\frac{M-1}{2}} \langle [\hat{H},\hat{n}_{p,\nu}];[\hat{H},\hat{n}_{p,\mu}]\rangle_{\omega+i\eta} \tag{24}
$$

where $\mathfrak{n} = \{L,\nu\}$, and $\mathfrak{m} = \{M,\mu\}$. The further calculation of the correlation functions $\mathfrak{C}_{\mathfrak{n}\mathfrak{m}}$ requires the specific Hamiltonian $\hat{H}$.

In the general case, the four-particle correlation function of creation and annihilation operators, arising after respective elementary transformations of the correlation function $\langle [\hat{H},\hat{n}_{p,\nu}];[\hat{H},\hat{n}_{p,\mu}]\rangle_{\omega+i\eta}$ with known Hamiltonian $\hat{H}$, can be expressed via thermodynamic Green functions [3,8]. Green function techniques allow one, in principle, to take into account all orders of interactions via the summation of respective Feynman diagrams [3,8,22]. Below we consider the first Born approximation, which follows at the lowest order with respect to the interaction either directly from the definition of the correlation functions in (24), or from the four-particle Green functions expressed as a product of single-particle Green functions, which are related to the correlation functions. As a result, we obtain concise and simple analytic results. It shall be noted that it can be reasonable to calculate the renormalization factor (18) in the Born or screened Born (see below) approximation and take into account strong-coupling effects only in the calculation of the collision frequency $\nu_1(\omega)$ (17), (18), see [18].

Below we look at two different cases:

(A) We consider individual interactions of electrons with each other and with randomly distributed ions. This is the case for ion temperatures higher than the melting one, where the long-range order of the ion lattice is destructed. The short-range order is described by the ionic structure factor. As an example, we can consider a metallic solid sample irradiated by intense short-pulse laser beams. The ion lattice disappears after a heating process longer than the characteristic melting time τ_m, which is of the order of the time between ion collisions. This time is given by the interatomic distance $r_a \sim (4\pi n_{at}/3)^{-1/3}$ divided by the sound velocity $v_s \sim \sqrt{ZT_e/m_{at}}$, where n_{at}, m_{at} are the concentration and the mass of the heavy particles, respectively, so that

$$
\begin{aligned}
\tau_m &= \frac{r_a}{v_s} = k_m A_{at}^{5/6} \sqrt{\frac{T_1}{ZT_e}} \varrho^{-1/3} \\
k_m &\approx 7.5\ \text{fs}, \quad T_1 = 1\ \text{eV}.
\end{aligned}
\tag{25}
$$

Here, A_{at} is the atomic number, and ϱ is the mass density of matter in g/cm^3. For example, for aluminum, $\tau_m \approx 11$ fs with $Z = 3$, $\varrho = 2.71$ g/cm^3 and $T_e = 20$ eV. We will not discuss the phenomenon of melting here, but we consider it as an example of a disordered configuration of ions.

(B) In the solid state, the interaction of the electrons with a perfect ionic lattice is already taken into account, introducing the band structure with the dispersion relation $E_{p,\nu}$, Equation (12). Only deviations from the perfect lattice lead to scattering of the electron quasiparticles. We consider here the collective interactions of electrons with ion lattice vibrations (electron–phonon interaction). In addition, we have electron–electron collisions that will not contribute to the conductivity because of the conservation of the total momentum at the Coulomb interaction. However, Umklapp processes are possible, and they lead to a transfer of momentum from the electron system to the ion lattice.

2.1. The Case of Individual Electron–Electron and Electron–Ion Interactions

For this case, the Hamiltonian accounting for only the electronic degrees of freedom can be written as

$$\hat{H} = \sum_p E_p \hat{a}_p^\dagger \hat{a}_p + \sum_{pk} V_{\rm ei}(k) \hat{a}_{p+k}^\dagger \hat{a}_p + \frac{1}{2} \sum_{p_1 p_2 k} V_{\rm ee}(k) \hat{a}_{p_1+k}^\dagger \hat{a}_{p_2-k}^\dagger \hat{a}_{p_2} \hat{a}_{p_1}, \tag{26}$$

with $E_p = \hbar^2 p^2/(2m)$. Only a single conduction band is considered in this subsection. The interactions between ions and electrons $V_{\rm ei}(k) = V(k)$ are given by the Coulomb potential. $V(k) = -Zv(k)$ and $V_{\rm ee}(k) = v(k) = 4\pi e^2/k^2$ is the potential of the $e-e$ interaction. The ions can be treated in adiabatic approximation via the static ion structure factor $S_{\rm ii}$ [23], which reflects the ion configuration. The ion component will be described in terms of an average charge number Z with the particle density $n_{\rm i} = n/Z$ due to charge neutrality. The ion temperature is denoted as $T_{\rm i}$.

In a more general case, pseudo-potentials $V_{\rm ei}^{\rm ps}(k)$ should be considered to take into account the structure of complex ions, the screening of the Coulomb potential, and the influence of bound and free electrons on their interaction with free electrons [12,24]. In particular, the expression for $|V_{\rm ei}|^2$, which appears in Born approximation can be rewritten as

$$|V_{\rm ei}(\mathbf{k})|^2 = |V_{\rm ei}^{\rm ps}(k)|^2 S_{\rm ii}(\mathbf{k}). \tag{27}$$

One can use the following expression for the individual $e-i$ interaction $V_{\rm ei}^{\rm ps}(k)$ [12]:

$$V_{\rm ei}^{\rm ps}(k) = V(k)[1 + \varkappa_{\rm ei}^2/k^2]^{-1} \cos(k r_{\rm cut}), \tag{28}$$

where the prefactor $V(k)$ is the electron–ion Coulomb potential. The second term on the r.h.s. is owing to the account of statical screening by the free electrons (the contribution of ions to screening is already taken into account by the ion structure factor $S_{\rm ii}$). It can be derived [12,25] in the low-frequency limit from the more sophisticated Lennard–Balescu approximation by summing up ring diagrams [8,22], leading to a characteristic inverse screening radius. It is $\varkappa_{\rm ee} = (4\pi n e^2/T_e)^{1/2}$ in the classical limit. The third term is due to an empty-core model pseudo-potential [24,26], where $r_{\rm cut}$ is a free parameter that can be fitted to match experimental data on transport and optical properties.

Similarly, in calculations within Born approximation, it is reasonable to replace the electron–electron Coulomb potential by a screened Coulomb potential:

$$V_{\rm ee}(k) = v(k)[1 + \varkappa_{\rm ee}^2/k^2]^{-1} \tag{29}$$

where the electron–electron Coulomb potential $v(k)$ is statically screened with the screening parameter $\varkappa_{ee}$.

Substituting (26)–(29) into the correlation function $\langle[\hat{H},\hat{n}_{p,\nu}];[\hat{H},\hat{n}_{p,\mu}]\rangle_{\omega+i\eta}$, one gets from (24), the following expressions for the real and imaginary parts of the correlation functions $\mathfrak{C}^{eq}_{\rm nm}$ (where superscript "eq" denotes electron–electron ("q"="e") or electron–ion ("q"="i") contributions to the full correlation function $\mathfrak{C}_{nm}=\mathfrak{C}^{\rm ee}_{nm}+\mathfrak{C}^{\rm ei}_{nm}$), see [12]:

$$\mathfrak{C}'^{eq}_{nm}=\alpha_q/(3\pi w)\times\int_0^\infty f^{eq}(y)dyR^{eq}_{nm}\left(\frac{w}{y},y\right)\ln\left[\frac{1+e^{\epsilon_\mu-(w/y-y)^2}}{1+e^{\epsilon_\mu-(w/y+y)^2}}\right] \tag{30}$$

$$\mathfrak{C}''^{eq}_{nm}=\frac{\alpha_q}{3\pi^2 w}\int\limits_0^\infty f^{eq}(y)dy\left[\sum_{l=\pm1}\mathcal{I}^{eq,l}_{nm}(y)-2\mathcal{I}^{eq,0}_{nm}(y)\right] \tag{31}$$

where $\alpha_{\rm i}=Z$, $\alpha_{\rm e}=1/\sqrt{2}$, and $\mathfrak{C}'^{eq}_{nm}$ and $\mathfrak{C}''^{eq}_{nm}$ denote real and imaginary parts of correlation functions, respectively;

$$\begin{aligned}\mathcal{I}^{eq,l}_{nm}&=\int\limits_0^\infty\frac{d\xi}{\xi}\sum_{\sigma=\pm1}\sigma R^{eq}_{nm}\left(\xi+\sigma\frac{lw}{y},y\right)\\&\times\ln\left[1+e^{\epsilon_\mu-[\xi+\sigma(y+lw/y)]^2}\right],\end{aligned} \tag{32}$$

with $l=0,\pm1$. The factors R^{eq}_{nm} are the following polynomials for $n,m=1,3$, see [9]:

$$\begin{aligned}&R^{\rm ei}_{11}=1\\&R^{\rm ei}_{31}(x,y)=R^{\rm ei}_{13}(x,y)=1+y^2+3x^2\\&R^{\rm ei}_{33}(x,y)=2+2y^2+y^4+2x^2(5+3y^2)+9x^4\\&R^{\rm ee}_{11}=R^{\rm ee}_{31}=R^{\rm ee}_{13}=0\\&R^{\rm ee}_{33}(x,y)=1+19x^2/4.\end{aligned} \tag{33}$$

Similar expressions can be given for the higher order polynomials, see [7,23]. The following dimensionless units are used hereafter:

$$\begin{aligned}&\tilde{k}=k/k_{\lambda},\ y=\tilde{k}/(2\sqrt{2}),\ k_{\lambda}^{-1}=\lambda=\hbar/\sqrt{mT_e};\\&\tilde{r}=k_{\lambda}r;\ \ w=\hbar\omega/(4T_e)\end{aligned} \tag{34}$$

(r is any quantity having the dimension of a coordinate).

The functions $f^{\rm eq}(y)$ occurring in Equation (30) are

$$f^{\rm ei}(y)=f^{\rm ei}_{\rm scr}(y)\cos^2(2\sqrt{2}y\tilde{r}_{\rm cut})S_{ii}(y),\quad f^{\rm ee}(y)=f^{\rm ee}_{\rm scr}(y) \tag{35}$$

where $f^{\rm ei}_{\rm scr}(y)$ and $f^{\rm ee}_{\rm scr}(y)$ are screening functions,

$$f^{\rm ei}_{\rm scr}(y)=y^3/[y^2+\kappa^2_{\rm ei}/8]\quad f^{\rm ee}_{\rm scr}(y)=y^3/[y^2+\kappa^2_{\rm ee}/4]. \tag{36}$$

Here,

$$\begin{aligned}&\kappa^2_{\rm ei}=\min\left\{\tilde{k}^2_{\rm D},\tilde{k}^2_{\rm max}\right\}\quad\kappa_{\rm ee}=\tilde{k}_{\rm D}\\&\tilde{k}^2_{\rm max}=C_{\tilde{k}_{\rm max}}8\epsilon_{\rm F}/(18\pi Z)^{2/3},\quad\tilde{k}^2_{\rm D}=[\tilde{R}^2_D(1+2\epsilon_{\rm F}/3)]^{-1}\end{aligned} \tag{37}$$

where $\tilde{R}_D = R_D/\lambda$ is the dimensionless Debye radius, $R_D = V_{th}/\omega_{pl}$, $V_{th} = \sqrt{T_e/m}$, and $C_{\tilde{k}_{max}} \approx 1$ is constant. Expressions for the ion–ion structure factor can be found in [12,27,28].

The value of $\tilde{k}_D$ leads to a proper interpolation between the degenerate and non-degenerate limits of screening and ensures a good agreement between Lennard–Balescu calculations and screened Born calculations everywhere, except for some frequency regions in the vicinity of the plasma frequency ω_{pl} [12]. The parameter $\tilde{k}_{max}$ gives a respective restriction of screening for strongly coupled plasmas [12,29] at distances of the order of the interatomic distance

$$R_0 = (4\pi n_i/3)^{-1/3}. \tag{38}$$

In the vicinity $\omega \sim \omega_{pl}$, a more precise expression for the screening function f_{scr}^{ei} can be derived by comparing it with the Lennard–Balescu expression for the dynamical collision frequency $\nu_1(\omega)$, see [12]:

$$f_{scr}^{ei} = f_{dyn}(y,w) = \varepsilon^*_{RPA}(y,w)/[y\varepsilon'_{RPA}(y,0)|\varepsilon_{RPA}(y,w)|^2] \tag{39}$$

where ε_{RPA} is the RPA (random phase approximation) permittivity, ε^*_{RPA} is its complex conjugate, and ε'_{RPA} is its real part;

$$\varepsilon_{RPA}(y,w) = 1 + \frac{\sqrt{\tilde{\omega}_{au}}}{8\sqrt{2\pi}}\frac{1}{y^3}\left[-\sum_{l=\pm1}\mathcal{I}^l_{11}(y) + i\pi\ln\left(\frac{1+\exp[\epsilon_\mu-(w/y-y)^2]}{1+\exp[\epsilon_\mu-(w/y+y)^2]}\right)\right] \tag{40}$$

$$\mathcal{I}^l_{11} = \int_0^\infty \frac{d\xi}{\xi}\sum_{\sigma=\pm1}\sigma\ln\left[1+e^{\epsilon_\mu-[\xi+\sigma(y+lw/y)]^2}\right]. \tag{41}$$

$l = 0, \pm1$.

Taking in mind that in the considered case of dynamical screening the screening function $f_{scr}(y,w)$ (39) is a complex function (note that in the case of statical screening f_{scr}^{ei} is dependent only on y, rather than on y and w), one can rewrite the expressions for real and imaginary parts of the correlation functions stipulated by electron–ion interactions as

$$\begin{aligned}\mathfrak{C}'^{ei}_{nm} &= \mathfrak{C}'^{ei}_{nm}(f'_{dyn}) - \mathfrak{C}''^{ei}_{nm}(f''_{dyn})\\ \mathfrak{C}''^{ei}_{nm} &= \mathfrak{C}''^{ei}_{nm}(f'_{dyn}) + \mathfrak{C}'^{ei}_{nm}(f''_{dyn})\end{aligned} \tag{42}$$

where designations $\mathfrak{C}'^{ei}_{nm}(f'_{dyn})$ and $\mathfrak{C}''^{ei}_{nm}(f'_{dyn})$ (where superscripts "ei" designate $e-i$ interactions) mean that in the respective Expressions (30) and (31) for the real and imaginary part of the correlation function, respectively, the real part of the screening function (39) is substituted by f_{scr}^{ei} in (36), and similarly designations $\mathfrak{C}'^{ei}_{nm}(f''_{dyn})$ and $\mathfrak{C}''^{ei}_{nm}(f''_{dyn})$ indicate the substitution of the imaginary part of f_{dyn} (39) by f_{scr}^{ei} in (36).

With the same arguments as for static screening (36), one can suppose that f'_{dyn} should be replaced by

$$f_{scr,min} = y^3/[y^2 + \tilde{k}^2_{max}/8] \tag{43}$$

where $\tilde{k}_{max}$ is given by (37) if $f'_{dyn} < f_{scr,min}$.

It should be noted that the restriction of screening at distances $\approx R_0$ occur at $\Gamma_{\rm ei,g} > 1/3$, where

$$\Gamma_{\rm ei,g} = \frac{\Gamma_{\rm ei}}{\epsilon_{\rm F}\left[4(1+e^{-\epsilon_\mu(\epsilon_{\rm F})})/(3\sqrt{\pi})\right]^{2/3}} \tag{44}$$

is the generalized electron–ion coupling parameter for plasma at arbitrary degeneracy [12], and $\Gamma_{\rm ei} = Ze^2/(R_0 T_e)$ is the classical plasma coupling parameter. In the non-degenerate case ($\epsilon_{\rm F} \ll 1$), the relation (44) gives the conventional expression $\Gamma_{\rm ei,g} \approx \Gamma_{\rm ei} = Ze^2/(R_0 T_e)$, while in the case of strongly degenerate ($\epsilon_{\rm F} \gg 1$) plasmas, the generalized coupling parameter depends on the Fermi energy, $\Gamma_{\rm ei,g} \approx (9\pi/16)^{1/3} Ze^2/(R_0 E_F) \approx 1.21 Ze^2/(R_0 E_F)$.

2.2. Collective Electron–Phonon Interactions and Electron–Electron Interactions via Umklapp Processes

For ion temperatures $T_{\rm i} < T_{\rm m}$ or when a lattice is heated to $T_{\rm i} > T_{\rm m}$ during times $t < \tau_m$, where τ_m is given by (25), one can assume that the electrons interact with lattice vibrations (phonons). In addition, electron–electron interactions can contribute to the change in the energy of the electron gas through electron momentum transfer to the lattice (Umklapp processes). This situation can be described by the Hamiltonian

$$\begin{aligned}\widehat{H} = &\sum_{k,i,\sigma} E_{k,i}\widehat{a}^{+}_{k,i,\sigma}\widehat{a}_{k,i,\sigma} + \sum_{q,\lambda} \hbar\omega_{q,\lambda}\widehat{b}^{+}_{q,\lambda}\widehat{b}_{q,\lambda} \\ &+ \sum_{k,q,i,i',\lambda,\sigma} g_k(q,i,i',\lambda)\widehat{a}^{+}_{k+q,i,\sigma}\widehat{a}_{k,i',\sigma}(\widehat{b}^{+}_{q,\lambda} + \widehat{b}_{-q,\lambda}) \\ &+ \frac{U}{2n}\sum_{k,k',q,g,i,\sigma} \widehat{a}^{+}_{k+q-g,i,\sigma}\widehat{a}^{+}_{k'-q,i,-\sigma}\widehat{a}_{k',i,-\sigma}\widehat{a}_{k,i,\sigma}\end{aligned} \tag{45}$$

where the first two terms on the r.h.s. of (45) represent electron and phonon kinetic energies, respectively. The third term represents the electron–phonon interaction in the Fröhlich form [30]. The fourth term represents the electron–electron interaction accounting for Umklapp processes in the Hubbard [31] form, where g is the wave vector of the inverse lattice. i, i' are electron band numbers, λ is the phonon mode number, σ is the spin quantum number, $\widehat{a}^{+}_{k,i}, \widehat{a}_{k,i}, \widehat{b}^{+}_{q,\lambda}, \widehat{b}_{-q,\lambda}$ are the creation and annihilation operators of electrons and phonons, respectively, $E_{k,i}$ and $\omega_{q,\lambda}$ are the energy of electrons in the i-th band, given by (12) and the frequency of phonons in λ-th mode, respectively, and $g_k(q,i,i',\lambda)$ is the coefficient of the electron–phonon interaction. U is the single-site approximation to the Coulomb interaction of electrons with opposite spin orientations.

This effective Hamiltonian (45) can be derived from a more fundamental Hamiltonian describing the Coulomb system consisting of electrons and ions. The phonon excitations are obtained from the dynamical structure factor, and the Hubbard term is obtained from the $e-e$ interaction. For our exploratory calculations, we consider the case of electrons interacting with a single phonon mode of longitudinal optical (LO) phonons with a frequency independent of the wave vector [30]. LO phonons have been considered for simplicity. One can expect that a consideration of acoustical phonons (see, e.g., [32]) gives similar results for ion temperatures greater than the Debye one.

We also disregard in this subsection *interband* transitions between different bands n, i and consider only the contribution due to free–free transitions of electrons with effective mass $m_i = m_*$ in the conduction band (the consideration of a two-level system for the case of electron–phonon interactions is given in the subsequent subsection). Besides that, we disregard cross terms from contributions of different types of interactions (normal and Umklapp processes) when calculating the correlation functions of the first moment of the density operator. Calculating commutators in (24) and making respective transformations, one obtains in the Born approximation

$$\mathfrak{C}_{11} = \mathfrak{C}_{\mathrm{e-ph}} + \mathfrak{C}_{\mathrm{U}} \tag{46}$$

where

$$\begin{aligned}\mathfrak{C}_{\mathrm{e-ph}} &= \frac{i\epsilon_{\mathrm{F}}^{-3/2}}{2\pi^{5/2}} \frac{w_{\mathrm{LO}}}{\widetilde{\omega}_{\mathrm{a.u.}}^{1/2}} m_*^2 C_{\mathrm{eph}} \int_0^\infty y dy \int_{-\infty}^\infty dx \\ &\times \left[\frac{1}{w - x + w_{\mathrm{LO}} + i\eta} + \frac{1}{w + x - w_{\mathrm{LO}} + i\eta} \right] \\ &\times \frac{(e^{4x} - 1)^{-1} - (e^{4\alpha w_{\mathrm{LO}}} - 1)^{-1}}{x - \alpha w_{\mathrm{LO}}} \\ &\times \ln \left[\frac{1 + \exp[\epsilon_\mu - (y - x/y)^2]}{1 + \exp[\epsilon_\mu - (y + x/y)^2]} \right]\end{aligned} \tag{47}$$

is the contribution due to electron–phonon interactions, derived earlier in [13], where C_{eph} is a constant of the order of unity, $\alpha = T_e/T_i$; $w = \hbar\omega/(4T_e)$, $\widetilde{\omega}_{\mathrm{au}} = \hbar\omega_{\mathrm{au}}/T_e$, $w_{\mathrm{LO}} = \hbar\omega_{\mathrm{LO}}/(4T_e)$ with the frequency of the longitudinal optical phonons ω_{LO}, and η is an infinitesimal small value.

The contribution of Umklapp processes to the correlation function is given by the second term in Equation (46),

$$\mathfrak{C}_{\mathrm{U}} = \frac{9im_*}{4} \frac{U^2 T_e^2}{E_F^3 E_H} \sum_{\mathbf{g}} g^2 J_\Omega(g) J_{\mathrm{E}}(W, \epsilon_B, \epsilon_\mu) \tag{48}$$

$$J_\Omega(g) = \frac{1}{(4\pi)^4} \iiiint d\Omega\, d\Omega' d\Omega_1 d\Omega_1' \times \delta\left(\mathbf{k}_1 + \mathbf{k}_1' - \mathbf{k} - \mathbf{k}' - \mathbf{g}\right) \tag{49}$$

$$J_{\mathrm{E}}(W, \epsilon_B, \epsilon_\mu) = \iiiint_{-\epsilon_\mu}^{\epsilon_B - \epsilon_\mu} \frac{n_{x_1} n_{x_1'} n_x n_{x'}\, dx_1 dx_1' dx\, dx'}{x_1 + x_1' - x - x' + W + i\eta} \times \frac{e^{x_1 + x_1'} - e^{x + x'}}{x_1 + x_1' - x - x'}. \tag{50}$$

In (49), the vectors $\mathbf{g}, \mathbf{k}_1, \mathbf{k}_1', \mathbf{k}$, and $\mathbf{k}'$ are taken dimensionless, as the ratio to the absolute value of the Fermi wave vector $k_F = k_F = (3\pi^2 n)^{1/3}$. The integration in (49) is performed on solid angles for each of the respective wavevectors $\mathbf{k}_1, \mathbf{k}_1', \mathbf{k}, \mathbf{k}'$. Therefore, the integral (49) is dependent only on $\mathbf{g}$. Furthermore, $W = \hbar\omega/T_e = 4w$; $\epsilon_B = E_B/T_e$, and E_B is the energy of electrons on the surface of the 1st Brillouin zone boundary. In (50), $n_x = 1/[1 + e^x]$ is the Bose distribution function.

The integral over dx in Equations (47) and (48) can be performed applying the Sokhotski–Plemelj formula

$$\int_{-\infty}^{\infty} \frac{f(x)}{x + i\eta} dx = -i\pi f(0) + \mathcal{P} \int_{-\infty}^{\infty} \frac{f(x)}{x} dx,$$

where $\mathcal{P}$ denotes the principal value of the integral. In this case, real and imaginary parts of the correlation function can easily be derived. Below we consider the real parts of the correlation functions (46):

$$\mathfrak{C}'_{\text{e-ph}} = \frac{\epsilon_F^{-3/2}}{2\pi^{3/2}} \frac{m_*^2 C_{\text{eph}} w_{\text{LO}}}{\tilde{\omega}_{\text{a.u.}}^{1/2}} \times \sum_{\sigma=\pm 1} \frac{(e^{4[w_{\text{LO}}+\sigma w]} - 1)^{-1} - (e^{4 w_{\text{LO}} \alpha} - 1)^{-1}}{w_{\text{LO}}(\alpha - 1) - \sigma w} \times \int_0^\infty y dy \ln \left[\frac{1 + \exp\left\{ \epsilon_\mu - \left[y - \frac{w_{\text{LO}} + \sigma w}{y} \right]^2 \right\}}{1 + \exp\left\{ \epsilon_\mu - \left[y + \frac{w_{\text{LO}} + \sigma w}{y} \right]^2 \right\}} \right] \tag{51}$$

and

$$\begin{aligned} \mathfrak{C}'_{\text{U}} &= \frac{9}{4} C_{\text{U}} N_g \bar{g}^2 m_* \frac{U^2 T_e^2}{E_F^3 E_H} J'_{\text{E}} \\ J'_{\text{E}} &= \frac{4}{W} \int_{-2\epsilon_\mu}^{2\epsilon_\Delta - 2\epsilon_\mu} dt \left[\frac{1}{e^{t-W} - 1} - \frac{1}{e^t - 1} \right] \\ &\times \ln \left[\frac{e^{t/2} + e^{-B/2}}{e^{t/2 - B/2} + 1} \right] \ln \left[\frac{e^{t/2 - W/2} + e^{-B/2}}{e^{t/2 - B/2 - W/2} + 1} \right] \end{aligned} \tag{52}$$

where $\epsilon_\Delta = \Delta_E / T_e$, where Δ_E is the energetic distance between the Fermi surface and the Brillouin zone boundary, $B = \epsilon_\mu + \epsilon_\Delta$.

While deriving Equation (52) from Equation (48), the substitution $x = (t + r)/2, x' = (t - r)/2, x_1 = (t_1 + r_1)/2, x'_1 = (t_1 - r_1)/2$ was done, the integrals over r and r_1 were calculated explicitly, and the δ-function was accounted for while integrating over t_1. To derive Expression (49), the approximation

$$\sum_g g^2 J_\Omega(g) \approx C_{\text{U}} \bar{g}^2 N_g$$

is made. C_{U} is a constant of the order of 1, which can be found, e.g., from optical measurements, as in [10,33,34]. N_g is the number of different wavevectors of the inverse lattice in the first Brillouin zone, which coincides with the number of nearest neighbors in the inverse lattice for the point g = 0. $\bar{g}^2$ is the average value of g^2 in the first Brillouin zone.

2.3. Interband Transitions in a Two-Level System

In this subsection, we consider expressions for the force–force correlation functions of first order moments $\mathfrak{C}_{\{1,\nu\}\{1,\mu\}} = \mathfrak{C}_{\nu\mu}$ for different energy bands $\nu, \mu = 1, 2$. The expressions will be derived for the case of collective electron–phonon interactions, when the electronic system Hamiltonian is described by (45) with the account of only the first three terms, i.e., without Umklapp processes. With this Hamiltonian and with an electron–phonon coupling function for longitudinal optical phonons, one can obtain from Equation (24) the following expression for correlation functions $\mathfrak{C}_{\nu\mu}$ similarly, as was done above:

(i) for the correlation functions related to intra-band electron transitions:

$$\mathfrak{C}_{\nu\nu} = -i m_*^2 \kappa \int_0^\infty y dy \int_{-\infty}^\infty dx X_{\nu\nu}(x) \Delta F_{\nu\nu}(x, y) - \sum_{\mu \neq \nu} \mathfrak{C}^0_{\mu\nu} \tag{53}$$

where $\kappa = \frac{\epsilon_F^{-3/2}}{2\pi^{5/2}} \frac{w_{LO}}{\tilde{\omega}_{a.u.}^{1/2}} C_{eph}$; $\mathfrak{C}^0_{\mu\nu}$ stands for the indirect influence of interband transitions:

$$\begin{aligned} \mathfrak{C}^0_{\mu\nu} = \; & im_*^2\kappa/4 \int_0^\infty dy \int_{-\infty}^\infty dx \Big\{ X_{\mu\nu}(x) \\ & \times \left[\left(\frac{x^2}{y^3} + \frac{2x}{y} + y \right) \Delta F_{\mu\nu}(x,y) + \frac{m_*^{-1}}{y} \Delta \widetilde{F}_{\mu\nu}(x,y) \right] \\ & + X_{\nu\mu}(x) \\ & \times \left[\left(\frac{x^2}{y^3} - \frac{2x}{y} + y \right) \Delta F_{\nu\mu}(x,y) + \frac{m_*^{-1}}{y} \Delta \widetilde{F}_{\nu\mu}(x,y) \right] \Big\} \end{aligned} \tag{54}$$

where

$$X_{\mu\nu}(x) = \left[\frac{1/\varphi_{\nu\mu}(x,\alpha)}{w + i\eta + \varphi_{\nu\mu}(x,1)} + \frac{1/\varphi_{\nu\mu}(x,\alpha)}{w + i\eta - \varphi_{\nu\mu}(x,1)} \right] \times \left[\frac{1}{e^{4x+4w_{\mu\nu}} - 1} - \frac{1}{e^{4\alpha w_{LO}} - 1} \right] \tag{55}$$

where $\varphi_{\nu\mu}(x,t) = x + w_{\nu\mu} - t w_{LO}$, $w_{\nu\mu} = \frac{1}{4}(E_\nu - E_\mu)/T_e$;

$$\begin{aligned} \Delta F_{\mu\nu}(x,y) &= F_1(A_-^\mu(x,y)) - F_1(A_+^\nu(x,y)), \\ \Delta \widetilde{F}_{\mu\nu}(x,y) &= F_2(A_-^\mu(x,y)) - F_2(A_+^\nu(x,y)) \\ A_\pm^\mu(x,y) &= \exp\left[(x/y \pm y)^2 + (E_\mu - \mu)/T_e \right] \\ F_1(t) &= \ln\left(1 + \tfrac{1}{t}\right), \quad F_2(t) = \ln^2(t) + 2\,\mathrm{Li}_2(-t). \end{aligned} \tag{56}$$

(Note that in the above expression, in the term $E_\mu - \mu$, the second value μ denotes the chemical potential, and the index μ in the first term E_μ denotes the energy band).

(ii) for the correlation functions related to interband electrons transitions:

$$\mathfrak{C}^{\mu\neq\nu}_{\mu\nu} = im_*^2\kappa/4 \int_0^\infty dy \int_{-\infty}^\infty dx \left\{ X_{\mu\nu}(x) \times \left[\left(\frac{x^2}{y^3} - y \right) \Delta F_{\mu\nu}(x,y) + \frac{m_*^{-1}}{y} \Delta \widetilde{F}_{\mu\nu}(x,y) \right] + \text{the same with } \mu \leftrightarrow \nu \right\}. \tag{57}$$

3. Calculations and Discussion

We perform exploratory calculations of the absorption coefficient of aluminum plasmas with the solid density $\varrho = 2.71$ g/cm^3 and the average ion charge $Z = 3$ (step-like density profile), irradiated by lasers with different wavelengths shown in Figures 1 and 2. The dielectric function (16) was determined for two cases: an ordered lattice with an account of collective electron–phonon interactions and Umklapp processes by means of Expressions (46), (51), and (52), assuming $T_i < T_{\text{melt}}$ or $t < \tau_m$ (25), and a disordered lattice, with an account of individual electron–ion and electron–electron interactions by means of Expressions (23), (30), and (31), with respect to a Percus–Yevick-like model [16] for S_{ii}, with the restrictions of screening (37) (see also [12]).

The effective mass m_* was calculated according to the Huttner model [35], see also [11]. The value of $C_{\text{eph}} \approx 5.73$ in (47) was chosen to reproduce the low-frequency cold reflectivity of aluminum [11,33] for the laser wavelength $\lambda = 0.4$ μm. The value of ω_{LO} was determined by the position of the maximum of the phonon spectrum for aluminum [36] as $\hbar\omega_{LO} \approx 0.006$ eV. Furthermore, the following parameters have been used: $C_U = 1.5$, $U = 2$ eV, $\Delta_E = 7.3$ eV, and $\bar{g}^2 = 2$. The value $N_g = 8$ is chosen, assuming the fcc lattice structure and the bcc inverse lattice structure for aluminum.

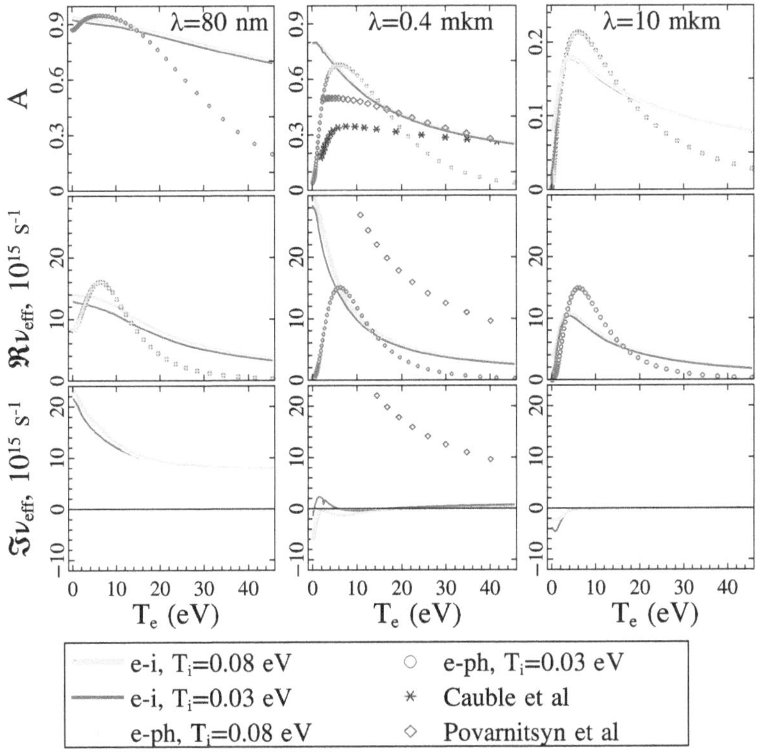

Figure 1. Absorption coefficient (first row) as well as real (second row) and imaginary (third row) parts of the complex collision frequency of electrons (46), as a function of the electron temperature T_e, for a solid-density aluminum plasma ($\varrho = 2.71\ \mathrm{g/cm^3}$) and laser radiation of different wavelengths λ (left column: 80 nm; center: 0.4 µm; right: 10 µm). Curves are shown for different ion temperatures (see legend), calculated for the case of an ordered lattice by Models (46), (51), and (52) (with an account of electron–phonon interactions and Umklapp processes, labeled by "e-ph"), as well as for the case of a disordered lattice (electron–ion and electron–electron interactions, labeled by "e-i"). Curves with the markers "*" and "◇" are according to the models cited in the text (see legend).

Figure 1 shows the dependence of the absorption coefficient A, Equation (2), the real and imaginary parts of the effective collision frequency $\nu(\omega)$ (17) on the electron temperature. Ordered (electron–phonon) and disordered ion lattices ($e-i$) are considered at different wavelengths of laser radiation ($\lambda = 0.08, 0.4, 10$ µm). The results for $\lambda = 0.4$ µm are compared with a semi-empirical model by Povarnitsyn et al. [33,37] and with calculations of the absorption coefficient taken from the work of Cauble et al. [38].

The most essential feature of the dependence of the effective collision frequency on electron temperature, for the case of ordered ion lattice with electron–phonon interactions and Umklapp processes, is that for $T_e > E_F$ ($E_F \approx 11.6$ eV for solid-density aluminum) the real part ν' is decreasing as

$$\nu' \sim T_e^{-4}$$

according to the asymptotic behavior of Expressions (52), see [14]. This is much faster than the scaling

$$\nu' \sim T_e^{-3/2}$$

for the case of electron–ion interaction in a high-temperature plasma [12]. This is shown by the solid and marked curves in Figure 1.

It should be noted that, in the case of an ordered ion lattice, unlike the case of a disordered ion lattice, the temperature dependence of the real part of the effective collision frequency as well as the absorption coefficient shows a clear peak in the vicinity of the Fermi temperature for all wavelengths. The maximum values of A, calculated by Models (46), (51), and (52) for an ordered ion lattice, are relatively close to that of the semi-empirical model [33] and to the values of A, calculated by Models (23), (30), and (31) for a disordered lattice.

It should also be noted that under the conditions of Figure 1 the contribution of Umklapp processes (52) exceeds the contribution of the electron–phonon contribution (51). The influence of different ion temperatures is mainly owing to the dependence of the effective electron mass m_* on the ion temperature T_i, as calculated according to the Huttner model [35] (compare the thin and thick solid curves in Figure 1).

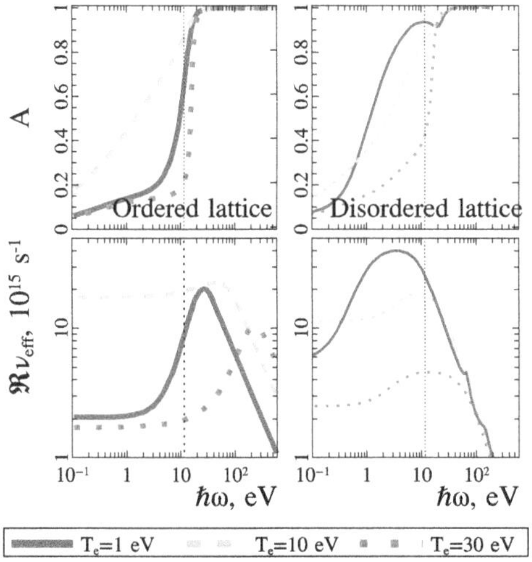

Figure 2. The absorption coefficient and the real part of the complex collision frequency of electrons (46) in a solid-density aluminum plasma are shown as a function of the laser frequency $\hbar\omega$ for ion temperatures $T_i = 0.04$ eV and different electron temperatures T_e (see legend). Thick curves (left column) refer to the case of an ordered lattice with electron–phonon interactions and Umklapp processes, and thin curves (right column) refer to a disordered lattice with electron–ion and electron–electron interactions.

The imaginary part of $\nu(\omega)$ calculated by a consequent quantum statistical model (for semi-empirical models, it can be calculated by equating the respective expressions for permittivity to the Drude-like expression (16), see [12]) is small for laser frequencies $\hbar\omega \ll E_F$ or for $\hbar\omega \gg E_F$, while for $\hbar\omega \sim E_F$ its value can be considerable, see the subfigure at the left corner of Figure 1.

For $\hbar\omega \ll E_F$ and $\hbar\omega < T_e$, $\mathrm{Re}\,\nu(\omega)$ (and hence the value of the density of absorbed power of laser radiation, which is proportional to $\mathrm{Im}\,\varepsilon \sim \mathrm{Re}\,\nu(\omega)$) is weakly dependent on ω, see Figure 2. For $\hbar\omega \gg T_e$

and $\hbar\omega \lesssim E_F$, the value of $\mathrm{Re}\,\nu(\omega)$ is increasing with ω (the rate of the increase is proportional to ω^2) for Umklapp processes in an ordered ion lattice, see [13]). For $\hbar\omega \gg T_e$ and $\hbar\omega \gg E_F$, the value of $\mathrm{Re}\,\nu(\omega)$ is decreasing with ω, see Figure 2. The rate of such a decrease is proportional to $\omega^{-3/2}$ for the case of a disordered ion lattice [12] and to ω^{-1} for the case of an ordered ion lattice [13]. One should note here that the contribution of interband transitions to the dielectric function should be taken into account for quantum energies exceeding the gap between the conductivity band and inner electron energy levels [17]. As described above, the respective theoretical approach can be elaborated on the basis of the nonequilibrium statistical operator method. Note also that in the case of a disordered ion lattice (individual electron–ion and electron–electron interactions), Expressions (30) and (31) for the correlation functions give rise to the Ziman–Evans formula [39,40] for the electric conductivity in the limit $\omega \to 0$ [12].

4. Conclusions

The NSO method allows one to describe consistently the dielectric function of WDM in a wide range of frequencies and plasma parameters. Different kinds of electron–ion interactions, in particular in systems with a disordered distribution of ions (individual electron–ion and electron–electron interactions) and systems with an ordered ion configuration, described as an ion lattice (with collective electron–phonon interactions and Umklapp processes), are successfully treated using this method.

A main peculiarity of the absorption of irradiated laser energy in the case of an ordered ion lattice, owing to collective electron–phonon interactions and Umklapp processes, is a much stronger ($\sim T_e^{-4}$) decrease of the real part of the effective collision frequency at electron temperatures exceeding the Fermi temperature, if compared to the case of individual electron–ion and electron–electron interactions (where $\mathrm{Re}\,\nu \sim T_e^{-3/2}$ for $T_e > E_F$). An essential feature of the electron–phonon interaction and the Umklapp process is that they show, as a function of the electron temperature, a clear peak structure of the absorption coefficient and of the real part of the effective collision frequency at $T_e \sim E_F$. In addition, in both cases of ordered and disordered ion lattices, the real part of the effective collision frequency as a function of the photon energy shows a peak structure: $\mathrm{Re}\,\nu(\omega)$ is nearly independent of ω for $\hbar\omega \ll E_F$ and $\hbar\omega < T_e$, but $\mathrm{Re}\,\nu(\omega)$ is rising with ω ($\sim \omega^2$ for the case of ordered ion lattice) for $\hbar\omega \gg T_e, \hbar\omega \lesssim E_F$, and $\mathrm{Re}\,\nu(\omega)$ is decreasing with ω ($\sim \omega^{-1}$ for the case of ordered ion lattice and $\sim \omega^{-3/2}$ for the case of disordered ion lattice) for $\hbar\omega \gg T_e$ and $\hbar\omega \gg E_F$.

The NSO method can be also applied for the description of interband contributions to the dielectric function, which are essential for photon energies exceeding the energy gaps between the conduction band and electron bands corresponding to excited electron energy levels. The relation to DFT calculation [17], which provides us with ab initio calculations of optimal single-electron states and replaces the approximation for the electron–ion potential used in our calculations, is of high interest. In addition, our approach allows one to take into account the contribution of electron–electron collisions to the dielectric function, which is not possible in mean-field approaches such as DFT. More detailed investigations of this case, as well as the calculation of the imaginary part of the effective collision frequency for the case of an ordered ion lattice with electron–phonon interactions and Umklapp processes, will be the subject of our future work.

Author Contributions: H.R. and G.R. have been working on the general concepts of the approach. M.V. has conducted the particular derivations and calculations.

Funding: The work of M.V. was partly supported by the Presidium of the RAS program "Thermo-physics of High Energy Density", No I.13P. H.R. and G.R. acknowledge support by the DFG (German research foundation) via RE 975/4-1 and RO 905/32-1, respectively. G.R. acknowledges support from the MEPhI Academic Excellence Program under contract number 02.a03.21.0005.

Acknowledgments: We are greatfull to N.E. Andreev for valuable comments

Conflicts of Interest: The authors declare no conflict of interest.

References

1. Zubarev, D.N. Relaxation and Hydrodynamic Processes, V 2. *Dokl. Akad. Nauk SSSR Russ.* **1961**, *140*, 92.
2. Zubarev, D.N. *Nonequilibrium Statistical Thermodynamics [in Russian: Neravnovesnaya Statistitsheskaya Termodinamika, Moscow, Nauka, 1971]*; Plenum Press: New York, NY, USA, 1974.
3. Zubarev, D.N.; Morozov, V.; Röpke, G. *Statistical Mechanics of Nonequilibrium Processes, V 1*; Akademie Verlag/Wiley: Berlin, Germany, 1997.
4. Zubarev, D.N.; Morozov, V.; Röpke, G. *Relaxation and Hydrodynamic Processes, V 2*; Akademie Verlag/Wiley: Berlin, Germany, 1997.
5. Röpke, G. Electrical Conductivity of Charged Particle Systems and Zubarev's Nonequilibrium Statistical Operator Method. *Theor. Math. Phys.* **2018**, *194*, 74–104. [CrossRef]
6. Kuzemsky, A.L. Nonequilibrium Statistical Operator Method and Generalized Kinetic Equations. *Theor. Math. Phys.* **2018**, *194*, 30–56. [CrossRef]
7. Redmer, R. Physical properties of dense, low-temperature plasmas. *Phys. Rep.* **1997**, *282*, 35–157. [CrossRef]
8. Reinholz, H. Dielectric and optical properties of dense plasmas. *Ann. Phys. Fr.* **2005**, *30*, 1–187. [CrossRef]
9. Reinholz, H.; Röpke, G. Dielectric function beyond the random-phase approximation: Kinetic theory versus linear response theory. *Phys. Rev. E* **2012**, *85*, 036401. [CrossRef]
10. Veysman, M.E.; Agranat, M.B.; Andreev, N.E.; Ashitkov, S.I.; Fortov, V.E.; Khishchenko, K.V.; Kostenko, O.F.; Levashov, P.R.; Ovchinnikov, A.V.; Sitnikov, D.S. Femtosecond optical diagnostics and hydrodynamic simulation of Ag plasma created by laser irradiation of a solid target. *J. Phys. B At. Mol. Opt. Phys.* **2008**, *41*, 125704. [CrossRef]
11. Veysman, M.E.; Andreev, N.E. Semi-empirical model for permittivity of warm dense matter. *J. Phys. Conf. Ser.* **2015**, *653*, 012004. [CrossRef]
12. Veysman, M.; Röpke, G.; Winkel, M.; Reinholz, H. Optical conductivity of warm dense matter within a wide frequency range using quantum statistical and kinetic approaches. *Phys. Rev. E* **2016**, *94*, 013203. [CrossRef]
13. Veysman, M.; Röpke, G.; Reinholz, H. Analytical expression for high-frequency dielectric function of metals at moderate temperatures. *J. Phys. Conf. Ser.* **2018**, *946*, 012012. [CrossRef]
14. Veysman, M.; Röpke, G.; Reinholz, H. High frequency dielectric function of metals taking into account Umklapp processes. *J. Phys. Conf. Ser.* **2019**, *1147*, 012071. [CrossRef]
15. Sperling, P.; Gamboa, E.J.; Lee, H.J.; Chung, H.K.; Galtier, E.; Omarbakiyeva, Y.; Reinholz, H.; Röpke, G.; Zastrau, U.; Hastings, J.; et al. Free-Electron X-Ray Laser Measurements of Collisional-Damped Plasmons in Isochorically Heated Warm Dense Matter. *Phys. Rev. Lett.* **2015**, *115*, 115001. [CrossRef]
16. Sperling, P.; Rosmej, S.; Bredow, R.; Fletcher, L.B.; Galtier, E.; Gamboa, E.J.; Lee, H.J.; Reinholz, H.; Röpke, G.; Zastrau, U.; et al. Electrical conductivity calculations in isochorically heated warm dense aluminum. *J. Phys. B At. Mol. Opt. Phys.* **2017**, *50*, 134002. [CrossRef]
17. Witte, B.B.L.; Fletcher, L.B.; Galtier, E.; Gamboa, E.; Lee, H.J.; Zastrau, U.; Redmer, R.; Glenzer, S.H.; Sperling, P. Warm Dense Matter Demonstrating Non-Drude Conductivity from Observations of Nonlinear Plasmon Damping. *Phys. Rev. Lett.* **2017**, *118*, 225001. [CrossRef]
18. Reinholz, H.; Röpke, G.; Rosmej, S.; Redmer, R. Conductivity of warm dense matter including electron–electron collisions. *Phys. Rev. E* **2015**, *91*, 043105. [CrossRef]
19. Alexandrov, A.F.; Bogdankevich, L.S.; Rukhadze, A.A. *Principles of Plasma Electrodynamics*; Springer: Berlin, Germany, 1984.
20. Kubo, R. Statistical-Mechanical Theory of Irreversible Processes. I. General Theory and Simple Applications to Magnetic and Conduction Problems. *J. Phys. Soc. Jpn.* **1957**, *12*, 570–586. [CrossRef]
21. Röpke, G. Quantum-statistical approach to the electrical conductivity of dense, high-temperature plasmas. *Phys. Rev. A* **1988**, *38*, 3001–3016. [CrossRef]

22. Reinholz, H.; Redmer, R.; Röpke, G.; Wierling, A. Long-wavelength limit of the dynamical local-field factor and dynamical conductivity of a two-component plasma. *Phys. Rev. E* **2000**, *62*, 5648. [CrossRef]
23. Karakhtanov, V.S.; Redmer, R.; Reinholz, H.; Ropke, G. The Influence of Dynamical Screening on the Transport Properties of Dense Plasmas. *Contrib. Plasma Phys.* **2013**, *53*, 639–652. [CrossRef]
24. Gericke, D.O.; Vorberger, J.; Wünsch, K.; Gregori, G. Screening of ionic cores in partially ionized plasmas within linear response. *Phys. Rev. E* **2010**, *81*, 065401. [CrossRef]
25. Röpke, G.; Redmer, R. Electrical conductivity of nondegenerate, fully ionized plasmas. *Phys. Rev. A* **1989**, *39*, 907–910. [CrossRef]
26. Ashcroft, N.; Stroud, D. Theory of the thermodynamics of simple liquid metals. *Solid State Phys.* **1978**, *33*, 1–81.
27. Thakor, P.; Sonvane, Y.; Jani, A. Structural properties of some liquid transition metals. *Phys. Chem. Liq.* **2011**, *49*, 530–549. [CrossRef]
28. Bretonnet, J.L.; Derouiche, A. Analytic form for the one-component plasma structure factor. *Phys. Rev. B* **1988**, *38*, 9255–9256. [CrossRef]
29. Skupsky, S. "Coulomb logarithm" for inverse-bremsstrahlung laser absorption. *Phys. Rev. A* **1987**, *36*, 5701–5712. [CrossRef]
30. Mahan, G.D. *Many Particle Physics*, 3rd ed.; Plenum: New York, NY, USA, 2000.
31. Hubbard, J. Electron correlations in narrow energy bands. *Proc. R. Soc. Lond. Ser. A* **1963**, *276*, 238–257.
32. Christoph, V.; Röpke, G. Theory of Inverse Linear Response Coefficients. *Phys. Status Solidi B* **1985**, *131*, 11–42. [CrossRef]
33. Povarnitsyn, M.E.; Andreev, N.E.; Apfelbaum, E.M.; Itina, T.E.; Khishchenko, K.V.; Kostenko, O.F.; Levashov, P.R.; Veysman, M.E. A wide-range model for simulation of pump-probe experiments with metals. *Appl. Surf. Sci.* **2012**, *258*, 9480–9483. [CrossRef]
34. Agranat, M.; Andreev, N.; Ashitkov, S.; Veysman, M.; Levashov, P.; Ovchinnikov, A.; Sitnikov, D.; Fortov, V.; Khishchenko, K. Determination of the transport and optical properties of a nonideal solid-density plasma produced by femtosecond laser pulses. *JETP Lett.* **2007**, *85*, 271–276. [CrossRef]
35. Huttner, B. A new method for the determination of the optical mass of electrons in metals. *J. Phys. Condens. Matter* **1996**, *8*, 11041. [CrossRef]
36. Maksimov, E.G.; Savrasov, D.Y.; Savrasov, S.Y. The electron–phonon interaction and the physical properties of metals. *Usp. Fiz. Nauk* **1997**, *167*, 353–376. [CrossRef]
37. Povarnitsyn, M.E.; Andreev, N.E. A wide-range model for simulation of aluminum plasma produced by femtosecond laser pulses. *J. Phys. Conf. Ser.* **2016**, *774*, 012105. [CrossRef]
38. Cauble, R.; Rozmus, W. Two-temperature frequency-dependent electrical resistivity in solid density plasmas produced by ultrashort laser pulses. *Phys. Rev. E* **1995**, *52*, 2974–2981. [CrossRef]
39. Ziman, J.M. A Theory of Electrical Properties of Liquid Metals. The Monovalent Metals. *Philos. Mag.* **1961**, *6*, 1013–1034. [CrossRef]
40. Evans, R. The resistivity and thermopower of liquid mercury and its alloys. *J. Phys. C Solid State Phys.* **1970**, *3*, S137–S152. [CrossRef]

particles

MDPI

Article

Nonequilibrium Pion Distribution within the Zubarev Approach

David Blaschke [1,2,3,*], Gerd Röpke [3,4], Dmitry N. Voskresensky [2,3] and Vladimir G. Morozov [5]

1 Institute of Theoretical Physics, University of Wroclaw, Max-Born place 9, 50-204 Wrocław, Poland
2 Bogoliubov Laboratory for Theoretical Physics, JINR Dubna, Joliot-Curie street 6, 141980 Dubna, Russia; d.voskresen@gmail.com
3 National Research Nuclear University (MEPhI), Kashirskoe shosse 31, Moscow 115409, Russia; gerd.roepke@uni-rostock.de
4 Institute of Physics, University of Rostock, Universitätsplatz 3, D-18055 Rostock, Germany
5 MIREA-Russian Technological University, Vernadsky Avenue 78, Moscow 119454, Russia; vladmorozov45@gmail.com
* Correspondence: david.blaschke@uwr.edu.pl

Received: 11 April 2020; Accepted: 30 April 2020; Published: 3 May 2020

Abstract: We discuss how the non-equilibrium process of pion production within the Zubarev approach of the non-equilibrium statistical operator leads to a theoretical foundation for the appearance of a non-equilibrium pion chemical potential for the pion distribution function for which there is experimental evidence in experiments at the CERN LHC.

Keywords: Zubarev formalism; non-equilibrium statistical operator; pion chemical potential; LHC

1. Introduction

The thermal statistical model [1–6] for chemical freeze-out of hadron species gives a successful description of a set of particle ratios produced in heavy-ion collisions (HIC) at different center of mass energies ranging from the energies provided by the Schwerionensynchrotron (SIS-18) at GSI Darmstadt over those of the Alternating Gradient Synchrotron (AGS) at BNL Brookhaven and the Super Proton Synchrotron (SPS) at CERN Geneva up to the highest energies at the Relativistic Heavy Ion Collider (RHIC) at BNL and the Large Hadron Collider (LHC) at CERN. It came therefore as a surprise that for LHC at $\sqrt{s} = 2.76$ TeV the measured proton abundances [7,8] do not agree with the most common version of the thermal mode (the inclusion of resonance formation due to (multi-)pion-nucleon interaction and further correlations in the continuum within the Beth–Uhlenbeck approach [9,10] improves the agreement with the experiment) based on the grand canonical ensemble [3,4]. As a possible explanation of this effect it has been suggested that the freeze-out may take place off chemical equilibrium [11–13]. Hereby, a key feature is the enhancement of low-transverse momentum pion spectra above the expectation from equilibrium statistical models which was seen already at lower energies in pion spectra at SPS and clearly seen in the RHIC and the LHC data. The effect can be seen as a precursor of pion Bose–Einstein condensation due to high phase space occupation at low momenta and has consequently been parametrized by adopting a pion chemical potential very close to the pion mass [14,15]. This concept is based on the assumption that the total pion number is dynamically fixed on a time scale between the pion chemical freeze out $t_{\pi,\mathrm{cfo}}$ and the thermal freeze-out (or simply freeze-out) t_{fo}, $t_{\pi,\mathrm{cfo}} < t < t_{\mathrm{fo}}$, where at $t_{\pi,\mathrm{cfo}}$ the pion number becomes frozen and at t_{fo} the momentum distributions stop to change [16]. Thereby, for pions, we assume dominance of elastic collisions over inelastic ones. We will assume that for pions the time typical for absorptive processes $t_{\pi,\mathrm{abs}}$, which change the pion particle number, is $t_{\pi,\mathrm{abs}} > t_{\mathrm{fo}}$.

In the present paper, we want to elucidate the non-equilibrium evolution of the initial fireball and the emergence of a non-equilibrium chemical potential for hadrons, in particular for the pions. The theoretical background shall be provided by the Zubarev formalism of the non-equilibrium statistical operator (NSO) [17] which introduces a generalization of the thermodynamical Gibbs ensemble by including non-equilibrium observables into the derivation of the statistical operator of the non-equilibrium, see also [18]. This is facilitated by extending the set of Lagrangian multipliers by the additional non-equilibrium chemical potentials for the hadrons will appear in the NSO. If the non-equilibrium chemical potential for the pions coincides with the pion effective mass, Bose–Einstein condensation will occur, and strong effects are expected on the measured pion spectra [19,20].

Many formulations have been given for the approach to equilibrium [21,22] and the kinetics of Bose–Einstein condensation, see for instance Refs. [23–27]. New ansätze have been developed, e.g., in References [28,29] with a state that is a fixed point and the evolution towards it is universal. Via this fixed point, the system develops then dynamically.

Such a behavior is long known in the context of the Zubarev formalism, which is able to describe, for example, the transition from the kinetic stage to the hydrodynamic stage. The short-time evolution goes to a relevant statistical operator with local time-dependent thermodynamic parameters. The long-time scale evolution is given by the time dependence of these thermodynamic parameters approaching thermodynamic equilibrium.

2. The Nonequilibrium Statistical Operator Method

HIC at ultrarelativistic energies are violent non-equilibrium processes which need, in principle, a genuine non-equilibrium approach. At present, simple approximations are used such as transport models based on the kinetic equations for single-particle distribution functions. Transport codes based on the relativistic Boltzmann–Uehling–Uhlenbeck (BUU) or Vlasov–Uehling–Uhlenbeck (VUU) equations have been worked out [23–25,30]. However, a non-equilibrium single-particle distribution is not sufficient to describe correlations in the evolving system. As example, cluster formation in an expanding fireball requires the inclusion of higher order correlation functions to describe bound states like hadrons or nuclei. Alternatively, the freeze-out concept assumes nuclear statistical equilibrium (NSE) during the expansion of the fireball, which is justified if the time $\tau_{\rm therm}$ for the relaxation to thermodynamic equilibrium is small compared to the variation time $\tau_{\rm exp} = q/\dot{q}$ of a parameter q describing the thermodynamic state of the expanding system. The treatment of thermodynamic equilibrium is able to include all equilibrium correlations, in particular cluster formation. At freeze-out, $t = t_{\rm fo}$, collision processes that change the composition and the distribution die out. For $t > t_{\rm fo}$, baryon distributions evolve according to the mean-field description of the expansion. Note that, at least under conditions of the LHC and highest RHIC energies for soft pions (with energies and momenta smaller than m_π), the time scales characterizing elastic and inelastic (absorptive) processes are such that $\tau_{\pi,\rm el} \ll t_{\rm fo} < \tau_{\pi,\rm abs}$. Thereby, we may speak about the evolution of $\mu_\pi(t)$ till thermal freeze-out. Although the expanding fireball approach with time dependent temperature $T(t)$ and chemical potentials $\mu_c(t)$ for all hadrons including pions is rather reasonable, it is just an approximation to a more sophisticated many-body non-equilibrium approach given below.

A systematic general approach to non-equilibrium is given by the NSO $\rho(t)$ which is the solution of the von Neumann equation with a given initial state [17],

$$\rho(t) = \lim_{\varepsilon \to 0} \varepsilon \int_{-\infty}^{t} dt' e^{\varepsilon(t-t')} U(t,t') \rho_{\rm rel}(t') U^{\dagger}(t,t'), \tag{1}$$

where for a Hamiltonian H which is not time-dependent holds $U(t,t') = \exp[(i/\hbar)H(t-t')]$, and the limit $\varepsilon \to 0$ has to be taken after the thermodynamic limit. Instead of a distribution $\rho_{\rm initial}(t_0)$ at an initial time t_0, according to Zubarev, a relevant statistical operator $\rho_{\rm rel}(t')$ has been introduced that contains all relevant information of the system in the past $t' < t$. This relevant information characterizes the state of the system in non-equilibrium and will be discussed below. The missing irrelevant correlations $\rho_{\rm irrel}(t) = \rho(t) - \rho_{\rm rel}(t)$ are assumed to be formed dynamically by the action of the time evolution operator $U(t, t')$.

The non-equilibrium state of the system is characterized by observables B_n in addition to the conserved observables such as total energy and particle numbers. The relevant information is given by the averages $\langle B_n \rangle^t = {\rm Tr}\{\rho(t) B_n\}$ of the relevant observables B_n. The maximum of the information entropy $S_{\rm inf} = -{\rm Tr}\{\rho_{\rm rel}(t) \ln \rho_{\rm rel}(t)\}$ at given averages is the generalized Gibbs distribution

$$\rho_{\rm rel}(t) = \frac{1}{Z_{\rm rel}(t)} e^{-\sum_n F_n(t) B_n}; \qquad Z_{\rm rel}(t) = {\rm Tr} e^{-\sum_n F_n(t) B_n} \tag{2}$$

where the Lagrange multipliers $F_n(t)$ are determined by the self-consistency conditions

$$\langle B_n \rangle^t_{\rm rel} = \langle B_n \rangle^t \tag{3}$$

with $\langle B_n \rangle^t_{\rm rel} \equiv {\rm Tr}\{\rho_{\rm rel}(t) B_n\}$. With respect to the selection of the set of relevant observables, B_n, it should contain all conserved quantities which cannot be changed owing to the dynamics of the system. In an ergodic system, all other correlations are produced dynamically. We can include any set of observables to the relevant ones. In particular, if we include all slowly varying observables in the set of relevant observables $\{B_n\}$, we can expect that a shorter time is necessary to produce the missing non-equilibrium correlations. This means that Eq. (2) already gives a good approximation for $\rho(t)$ at finite ε so that memory effects are less important.

According to the NSO method, the equations of evolution (generalized kinetic equations) are obtained from

$$\frac{d}{dt} \langle B_n \rangle^t = \lim_{\varepsilon \to 0} \frac{i\varepsilon}{\hbar} \int_{-\infty}^{t} dt' e^{\epsilon(t'-t)} {\rm Tr} \left\{ \rho_{\rm rel}(t') e^{iH(t'-t)/\hbar} [H, B_n] e^{iH(t-t')/\hbar} \right\}, \tag{4}$$

where we inserted the time derivative of the NSO (1) and used the self-consistency conditions (3).

The correct reproduction of the relevant information in the past gives the possibility to form the irrelevant correlations very fast so that a perturbation expansion is possible. Although the expression (1) is correct for any choice of relevant observables after performing the limit $\varepsilon \to 0$, an appropriate choice of the set of relevant observables $\{B_n\}$ allows us to make expansions quickly convergent so that, for instance, the Markov approximation can be performed (We speak here about memory effects associated with dying initial correlations. There are memory effects related to processes described by diagrams with more than two vertices in the non-equilibrium Greens function technique. These effects can be neglected only for dilute gases, but, in general, they are important. They result in the famous $T^3 \ln T$ correction to the specific heat of ^{3}He, cf. [31,32]. Since this correction is quite comparable (numerically) to the leading term in the specific heat ($\propto T$), one may claim that liquid ^{3}He is a liquid with quite strong memory effects from the point of view of kinetics). In Section 4, we discuss this issue in detail. It is our main goal to show that the optimal path for the non-equilibrium evolution (i.e., a sufficient broad choice of relevant observables B_n) must be found to provide us with a precise description already in low orders of perturbation theory.

A correct description of the evolution is also necessary for the expanding fireball if the freeze-out approximation is used. We cannot assume that the system at freeze-out is strictly in thermodynamic equilibrium. A simple relaxation-time ansatz is not sufficient, but a more detailed description of the time evolution is necessary. An important feature of the evolution is that a perturbation expansion in powers of the interaction which is often used cannot give the formation of bound states or quantum condensates in any finite order of perturbation theory. The introduction of the relevant NSO provides us with the description of those phenomena. In particular, we show that the formation of an intermediate pion Bose–Einstein condensate can be described in our approach. It is an advantage of the Zubarev approach that initial correlations are included via the relevant statistical operator $\rho_{\rm rel}(t)$, in contrast to the kinetic theory which is based on the single-particle distribution function.

3. Model for Pions in Heavy-Ion Collisions at Ultra High Energies

To explain our approach denoted as the NSO method, we discuss the pion production in heavy-ion collisions. After an initial stage where hadrons are formed, we consider a fireball consisting of pions, nucleons N, Δ resonances, and further hadronic states such as N^* and K mesons containing strangeness degrees of freedom. In occupation number representation, $a^+_{\mathbf{p},c}, a_{\mathbf{p},c}$ are the creation/annihilation operators of a particle in the quantum state $\mathbf{p}, c$ given by the species c (including spin) and momentum $\mathbf{p}$. The Hamiltonian $H = H^0 + H'$ contains the kinetic part

$$H^0 = \sum_{\mathbf{p},c} \sqrt{p^2 + m_c^2} a^+_{\mathbf{p},c} a_{\mathbf{p},c} = \sum_{\mathbf{p},c} E_{\mathbf{p},c}\, a^+_{\mathbf{p},c} a_{\mathbf{p},c} \tag{5}$$

and the interaction part H'. At highest RHIC and LHC energies, the fireball is dominated by pions. Approximately, one may speak of a pure pion gas. Thus, further within our model, we consider only special processes, which concern the pion distribution, c, that runs over pion species. We split the interaction into an elastic part describing collisions which conserve the pion number, $H_{\rm col}$, and an inelastic part describing reactions, $H_{\rm reac}$, where the pion number is changed, $H' = H_{\rm col} + H_{\rm reac}$.

Expressions for the meson–meson interaction are found in the literature [16,30]. $\pi - \pi$ interactions at high energies are predominantly elastic implying that at low density the number of pions is effectively conserved. We assume elastic $\pi - \pi$ scattering of the form

$$H_{\rm col} = \frac{1}{2} \sum_{\mathbf{p}_1, \mathbf{p}_2, \mathbf{p}'_1, \mathbf{p}'_2; c,d} \lambda_{c,d}(\mathbf{p}_1, \mathbf{p}_2; \mathbf{p}'_1, \mathbf{p}'_2) a^+_{\mathbf{p}_1,c} a^+_{\mathbf{p}_2,d} a_{\mathbf{p}'_2,d} a_{\mathbf{p}'_1,c}. \tag{6}$$

We assume that at $t < t_{\pi,\rm cfo}$ a state overpopulated by soft pions is formed, for $t > t_{\pi,\rm cfo}$ the collisions conserve the particle number, but evolve the distribution function to a thermal equilibrium distribution with a corresponding short relaxation time $\tau_{\rm col}$. These collision processes may happen via a virtual states such as the ρ and σ mesons or other resonances. We note that the matrix element $\lambda_{\pi,\pi}(\mathbf{p}_1, \mathbf{p}_2; \mathbf{p}'_1, \mathbf{p}'_2)$ of the $\pi - \pi$ interaction can be taken in a separable form [33,34] so that the Bethe–Goldstone equation for the T-matrix of the $\pi - \pi$ scattering in the pion gas can be solved straightforwardly, resulting in in-medium scattering phase shifts and cross sections with resonances [34–36] as well as the corresponding equation of state [37,38].

Interactions of pions with baryons can also be described as particle number conserving $2 \to 2$ processes with a Hamiltonian of the form (6). See, for example, the recent work [39] on the ANL-Osaka model which provides an excellent description of existing $\pi - N$ scattering data. These processes contain, in particular, the Δ and N resonances that become very important for heavy-ion collision experiments with lower c.m. energies at SPS, SIS-18, and the future FAIR and NICA experiments. For our discussion of results from the LHC experiment in the present work, the processes involving baryons are not important and will not be treated explicitly here.

If the particle number is fixed, neglecting processes described by $H_{\rm reac}$, a pion gas in thermodynamic equilibrium may form a Bose–Einstein condensate at high phase space occupation densities and sufficiently low temperatures. It is possible that the expanding fireball will meet such parameter values of the pion phase space during the non-equilibrium evolution.

There are also processes which change the particle numbers of the different species which contribute to the interaction part of the Hamiltonian $H_{\rm reac}$. As an example, we have $\pi + \pi \rightleftharpoons 4\pi$ [40] or the formation of other mesons such as $\pi + \pi \to \bar{K} + K$ which decay in other channels, see Lin and Ko [30]. As shown there, because of the threshold for these reactions and the small cross sections compared to the elastic collisions, the corresponding relaxation time $\tau_{\rm reac}$ to establish chemical equilibrium is large. This is a slow process not of relevance for the time scales considered here. Other reactions involving resonant correlations such as $\Delta \rightleftharpoons N + \pi$ contribute to collision processes via virtual states and conserve the particle number, but also have a small branching ratio for a number of non-conserving processes. These reactive collisions which change the pion number are assumed to be weak in comparison to the quasielastic collisions and can be discarded for the short-time evolution, but are relevant for the evolution on long time scales to produce chemical equilibrium.

The $\pi - \pi$ collision term was treated in Boltzmann equation calculations by Welke and Bertsch [30]. Strong pion interaction processes which change the pion number have been considered, e.g., in Reference [40].

In addition, other work has been performed using transport codes to describe the time evolution of the pion distribution function and to solve the low-p_T enhancement puzzle. We discuss here the more general NSO approach to give an approach which goes beyond the single-particle distribution function considered in the transport codes which are based on kinetic equations.

4. The Relevant Statistical Operator

Our main point is the selection of the set of relevant observables B_n which determines the convergence and the accuracy of the non-equilibrium description. We discuss three examples, the Kubo case considering only conserved quantities, the kinetic theory considering the single-particle occupation numbers, and the formation of a condensate where amplitudes are added. In principle, all three choices for the set of relevant observables should give the same results if the limit $\varepsilon \to 0$ is correctly performed. However, because we use perturbation expansions and Fermi's Golden rule, these approximations lead to different results.

4.1. Kubo Case

Within the NSO method, there is no prescription for the choice of the set $\{B_n\}$ of relevant observables. Only conserved observables have to be included because their averages cannot be changed dynamically.

A minimum set of relevant observables of the pion–nucleon system (Kubo case) is the energy H that is conserved. The number of pions is not strictly conserved. Because the pion number is not prescribed, in equilibrium, no corresponding chemical potential μ_π can be introduced. Formally, one takes $\mu_\pi = 0$ similar to the photon system. Thus, in the Kubo case, one supposes that $\tau_{\pi,\mathrm{abs}} \ll t_{\mathrm{fo}}$ (contrary to the case studied by us in this paper). The number of baryons N_b is conserved. In addition, the charge has to be considered as conserved quantity. With this selection of relevant observables, we obtain from the maximum principle for the relevant entropy the grand canonical distribution

$$\rho^{(0)}_{\mathrm{rel}}(t) = \frac{1}{Z^{(0)}_{\mathrm{rel}}(t)} e^{-\beta(t)(H-\sum_\alpha \mu_\alpha(t) N_\alpha)} . \quad (7)$$

Because the system is expanding, the thermodynamic averages are also changing with time and also the corresponding Lagrange parameters. We can adopt the blast wave model [41–45] to describe the expansion of the fireball. If we assume that the velocity is proportional to the distance from the center, the density is decreasing with time. Assuming adiabatic expansion, the entropy is constant, but the temperature is also decreasing. This hydrodynamical model may serve as an approximation to describe the time dependence of the average density and energy and, according to the self-consistency conditions (3), $\mu_\alpha(t)$ and $\beta(t)$.

Starting from a non-equilibrium state, we consider the relaxation to the local thermodynamic equilibrium. The time behavior of the observables N_c and H_c^{MF} of the particle number of the species c and its mean-field energy (see below) are given by

$$\frac{d}{dt}\langle N_c\rangle^t = \frac{i}{\hbar}\langle [H, N_c]\rangle^t_{\mathrm{rel}} - \frac{1}{\hbar^2}\int_{-\infty}^0 dt' e^{\epsilon t'} \mathrm{Tr}\{\rho_{\mathrm{rel}}(t)[H(t'), [H, N_c]]\} , \quad (8)$$

$$\frac{d}{dt}\langle H_c^{\mathrm{MF}}\rangle^t = \frac{i}{\hbar}\langle [H, H_c^{\mathrm{MF}}]\rangle^t_{\mathrm{rel}} - \frac{1}{\hbar^2}\int_{-\infty}^0 dt' e^{\epsilon t'} \mathrm{Tr}\{\rho_{\mathrm{rel}}(t)[H(t'), [H, H_c^{\mathrm{MF}}]]\} . \quad (9)$$

Evaluating the correlation functions in Born approximation for the pion system, we observe a behavior different from the one that would be consistent with the assumption of $\mu_\pi = 0$. Because the particle numbers N_π are conserved with respect to the elastic collisions $H_{\rm col}$, only the inelastic collisions $H_{\rm reac}$ contribute. This makes the time derivative (8) small. In contrast, the thermalization process (9) is dominated by $H_{\rm col}$ so that the exchange of energy between the different components c and the momentum states is a fast process.

We can calculate the corresponding relaxation times $\tau_i^{-1} = -[d\langle B_i\rangle^t/dt]/\langle B_i\rangle^t$ for the observables of local thermodynamic equilibrium and compare it with the expansion time scale $\tau_{\rm exp}^{-1} = \partial_\mu u^\mu \approx -n_b^{-1}[dn_b/dt]$. The freeze-out time $t_{\rm fo}$ is given by the condition that the increasing $\tau_i(t)$ becomes equal to $\tau_{\rm exp}$.

It is evident that this is a very global approach. We cannot assume that at any freeze-out time $t_{\rm fo}$ the system is well approximated by the equilibrium distribution (7). A more detailed description of the non-equilibrium state is necessary, in particular if there exist long-living correlations. Indeed, the relaxation to thermodynamic equilibrium (7) also implies the achievement of the total pion number in equilibrium which is determined only by T and $\mu_\pi = 0$ in thermodynamic equilibrium. Because the processes which change the pion number are weak under conditions at RHIC and LHC which we focus on, the corresponding relaxation times are long and the Kubo case is not valid for our considerations. To have an appropriate description of the non-equilibrium process, these slow modes should be included in $\rho_{\rm rel}(t)$. At freeze-out, we therefore expect that not the thermodynamic equilibrium but a more general non-equilibrium distribution is seen.

4.2. Pion Number as a Relevant Observable

Long-living correlations have to be implemented in the set of relevant observables to improve the convergence of the perturbation expansion, and to apply the Markov approximation. For the pion system considered here, we have elastic collisions which conserve the particle numbers and in general inelastic reactions where the particle numbers of the constituents c are changed. Because the conserving interaction $H_{\rm col}$ leads to cross sections which are large compared with cross sections for the non-conserving interaction $H_{\rm reac}$, the pion number N_π is an observable which changes slowly with time and should be included in the set of relevant observables so that the index α in Equation (7) goes over all pion species c. The new condition

$$\langle N_\pi\rangle_{\rm rel}^t = \langle N_\pi\rangle^t \tag{10}$$

is not given by the external condition of the expanding fireball but must be calculated self-consistently solving the corresponding equation of evolution (8).

A new feature of the relevant distribution including the pion number is the possibility of a singularity when the self-consistency conditions (3) are solved. As well known from the ideal Bose gas, we have to treat the occupation of the ground state separately so that below a critical temperature we have $\langle N_\pi\rangle = \langle N_\pi^{\rm norm}\rangle + \langle N_\pi^{\rm cond}\rangle$ with the normal component $N_\pi^{\rm norm} = \sum_{p>0} a^+_{\mathbf{p},\pi} a_{\mathbf{p},\pi}$ and the condensate $N_\pi^{\rm cond} = a^+_{0,\pi} a_{0,\pi}$. The corresponding relevant operator reads

$$\rho_{\rm rel}^{\rm Bose}(t) = \frac{1}{Z_{\rm rel}^{\rm Bose}(t)} e^{-\beta(t)[H-\sum_c \mu_c(t) N_c^{\rm norm}] - F_{0,\pi}(t) a^+_{0,\pi} a_{0,\pi}}\,. \tag{11}$$

The new Lagrange parameter $F_{0,\pi}(t)$ follows from the self-consistency relation (10) in perturbation expansion with respect to H' as

$$\langle N_\pi^{\rm cond}\rangle_{\rm rel}^t = \frac{1}{e^{\beta(t)[E_{0,\pi}-\mu_\pi(t)]+F_{0,\pi}(t)} - 1}\,, \tag{12}$$

which is a macroscopic number if the temperature is below the critical one. The normal component $\langle N_\pi^{\rm norm}\rangle^t_{\rm rel}$ is only a function of $\beta(t)$ as is well known; we have $E_{0,\pi} - \mu_\pi(t) = 0$ in the condensate state. Then, the Bose condensate $\langle N_\pi^{\rm cond}\rangle^t_{\rm rel}$ is a macroscopic number so that $F_{0,\pi}(t)$ is infinitesimally small. Below, we improve this shortcoming introducing coherent states.

We can also solve the evolution equations (8) with the relevant statistical operator (11). The corresponding relaxation times are given by the interaction part H'. However, they are very different. As before, the elastic collisions thermalize the kinetic energies of the components (9) leading to the relaxation time $\tau_{\rm therm}$.

To describe chemical relaxation (8), we can simplify the von Neumann equation as

$$\frac{\partial}{\partial t}\rho(t) = \frac{1}{i\hbar}\left[(H^0 + H_{\rm reac}), \rho(t)\right] - \frac{1}{\tau_{\rm therm}}\left(\rho(t) - \rho_{\rm rel}^{\rm Bose}(t)\right). \tag{13}$$

This is possible if the thermalization is very fast compared to the formation of the chemical equilibrium. The solution is given by Equation (1) after replacing ϵ by $1/\tau_{\rm therm}$ and H' by $H_{\rm reac}$.

With respect to the evolution of the fireball, we have the result that full thermodynamic equilibrium must not necessarily occur at the freeze-out time. The reaction rates become small during the expansion so that the relevant distribution (11) at $t_{\rm fo}$ is seen. In contrast to the thermodynamic equilibrium (7), a Bose–Einstein condensate of pions is possible.

4.3. Kinetic Equations

We can further improve the relevant statistical operator considering the occupation numbers $n_{\mathbf{p},c} = a^+_{\mathbf{p},c}a_{\mathbf{p},c}$ of the single-particle states as relevant observables. Formally, instead of N_c, each single-particle state is taken similar to a new species. The time dependence of the mean occupation of this state leads to the kinetic equations. For details of the derivation, see, e.g., Reference [46], Equation (4.100).

We consider the time evolution of the pion distribution function $\langle n_{\mathbf{p},c}\rangle^t$ as the diagonal part of the Wigner distribution function [46]. The relevant statistical operator has the form

$$\rho_{\rm rel}^{\rm kin}(t) = \frac{1}{Z_{\rm rel}^{\rm kin}(t)} e^{-\sum_{\mathbf{p},c} s_{\mathbf{p},c}(t) a^+_{\mathbf{p},c}a_{\mathbf{p},c}} \tag{14}$$

with the corresponding self-consistency conditions to eliminate the Lagrange parameters $s_{\mathbf{p},c}(t)$,

$$\langle n_{\mathbf{p},c}\rangle^t = \frac{1}{e^{s_{\mathbf{p},c}(t)} - 1}. \tag{15}$$

For the time evolution, the following kinetic equation is obtained from (4) after integration by parts and using (3), see also [46]

$$\frac{d}{dt}\langle n_{\mathbf{p},c}\rangle^t = \frac{1}{\hbar^2}\int_{-\infty}^0 dt' e^{\epsilon t'} {\rm Tr}\left\{[H, n_{\mathbf{p},c}] e^{(i/\hbar)Ht'} [H, \rho_{\rm rel}^{\rm kin}(t)] e^{-(i/\hbar)Ht'}\right\} \tag{16}$$

if we neglect the explicit time dependence of $\rho_{\rm rel}^{\rm kin}(t)$. In the approximation of binary collisions, we get the quantum statistical Boltzmann equation

$$\begin{aligned} \frac{d}{dt}\langle n_{\mathbf{p}_1}\rangle^t_{\rm coll} \;=\; & \frac{2\pi}{\hbar}\sum_{\mathbf{p}_2,\mathbf{p}'_1,\mathbf{p}'_2} \delta(E_{\mathbf{p}_1} + E_{\mathbf{p}_2} - E_{\mathbf{p}'_1} - E_{\mathbf{p}'_2})\delta_{\mathbf{p}_1+\mathbf{p}_2-\mathbf{p}'_1-\mathbf{p}'_2} |t(\mathbf{p}_1\mathbf{p}_2, \mathbf{p}'_1\mathbf{p}'_2) + t(\mathbf{p}_1\mathbf{p}_2, \mathbf{p}'_2\mathbf{p}'_1)|^2 \\ & \times \left\{\langle n_{\mathbf{p}'_1}\rangle^t \langle n_{\mathbf{p}'_2}\rangle^t [1 + \langle n_{\mathbf{p}_1}\rangle^t][1 + \langle n_{\mathbf{p}_2}\rangle^t] - \langle n_{\mathbf{p}_1}\rangle^t \langle n_{\mathbf{p}_2}\rangle^t [1 + \langle n_{\mathbf{p}'_1}\rangle^t][1 + \langle n_{\mathbf{p}'}\rangle^t]\right\} \end{aligned} \tag{17}$$

where the two-particle T-matrix is given by the interaction potential in Born approximation [46]. Near thermodynamic equilibrium,

$$\langle n_{\mathbf{p},c}\rangle_{\rm eq} = \frac{1}{e^{E_{\mathbf{p},c}/T - \mu_c/T} - 1}, \tag{18}$$

we can approximate the Boltzmann equation in relaxation time approximation as:

$$\frac{d}{dt}\langle n_{\mathbf{p},c}\rangle^t = -\frac{1}{\tau_{\mathbf{p},c}}(\langle n_{\mathbf{p},c}\rangle^t - \langle n_{\mathbf{p},c}\rangle_{\rm eq}) , \tag{19}$$

where the relaxation time $\tau_{\mathbf{p},c}$ is calculated from a microscopic collision process. This approach of a relaxation time $\tau_{\rm col}$ of collisions as the thermal average over $\tau_{\mathbf{p},c}$ [46] or the corresponding collision frequency is used in the relevant literature (see, e.g., [30]). Note that the relaxation time ansatz (19) with $\mathbf{p}$-dependent relaxation time does not obey, in general, the conservation of particle number. According to Mermin [47], this defect is removed if the relaxation occurs not to the equilibrium state but to a relevant operator which accounts for the conservation of particle number, see also [48].

Thermal freeze-out is obtained at the time $t_{\rm fo}$ when $\tau_{\rm col}(t_{\rm fo}) = \tau_{\rm exp}(t_{\rm fo})$, where the scattering time scale for a given particle species c, working in favor of equilibration, can be computed locally from the local densities n_d, thermal (relative) velocities v_{cd}, and total scattering cross sections σ_{cd} between the particles c and d [42–44] after momentum average

$$\frac{1}{\tau_{\rm col}} = \sum_d \langle v_{cd}\sigma_{cd}\rangle n_d \,. \tag{20}$$

4.4. Nonequilibrium State with Condensate Formation

Alternatively, we can construct another relevant operator with the single-particle occupation numbers $n_{\mathbf{p},c}$, but containing also non-diagonal parts and, in addition, also single construction operators $a_{\mathbf{p},c}$ and $a^+_{\mathbf{p},c}$. Corresponding expressions are known from the theory of coherent states which are of interest to describe Bose–Einstein condensates. We can construct the relevant entropy with arbitrary powers of the creation and annihilation operators, corresponding to a very general expansion of the entropy operator in occupation number representation.

As a simple case, we construct the relevant statistical operator

$$\rho^{\rm coh}_{\rm rel}(t) = \frac{1}{Z^{\rm coh}_{\rm rel}(t)} e^{\sum_{\mathbf{p},c}[F^*_{\mathbf{p},c}(t)a_{\mathbf{p},c} + F_{\mathbf{p},c}(t)a^+_{\mathbf{p},c} - s_{\mathbf{p},c}(t)a^+_{\mathbf{p},c}a_{\mathbf{p},c}]} = e^{-S^{(2)}(t)} \tag{21}$$

with the corresponding expression for the partition function $Z^{\rm coh}_{\rm rel}(t)$. Higher order contributions such as $a^+_{\mathbf{p},c}a^+_{\mathbf{p},c}$ are also possible, as well as non-diagonal terms (describing systems which are not homogeneous in space) but will not be considered here. A similar approach has been used for superfluidity in strongly coupled fermion systems [49]. Note that this bilinear form of the entropy $S^{(2)}(t)$ may be extended including higher than second order terms in $a^+_{\mathbf{p},c}$ and $a_{\mathbf{p},c}$. This is necessary to describe, e.g., total energy conservation or the formation of bound states.

We have to eliminate the Lagrange multipliers $F^*_{\mathbf{p},c}(t), F_{\mathbf{p},c}(t), s_{\mathbf{p},c}(t)$ using the self-consistency conditions (3). The evaluation of correlation functions becomes quite simple if the relevant statistical operator (7) is diagonal in the occupation number representation. We transform $a_{\mathbf{p},c} = b_{\mathbf{p},c} + B_{\mathbf{p},c}(t)$ where $b_{\mathbf{p},c}$ obey the usual commutation relations for bosons, and $B_{\mathbf{p},c}(t) = F_{\mathbf{p},c}(t)/s_{\mathbf{p},c}(t)$ is a c-number. We obtain the diagonal form

$$S^{(2)}(t) = \sum_{\mathbf{p},c}[s_{\mathbf{p},c}(t)b^+_{\mathbf{p},c}b_{\mathbf{p},c} - |F_{\mathbf{p},c}(t)|^2/s_{\mathbf{p},c}(t)] \tag{22}$$

for the bilinear relevant entropy $S^{(2)}(t)$, the c-number term can be canceled with $Z^{\rm coh}_{\rm rel}(t)$. Then, the evaluation of $\langle n_{\mathbf{p},c}\rangle_{\rm rel}$ is quite simple and yields the well-known result

$$\langle b^+_{\mathbf{p},c}b_{\mathbf{p},c}\rangle^t_{\rm rel} = \frac{1}{e^{s_{\mathbf{p},c}(t)} - 1} = f_{\mathbf{p},c}(t), \qquad \langle b^+_{\mathbf{p},c}\rangle^t_{\rm rel} = \langle b_{\mathbf{p},c}\rangle^t_{\rm rel} = 0, \tag{23}$$

which is the Bose distribution for the ideal quantum gas, but with non-equilibrium parameter $s_{\mathbf{p},c}(t) \geq 0$ which are determined by the given averages. The mean occupation numbers follow as $\langle n_{\mathbf{p},c}\rangle^t_{\rm rel} = [e^{s_{\mathbf{p},c}(t)} - 1]^{-1} + |B_{\mathbf{p},c}(t)|^2$. In addition, we find $\langle a_{\mathbf{p},c}\rangle^t_{\rm rel} = B_{\mathbf{p},c}(t)$. With these relations, the Lagrange parameters in Equation (21) can be eliminated.

As before, the dynamics of the many-particle system is described by the Hamiltonian $H = H^0 + H_{\rm col} + H_{\rm reac}$, defined in Equations (5) and (6). We extract the mean-field terms (MF) from the interaction $(1 = \{\mathbf{p}, c\})$

$$H = \sum_1 E^{\rm MF}(1,t)a_1^+ a_1 + \frac{1}{2}\sum_{12} \Delta^{\rm MF}_{\rm pair}(12,t)a_1^+ a_2^+ + \text{c.c.} + \frac{1}{2}\sum_{121'2'} V(12,1'2')a_1^+ a_2^+ a_{2'} a_{1'} - (\text{MF}) \quad (24)$$

with $E^{\rm MF}(1,t) = E(1) + \sum_2 V(12,12)_{\rm ex}\langle n_2\rangle^t$ and $\Delta^{\rm MF}_{\rm pair}(12,t) = \sum_{1'2'} V(12,1'2')\langle a_{2'} a_{1'}\rangle^t$. We will not consider pairing so that $\Delta^{\rm MF}_{\rm pair}(12,t) = 0$. In the case of fermions, pairing was considered in Reference [49], which can also transformed to the bilinear form (22) applying the Bogoliubov transformation. In the case of a Bose gas considered here, the mean-field terms contain also averages $\langle a_2^+ a_{2'} a_{1'}\rangle^t$ of the condensate mode so that

$$H^{\rm MF}(t) = \sum_1 E^{\rm MF}(1,t)a_1^+ a_1 + \frac{1}{2}\Delta^{\rm MF}_{\rm cond}(1,t)a_1^+ + \text{c.c.} \quad (25)$$

with $\Delta^{\rm MF}_{\rm cond}(1,t) = \sum_{21'2'} V(12,1'2')\langle a_2^+ a_{2'} a_{1'}\rangle^t$.

According to the NSO method, the kinetic equations are obtained from the equations of evolution (4) for the relevant observables

$$\frac{d}{dt}\langle B_n\rangle^t = \lim_{\epsilon\to 0}\frac{i\epsilon}{\hbar}\int_{-\infty}^t dt' e^{\epsilon(t'-t)}\text{Tr}\left\{e^{-S^{(2)}(t')}e^{iH(t'-t)/\hbar}[H, B_n]e^{-iH(t-t')/\hbar}\right\}. \quad (26)$$

We apply perturbation theory with respect to the deviation ΔH from the mean-field expression which can be incorporated into $s_{\mathbf{p},c}(t) = \beta_c(t)[E^{\rm MF}_{\mathbf{p},c}(t) - \mu_c(t)] + \delta f_{\mathbf{p},c}(t) = f^{\rm MF}_{\mathbf{p},c}(t) + \delta f_{\mathbf{p},c}(t)$. The new Lagrange parameters $\beta_c(t), \mu_c(t)$ are introduced to describe the total particle number N_c and mean-field energy $H^{\rm MF}_c$ of the species c. The perturbation expansion is performed with respect to $\Delta S(t) = S^{(2)}(t) - S^0(t)$ with $S^0(t) = \beta(t)[H^{\rm MF}(t) - \sum_c \mu_c(t)N_c]$, where $\beta(t)$ is determined by the average of the total energy H. We have ($S^{(2)}(t)$ commutes with $S^0(t)$ in the lowest order of perturbation theory)

$$\frac{d}{dt}\langle a_1^+\rangle^t = \lim_{\epsilon\to 0}\frac{i\epsilon}{\hbar}\int_{-\infty}^0 dt' e^{\epsilon t'}e^{-i\mu_1 t'/\hbar}\text{Tr}\left\{e^{-S^{(2)}(t'+t)}\left[E(1)a_1^+ + \frac{1}{2}\sum_{1'22'} V(1'2',12)a_{1'}^+ a_{2'}^+ a_2\right]\right\} \quad (27)$$

and the corresponding equations of evolution for the other relevant observables $N_c, H^{\rm MF}_c, a_{\mathbf{p},c}$. To evaluate the trace, we perform the transformation of the relevant statistical operator (7) to the diagonal form (22) and have

$$\frac{d}{dt}\langle a_1^+\rangle^t = \frac{i}{\hbar}E^{\rm MF}(1,t)\lim_{\epsilon\to 0}\epsilon\int_{-\infty}^0 dt' e^{\epsilon t'}e^{-i\mu_1 t'/\hbar}F_1^*(t+t'), \quad (28)$$

where it was assumed that the mean-field energy $E^{\rm MF}(1,t) = E(1) + \sum_2 V(12,12)_{\rm ex} f_2(t)$ depends only weakly on time so that it can be extracted from the integral which is determined by the collisions. In addition, we suppose that a condensate mode is only in the state $\mathbf{p}_1, c_1$ and $V(11,11) = 0$ with 1 denoting the state of lowest mean field energy. In the stationary state, we assume a periodic dependence on time, $F_1(t) = F_1^0 e^{i\omega t}$. Then, the integral can be performed with the result $\omega = \mu_1/\hbar$. The amplitude $\langle a_1\rangle^t = F(t)$ depends periodically on time. We obtain the condition $\hbar\omega = \mu_1 = E^{\rm MF}(1)$ for a stationary solution, considering the lowest order (mean-field approximation). Similar results hold for $\langle a_1^+\rangle^t$.

For the other relevant observables, the time derivative vanishes in the lowest order of perturbation expansion with respect to the interaction.

To obtain the evolution of the averages, one has to consider higher orders of the interaction. It is convenient to use the following expression for the NSO obtained from (1) after integration by parts

$$\rho(t) = \rho_{\rm rel}(t) - \lim_{\epsilon\to 0}\int_{-\infty}^{t} e^{\epsilon(t'-t)}U(t,t')\left\{\frac{i}{\hbar}[H,\rho_{\rm rel}(t')] + \frac{\partial}{\partial t'}\rho_{\rm rel}(t'),\right\}U(t',t)dt'. \tag{29}$$

so that, for the averages,

$$\frac{d}{dt}\langle B_n\rangle^t = \frac{i}{\hbar}{\rm Tr}\{\rho_{\rm rel}(t)[H,B_n]\}$$
$$+\frac{1}{\hbar^2}\int_{-\infty}^{0} dt' e^{\epsilon t'}{\rm Tr}\left\{[H,B_n]e^{iHt'/\hbar}\left([H,\rho_{\rm rel}(t')] + \frac{\hbar\partial}{i\partial t'}\rho_{\rm rel}(t')\right)e^{-iHt'/\hbar}\right\}. \tag{30}$$

In Markov approximation, the time dependence of $\rho_{\rm rel}(t')$ is neglected, and we have the Boltzmann-like form of the equations of evolution; see also (8), (9), which is obtained after cyclic permutation within the trace. In our case, we cannot assume that the time dependence of $F_1(t) \propto \exp(i\omega t)$ is slow; only after the transformation to the diagonal form may the remaining $s_1(t)$ be slow.

Using Wick's theorem, the evaluation of the first term of the r.h.s. of (30) is immediately done if we transform to the diagonal form of the relevant statistical operator. The second term describes the collision between the pions and gives the relaxation to the intermediate relevant state showing the condensate distribution. The evaluation of the time dependence of occupation numbers $\langle n_{\mathbf{p},c}\rangle^t$ coincides with the expression (17) but replacing $\langle n_{\mathbf{p},c}\rangle^t$ by $f_{\mathbf{p},c}(t) + |B_{\mathbf{p},c}(t)|^2$.

The time evolution of the amplitude follows in Born approximation as

$$\begin{aligned}\frac{d}{dt}\langle a_1^+\rangle^t \;=\; & \frac{i}{\hbar}E_1^{\rm MF}B_1^*(t) + \frac{\pi}{2\hbar}B_1^*(t)\sum_{1'22'}|V_{\rm ex}(12,1'2')|^2\delta(E_{\mathbf{p}_1}+E_{\mathbf{p}_2}-E_{\mathbf{p}'_1}-E_{\mathbf{p}'_2})\delta_{\mathbf{p}_1+\mathbf{p}_2-\mathbf{p}'_1-\mathbf{p}'_2}\\ & \times\{f_{1'}f_{2'}(1+f_2) - f_2(1+f_{2'})(1+f_{1'})\}.\end{aligned} \tag{31}$$

Stationary solution is the grand canonical distribution with the chemical potential given by the pion number density. If the pion chemical potential approaches the lowest pion energy state, a quantum condensate will be formed which is described by a coherent state. The time evolution of the condensate is characterized by the collision time $\tau_{\rm cond}$.

4.5. Quantum Master Equation

The non-equilibrium evolution of the pion system can also be treated considering it as an open system coupled to a bath. We can consider the gluon system as the bath in the stage of evolution where the pions are formed from the hot quark–gluon plasma, or we can consider the interaction between pions (e.g., via ρ mesons) as a bath. We also can consider the pion Bose–Einstein condensate as the relevant subsystem interacting with the normal pion gas. A quantum master equation is derived that contains a Lindblad term [17], and a solution can be performed using coherent states. We will not discuss this interesting approach here but mention that the treatment of open many-particle systems is also possible within the Zubarev NSO method, leading to quantum master equations [17]. See, for instance, Reference [50] for the treatment of heavy quarkonia kinetics in a quark–gluon plasma.

5. Discussion

We refer to the central 200 AGeV ^{16}O+Au data of the NA35 Collaboration, see [30]. For more recent data, see also the discussion of Reference [51]. Assuming hadronization (formation time) at $t_0 \sim 1$ fm/c and temperature of about 160 MeV, the equilibrium pion density at $\mu_\pi = 0$ is $n_{\pi,\rm normal} \approx 0.15$ fm^{-3}, in contrast to the observed density $n_\pi(t_0) \sim 1$ fm^{-3}. This motivates the consideration of a strong macroscopic occupation of the lowest momentum state, forming a pion Bose–Einstein condensate.

We use the hydrodynamical expansion under conservation of the initial entropy S_0 which determines the temperature evolution according to $s(T)V(\tau) = S_0 = \text{const.}$, where for the entropy density we use a fit to lattice QCD data from Reference [52].

For the expansion of the fireball, we can adopt a Bjorken like picture where in the first stage ($t < 10$ fm/c) we have one-dimensional expansion with $n_\pi(t) \sim n_\pi(t_0)t_0/t$, and afterwards three-dimensional expansion where $n_\pi(t) \propto t^{-3}$. The expansion rate $\tau_{\rm exp}^{-1} = |\dot{n}|/n \sim 1/t$ drops down as $1/t$.

The relaxation $\tau_{\rm col} = 1/[\langle\sigma v\rangle n(t)]$ is estimated by a thermal average of the elastic $\pi - \pi$ cross section $\sigma \approx 23$ mb [30], determined by scattering phase shift data. The thermal average $\langle\sigma v\rangle \sim 7 - -10$ mb is nearly not depending on time, so that the collision time drops down proportional to $1/t$ in the first stage, but proportional to $1/t^3$ in the later stage which induces the freeze-out which occurs at $t \approx 10$ fm/c, where this transition occurs. The relaxation of the condensate mode $\langle a_1^+\rangle$ differs from that of the normal modes. A slower relaxation entails that this mode freezes out while the normal part is further thermalizing.

For a recent discussion of the chemical freeze-out in the phase diagram on the basis of a kinetic criterion, see Reference [53] and references therein.

The experimental data are well reproduced by the fit of a pion (and kaon) distribution with a non-equilibrium chemical potential as a Lagrangian multiplier in CERN SPS [14]. The thermal freeze-out process of pions and kaons at LHC conditions is characterized by just two parameters, the freeze-out time $\tau_{\rm fo}$ and the transverse size $r_{\rm max}$, whereby the shape of the transverse momentum spectra is described with only one parameter, $r_{\rm max}/\tau_{\rm fo}$ because the volume at freeze-out $V = \pi\tau_{\rm fo}r_{\rm max}^2$ fixes the overall normalization [13]. For an excellent simultaneous fit of pion, kaon, and proton spectra in most central Pb+Pb collisions at $\sqrt{s} = 2.76$ TeV, including the low-momentum enhancement of pions, a non-equilibrium chemical potential of pions $\mu_\pi = 134.9$ MeV is required which is very close to the neutral pion mass $m_\pi = 134.98$ MeV. The other parameters are $T_{\rm kin} = 138$ MeV, $\tau_{\rm fo} = 7.68$ fm/c and $r_{\rm max} = 11.7$ fm, according to [13]. A scenario as described by the Zubarev approach to the non-equilibrium statistical operator, with a fast relaxation to an intermediate relevant operator describing a Bose–Einstein condensate of pions and the slow relaxation to full thermodynamic equilibrium seems to be realistic with these estimates of time scales.

A detailed numerical calculation within the presented approach, e.g., on the basis of a separable model Hamiltonian for $\pi - \pi$ scattering as discussed in Section 3 is the subject of ongoing work that shall be reported in a subsequent publication.

6. Conclusions

There are different models to describe the low momentum enhancement of pions observed in HIC at SPS, RHIC, and LHC energies. We discuss this effect as a signature of a quantum condensate of the high-density pion gas. As an origin for the high phase space density of pions, one may think of an initial state in the form of a color glass condensate state (gluon saturation) which gets converted to a pion gas by particle number conserving process as described, e.g., [54,55].

After the hadronization time, a hadron gas is formed, which, under LHC conditions, mainly consists of pions. The time evolution of the fireball is governed by particle-conserving binary collisions; processes that change the pion number are weak and influence only the long-time evolution. In the oversaturated pion gas, the cross sections of pion rescattering processes are relatively large. As a consequence, the pion distribution function quickly relaxes to local thermodynamic equilibrium (here denoted as relevant distribution) which slowly evolves to full equilibrium.

The expansion of the fireball produced in HIC changes not only the parameter of the local thermodynamic equilibrium but influences also the relaxation time, and freeze-out happens if the relaxation rate becomes smaller than the expansion rate. A general description of this non-equilibrium process is given here within the Zubarev method of the non-equilibrium statistical operator. As discussed in the literature, it appears that one can capture the essence of the effect with fixed point dynamics. The relevant statistical operator may be considered as a transient distribution proposed also recently from other approaches [28,29]. Here, we formulate this behavior using the Zubarev concept of a relevant statistical operator. The system quickly relaxes to a relevant distribution (pre-equilibrium state) which evolves slowly to equilibrium, but is frozen out at the freeze-out time. This relevant distribution at $t_{\rm fo}$ describes the composition to be observed in the experiments.

We show different possibilities to introduce a relevant statistical operator to derive the corresponding equations of evolution of the state. Treating the binary collisions in relaxation time approximation, a quantum condensate may appear in the relevant statistical operator. After freeze-out, where this relevant distribution stops evolving further, the non-equilibrium evolution of the pion system is described by kinetic equations with initial condition at freeze-out time for the distribution function, which is approximated by the relevant statistical operator at $t_{\rm fo}$. To obtain a optimum description already in lowest order perturbation theory (Markov approximation), the relevant statistical operator should contain already all relevant correlations, in particular the formation of quantum condensates.

The method of the Zubarev NSO as presented here for the application to the pion production in heavy-ion collision experiments considers not only a systematic description of the collision processes but also a simultaneous treatment of the hydrodynamical evolution as well as the evolution of the condensate.

Author Contributions: Conceptualization, G.R. and D.B.; methodology, G.R.; validation, D.B., D.N.V. and V.G.M.; formal analysis, G.R.; investigation, D.B.; writing–original draft preparation, G.R.; writing–review and editing, D.B. and D.N.V.; funding acquisition, D.B. and G.R. All authors have read and agreed to the published version of the manuscript.

Funding: This work was supported by the MEPhI Academic Excellence Program under contract number 02.a03.21.0005.

Conflicts of Interest: The authors declare no conflict of interest.

References

1. Braun-Munzinger, P.; Magestro, D.; Redlich, K.; Stachel, J. Hadron production in Au–Au collisions at RHIC. *Phys. Lett. B.* **2001**, *518*, 41–46. [CrossRef]
2. Andronic, A.; Braun-Munzinger, P.; Redlich, K.; Stachel, J. Decoding the phase structure of QCD via particle production at high energy. *Nature* **2018**, *561*, 321–330. [CrossRef]
3. Stachel, J.; Andronic, A.; Braun-Munzinger, P.; Redlich, K. Confronting LHC data with the statistical hadronization model. *J. Phys. Conf. Ser.* **2014**, *509*, 012019. [CrossRef]
4. Becattini, F.; Bleicher, M.; Kollegger, T.; Schuster, T.; Steinheimer, J.; Stock, R. Hadron formation in relativistic nuclear collisions and the QCD phase diagram. *Phys. Lett. B.* **2013**, *111*, 082302. [CrossRef] [PubMed]
5. Cleymans, J.; Kraus, I.; Oeschler, H.; Redlich, K.; Wheaton, S. Statistical model predictions for particle ratios at $\sqrt{s_{NN}}$ = 5.5 TeV. *Phys. Rev. C* **2006**, *74*, 034903. [CrossRef]
6. Cleymans, J. The thermal-statistical model for particle production. *EPJ Web Conf.* **2010**, *7*, 01001. [CrossRef]
7. Abelev, B.; Adam, J.; Adamova, D.; Adare, A.M.; Aggarwal, M.M.; Rinella, G. A.; Agocs, A.G.; Agostinelli, A.; Aguilar Salazar, S.; Ahammed, Z.; et al. Pion, kaon, and proton production in central Pb-Pb collisions at $\sqrt{s_{NN}} = 2.76$ TeV. *Phys. Lett. B.* **2012**, *109*, 252301. [CrossRef] [PubMed]
8. Abelev, B.; Adam, J.; Adamova, D.; ALICE Collaboration. Centrality dependence of π, K, p production in Pb-Pb collisions at $\sqrt{s_{NN}}$ = 2.76 TeV. *Phys. Rev. C* **2013**, *88*, 044910. [CrossRef]
9. Andronic, A.; Braun-Munzinger, P.; Friman, B.; Lo, P. M.; Redlich, K.; Stachel, J. The thermal proton yield anomaly in Pb-Pb collisions at the LHC and its resolution. *Phys. Lett. B.* **2019**, *792*, 304. [CrossRef]
10. Weinhold, W.; Friman, B.; Norenberg, W. Thermodynamics of Delta resonances. *Phys. Lett. B.* **1998**, *433*, 236. [CrossRef]
11. Petran, M.; Rafelski, J. Universal hadronization condition in heavy ion collisions at $\sqrt{s_{\rm NN}} = 62$ GeV and at $\sqrt{s_{\rm NN}} = 2.76$ TeV. *Phys. Rev. C* **2013**, *88*, 021901. [CrossRef]
12. Petran, M.; Letessier, J.; Petracek, V.; Rafelski, J. Hadron production and quark–gluon plasma hadronization in Pb-Pb collisions at $\sqrt{s_{NN}} = 2.76$ TeV. *Phys. Rev. C* **2013**, *88*, 034907. [CrossRef]

13. Begun, V.; Florkowski, W.; Rybczynski, M. Explanation of hadron transverse-momentum spectra in heavy-ion collisions at $\sqrt{s}_{NN} = 2.76$ TeV within chemical non-equilibrium statistical hadronization model. *Phys. Rev. C* **2014**, *90*, 014906. [CrossRef]
14. Kataja, M.; Ruuskanen, P.V. Nonzero Chemical Potential and the Shape of the p_T Distribution of Hadrons in Heavy Ion Collisions. *Phys. Lett. B.* **1990**, *243*, 181. [CrossRef]
15. Gavin, S.; Ruuskanen, P.V. Low-pT pion enhancement from partial thermalization in nuclear collision. *Phys. Lett. B.* **1991**, *262*, 326. [CrossRef]
16. Gerber, P.; Leutwyler, H.; Goity, J.L. Kinetics of an expanding pion gas. *Phys. Lett. B.* **1990**, *246*, 513. [CrossRef]
17. Zubarev, D.N.; Morozov,V.; Röpke, G. *Statistical Mechanics of Nonequilibrium Processes*; Akademie Verlag: Berlin, Germany, 1996; Volume I, II.
18. Zubarev, D.N. *Nonequilibrium Statistical Thermodynamics*; Nauka: Moscow, Russia, 1971.
19. Voskresensky, D.N. On the possibility of Bose-condensation of pions in ultrarelativistic collisions of nuclei. *J. Exp. Theor. Phys.* **1994**, *78*, 793.
20. Kolomeitsev, E.E.; Voskresensky, D.N. Fluctuations in non-ideal pion gas with dynamically fixed particle number. *Nucl. Phys. A* **2018**, *973*, 89. [CrossRef]
21. Welke, G.M.; Venugopalan, R.; Prakash, M. The Speed of sound in an interacting pion gas. *Phys. Lett. B.* **1990**, *245*, 137. [CrossRef]
22. Fore, B.; Reddy, S. Pions in hot dense matter and their astrophysical implications. *Phys. Rev. C* **2020**, *101*, 035809. [CrossRef]
23. Semikoz, D.V.; Tkachev, I.I. Kinetics of Bose condensation. *Phys. Rev. Lett.* **1995**, *74*, 3093. [CrossRef] [PubMed]
24. Semikoz, D.V.; Tkachev, I.I. Condensation of bosons in kinetic regime. *Phys. Rev. D* **1997**, *55*, 489. [CrossRef]
25. Voskresensky, D.N. Kinetic description of a pion gas in ultrarelativistic collisions of nuclei: Turbulence and Bose condensation. *Phys. Atom. Nucl.* **1996**, *59*, 2015–2023.
26. Berges, J.; Floerchinger, S.; Venugopalan, R. Entanglement and thermalization. *Nucl. Phys. A* **2019**, *982*, 819. [CrossRef]
27. Berges, J.; Floerchinger, S.; Venugopalan, R. Dynamics of entanglement in expanding quantum fields. *JHEP* **2018**, *1804*, 145. [CrossRef]
28. Erne, S.; Büker, R.; Gasenzer, T.; Berges, J.; Schmiedmayer, J. Universal dynamics in an isolated one-dimensional Bose gas far from equilibrium. *Nature* **2018**, *563*, 225. [CrossRef]
29. Mazeliauskas, A.; Berges, J. Prescaling and far-from-equilibrium hydrodynamics in the quark–gluon plasma. *Phys. Rev. Lett.* **2019**, *122*, 122301. [CrossRef]
30. Welke, G.M.; Bertsch, G.F. Bosonic kinetics and the pion transverse momentum in heavy ion collisions. *Phys. Rev. C* **1992**, *45*, 1403. [CrossRef]
31. Carneiro, G.M.; Pethick, C.J. Specific heat of a normal Fermi liquid. II. Microscopic approach. *Phys. Rev. B* **1975**, *11*, 1106. [CrossRef]
32. Ivanov, Y.B.; Knoll, J.; Voskresensky, D.N. Resonance transport and kinetic entropy. *Nucl. Phys. A* **2000**, *672*, 313. [CrossRef]
33. Aouissat, Z.; Chanfray, G.; Schuck, P.; Welke, G. $\pi - \pi$ scattering in a hot pion gas at URHIC conditions. *Zeitschrift für Physik A Hadrons and Nuclei* **1991**, *340*, 347. [CrossRef]
34. Barz, H.W.; Schulz, H.; Bertsch, G.; Danielewicz, P. Pion-pion cross section in a dense and hot pionic gas. *Phys. Lett. B.* **1992**, *275*, 19. [CrossRef]
35. Barz, H.W.; Danielewicz, P.; Schulz, H.; Welke, G.M. Thermalization of mesons in ultrarelativistic heavy ion reactions. *Phys. Lett. B.* **1992**, *287*, 40. [CrossRef]
36. Emelyanov, V.; Pantis, G. Pion thermalization in relativistic heavy ion collisions. *Nucl. Phys. A* **1995**, *592*, 581. [CrossRef]
37. Rapp, R.; Durso, J.W.; Wambach, J. Chirally constraining the $\pi\pi$ interaction in nuclear matter. *Nucl. Phys. A* **1996**, *596*, 436. [CrossRef]
38. Rapp, R.M.; Wambach, J. Equation of state of an interacting pion gas with realistic $\pi\pi$ interactions. *Phys. Rev. C* **1996**, *53*, 3057. [CrossRef]
39. Kamano, H.; Lee, T.S.; Nakamura, S.X.; Sato, T. The ANL-Osaka Partial-Wave Amplitudes of πN and γN Reactions. *arXiv* **2019**, arXiv:1909.11935.

40. Voskresensky, D.N.; Blaschke, D.; Röpke, G.; Schulz, H. Nonequilibrium approach to dense hadronic matter. *Int. J. Mod. Phys. E* **1995**, *4*, 1. [CrossRef]
41. Siemens, P.J.; Rasmussen, J.O. Evidence for a blast wave from compress nuclear matter. *Phys. Rev Lett.* **1979**, *42*, 880. [CrossRef]
42. Schnedermann, E.; Heinz, U. Relativistic hydrodynamics in a global fashion. *Phys. Rev. C* **1993**, *47*, 1738. [CrossRef]
43. Schnedermann, E.; Sollfrank, J.; Heinz, U. Thermal phenomenology of hadrons from 200-A/GeV S+S collisions. *Phys. Rev. C* **1993**, *48*, 2462. [CrossRef] [PubMed]
44. Jaiswal, A.; Koch, V. A viscous blast-wave model for heavy-ion collisions. *IOP Conf. Ser. J. Phys. Conf. Ser.* **2017**, *779*, 012065. [CrossRef]
45. Florkowski, W. *Phenomenology of Ultra-Relativistic Heavy-Ion Collisions*; World Scientific: Singapore, 2010.
46. Röpke, G. *Nonequilibrium Statistical Physics*; Wiley-VCH: Weinheim, Germany, 2013.
47. Mermin, N.D. Lindhard Dielectric Function in the Relaxation-Time Approximation. *Phys. Rev. B* **1970**, *1*, 2362. [CrossRef]
48. Selchow, A.; Röpke, G.; Wierling, A. Extended Mermin-like Dielectric Function for a Two-Component Plasma. *Wierling, Contrib. Plasma Phys.* **2002**, *42*, 43. [CrossRef]
49. Röpke, G. Bound states and superfluidity in strongly coupled Fermion systems. *Annalen der Physik (Leipzig)* **1994**, *3*, 145. [CrossRef]
50. Akamatsu, Y. Heavy quark master equations in the Lindblad form at high temperatures. *Phys. Rev. D* **2015**, *91*, 056002. [CrossRef]
51. Begun, V.; Florkowski, W. Bose–Einstein condensation of pions in heavy-ion collisions at the CERN Large Hadron Collider (LHC) energies. *Phys. Rev. C* **2015**, *91*, 054909. [CrossRef]
52. Pena, C.; Blaschke, D. Quantum mechanical model for J/? suppression in the LHC era. *Nucl. Phys. A* **2014**, *927*, 1. [CrossRef]
53. Blaschke, D.; Jankowski, J.; Naskret, M. Formation of hadrons at chemical freeze-out. *arXiv* **2017**, arXiv:1705.00169.
54. Nazarova, E.; Juchnowski, L.; Blaschke, D.; Fischer, T. Low-momentum pion enhancement from schematic hadronization of a gluon-saturated initial state. *Particles* **2019**, *2*, 10. [CrossRef]
55. Harrison, B.; Peshier, A. Bose–Einstein Condensation from the QCD Boltzmann Equation. *Particles* **2019**, *2*, 16. [CrossRef]

particles

MDPI

Article

Calculation of Acceleration Effects Using the Zubarev Density Operator

Georgy Prokhorov [1,*], Oleg Teryaev [1,2,3] and Valentin Zakharov [2,4,5]

1 Joint Institute for Nuclear Research, 141980 Dubna, Russia; teryaev@jinr.ru
2 Institute of Theoretical and Experimental Physics, NRC Kurchatov Institute, 117218 Moscow, Russia; vzakharov@itep.ru
3 Department of Physics, M. V. Lomonosov Moscow State University, 117234 Moscow, Russia
4 School of Biomedicine, Far Eastern Federal University, 690950 Vladivostok, Russia
5 Moscow Institute of Physics and Technology, 141700 Dolgoprudny, Russia
* Correspondence: prokhorov@theor.jinr.ru

Received: 16 November 2019; Accepted: 23 December 2019; Published: 3 January 2020

Abstract: The relativistic form of the Zubarev density operator can be used to study quantum effects associated with acceleration of the medium. In particular, it was recently shown that the calculation of perturbative corrections in acceleration based on the Zubarev density operator makes it possible to show the existence of the Unruh effect. In this paper, we present the details of the calculation of quantum correlators arising in the fourth order of the perturbation theory needed to demonstrate the Unruh effect. Expressions for the quantum corrections for massive fermions are also obtained.

Keywords: Zubarev operator; Unruh effect; acceleration

1. Introduction

There are wonderful quantum-field effects associated with non-uniform motion of the medium. A well-known example of such an effect is the Unruh effect, according to which an accelerated observer perceives the Minkowski vacuum as a medium filled with particles with a temperature depending on the acceleration [1]. This temperature is called the Unruh temperature, and it is equal to

$$T_U = \frac{\hbar |a|}{2\pi c k} . \tag{1}$$

The Unruh effect is similar to the Hawking effect, since it is also associated with the appearance of the event horizon in the accelerated system. This effect continues to be the focus of theorists [2–5]. The possibility of experimental observation of the Unruh effect needs the generation of ultrahigh acceleration in a system, which is relevant, in particular, for particle collisions [6,7] and systems with two-level atoms in quantum optics [8–10].

There is a universal fundamental statistical approach to describing the equilibrium thermodynamics of quantized fields. This approach is based on the relativistic form of the Zubarev density operator [11,12]. It has recently been shown that this approach allows to study in a regular way the effects of rotation and acceleration in a medium of relativistic particles [13–15].

Using the Zubarev operator method, various effects associated with the motion of the medium are shown. In particular, the well-known chiral vortical effect is shown and corrections to this effect are calculated [13,14,16]. Since the chiral vortical effect is associated with the axial electromagnetic anomaly [17–19], as well as with the gravitational anomaly [20,21], it turns out that the approach with the Zubarev operator carries information about the most fundamental properties of matter.

A remarkable observation made recently is that the Unruh effect can also be obtained from the Zubarev density operator [22,23]. Relativistic quantum statistical mechanics considers a continuous medium filled with particles described by quantized fields. This medium in equilibrium is characterized by a number of thermodynamic parameters, such as temperature, energy density, pressure, and others. Non-trivial aspect is connected with the need for normalization of the thermodynamic quantities of the system to a specific vacuum, as a rule, the Minkowski vacuum. With such a statement of the problem, a direct consequence of the Unruh effect from the point of view of quantum statistical mechanics is the vanishing of the observables, in particular, the energy-momentum tensor, at a proper temperature equal to the Unruh temperature [24,25]. This is exactly what was found in [23].

This means that, in the Zubarev approach, nontrivial gravitational effects, associated with the occurrence of an event horizon, and the changes in vacuum properties depending on the reference system, are reproduced. This observation seems even more surprising because the corresponding calculation was carried out in ordinary flat Minkowski space-time, that is, by observing an accelerated medium from an inertial frame. Nevertheless, nontrivial physics associated with Unruh effect is reproduced.

Moreover, as discussed in [26], the Zubarev density operator exactly reproduces quantum corrections that were derived in space of a cosmic string, characterized by a conical singularity [25,27]. The existence of such exact duality means that the Zubarev operator of the accelerated medium leads to emergent conical geometry.

To justify the Unruh effect in [23], it was necessary to calculate a five-point correlator with boost operators and energy-momentum tensor. This calculation in [23] was made for the massless Dirac field. The method we used was developed in a series of works [13–15], where the perturbation theory with the boost operator was developed and corrections up to the second order were calculated. It is well known [13] that the boost operator does not commute with the Hamiltonian of the system. Because of this, with each subsequent order of the perturbation theory, the complexity of calculation of the corresponding quantum correlators increases. The fourth order found in [23] is currently a record one. In the present paper, we describe a never before given scheme for calculating higher orders of the perturbation theory with the boost operator and also derive expressions for the fourth-order corrections to the energy-momentum tensor at nonzero mass.

To date, the Unruh effect has been considered from various points of view. In particular, in the framework of quantum optics [8–10], the Unruh effect manifests itself in the thermal distribution with the Unruh temperature, in the probability of absorption and emission of gamma quanta by accelerated two-level atoms. It is necessary to consider the interaction of atoms with an electromagnetic field in the framework of perturbation theory with respect to the coupling constant, while acceleration effects can be taken into account in a nonperturbative way through Rindler coordinates.

Despite the difference in approaches, a parallel can be established between our consideration and the usual approach to the Unruh effect, as well as quantum optics. In particular, in the statistical approach we also obtained a term in the energy density (which is the last term in Equation (3.1) in [23]), which corresponds to the Bose distribution of gamma quanta at the Unruh temperature.

The paper has the following structure. Section 2 introduces the basic concepts of the method of Zubarev density operator. An algorithm of constructing a perturbation theory in acceleration is also discussed. In the Section 3 we describe in details the calculation of the corrections of the fourth-order in acceleration to the energy-momentum tensor. The interpretation associated with the Unruh effect is given in Section 4. In Section 5 the conclusions are given. In the Appendix A the formulas for the coefficients at finite mass are presented.

The system of units $\hbar = c = k = 1$ is used.

2. Perturbation Theory in Acceleration Based on the Zubarev Density Operator

In this section, we introduce the basic concepts related to the density operator and describe how the acceleration perturbation theory can be constructed. In general, in this section we follow the paper [13]. In [11,12], a relativistic form of the Zubarev density operator was obtained for a medium in a state of local thermodynamic equilibrium

$$\hat{\rho} = \frac{1}{Z}\exp\Big\{ -\int_{\Sigma} d\Sigma_{\mu}[\hat{T}^{\mu\nu}(x)\beta_{\nu}(x) - \xi(x)\hat{j}^{\mu}(x)]\Big\}, \tag{2}$$

where integration over the three-dimensional hypersurface Σ is performed. Here, $\beta_{\mu} = \frac{u_{\mu}}{T}$ is the inverse temperature 4-vector, T is the proper temperature, $\xi = \frac{\mu}{T}$ is the ratio of the chemical potential in the co-moving frame to temperature, $\hat{T}^{\mu\nu}$ and $\hat{j}^{\mu}$ are the energy-momentum tensor and current operators. The conditions of global thermodynamic equilibrium for a medium with rotation and acceleration, that is, conditions under which the density operator (2) becomes independent on the choice of the hypersurface Σ, over which the integration occurs, thus acquiring the properties of a density operator in a state of global thermodynamic equilibrium, have the form [13,15,28,29]

$$\begin{aligned} \beta_{\mu} &= b_{\mu} + \varpi_{\mu\nu}x_{\nu}, \quad b_{\mu} = \text{const}, \quad \varpi_{\mu\nu} = \text{const}, \\ \varpi_{\mu\nu} &= -\frac{1}{2}(\partial_{\mu}\beta_{\nu} - \partial_{\nu}\beta_{\mu}), \quad \xi = \text{const}, \end{aligned} \tag{3}$$

where $\varpi_{\mu\nu}$ is the thermal vorticity tensor. In the general case, integration over the hypersurface is to be done and the quantum statistical theory should be projected to this hypersurface [30–32]. So under the condition (3), the density operator (2) becomes the global equilibrium density operator [13,15,22]

$$\hat{\rho} = \frac{1}{Z}\exp\Big\{ -\beta_{\mu}(x)\hat{P}^{\mu} + \frac{1}{2}\varpi_{\mu\nu}\hat{J}^{\mu\nu}_x + \xi\hat{Q}\Big\}, \tag{4}$$

where $\hat{P}$ is the 4-momentum operator, $\hat{Q}$ is the charge operator, and $\hat{J}_x$ are the generators of the Lorentz transformations shifted to the point x

$$\hat{J}^{\mu\nu}_x = \int d\Sigma_{\lambda}\left[(y^{\mu} - x^{\mu})\hat{T}^{\lambda\nu}(y) - (y^{\nu} - x^{\nu})\hat{T}^{\lambda\mu}(y)\right]. \tag{5}$$

The technique of calculating the mean values of physical quantities based on (4) was developed in [13,15], in which second-order corrections in the thermal vorticity tensor were calculated to various thermodynamic quantities for scalar and Dirac fields.

Note that the condition (3) also lead to a system of kinematic equations of motion, solving which, we can construct trajectories of motion. Particular cases of this solution are the rotation of the medium as a solid, as well as uniformly accelerated motion.

Following [13], we introduce the thermal acceleration vector α_{μ} and the thermal vorticity pseudo-vector w_{μ}

$$\alpha_{\mu} = \varpi_{\mu\nu}u^{\nu}, \quad w_{\mu} = -\frac{1}{2}\epsilon_{\mu\nu\alpha\beta}u^{\nu}\varpi^{\alpha\beta}. \tag{6}$$

Drawing a parallel with the electrodynamics, α_{μ} and w_{μ} can be called the "electrical" and "magnetic" components of the tensor ϖ. The tensor $\varpi_{\mu\nu}$ can be decomposed into these components as follows

$$\varpi_{\mu\nu} = \epsilon_{\mu\nu\alpha\beta}w^{\alpha}u^{\beta} + \alpha_{\mu}u_{\nu} - \alpha_{\nu}u_{\mu}. \tag{7}$$

The meaning of the vectors α_μ and w_μ becomes clear when considering the case of global thermodynamic equilibrium, in which they are proportional to the usual kinematic 4-acceleration a_μ and vorticity ω_μ

$$\alpha^\mu = \varpi^\mu{}_\nu u^\nu = u^\nu \partial_\nu \beta^\mu = \frac{1}{T} u^\nu \partial_\nu u^\mu = \frac{a^\mu}{T}, \tag{8}$$

and for thermal vorticity, we get

$$w_\mu = -\frac{1}{2}\epsilon_{\mu\nu\alpha\beta} u^\nu \varpi^{\alpha\beta} = -\frac{1}{2}\epsilon_{\mu\nu\alpha\beta} u^\nu \partial^\beta \beta^\alpha = \frac{1}{2T}\epsilon_{\mu\nu\alpha\beta} u^\nu \partial^\alpha u^\beta = \frac{\omega_\mu}{T}. \tag{9}$$

In the rest frame, a^μ and ω^μ are expressed in terms of three-dimensional vectors

$$a^\mu = (0, \mathbf{a}), \quad \omega^\mu = (0, \mathbf{w}), \tag{10}$$

where **a** and **w** are three-dimensional acceleration and angular velocity.

The density operator (4) allows one to find corrections related to thermal vorticity in the framework of perturbation theory. To do this, it is necessary to expand (4) in a series taking into account the fact that we are constructing a perturbation theory with non-commuting operators. According to [13] we have

$$\langle \hat{O}(x) \rangle = \langle \hat{O}(0) \rangle_{\beta(x)} + \sum_{N=1}^{\infty} \frac{\varpi^N}{2^N N! |\beta|^N} \int_0^{|\beta|} d\tau_1 d\tau_2 ... d\tau_N \langle T_\tau \hat{J}_{-i\tau_1 u} ... \hat{J}_{-i\tau_N u} \hat{O}(0) \rangle_{\beta(x),c}, \tag{11}$$

where it is assumed that each of the thermal vorticity tensors is contracted with the tensor $\hat{J}$ so that $\varpi_{\mu\nu}\hat{J}^{\mu\nu}$. Equation (11) includes only connected correlators, all disconnected correlators are reduced due to the contribution of the denominator $1/Z$ to (4). This fact is reflected in the subscript c; the subscript $\beta(x)$ means that the mean values are taken at $\varpi = 0$, that is, averaging is performed over a grand canonical distribution. The T_τ operator orders in imaginary time τ, and $|\beta| = \sqrt{\beta^\mu \beta_\mu} = \frac{1}{T}$.

It is convenient to introduce the boost operator $\hat{K}$ and the angular momentum operator $\hat{J}$

$$\hat{J}^{\mu\nu} = u^\mu \hat{K}^\nu - u^\nu \hat{K}^\mu - \epsilon^{\mu\nu\rho\sigma} u_\rho \hat{J}_\sigma. \tag{12}$$

From (7) and (12), it follows that scalar products with vorticity tensor in (4) and (11) decompose into terms with boost and angular momentum

$$\varpi_{\mu\nu} \hat{J}^{\mu\nu}_x = -2\alpha_\mu \hat{K}^\mu_x - 2w_\mu \hat{J}^\mu_x. \tag{13}$$

Further, we will consider uniformly accelerated media without vorticity and chemical potential; therefore (4), transforms to the density operator of the form

$$\hat{\rho} = \frac{1}{Z} \exp\Big\{ -\beta_\mu \hat{P}^\mu - \alpha_\mu \hat{K}^\mu_x \Big\}, \tag{14}$$

and the perturbation theory in (11) takes the form of the series in acceleration

$$\langle \hat{O}(x) \rangle = \langle \hat{O}(0) \rangle_{\beta(x)} + \sum_{N=1}^{\infty} \frac{(-1)^N a^N}{N!} \int_0^{|\beta|} d\tau_1 d\tau_2 ... d\tau_N \langle T_\tau \hat{K}_{-i\tau_1 u} ... \hat{K}_{-i\tau_N u} \hat{O}(0) \rangle_{\beta(x),c}, \tag{15}$$

3. Calculation of Fourth-Order Coefficients in Acceleration

The second-order coefficients in acceleration in the energy-momentum tensor of the Dirac field were calculated in [13,14]. In this section, we present the details of calculation of the fourth-order coefficient.

The operator form of the energy-momentum tensor of the mass-less Dirac fields is well known. We will use the symmetrized Belinfante energy-momentum tensor

$$\hat{T}^{\mu\nu} = \frac{i}{4}\left(\bar{\Psi}\gamma^{\mu}\partial^{\nu}\Psi - \partial^{\nu}\bar{\Psi}\gamma^{\mu}\Psi + \bar{\Psi}\gamma^{\nu}\partial^{\mu}\Psi - \partial^{\mu}\bar{\Psi}\gamma^{\nu}\Psi\right). \tag{16}$$

As follows from (15), the calculation of the necessary correlators is performed in imaginary time—a time shift is made along the imaginary axis. Thus, it is necessary to pass to the Euclidean formalism in imaginary time. The Euclidean version of the energy-momentum tensor (16) has the form

$$\hat{T}^{\mu\nu} = \frac{i^{\delta_{0\mu}+\delta_{0\nu}}}{4}\left(\bar{\Psi}\tilde{\gamma}^{\mu}\partial^{\nu}\Psi - \partial^{\nu}\bar{\Psi}\tilde{\gamma}^{\mu}\Psi + \bar{\Psi}\tilde{\gamma}^{\nu}\partial^{\mu}\Psi - \partial^{\mu}\bar{\Psi}\tilde{\gamma}^{\nu}\Psi\right), \tag{17}$$

where $\tilde{\gamma}$ are the Euclidean Dirac matrices

$$\tilde{\gamma}_{\mu} = i^{1-\delta_{0\mu}}\gamma_{\mu}, \quad \tilde{\gamma}^{\mu} = i^{1-\delta_{0\mu}}\gamma^{\mu}, \quad \{\tilde{\gamma}_{\mu}\tilde{\gamma}_{\nu}\} = 2\delta_{\mu\nu}, \tag{18}$$

and derivatives are also taken in Euclidean space-time, so that

$$\tilde{\partial}_{\mu} = (-i)^{\delta_{0\mu}}\partial_{\mu}. \tag{19}$$

However, we will omit the tilde sign for derivatives. Consider the mean value of the energy-momentum tensor in the fourth order of the perturbation theory in acceleration using (15)

$$\begin{aligned}\langle\hat{T}^{\mu\nu}(x)\rangle &= \langle\hat{T}^{\mu\nu}(0)\rangle_{\beta(x)} + \frac{a_{\rho}a_{\sigma}}{2}\int_0^{|\beta|} d\tau_1 d\tau_2 \langle T_{\tau}\hat{K}^{\rho}_{-i\tau_1 u}\hat{K}^{\sigma}_{-i\tau_2 u}\hat{T}^{\mu\nu}(0)\rangle_{\beta(x),c} \\ &+\frac{8a_{\rho}a_{\sigma}a_{\gamma}a_{\eta}}{4!}\int_0^{|\beta|} d\tau_1 d\tau_2 d\tau_3 d\tau_4 \langle T_{\tau}\hat{K}^{\rho}_{-i\tau_1 u}\hat{K}^{\sigma}_{-i\tau_2 u}\hat{K}^{\gamma}_{-i\tau_3 u}\hat{K}^{\eta}_{-i\tau_4 u}\hat{T}^{\mu\nu}(0)\rangle_{\beta(x),c} + \mathcal{O}(a^6).\end{aligned} \tag{20}$$

Symmetry and parity considerations fix the form of the energy-momentum tensor in the fourth order of perturbation theory

$$\begin{aligned}\langle\hat{T}^{\mu\nu}\rangle &= (\rho_0 - A_1T^2a^2 + A_2a^4)u^{\mu}u^{\nu} - (p_0 - A_3T^2a^2 + A_4a^4)\Delta^{\mu\nu} \\ &+(A_5T^2 - A_6a^2)a^{\mu}a^{\nu} + \mathcal{O}(a^6) \qquad \Delta^{\mu\nu} = g^{\mu\nu} - u^{\mu}u^{\nu},\end{aligned} \tag{21}$$

where $a^2 = a_{\mu}a^{\mu}$. As already mentioned, 2-order coefficients were calculated earlier in [13,14]. Our goal is to calculate coefficients of the 4th order A_2, A_4, A_6. Comparing (20) with (21), we obtain

$$\begin{aligned}A_2a^4u^{\mu}u^{\nu} - A_4a^4\Delta^{\mu\nu} - A_6a^2a^{\mu}a^{\nu} &= \frac{a_{\rho}a_{\sigma}a_{\gamma}a_{\eta}}{4!}\int_0^{|\beta|} d\tau_1 d\tau_2 d\tau_3 d\tau_4 \\ &\times\langle T_{\tau}\hat{K}^{\rho}_{-i\tau_1 u}\hat{K}^{\sigma}_{-i\tau_2 u}\hat{K}^{\gamma}_{-i\tau_3 u}\hat{K}^{\eta}_{-i\tau_4 u}\hat{T}^{\mu\nu}(0)\rangle_{\beta(x),c}.\end{aligned} \tag{22}$$

The coefficients A_2, A_4, A_6 are Lorentz invariants, and the relation (22) is valid for any choice of the vectors u_μ, a_μ. Therefore, to determine the coefficient, we can choose the vectors u_μ, a_μ in any form convenient for us. To determine A_2, we choose $a^\mu = (0,0,0,|a|)$ and $u^\mu = (1,0,0,0)$ and consider the components $\mu = 0, \nu = 0$, to determine A_4 we choose $a^\mu = (0,0,|a|,0)$ and $u^\mu = (1,0,0,0)$ and consider the components $\mu = 3, \nu = 3$, and to determine A_6 we choose $a^\mu = (0,0,0,|a|)$ and $u^\mu = (1,0,0,0)$ and consider the components $\mu = 3, \nu = 3$. As a result, we obtain

$$\begin{aligned} A_2 &= \frac{1}{4!}\int_0^{|\beta|} d\tau_1 d\tau_2 d\tau_3 d\tau_4 \langle T_\tau \hat{K}^3_{-i\tau_1 u}\hat{K}^3_{-i\tau_2 u}\hat{K}^3_{-i\tau_3 u}\hat{K}^3_{-i\tau_4 u}\hat{T}^{00}(0)\rangle_{\beta(x),c}, \\ A_4 &= \frac{1}{4!}\int_0^{|\beta|} d\tau_1 d\tau_2 d\tau_3 d\tau_4 \langle T_\tau \hat{K}^2_{-i\tau_1 u}\hat{K}^2_{-i\tau_2 u}\hat{K}^2_{-i\tau_3 u}\hat{K}^2_{-i\tau_4 u}\hat{T}^{33}(0)\rangle_{\beta(x),c}, \\ A_6 &= -A_4 + \frac{1}{4!}\int_0^{|\beta|} d\tau_1 d\tau_2 d\tau_3 d\tau_4 \langle T_\tau \hat{K}^3_{-i\tau_1 u}\hat{K}^3_{-i\tau_2 u}\hat{K}^3_{-i\tau_3 u}\hat{K}^3_{-i\tau_4 u}\hat{T}^{33}(0)\rangle_{\beta(x),c}. \end{aligned} \tag{23}$$

We now use the representation of the boost operator through the energy-momentum tensor. According to (5) and (12), we have

$$\begin{aligned} \hat{K}^3_{-i\tau u} &= \hat{J}^{03}_{-i\tau u} = \int d^3x(-1)x^3\hat{T}^{00}(\tau,\mathbf{x}), \\ \hat{K}^2_{-i\tau u} &= \hat{J}^{02}_{-i\tau u} = \int d^3x(-1)x^2\hat{T}^{00}(\tau,\mathbf{x}), \end{aligned} \tag{24}$$

Substituting (24) into (23), we come to the need of calculating quantities of the form

$$\begin{aligned} C^{\alpha_1\alpha_2|\alpha_3\alpha_4|\alpha_5\alpha_6|\alpha_7\alpha_8|\alpha_9\alpha_{10}|ijkl} &= \int_0^{|\beta|} d\tau_x d\tau_y d\tau_z d\tau_f d^3x d^3y d^3z d^3f \\ \times x^i y^j z^k f^l \langle T_\tau \hat{T}^{\alpha_1\alpha_2}(\tau_x,\mathbf{x})&\hat{T}^{\alpha_3\alpha_4}(\tau_y,\mathbf{y})\hat{T}^{\alpha_5\alpha_6}(\tau_z,\mathbf{z})\hat{T}^{\alpha_7\alpha_8}(\tau_f,\mathbf{f})\hat{T}^{\alpha_9\alpha_{10}}(0)\rangle_{\beta(x),c}. \end{aligned} \tag{25}$$

In particular, from (23), we have

$$A_2 = \frac{1}{4!}C^{00|00|00|00|00|3333}, \; A_4 = \frac{1}{4!}C^{00|00|00|00|33|2222}, \; A_6 = -A_4 + \frac{1}{4!}C^{00|00|00|00|33|3333}. \tag{26}$$

Next, we will focus on calculating the coefficient in energy A_2; the remaining coefficients can be calculated by analogy.

We represent the energy-momentum tensor (17) in a split form

$$\begin{aligned} \hat{T}^{\alpha\beta}(X) &= \lim_{X_1,X_2\to X} \mathcal{D}^{\alpha\beta}_{ab}(\partial_{X_1},\partial_{X_2})\bar{\Psi}_a(X_1)\Psi_b(X_2), \\ \mathcal{D}^{\alpha\beta}_{ab}(\partial_{X_1},\partial_{X_2}) &= \frac{i^{\delta_{0\alpha}+\delta_{0\beta}}}{4}[\tilde{\gamma}^\alpha_{ab}(\partial_{X_2}-\partial_{X_1})^\beta + \tilde{\gamma}^\beta_{ab}(\partial_{X_2}-\partial_{X_1})^\alpha], \end{aligned} \tag{27}$$

and substitute it in (26). As a result, we get for the corresponding correlator

$$\begin{aligned} \langle T_\tau \hat{T}^{00}(X)\hat{T}^{00}(Y)\hat{T}^{00}(Z)\hat{T}^{00}(F)\hat{T}^{00}(0)\rangle_{\beta(x),c} = \lim_{\substack{X_1,X_2\to X\\ Y_1,Y_2\to Y\\ Z_1,Z_2\to Z\\ F_1,F_2\to F\\ H_1,H_2\to H=0}} \mathcal{D}^{00}_{a_1a_2}(\partial_{X_1},\partial_{X_2}) \\ \mathcal{D}^{00}_{a_3a_4}(\partial_{Y_1},\partial_{Y_2})\mathcal{D}^{00}_{a_5a_6}(\partial_{Z_1},\partial_{Z_2})\mathcal{D}^{00}_{a_7a_8}(\partial_{F_1},\partial_{F_2})\mathcal{D}^{00}_{a_9a_{10}}(\partial_{H_1},\partial_{H_2})\langle T_\tau \overline{\Psi}_{a_1}(X_1)\Psi_{a_2}(X_2) \\ \times\overline{\Psi}_{a_3}(Y_1)\Psi_{a_4}(Y_2)\overline{\Psi}_{a_5}(Z_1)\Psi_{a_6}(Z_2)\overline{\Psi}_{a_7}(F_1)\Psi_{a_8}(F_2)\overline{\Psi}_{a_9}(H_1)\Psi_{a_{10}}(H_2)\rangle_{\beta(x),c}. \end{aligned} \tag{28}$$

When calculating the correlator with 10 Dirac fields of the form (28), it is necessary to use an analogue of Wick theorem for field theory at finite temperatures. Then, the five-point correlator in (28) leads to the product of mean values of quadratic combinations of Dirac fields, that is, thermal propagators. For short, we denote $\Psi_{a_n} \to n$, and $\overline{\Psi}_{a_n} \to \bar{n}$ and omit T_τ and the index $\beta(x)$. Then, after extraction on the connected part in (28) according to Wick theorem, we obtain 24 terms

$$
\begin{aligned}
&\langle T_\tau \overline{\Psi}_{a_1}(X_1)\Psi_{a_2}(X_2)\overline{\Psi}_{a_3}(Y_1)\Psi_{a_4}(Y_2)\overline{\Psi}_{a_5}(Z_1)\Psi_{a_6}(Z_2)\overline{\Psi}_{a_7}(F_1)\Psi_{a_8}(F_2)\\
&\overline{\Psi}_{a_9}(H_1)\Psi_{a_{10}}(H_2)\rangle_{\beta(x),c} = \langle \bar{1}2\bar{3}4\bar{5}6\bar{7}8\bar{9}10\rangle = -\langle\bar{1}4\rangle\langle 2\bar{9}\rangle\langle\bar{3}6\rangle\langle\bar{5}8\rangle\langle\bar{7}10\rangle\\
&+\langle\bar{1}4\rangle\langle 2\bar{7}\rangle\langle\bar{3}6\rangle\langle\bar{5}10\rangle\langle 8\bar{9}\rangle + \langle\bar{1}4\rangle\langle 2\bar{9}\rangle\langle\bar{3}8\rangle\langle\bar{5}10\rangle\langle 6\bar{7}\rangle + \langle\bar{1}4\rangle\langle 2\bar{5}\rangle\langle\bar{3}8\rangle\langle 6\bar{9}\rangle\langle\bar{7}10\rangle\\
&+\langle\bar{1}4\rangle\langle 2\bar{7}\rangle\langle\bar{3}10\rangle\langle\bar{5}8\rangle\langle 6\bar{9}\rangle - \langle\bar{1}4\rangle\langle 2\bar{5}\rangle\langle\bar{3}10\rangle\langle 6\bar{7}\rangle\langle 8\bar{9}\rangle + \langle\bar{1}6\rangle\langle 2\bar{9}\rangle\langle\bar{3}8\rangle\langle 4\bar{5}\rangle\langle\bar{7}10\rangle\\
&-\langle\bar{1}6\rangle\langle 2\bar{7}\rangle\langle\bar{3}10\rangle\langle 4\bar{5}\rangle\langle 8\bar{9}\rangle + \langle\bar{1}6\rangle\langle 2\bar{9}\rangle\langle\bar{3}10\rangle\langle 4\bar{7}\rangle\langle\bar{5}8\rangle + \langle\bar{1}6\rangle\langle 2\bar{3}\rangle\langle 4\bar{9}\rangle\langle\bar{5}8\rangle\langle\bar{7}10\rangle\\
&+\langle\bar{1}6\rangle\langle 2\bar{7}\rangle\langle\bar{3}8\rangle\langle 4\bar{9}\rangle\langle\bar{5}10\rangle - \langle\bar{1}6\rangle\langle 2\bar{3}\rangle\langle 4\bar{7}\rangle\langle\bar{5}10\rangle\langle 8\bar{9}\rangle + \langle\bar{1}8\rangle\langle 2\bar{9}\rangle\langle\bar{3}6\rangle\langle 4\bar{7}\rangle\langle\bar{5}10\rangle\\
&-\langle\bar{1}8\rangle\langle 2\bar{5}\rangle\langle\bar{3}10\rangle\langle 4\bar{7}\rangle\langle 6\bar{9}\rangle - \langle\bar{1}8\rangle\langle 2\bar{9}\rangle\langle\bar{3}10\rangle\langle 4\bar{5}\rangle\langle 6\bar{7}\rangle - \langle\bar{1}8\rangle\langle 2\bar{3}\rangle\langle 4\bar{9}\rangle\langle\bar{5}10\rangle\langle 6\bar{7}\rangle\\
&+\langle\bar{1}8\rangle\langle 2\bar{5}\rangle\langle\bar{3}6\rangle\langle 4\bar{9}\rangle\langle\bar{7}10\rangle - \langle\bar{1}8\rangle\langle 2\bar{3}\rangle\langle 4\bar{5}\rangle\langle 6\bar{9}\rangle\langle\bar{7}10\rangle + \langle\bar{1}10\rangle\langle 2\bar{7}\rangle\langle\bar{3}6\rangle\langle 4\bar{9}\rangle\langle\bar{5}8\rangle\\
&-\langle\bar{1}10\rangle\langle 2\bar{5}\rangle\langle\bar{3}8\rangle\langle 4\bar{9}\rangle\langle 6\bar{7}\rangle - \langle\bar{1}10\rangle\langle 2\bar{7}\rangle\langle\bar{3}8\rangle\langle 4\bar{5}\rangle\langle 6\bar{9}\rangle - \langle\bar{1}10\rangle\langle 2\bar{3}\rangle\langle 4\bar{7}\rangle\langle\bar{5}8\rangle\langle 6\bar{9}\rangle\\
&-\langle\bar{1}10\rangle\langle 2\bar{5}\rangle\langle\bar{3}6\rangle\langle 4\bar{7}\rangle\langle 8\bar{9}\rangle + \langle\bar{1}10\rangle\langle 2\bar{3}\rangle\langle 4\bar{5}\rangle\langle 6\bar{7}\rangle\langle 8\bar{9}\rangle,
\end{aligned} \tag{29}
$$

where signs correspond to the number of permutations of anti-commuting fields. Thermal propagators have a standard form [13,33]

$$
\begin{aligned}
G_{a_1a_2}(X_1,X_2) &= \langle T_\tau \Psi_{a_1}(X_1)\overline{\Psi}_{a_2}(X_2)\rangle_{\beta(x)} = \sum\!\!\!\!\!\!\int_P e^{iP^+(X_1-X_2)}(-iP^+_\mu\tilde{\gamma}_\mu + m)_{a_1a_2}\Delta(P^+),\\
\bar{G}_{a_1a_2}(X_1,X_2) &= \langle T_\tau \overline{\Psi}_{a_1}(X_1)\Psi_{a_2}(X_2)\rangle_{\beta(x)} = -\langle T_\tau \Psi_{a_2}(X_2)\overline{\Psi}_{a_1}(X_1)\rangle_{\beta(x)}\\
&= -\sum\!\!\!\!\!\!\int_P e^{iP^-(X_1-X_2)}(iP^-_\mu\tilde{\gamma}_\mu + m)_{a_2a_1}\Delta(P^-),
\end{aligned} \tag{30}
$$

where integration over the three-dimensional components of the momentum and summation over the Matsubara frequencies of fermion field appear. The following notations are used in (30): $P^\pm = (p_n^\pm, \mathbf{p})$, $p_n^\pm = \pi(2n+1)/|\beta| \pm i\mu$, $n = 0, \pm1, \pm2, \cdots$, $X = (\tau, \mathbf{x})$, $\sum\!\!\!\!\!\!\int_P = \frac{1}{|\beta|}\sum_{n=-\infty}^{\infty}\int\frac{d^3p}{(2\pi)^3}$, and $\Delta(P) = \frac{1}{P^2+m^2}$, where the square is taken with the Euclidean metric, as also in $P^\pm_\mu\tilde{\gamma}_\mu = \not{P}^\pm$ (unlike $P^+(X_1 - X_2)$ according to [33]). Since we consider mass-less field at zero chemical potential, the mass and chemical potential must be set equal to zero $m = 0, \mu = 0$. Nevertheless, we retain the notation $P^\pm$, bearing in mind the possibility of generalization to the case with nonzero chemical potential in the future.

Next, substitute (30) in (29). We will describe the calculations for the first term in (29), while all other terms can be calculated by analogy

$$
\begin{aligned}
&- \lim_{\substack{X_1,X_2\to X\\ Y_1,Y_2\to Y\\ Z_1,Z_2\to Z\\ F_1,F_2\to F\\ H_1,H_2\to H=0}} \mathcal{D}^{00}_{a_1a_2}(\partial_{X_1},\partial_{X_2})\mathcal{D}^{00}_{a_3a_4}(\partial_{Y_1},\partial_{Y_2})\mathcal{D}^{00}_{a_5a_6}(\partial_{Z_1},\partial_{Z_2})\mathcal{D}^{00}_{a_7a_8}(\partial_{F_1},\partial_{F_2})\mathcal{D}^{00}_{a_9a_{10}}(\partial_{H_1},\partial_{H_2})\\
&\times \bar{G}_{a_1a_4}(X_1,Y_2)G_{a_2a_9}(X_2,H_1)\bar{G}_{a_3a_6}(Y_1,Z_2)\bar{G}_{a_5a_8}(Z_1,F_2)\bar{G}_{a_7a_{10}}(F_1,H_2) =\\
&- \sum\!\!\!\!\!\!\int_{\{P,Q,K,R,L\}} e^{-i\mathbf{p}(\mathbf{x}-\mathbf{y})-i\mathbf{q}\mathbf{x}-i\mathbf{k}(\mathbf{y}-\mathbf{z})-i\mathbf{r}(\mathbf{z}-\mathbf{f})-i\mathbf{l}\mathbf{f}} e^{ip_n^-(\tau_x-\tau_y)+iq_n^+\tau_x+ik_n^-(\tau_y-\tau_z)+ir_n^-(\tau_z-\tau_f)+il_n^-\tau_f}\\
&\times \Delta(P^-)\Delta(Q^+)\Delta(K^-)\Delta(R^-)\Delta(L^-)\\
&\times \mathrm{tr}\Big[(-i\not{L}^-)\mathcal{D}^{00}(iL^-,-iR^-)(-i\not{R}^-)\mathcal{D}^{00}(iR^-,-iK^-)(-i\not{K}^-)\\
&\times \mathcal{D}^{00}(iK^-,-iP^-)(-i\not{P}^-)\mathcal{D}^{00}(iP^-,iQ^+)(-i\not{Q}^+)\mathcal{D}^{00}(-iQ^+,-iL^-)\Big],
\end{aligned} \tag{31}
$$

where it was necessary to arrange all the matrices under the trace in accordance with the order of the spinor indices. To calculate (31), it is necessary to find a trace of the form

$$
\mathrm{tr}\Big[\not{P}_1\mathcal{D}^{00}(P_2,P_3)\not{P}_4\mathcal{D}^{00}(P_5,P_6)\not{P}_7\mathcal{D}^{00}(P_8,P_9)\not{P}_{10}\mathcal{D}^{00}(P_{11},P_{12})\not{P}_{13}\mathcal{D}^{00}(P_{14},P_{15})\Big]. \tag{32}
$$

The subsequent calculations are more convenient to carry out using special software applications. Calculation (32) requires finding the trace of 10 Euclidean Dirac matrices

$$
\mathrm{tr}\Big[\tilde{\gamma}^{\alpha_1}\tilde{\gamma}^{\alpha_2}\tilde{\gamma}^{\alpha_3}\tilde{\gamma}^{\alpha_4}\tilde{\gamma}^{\alpha_5}\tilde{\gamma}^{\alpha_6}\tilde{\gamma}^{\alpha_7}\tilde{\gamma}^{\alpha_8}\tilde{\gamma}^{\alpha_9}\tilde{\gamma}^{\alpha_{10}}\Big]. \tag{33}
$$

Using the definition (18), this trace can be easily transformed to the trace of ordinary Dirac matrices, which can be found using standard methods. We denote the trace in (32) as $A(P_1,P_2,P_3,P_4,P_5,P_6,P_7,P_8,P_9,P_{10},P_{11},P_{12},P_{13},P_{14},P_{15})$. Then (31) will be presented in the form

$$
\begin{aligned}
&-\int \frac{d^3p d^3q d^3k d^3r d^3l}{(2\pi)^{15}} e^{-i\mathbf{p}(\mathbf{x}-\mathbf{y})-i\mathbf{q}\mathbf{x}-i\mathbf{k}(\mathbf{y}-\mathbf{z})-i\mathbf{r}(\mathbf{z}-\mathbf{f})-i\mathbf{l}\mathbf{f}}\\
&\times \sum_{p_n,q_n,k_n,r_n,l_n} \frac{1}{|\beta|^5} e^{ip_n^-(\tau_x-\tau_y)+iq_n^+\tau_x+ik_n^-(\tau_y-\tau_z)+ir_n^-(\tau_z-\tau_f)+il_n^-\tau_f}\\
&\times \Delta(P^-)\Delta(Q^+)\Delta(K^-)\Delta(R^-)\Delta(L^-)\\
&\times A(-iL^-,iL^-,-iR^-,-iR^-,iR^-,-iK^-,-iK^-,iK^-,-iP^-,-iP^-,iP^-,iQ^+,\\
&-iQ^+,-iQ^+,-iL^-).
\end{aligned} \tag{34}
$$

Next, one needs to sum over the Matsubara frequencies in (34) using the relation

$$
\frac{1}{|\beta|}\sum_{\omega_n}\frac{(\omega_n \pm i\mu)^k e^{i(\omega_n\pm i\mu)\tau}}{(\omega_n\pm i\mu)^2+E^2} = \frac{1}{2E}\sum_{s=\pm1}(-isE)^k e^{\tau s E}[\theta(-s\tau)-n_F(E\pm s\mu)], \tag{35}
$$

where $E=\sqrt{\mathbf{p}^2+m^2}$, $n_F(E)=1/(1+e^{E/T})$ is the Fermi distribution, and θ is the Heaviside theta function. Again, we can take $m=0,\mu=0$. As a result, we obtain

$$
\begin{aligned}
&-\int \frac{d^3pd^3qd^3kd^3rd^3l}{(2\pi)^{15}} e^{-i\mathbf{p}(\mathbf{x}-\mathbf{y})-i\mathbf{q}\mathbf{x}-i\mathbf{k}(\mathbf{y}-\mathbf{z})-i\mathbf{r}(\mathbf{z}-\mathbf{f})-i\mathbf{l}\mathbf{f}} \\
&\times \frac{1}{32E_pE_qE_kE_rE_l} \sum_{s_1,s_2,s_3,s_4,s_5} e^{(\tau_x-\tau_y)s_1E_p+\tau_xs_2E_q+(\tau_y-\tau_z)s_3E_k+(\tau_z-\tau_f)s_4E_r+\tau_fs_5E_l} \\
&\times A(-i\widetilde{L}, i\widetilde{L}, -i\widetilde{R}, -i\widetilde{R}, i\widetilde{R}, -i\widetilde{K}, -i\widetilde{K}, i\widetilde{K}, -i\widetilde{P}, -i\widetilde{P}, i\widetilde{P}, i\widetilde{Q}, -i\widetilde{Q}, -i\widetilde{Q}, -i\widetilde{L}) \\
&\times \left(\theta\left[-s_1(\tau_x-\tau_y)\right] - n_F\left(E_p\right)\right)\left(\theta\left[-s_2\right] - n_F\left(E_q\right)\right) \\
&\times \left(\theta\left[-s_3(\tau_y-\tau_z)\right] - n_F\left(E_k\right)\right)\left(\theta\left[-s_4(\tau_z-\tau_f)\right] - n_F\left(E_r\right)\right)\left(\theta\left[-s_5\right] - n_F\left(E_l\right)\right). \qquad (36)
\end{aligned}
$$

Here, following [13], the notations $\widetilde{P} = \widetilde{P}(s_1) = (-is_1E_p, \mathbf{p})$, $\widetilde{Q} = \widetilde{Q}(s_2), \cdots$ are introduced. We return now to the formula for A_2 (26) with spatial integrals and calculate the contribution of the term (36). This contribution has the form

$$
\begin{aligned}
A_2 \;=\; &\int \frac{d\tau_xd\tau_yd\tau_zd\tau_fd^3xd^3yd^3zd^3fd^3pd^3qd^3kd^3rd^3l}{4!(2\pi)^{15}} e^{-i\mathbf{p}(\mathbf{x}-\mathbf{y})-i\mathbf{q}\mathbf{x}-i\mathbf{k}(\mathbf{y}-\mathbf{z})-i\mathbf{r}(\mathbf{z}-\mathbf{f})-i\mathbf{l}\mathbf{f}} \\
&\times x^3y^3z^3f^3D + \cdots, \qquad (37)
\end{aligned}
$$

where the ellipsis indicates the contribution of the remaining 23 terms from (29), and D equals to

$$
\begin{aligned}
D \;=\; &-\frac{1}{32E_pE_qE_kE_rE_l} \sum_{s_1,s_2,s_3,s_4,s_5} e^{(\tau_x-\tau_y)s_1E_p+\tau_xs_2E_q+(\tau_y-\tau_z)s_3E_k+(\tau_z-\tau_f)s_4E_r+\tau_fs_5E_l} \\
&\times A(-i\widetilde{L}, i\widetilde{L}, -i\widetilde{R}, -i\widetilde{R}, i\widetilde{R}, -i\widetilde{K}, -i\widetilde{K}, i\widetilde{K}, -i\widetilde{P}, -i\widetilde{P}, i\widetilde{P}, i\widetilde{Q}, -i\widetilde{Q}, -i\widetilde{Q}, -i\widetilde{L}) \\
&\times \left(\theta\left[-s_1(\tau_x-\tau_y)\right] - n_F\left(E_p\right)\right)\left(\theta\left[-s_2\right] - n_F\left(E_q\right)\right) \\
&\times \left(\theta\left[-s_3(\tau_y-\tau_z)\right] - n_F\left(E_k\right)\right)\left(\theta\left[-s_4(\tau_z-\tau_f)\right] - n_F\left(E_r\right)\right)\left(\theta\left[-s_5\right] - n_F\left(E_l\right)\right). \qquad (38)
\end{aligned}
$$

Next, one needs to rewrite the product of spatial coordinates in the integral through derivatives using the formula

$$
\begin{aligned}
&\int d^3pd^3qd^3kd^3rd^3xd^3yd^3zd^3f\, F(\mathbf{p},\mathbf{q},\mathbf{k},\mathbf{r},\mathbf{l}) e^{-i\mathbf{p}(\mathbf{x}-\mathbf{y})-i\mathbf{q}\mathbf{x}-i\mathbf{k}(\mathbf{y}-\mathbf{z})-i\mathbf{r}(\mathbf{z}-\mathbf{f})-i\mathbf{l}\mathbf{f}} x^3y^3z^3f^3 \\
&= (2\pi)^{12} \int d^3p \Big(-\frac{\partial^3}{\partial q^3\partial l^3\partial p^3\partial r^3} - \frac{\partial^3}{\partial q^3\partial l^3\partial p^3\partial l^3} \\
&+ \frac{\partial^3}{\partial q^3\partial l^3\partial r^3\partial q^3} + \frac{\partial^3}{\partial q^3\partial q^3\partial l^3\partial l^3} \Big) F(\mathbf{p},\mathbf{q},\mathbf{k},\mathbf{r},\mathbf{l}) \Big|_{\substack{\mathbf{l}=\mathbf{p}\\ \mathbf{r}=\mathbf{p}\\ \mathbf{k}=\mathbf{p}\\ \mathbf{q}=-\mathbf{p}}}, \qquad (39)
\end{aligned}
$$

resulting from integration by parts and properties of the delta function. After that, (37) is converted to the form

$$
\begin{aligned}
A_2 \;=\; &\frac{1}{4!(2\pi)^3} \int d\tau_xd\tau_yd\tau_zd\tau_fd^3p \Big(-\frac{\partial^3}{\partial q^3\partial l^3\partial p^3\partial r^3} - \frac{\partial^3}{\partial q^3\partial l^3\partial p^3\partial l^3} \\
&+ \frac{\partial^3}{\partial q^3\partial l^3\partial r^3\partial q^3} + \frac{\partial^3}{\partial q^3\partial q^3\partial l^3\partial l^3} \Big) D(\mathbf{p},\mathbf{q},\mathbf{k},\mathbf{r},\mathbf{l}) \Big|_{\substack{\mathbf{l}=\mathbf{p}\\ \mathbf{r}=\mathbf{p}\\ \mathbf{k}=\mathbf{p}\\ \mathbf{q}=-\mathbf{p}}} + \cdots. \qquad (40)
\end{aligned}
$$

Now, it remains to integrate over the imaginary time and also over the last momentum, which can be done directly in spherical coordinates $d^3p = |\mathbf{p}|^2 d|\mathbf{p}| \sin(\theta) d\theta d\phi$. The sequence of actions in this case, from the point of view of calculation speed, will be most convenient as follows: first one needs to make differentiations with respect to the four momentum variables in (40), then make the corresponding changes of the variables following from the delta functions, then sum over the indices s_n from (38), then integrate over the angles in d^3p, and then integrate over imaginary time variables, which requires careful handling of theta functions. The transformations with each of the 24 terms in (29) can be performed independently and using parallel computing tools. We do not give the described intermediate steps, since they are most conveniently performed using the program, and the intermediate formulas themselves are extremely long, while the calculations themselves are not difficult from a mathematical point of view and are done directly. As a result, we obtain the following integral

$$
\begin{aligned}
A_2 \quad = \quad & \int_0^\infty d\tilde{p} e^{\frac{9\tilde{p}}{2}} \tilde{p}^3 \Big(5600\tilde{p}\left(49\tilde{p}^2 - 95\right) \cosh\left(\frac{\tilde{p}}{2}\right) + 2016\tilde{p}\left(25 - 119\tilde{p}^2\right) \cosh\left(\frac{3\tilde{p}}{2}\right) \\
& +53200\left(\sinh\left(\frac{3\tilde{p}}{2}\right) - 11\sinh\left(\frac{\tilde{p}}{2}\right)\right) \cosh^4\left(\frac{\tilde{p}}{2}\right) + \tilde{p}\Big(- 224\left(\tilde{p}^2 + 25\right) \cosh\left(\frac{7\tilde{p}}{2}\right) \\
& +224\left(119\tilde{p}^2 + 575\right) \cosh\left(\frac{5\tilde{p}}{2}\right) + 18\tilde{p} \sinh\left(\frac{\tilde{p}}{2}\right) \Big(- 5786\tilde{p}^2 + \left(\tilde{p}^2 + 210\right) \cosh(3\tilde{p}) \\
& -6\left(41\tilde{p}^2 + 1890\right) \cosh(2\tilde{p}) + 3\left(1349\tilde{p}^2 + 9450\right) \cosh(\tilde{p}) \\
& +39900\Big)\Big)\Big)\left(50400\pi^2 \left(e^{\tilde{p}} + 1\right)^9\right)^{-1},
\end{aligned} \tag{41}
$$

where the dimensionless variable $\tilde{p} = |\mathbf{p}|/T$ was introduced. This integral converges and can be found analytically:

$$
A_2 \quad = \quad -\frac{17}{960\pi^2}. \tag{42}
$$

Repeating the entire calculation algorithm for the coefficients A_4, A_6 in (26), we obtain at $m = 0$

$$
A_4 = -\frac{17}{2880\pi^2}, \quad A_6 = 0. \tag{43}
$$

Saving the mass in all formulas, in particular, in the propagators (30), we get more complicated expressions for the coefficients at finite mass given in the Appendix A.

4. Discussion

In the previous section, we described the details of the calculation of the corrections of the fourth order in acceleration to the energy-momentum tensor of the Dirac field, first obtained in [23]. Taking into account (42) and (43), we obtain the next formula for the energy-momentum tensor at $m = 0$

$$
\langle \hat{T}^{\mu\nu} \rangle \quad = \quad \Big(\frac{7\pi^2 T^4}{60} + \frac{T^2|a|^2}{24} - \frac{17|a|^4}{960\pi^2}\Big) u^\mu u^\nu - \Big(\frac{7\pi^2 T^4}{180} + \frac{T^2|a|^2}{72} - \frac{17|a|^4}{2880\pi^2}\Big) \Delta^{\mu\nu} + \mathcal{O}(a^6), \tag{44}
$$

where the notation $|a| = \sqrt{-a_\mu a^\mu}$ is used.

As discussed in [22,24,25,27], the mean value of the energy-momentum tensor calculated in this way should vanish at the proper temperature equal to Unruh temperature. Since the energy-momentum tensor is normalized with respect to the Minkowski vacuum, such a vanishing is a direct consequence of the Unruh effect—an accelerated medium with Unruh temperature corresponds to the Minkowski vacuum. It is easy to see that energy-momentum tensor (44) satisfies this condition following from the Unruh effect

$$\langle \hat{T}^{\mu\nu} \rangle (T = T_U) = 0 \,. \tag{45}$$

Moreover, as discussed in [26], from the presentation of the result (44) in the form of Sommerfeld integrals, as well as comparison with the field theory in a space with a conical singularity, it follows that the calculated fourth order of perturbation theory is maximal; that is, $\mathcal{O}(a^6) = 0$ at least at $T > T_U$ [26]. Thus, Equation (44) is an exact non-perturbative formula in this region.

We also note that expression (44) can be obtained from the point of view of another approach, where field theory in a space with a conical singularity is considered [25,27]. As discussed in [26], this indicates the duality of the statistical and geometrical approaches to the description of accelerated media.

5. Conclusions

The Zubarev density operator provides a powerful fundamental theoretical method for studying quantum-field effects in the accelerated medium. This makes it possible to obtain information about such a medium from the point of view of an inertial observer and there is no need to go to the curvilinear coordinates of the accelerated frame and consider the features of nontrivial space with a boundary. All effects can be calculated in ordinary flat space described by the Minkowski metric using standard Green functions at finite temperature. In this case, the effects of acceleration are calculated in a regular way in the framework of perturbation theory with the boost operator. However, it is possible to obtain exact non-perturbative expressions in the chiral limit, since the first few orders of the perturbation theory are to give a complete perturbative series.

In particular, earlier in [23], the Unruh effect for fermions was demonstrated by calculating fourth-order quantum corrections. In the language of the statistical approach with the Zubarev operator, the Unruh effect should lead to the vanishing of the energy-momentum tensor at the proper temperature equal to the Unruh temperature. Thus, the Zubarev density operator allows one to obtain information about the effects associated with the occurrence of an event horizon in an accelerated system and the radiation associated with it.

In more usual formulation or from the point of view of modern developments in the quantum optics [8–10], the Unruh effect should be manifested in the thermal distribution of photons with Unruh temperature. However, it can be shown that the formula we obtained (44) also contains such a distribution with the Unruh temperature [23].

In this paper, we described the details of the calculations of the coefficients with acceleration in the energy-momentum tensor given in [23], focusing on the calculation of the quantum correction to the energy density. The calculation of this correction consists in finding the mean value of the product of the boost operators and operator of the energy-momentum tensor. Applying Wick theorem, one can transform the average of the product of operators to the product of five thermal propagators. Each of the propagators adds one summation over the Matsubara frequencies and a three-dimensional integral over the momentum, and also each boost operator adds three-dimensional integral over the coordinate and one integral over the imaginary time. The procedure for calculating these sums and integrals is described. In addition, expressions for the coefficients at a finite mass are given.

The effects of acceleration we are discussing are of interest from the experimental point of view, in particular, in heavy-ion collisions, where large acceleration can occur. A systematic study of the effects of acceleration requires calculating the acceleration resulting from particle collisions, similar to calculating the vorticity [34–36]. Since the vorticity turns out to be significant in the collision of particles, acceleration, being another combination of derivatives, is also expected to affect the observables. We predict that the effects of acceleration should be significant at early stages of the collision, when the system is not yet fully thermalized and the terms with acceleration are not suppressed with respect to temperature. In this case, non-equilibrium processes can arise that are associated with instability at the Unruh temperature, which were discussed in [26]. One can also make a prediction that the discussed electron-ion collider (EIC) can become a good laboratory for studying effects of acceleration [37]. An elementary particle like an electron, colliding with an ion, behaves like a wave, which allows us to separate the effects of acceleration from the effects of vorticity.

Author Contributions: Conceptualization, G.P., O.T. and V.Z.; investigation, G.P., O.T. and V.Z.; draft preparation, G.P.; supervision, O.T. and V.Z. All authors have read and agreed to the published version of the manuscript.

Funding: The work was supported by Russian Science Foundation Grant No 16-12-10059.

Acknowledgments: Useful discussions with F. Becattini are gratefully acknowledged.

Conflicts of Interest: The authors declare no conflict of interest.

Appendix A. The Coefficients a^4 at Finite Mass

The coefficient A_2 at a finite mass is described by the expression

$$\begin{aligned} A_2 \;=\; & \int_0^\infty d\tilde{p}\tilde{p}^2 e^{\frac{9\tilde{E}_p}{2}} \Big(\tilde{E}_p\Big(9\left(51450-15619\tilde{m}^2\right)\tilde{p}^4+175\left(2450\tilde{m}^2-361\right)\tilde{p}^2 \\ & +175\tilde{m}^2\left(392\tilde{m}^2-285\right)-140571\tilde{p}^6\Big)\sinh\left(\frac{\tilde{E}_p}{2}\right)+27\tilde{E}_p\Big(27\left(53\tilde{m}^2+490\right)\tilde{p}^4 \\ & +175\left(70\tilde{m}^2-19\right)\tilde{p}^2+35\tilde{m}^2\left(56\tilde{m}^2-75\right)+1431\tilde{p}^6\Big)\sinh\left(\frac{3\tilde{E}_p}{2}\right) \\ & -\tilde{E}_p\Big(9\left(247\tilde{m}^2+11550\right)\tilde{p}^4+175\left(550\tilde{m}^2+133\right)\tilde{p}^2+175\tilde{m}^2\left(88\tilde{m}^2+105\right) \\ & +2223\tilde{p}^6\Big)\sinh\left(\frac{5\tilde{E}_p}{2}\right)+\tilde{E}_p\Big(9\left(\tilde{m}^2+210\right)\tilde{p}^4+175\left(10\tilde{m}^2+19\right)\tilde{p}^2 \\ & +35\tilde{m}^2\left(8\tilde{m}^2+75\right)+9\tilde{p}^6\Big)\sinh\left(\frac{7\tilde{E}_p}{2}\right)-8\left(\tilde{m}^2+\tilde{p}^2\right)\Big(5\tilde{m}^2\left(2\tilde{p}^2+63\right) \\ & +28\tilde{p}^2\left(\tilde{p}^2+25\right)\Big)\cosh\left(\frac{7\tilde{E}_p}{2}\right)-504\left(\tilde{m}^2+\tilde{p}^2\right)\Big(5\tilde{m}^2\left(34\tilde{p}^2-9\right) \\ & +476\tilde{p}^4-100\tilde{p}^2\Big)\cosh\left(\frac{3\tilde{E}_p}{2}\right)+56\left(\tilde{m}^2+\tilde{p}^2\right)\Big(5\tilde{m}^2\left(34\tilde{p}^2+207\right) \\ & +476\tilde{p}^4+2300\tilde{p}^2\Big)\cosh\left(\frac{5\tilde{E}_p}{2}\right)+1400\left(\tilde{m}^2+\tilde{p}^2\right)\Big(\tilde{m}^2\left(70\tilde{p}^2-171\right) \\ & +4\tilde{p}^2\left(49\tilde{p}^2-95\right)\Big)\cosh\left(\frac{\tilde{E}_p}{2}\right)\Big)\left(50400\pi^2\left(e^{\tilde{E}_p}+1\right)^9\tilde{E}_p^2\right)^{-1}, \end{aligned} \tag{A1}$$

where the dimensionless quantities $\tilde{m} = m/T, \tilde{E}_p = \sqrt{p^2 + m^2}/T$ are introduced. The coefficient A_4 at a finite mass has the form

$$
\begin{aligned}
A_4 \; = \; & \int_0^\infty d\tilde{p}\Big(\tilde{p}^4 e^{\frac{9\tilde{E}_p}{2}}\Big(1960\sinh\left(\frac{\tilde{E}_p}{2}\right)\cosh^2\left(\frac{\tilde{E}_p}{2}\right)\Big(\left(8\tilde{m}^2+15\right)\cosh\left(2\tilde{E}_p\right) \\
& -8\left(56\tilde{m}^2+15\right)\cosh\left(\tilde{E}_p\right)+984\tilde{m}^2-135\Big)+\tilde{p}^2\left(408170-421713\tilde{p}^2\right)\sinh\left(\frac{\tilde{E}_p}{2}\right) \\
& +27\tilde{p}^2\left(4293\tilde{p}^2+11662\right)\sinh\left(\frac{3\tilde{E}_p}{2}\right)-\tilde{p}^2\left(6669\tilde{p}^2+91630\right)\sinh\left(\frac{5\tilde{E}_p}{2}\right) \\
& +\tilde{p}^2\left(27\tilde{p}^2+1666\right)\sinh\left(\frac{7\tilde{E}_p}{2}\right)+29400\left(14\tilde{p}^2-19\right)\tilde{E}_p\cosh\left(\frac{\tilde{E}_p}{2}\right) \\
& -168\left(2\tilde{p}^2+35\right)\tilde{E}_p\cosh\left(\frac{7\tilde{E}_p}{2}\right)-10584\left(34\tilde{p}^2-5\right)\tilde{E}_p\cosh\left(\frac{3\tilde{E}_p}{2}\right) \\
& +1176\left(34\tilde{p}^2+115\right)\tilde{E}_p\cosh\left(\frac{5\tilde{E}_p}{2}\right)\Big)\Big)\left(1058400\pi^2\left(e^{\tilde{E}_p}+1\right)^9\tilde{E}_p\right)^{-1}.
\end{aligned}
\tag{A2}
$$

The coefficient A_6 is zero both for massless and massive Dirac fields

$$
A_6 \; = \; 0 \, . \tag{A3}
$$

References

1. Unruh, W.G. Notes on black hole evaporation. *Phys. Rev. D* **1976**, *14*, 870. [CrossRef]
2. Castorina, P.; Finocchiaro, M. Symmetry Restoration By Acceleration. *J. Mod. Phys.* **2012**, *3*, 1703, [CrossRef]
3. Ohsaku, T. Dynamical chiral symmetry breaking and its restoration for an accelerated observer. *Phys. Lett. B* **2004**, *599*, 102. [CrossRef]
4. Takeuchi, S. Bose–Einstein condensation in the Rindler space. *Phys. Lett. B* **2015**, *750*, 209. [CrossRef]
5. Fulling, S.A.; Wilson, J.H. The Equivalence Principle at Work in Radiation from Unaccelerated Atoms and Mirrors. *Phys. Scr.* **2019**, *94*, 014004. [CrossRef]
6. Castorina, P.; Kharzeev, D.; Satz, H. Thermal Hadronization and Hawking-Unruh Radiation in QCD. *Eur. Phys. J. C* **2007**, *52*, 187. [CrossRef]
7. Becattini, F.; Castorina, P.; Manninen, J.; Satz, H. The Thermal Production of Strange and Non-Strange Hadrons in e+ e- Collisions. *Eur. Phys. J. C* **2008**, *56*, 493. [CrossRef]
8. Scully, M.O.; Svidzinsky, A.A.; Unruh, W. Causality in acceleration radiation. *Phys. Rev. Res.* **2019**, *1*, 033115. [CrossRef]
9. Scully, M.O.; Kocharovsky, V.V.; Belyanin, A.; Fry, E.; Capasso, F. Enhancing Acceleration Radiation from Ground-State Atoms via Cavity Quantum Electrodynamics. *Phys. Rev. Lett.* **2003**, *91*, 243004. [CrossRef]
10. Scully, M.O.; Fulling, S.; Lee, D.; Page, D.N.; Schleich, W.; Svidzinsky, A. Quantum optics approach to radiation from atoms falling into a black hole. *Proc. Nat. Acad. Sci. USA* **2018**, *115*, 8131–8136. [CrossRef]
11. Zubarev, D.N.; Prozorkevich, A.V.; Smolyanskii, S.A. Derivation of nonlinear generalized equations of quantum relativistic hydrodynamics. *Theoret. Math. Phys.* **1979**, *40*, 821–831. [CrossRef]
12. Zubarev, D.N. *Nonequilibrium Statistical Thermodynamics;* Nauka: Moscow, Russia, 1971. (English translation: New York, Consultant Bureau, 1974)
13. Buzzegoli, M.; Grossi, E.; Becattini, F. General equilibrium second-order hydrodynamic coefficients for free quantum fields. *J. High Energy Phys.* **2017**, *2017*, 91. [CrossRef]
14. Buzzegoli, M.; Becattini, F. General thermodynamic equilibrium with axial chemical potential for the free Dirac field. *J. High Energy Phys.* **2018**, *2018*, 2. [CrossRef]
15. Becattini, F.; Grossi, E. Quantum corrections to the stress-energy tensor in thermodynamic equilibrium with acceleration. *Phys. Rev. D* **2015**, *92*, 045037. [CrossRef]

16. Prokhorov, G.Y.; Teryaev, O.V.; Zakharov, V.I. Effects of rotation and acceleration in the axial current: Density operator vs. Wigner function. *J. High Energy Phys.* **2019**, *1902*, 146. [CrossRef]
17. Kharzeev, D.E.; Landsteiner, K.; Schmitt, A.; Yee, H.U. Strongly Interacting Matter in Magnetic Fields: A Guide to This Volume. *Lect. Notes Phys.* **2013**, *871*, 1–11. [CrossRef]
18. Son, D.T.; Surowka, P. Hydrodynamics with Triangle Anomalies. *Phys. Rev. Lett.* **2009**, *103*, 191601. [CrossRef]
19. Sadofyev, A.V.; Shevchenko, V.I.; Zakharov, V.I. Notes on chiral hydrodynamics within effective theory approach. *Phys. Rev. D* **2011**, *83*, 105025. [CrossRef]
20. Stone, M.; Kim, J. Mixed Anomalies: Chiral Vortical Effect and the Sommerfeld Expansion. *Phys. Rev. D* **2018**, *98*, 025012. [CrossRef]
21. Landsteiner, K.; Megias, E.; Pena-Benitez, F. Anomalous Transport from Kubo Formulae. *Lect. Notes Phys.* **2013**, *871*, 433. [CrossRef]
22. Becattini, F. Thermodynamic equilibrium with acceleration and the Unruh effect. *Phys. Rev. D* **2018**, *97*, 085013. [CrossRef]
23. Prokhorov, G.Y.; Teryaev, O.V.; Zakharov, V.I. Unruh effect for fermions from the Zubarev density operator. *Phys. Rev. D* **2019**, *99*, 071901. [CrossRef]
24. Florkowski, W.; Speranza, E.; Becattini, F. Perfect-fluid hydrodynamics with constant acceleration along the stream lines and spin polarization. *Acta Phys. Polon. B* **2018**, *49*, 1409. [CrossRef]
25. Dowker, J.S. Remarks on geometric entropy. *Class. Quant. Grav.* **1994**, *11*, L55. [CrossRef]
26. Prokhorov, G.Y.; Teryaev, O.V.; Zakharov, V.I. Thermodynamics of accelerated fermion gases and their instability at the Unruh temperature *Phys. Rev. D* **2019**, *100*, 125009. [CrossRef]
27. Frolov, V.P.; Serebryanyi, E.M. Vacuum Polarization in the Gravitational Field of a Cosmic String. *Phys. Rev. D* **1987**, *35*, 3779. [CrossRef]
28. Becattini, F. Covariant statistical mechanics and the stress-energy tensor. *Phys. Rev. Lett.* **2012**, *108*, 244502. [CrossRef]
29. Groot, S.R.D.; Leeuwen, W.A.V.; Weert, C.G.V. *Relativistic Kinetic Theory. Principles and Applications*; North-Holland: Amsterdam, The Netherlands, 1980; p. 417.
30. Morozov, V.G.; Ropke, G.; Holl, A. Kinetic theory of quantum electrodynamic plasma in a strong electromagnetic field. I: The covariant formalism. *Theor. Math. Phys.* **2002**, *131*, 812. [CrossRef]
31. Holl, A.; Morozov, V.G.; Ropke, G. Kinetic theory of QED plasmas in a strong electromagnetic field. 2. The Mean field description. *Theor. Math. Phys.* **2002**, *132*, 1029. [CrossRef]
32. Höll, A.; Morozov, V.G.; Röpke, G. Covariant linear response theory of relativistic qed plasmas. *Phys. A Stat. Mech. Its Appl.* **2003**, *319*, 371–403. [CrossRef]
33. Laine, M.; Vuorinen, A. Basics of Thermal Field Theory. *Lect. Notes Phys.* **2016**, *925*, 1. [CrossRef]
34. Karpenko, I.; Becattini, F. Lambda polarization in heavy ion collisions: From RHIC BES to LHC energies. *Nucl. Phys. A* **2019**, *982*, 519. [CrossRef]
35. Baznat, M.; Gudima, K.; Sorin, A.; Teryaev, O. Hyperon polarization in heavy-ion collisions and holographic gravitational anomaly. *Phys. Rev. C* **2018**, *97*, 041902. [CrossRef]
36. Ivanov, Y.B.; Toneev, V.D.; Soldatov, A.A. Vorticity and Particle Polarization in Relativistic Heavy-Ion Collisions. *arXiv* **2019**, arXiv:1910.01332.
37. Prokhorov, G.; Teryaev, O.; Zakharov, V.I. Energy and atomic number scan in electron-ion collisions. In Proceedings of the XXVII International Workshop on Deep-Inelastic Scattering and Related Subjects, Torino, Italy, 8–12 April 2019; p. 241. [CrossRef]

particles

MDPI

Article

Generalizing Bogoliubov–Zubarev Theorem to Account for Pressure Fluctuations: Application to Relativistic Gas

Yuri G. Rudoy * and Yuri P. Rybakov

Institute for Physical Research and Technologies, RUDN University, Miklukho-Maklay Str. 6, Moscow 117198, Russia; soliton4@mail.ru

* Correspondence: rudikar@mail.ru

Received: 18 January 2019; Accepted: 17 March 2019; Published: 21 March 2019

Abstract: The problem of pressure fluctuations in the thermal equilibrium state of some objects is discussed, its solution being suggested via generalizing the Bogoliubov–Zubarev theorem. This theorem relates the thermodynamic pressure with the Hamilton function and its derivatives describing the object in question. It is shown that unlike to other thermodynamic quantities (e.g., the energy or the volume) the pressure fluctuations are described not only by a purely thermodynamic quantity (namely, the corresponding thermodynamic susceptibility) but also by some non-thermodynamic quantities. The attempt is made to apply these results to the relativistic ideal gases, with some numerical results being valid for the limiting ultra-relativistic or high-temperature case.

Keywords: Gibbs equilibrium statistical mechanics; Bogoliubov's quasi-averages; pressure fluctuations; relativistic ideal gas

PACS: 05.70.-a; 05.30.-d; 05.40.-a

1. Introduction

The long-standing and rather non-trivial problem of calculating pressure fluctuations in the Gibbs equilibrium statistical mechanics is revised. The previous attempts are critically analyzed and it is shown that the application of the Bogoliubov's ideas gives the full and unambiguous solution to this problem. The crucial role plays the Bogoliubov's idea of quasi-average (in our case—quasi-dynamic) quantities—specifically, the pressure P and the dynamic compressibility Ψ. Following the Bogoliubov's idea of spontaneous symmetry breaking, we introduce the virtual conjugate field, which appears to be the singular potential εU of the container impenetrable walls. The translational invariance of the Hamilton function H being broken, finally we consider the limiting case $\varepsilon \to 0$. General relations expressing P and Ψ in terms of the derivatives of H are presented and some examples are studied. In particular, we consider the cases when the Hamilton function can be expressed as the sum of uniform functions (in the Euler sense).

In our case the virtual conjugate field, which in the limit $\varepsilon \to 0$ breaks the translational invariance of the Hamilton function H, appears to be the singular potential εU of the container impenetrable walls. The general relations expressing P and Ψ in terms of the derivatives of H are presented and some examples are studied—i.e., the cases of the ideal vs. non-ideal as well as those of uniform vs. non- and quasi-uniform (in the Euler sense) Hamilton function H describing the system (here—the gas, presumably in the classical regime).

The problem of the equilibrium pressure fluctuations is one of the oldest and most difficult problems in classical statistical mechanics. In 1902, Gibbs [1] in Ch.VII wrote down the appropriate expression, which included the quantity named by him the "dynamical compressibility" (see also Fowler [2], Hill [3], Kittel [4], Terletzky [5]), the latter one being important for the problem of thermodynamic stability (more precise definitions are given below).

Many unsuccessful attempts were undertaken for calculating this quantity even for the simplest case of 'ordinary' non-relativistic ideal gas. One can find the details in the works by Fowler [2], Wergeland [6], Münster [7], and M. Klein [8].

A 'pessimistic' point of view was expressed in [3], Ch. 4, §19 (see also [5], §69), where the calculation of the pressure fluctuations was connected with the detailed knowledge of the kind of forces acting between the gas particles and the container walls. Some attempts [2,3] to follow this route brought physically unsatisfactory—i.e., divergent—results. This appears to be unphysical because, due to Maxwell, the gas in the container should relax to the thermal equilibrium state quite independently on physical properties of the walls.

Finally, it was even claimed (see, e.g., [4], Ch. 11) that the solution to the problem of Gibbs' pressure fluctuations is generally outside the scope of the equilibrium theory, so all these failures were sometimes considered as the inconsistency of the Gibbs's approach as a whole. The situation becomes even more involved by noting that some of the physically acceptable results for the pressure fluctuations obtained earlier [6–8] refer in fact not to the Gibbs's approach itself, but to the Einstein's one, which is called "quasi-thermodynamic" by Landau and Lifshitz [9]. These approaches differ significantly by the choice of the thermodynamic variables fixed by calculation. For example, in the case of the pressure fluctuations it is the entropy in the Einstein's approach, though it is the volume in the Gibbs's ensemble approach (more details relating to these approaches are given in [10]). The goal of our paper is to show the efficiency of the Gibbs approach.

Concerning the problem of application, it is not obvious that just Gibbs approach (and thus BZ and our results) should be more useful than Einstein one. To decide this one should analyze the specific experimental situation but it is outside scope of our paper.

The way out concerning only the Gibbs approach was actually outlined in 1946 by Bogoliubov [11], who used the coordinate scale transformation in order to connect the thermodynamic pressure with the dynamical quantities—namely, with the first derivatives of the Hamilton function and the particles' pair distribution function. Later on in 1971, Zubarev [12] obtained the analogous expression for the dynamic (yet not somehow thermally-averaged) pressure as the function defined only in the phase space.

In fact, in [12] there was implicitly used the idea of quasi-averages—or, in our case, quasi-dynamic quantities—which was also formulated by Bogoliubov [13] in 1961. From the computational point of view, the Zubarev's result became possible by virtue of the explicit usage of generalized functions (in this case—the singular potential of the container walls) following the lines of Vladimirov [14].

However, it was only in 2000 one of the present authors with Sukhanov [10] succeeded to extend the Bogoliubov–Zubarev approach and obtained for the first time the general expression for the Gibbs 'dynamical compressibility' in terms of the second derivatives of the Hamilton function. This generalized form of the Bogoliubov–Zubarev theorem is valid for any reasonable kind of the kinetic energy and the interaction potential, but only the non-relativistic Maxwell gas was considered in [10] as an example.

Later on in [15–17], these results were extended to the ideal gas with any uniform (in the Euler sense) dependence of the Hamilton function upon the (quasi)particle momentum. The most general case of the non-uniform Hamilton function—i.e., that of Lorentz as well as Lorentz-violated form [16]—was considered for the classical ideal gas. In the present paper the pressure fluctuation problem is considered for the more complicated case—the non-uniform gas in the ultra-relativistic limiting case—both from dynamic as well as thermodynamic points of view. We stress that the logical and computational completeness of the Gibbs statistical mechanics, which was sometimes brought to doubt—especially in connection with the problem of the pressure fluctuations—is fully restored by means of Bogoliubov's seminal ideas.

This paper is organized as follows. In Section 2, the problem of pressure fluctuations is formulated and in Section 3 the solution to this problem is given in general form. Sections 4 and 5 are devoted to some illustrative examples, whereas Section 6 contains the main result for the thermodynamic properties of the ideal gas in the ultra-relativistic approximation. Section 7 provides the short summary. Appendix A clears some computational problems encountered in Section 6.

2. Rigorous Formulation of the Pressure Fluctuations Problem

The equilibrium pressure fluctuations $<(\Delta P(\Gamma))^2>$ are defined in a standard way as $<(\Delta P(\Gamma))^2> = <(P(\Gamma))^2> - <P(\Gamma)>^2$, where $\Gamma = \{q,p\}$ is the phase space of coordinates q and momenta p and $<\ldots>$ denotes the canonical averaging for the system in the isothermal-isochoric ensemble with fixed values of the inverse temperature β and the volume V. The value of β is introduced by the canonical distribution function whereas V—by the restriction of the region of Γ.

Following Gibbs [1], if the Hamilton function $H(\Gamma)$ for the dynamic system is given, then

$$<\ldots> = Z^{-1}(\beta,V)\int d\Gamma \exp[-\beta H(\Gamma)](\ldots),\; Z(\beta,V) = \int d\Gamma \exp[-\beta H(\Gamma)],\; \Phi(\beta,V) = \ln Z(\beta,V), \quad (1)$$

where the partition function $Z(\beta,V)$is supposed to be finite and strictly positive, so that the Massieu—Planck thermodynamic potential $\Phi(\beta,V)$ does exist. The latter one is usually a smooth function of $\beta$and V, so there exist also the relevant thermodynamic derivatives, in particular the equilibrium (i.e., isothermal) pressure $P(\beta,V)$ and the compressibility $\chi(\beta,V) < 0$

$$P(\beta,V) = (1/\beta)[\partial\Phi(\beta,V)/\partial V],\; \chi(\beta,V) \equiv \partial P(\beta,V)/\partial V = (1/\beta)[\partial^2\Phi(\beta,V)/\partial V^2]; \quad (2)$$

the expressions (2) being known in thermodynamics as thermic equations of state.

According to the Gibbs lemma [1] (Ch. VII, Equations (252) and (255), see also [3,5]), the equilibrium pressure fluctuations $<(\Delta P(\Gamma))^2>$ are given by the expression

$$\beta<(\Delta P(\Gamma))^2> = \chi(\beta,V) + \Psi(\beta,V),\; \chi(\beta,V) = \partial<P(\Gamma)>/\partial V,\; \Psi(\beta,V) = -<\partial P(\Gamma)/\partial V>, \quad (3)$$

or, following Gibbs and introducing the additional dynamic quantity $\Psi(\Gamma)$,

$$\Psi(\beta,V) = <\Psi(\Gamma)>,\; \Psi(\Gamma) = -\partial P(\Gamma)/\partial V = \partial^2 H(\Gamma)/\partial V^2,\; P(\Gamma) = -\partial H(\Gamma)/\partial V. \quad (4)$$

Gibbs called the quantity $\Psi(\Gamma)$ dynamic compressibility, but gave no example of its calculation; in general, calculation of quantities in (3) and (4) consists of two stages: firstly, the adequate definition of $P(\Gamma)$ and $\Psi(\Gamma)$, and secondly—their correct averaging according to (1).

Note that for the pressure P the first stage may be in fact bypassed due to the first of Equation (2) along with definitions in (1), and thus the pressure $P(\beta,V)$ is called the 'thermodynamic' average. On the contrary, though according to (3) $\Psi(\beta,V)$ also belongs to the set of Gibbs's averages, it is a 'non-thermodynamic' one because it needs a direct calculation according to (1).

Furthermore, in order to satisfy the conditions of thermodynamic stability relative to the external mechanical disturbance, it is necessary for$<(\Delta P(\Gamma))^2>$ to be *positive*. It requires $\Psi(\beta,V)$ not only to be positive but also to exceed $-\chi(\beta,V)$. Hence $\Psi(\beta,V)$ cannot be equal to $-\chi(\beta,V)$, this fact implying (with the account for (3) and (4)) that the operation $<\ldots>$ is in general not permutable with the operation $\partial/\partial V$—just this circumstance is of decisive significance for further presentation.

It is worthwhile to note, that due to the Gibbs lemma the expressions analogous to (3) hold also for the equilibrium thermal fluctuations of other (thermo)dynamic quantities—e.g., the energy H or the generalized force $A = -\partial H/\partial a$. In all cases the relevant derivatives in the Gibbs lemma refer to the (thermo)dynamically conjugate variables (for H and A those are the inverse temperature $\beta = 1/k_B T$ and the relevant generalized parameter a respectively), but in the cases with H and A the terms $\partial H(\Gamma)/\partial\beta$ and $-\partial A/\partial a = \partial^2 H/\partial a^2$ fully disappear and thus no difficulties arise at all. Indeed, the energy $H(\Gamma)$

is a pure dynamic variable and so—by definition—does not depend upon the thermal parameter β, whereas variables A and a are mutually independent and enter $H(\Gamma)$ in the bilinear form $(-Aa)$.

Quite a different situation takes place for the pair of relevant (thermo)dynamically conjugate variables—the pressure P and the volume V. Strictly speaking, all the derivatives of the energy $H(\Gamma)$ with respect to the volume V, entering the definitions (4), are identically zero by definition. Indeed, all the quantities $H(\Gamma)$, $P(\Gamma)$, and $\Psi(\Gamma)$ in (4) have pure dynamical origin and do not contain the kinematical parameter V. All these quantities are defined in the whole phase space Γ for the 'free' system without any 'walls' (therefore, for $V \to \infty$), while the finite value V enters only at the final stage, that is, after the averaging procedure.

Let us recall here, that the method of quasi-averages was created by Bogoliubov [13] just in order to cope those frequently encountered problems, when the symmetry of the Hamiltonian H of the physical system is higher than that of the ground state or of the state of thermal equilibrium. In these cases, the formal calculations in accordance with (1) prescribed by the Gibbs approach [1] (as well as by its quantum generalization) give unphysical zero results for ordinary average values. It was shown by Bogoliubov [13], that the reason lies in the existence of some kind of degeneration in the system's energy, so the notion of quasi-averages was suggested in order to obtain physically meaningful results.

Note that the term 'degeneration' is fully deprived here of any 'quantum' sense and is used only to designate the presence of some additional symmetry in H (e.g., with respect to translations or rotations in the configuration part of the phase space Γ). The ingenious—though almost 'obvious'—Bogoliubov's idea was to remove this 'degeneration' by means of relevant conjugate (in wide sense) infinitesimal 'external field' before the averaging procedure is carried out and then, after all calculations are made, fully eliminate the field. Spoken figuratively, the quasi-averages are alike to such fictitious personages as the Moor of Venice or the Cheshire Cat.

To be specific, in our case the Hamilton function $H(p,q) \equiv H(\Gamma)$ describing the energy of the system of particles in classical regime, is translation invariant and does not distinguish between the 'interior' and the 'exterior' of some 'container'. Therefore, $H(\Gamma)$ does not depend upon the volume V of this container and thus both quantities P and Ψ are formally identically equal to zero. But in fact, any system in thermal equilibrium should be confined in space, so the system's energy should depend upon the value of the volume V—in the opposite case no pressure and no dynamic compressibility may be formally defined at all.

3. Solution to the Problem of Pressure Fluctuations

In order to overcome this contradiction and to obtain the adequate definitions of P and Ψ, we act in the spirit of the Bogoliubov's method [13] and, following partly to Zubarev [12], violate (may be virtually) the translational symmetry of 'free' Hamilton function $H(\Gamma)$. To this end, one can simply add to $H(\Gamma)$ the singular repulsive potential $U_V(q)$

$$H_V{}^{(\varepsilon)}(\Gamma) = H(\Gamma) + \varepsilon U_V(q); U_V(q) = \begin{cases} 0, q \notin S_V, \\ \infty, q \in S_V. \end{cases} \tag{5}$$

The potential $U_V(q)$ is called also the 'contact delta-like', or the 'hard core' potential, which describes dynamically the container of the volume V and the surrounding surface S_V with the idealized 'impenetrable' walls. Evidently, $U_V(q)$ should not depend on the form of any actually present 'wall–particle' interaction. Its role reduces to introducing the dependence of the ε-deformed Hamilton function (5) on the volume V.

By virtue of the suggested properties (5) of $U_V(q)$, the configuration part of Γ is divided into the 'interior' and the 'exterior' parts (relative to the container). Therefore, the potential $U_V(q)$ acquires the properties of the generalized function (in particular, see [10]). Possibly, just these circumstances have led to the failure of perturbation approaches in papers [2,6].

Taking into account these definitions, it is natural to define the quantities P and Ψ in the proper and unambiguous way as the 'quasi-dynamical' variables in the following 'limiting' sense

$$P_V(\Gamma) \equiv \lim[-\partial H_V{}^{(\varepsilon)}(\Gamma)/\partial V],\ \Psi_V(\Gamma) = \lim[\partial^2 H_V{}^{(\varepsilon)}(\Gamma)/\partial V^2]\ (\varepsilon\to 0);\ \Psi_V(\Gamma) \neq -\partial P_V(\Gamma)/\partial V. \quad (6)$$

Note that the mathematical hallmark of the Bogoliubov's method of quasi-averages [13] consists in their non-analytic dependence upon the infinitesimal parameter ε, and this is just the main reason why the results of the limiting procedure (6) differ drastically from the identically zero results for $P(\Gamma)$ and $\Psi(\Gamma)$, when ε is taken equal to zero from the very beginning.

It can be shown (details of calculation see in [10], App. 6) that in accordance with the definition (6), $P_V(\Gamma)$ coincides exactly with the previously known result of Zubarev [12], whereas $\Psi_V(\Gamma)$ in the form (6) was presented in [10] explicitly for the first time. It is worthwhile to note that, in [10], the quantum generalization of these results was also obtained based on the well-known Hellman—Feynman theorem for the operator's parameter differentiation.

Finally, the averaging of $\Psi_V(\Gamma)$ according to (1) gives $\Psi(\beta,V)$ and thus allows one to obtain in quite general way the solution of the long standing and rather controversial problem (see [2–8]) of thermal equilibrium pressure fluctuations (3) in the isothermal-isochoric Gibbs ensemble for the non-ideal systems of particles in classical regime.

The key mathematical device for obtaining the quasi-dynamical equations of state (6) is the equality of volume derivatives of the n-th order for the two types of functionals, namely $Z_V(\beta) = \int d\Gamma \exp[-\beta H(\Gamma)]$ and $Z_V(\varepsilon)(\beta) = \int d\Gamma \exp[-\beta H_V(\varepsilon)(\Gamma)$. In the first case the integral is taken over the kinematic-confined coordinate subspace of Γ with the volume V. On the contrary, in the second case, the integral is taken over the whole coordinate subspace of Γ and only after this the limiting procedure $\varepsilon\to 0$ is performed.

For $n = 0$ the equality is quite obvious because the dynamical factor $\Delta_V(\Gamma) = \exp[-\beta U_V(q)]$ acts as the projection operator onto the relevant coordinate subspace of Γ. Indeed, according to the definition (5) of the external wall potential $U_V(q)$, $\Delta_V(\Gamma) = 1$, if $U_V(q) = 0$—i.e., when q belongs to the interior of the container, and $\Delta_V(\Gamma) = 0$, if $U_V(q)\to\infty$, when q belongs to the exterior of the container or even to its walls. Details of calculations for $n = 1$ and $n = 2$, which give the constructive realization of the definitions (6), can be found in [10], App. 7, and were repeated in the recent paper [18]. The main result is the following.

Suppose that a macroscopic dynamic system is confined within the finite volume V and is described by the Hamilton function of the form (5). Then the explicit expressions for $P_V(\Gamma)$ and $\Psi_V(\Gamma)$ are determined only by the 'free' part $H(\Gamma)$ of the Hamilton function (5) and are quite independent upon the specific form of the "wall potential" $U_V(\Gamma)$. This result is quite typical when one works with the generalized functions.

Furthermore, the canonical scale transformation in the phase space $\Gamma = (q,p)\to\Gamma_\lambda = (\lambda q,p/\lambda)$ is performed, and thus we obtain the following expressions for $P_V(\Gamma)$and $\Psi_V(\Gamma)$ in terms of the partial derivatives of the Hamilton function $H(\Gamma_\lambda)$ for the "free", or unconfined, system but with λ-deformed phase space (f is the degree of freedom)

$$\begin{gathered} P_V(\Gamma) = -(1/fV)[D_\lambda H(\Gamma_\lambda)]|_{\lambda=1},\ \Psi_V(\Gamma) \equiv (1/V)P_V(\Gamma) + \Delta\Psi_V(\Gamma), \\ \Delta\Psi_V(\Gamma) = (1/fV)^2[D_\lambda(1 + D_\lambda)H(\Gamma_\lambda)]|_{\lambda=1}. \end{gathered} \quad (7)$$

Here $D_\lambda \equiv d/d\lambda$, and $1 \equiv D_\lambda{}^0$ is the symbolic designation of the unity operator in the operator family, $\{D_\lambda{}^n\}$ ($n \geq 0$—integer) is the n-fold differentiation with respect to λ. Finally, one should put everywhere $\lambda = 1$. Expressions (7) are well defined for sufficiently smooth Hamilton function $H(q,p)$—i.e., twice differentiable with respect to the arguments puq, while this operation does not yield the dependence of $P_V(\Gamma)$ and $\Psi_V(\Gamma)$ upon V.

The auxiliary variable λ establishes the connection between the change of the volume V and the equivalent change of the coordinates q, where the condition of canonicity requires also the corresponding change of the momenta p. In other words, λ is a parameter of canonical scaling transformation preserving the Liouville dynamic measure—i.e., the volume element of phase space $d\Gamma$: clearly, $d\Gamma_\lambda = (\lambda dq)(dp/\lambda) = (dqdp) = d\Gamma$.

Note that terms of different order in D_λ entering $\Delta\Psi_V(\Gamma)$ may give contributions of the same order; e.g., in the case (7) and (8) (see below) the terms in (6) take the form—e.g., for $H_k(p)$ (just the same expressions will be valid for the contribution of $H_p(q)$into (6), with replacing m with l.):

$$[D_\lambda H_k(p/\lambda)]|_{\lambda=1} = -mH_k(p), [D_\lambda{}^2 H_k(p/\lambda)]|_{\lambda=1} = m(m+1)H_k(p),$$

$$P_V(p) = (1/fV)mH_k(p), \Delta\Psi_V(p) = (1/fV)^2 m^2 H_k(p).$$

The expression for $P_V(\Gamma)$ in (7) is usually cited as the Bogoliubov–Zubarev theorem [11,12], whereas the expression for $\Psi_V(\Gamma)$ for the first time was obtained in the paper byRudoy and Sukhanov [10]. It is natural to call the expressions (7) (quasi)-dynamical equations of state, because they connect the (quasi)-dynamic quantities—the pressure $P(\Gamma)$ and the compressibility $\Psi(\Gamma)$ with the main characteristic of the dynamic system—the Hamilton function $H(\Gamma)$.

It is essential that thermodynamic equations of state (7) do not include external thermal parameter—the temperature T, but they explicitly depend on the external mechanical parameter—the volume V. It is evident that the dynamic functions H, P and Ψ are defined in the system's phase space Γ. Note also that all functions entering (7) are usually (but not always!) additive, so their average values are proportional to particle's number N. Moreover, functions entering (7) possess various – but universal for all dynamical systems – kinds of behavior relative to deformations of the volume V, namely $H(\Gamma) = O(V^0)$, $P_V(\Gamma) = O(V^{-1})$, $\Psi_V(\Gamma) = O(V^{-2})$. Indeed, the external parameter V enters the right-hand parts of (6) only as entire negative (or zero) powers, so in the limit $V \to \infty$ (i.e., for the case of 'free' system) quantities $P_V(\Gamma)$ and $\Psi_V(\Gamma)$ really tend to zero in full accord with (2), whereas $H_V(\Gamma)$ rests in this limit invariable.

For most non-ideal macroscopic non-relativistic systems the Hamilton functions $H(q,p)$ appear to have additive and separable nature in q and p, so they can be represented as sums of three terms: the constant rest energy E_0, the kinetic energy $H_k(p)$ and the potential energy $H_p(q)$. These energies usually are also additive relative to all particles (E_0 and $H_k(p)$) and to their pairs ($H_p(q)$. Evidently, the energy E_0 gives no contribution to the Equation (7) for the pressure P and the compressibility Ψ.

4. Uniform Ideal and Non-Ideal Systems

4.1. Uniform Non-Ideal Case

In [10] the particular case was considered, where both energies $H_K(p)$ and $H_p(q)$ are *uniform* (in the Euler's sense) functions of their arguments with exponents m and l respectively. This means that

$$H_p(\lambda q) = \lambda^l H_p(q), H_k(\lambda^{-1} p) = \lambda^{-m} H_k(p), \tag{8}$$

so the expressions (7) can be represented as

$$P_V(q,p) = (1/fV)[mH_k(p) - lH_p(q)], \Delta\Psi_V(q,p) = (1/fV)^2[m^2 H_k(p) + l^2 H_p(q)]. \tag{9}$$

It should be remarked that the expression for $P_V(q,p)$ in (9) includes the quantity $(-lH_p(q)) = qF(q)$, where $F(q) = -\partial H_p(q)/\partial q$, which is in fact the *Clausius force virial*. Therefore, after the Gibbs averaging the resulting expression is nothing else as the virial theorem. The "uniform" expressions (8) and (9) possess the following useful properties. Note, that in this approach it is not necessary to invoke the dynamical equations of motion with the additional assumptions of their stationary behavior relative to the time averaging: here we operate only with the phase space variables without using the time variable.

1. For any non-zero exponents m and l in (8) both energies $H_k(p)$ and $H_p(q)$ enter the right-hand parts of (8) *linearly*, every differentiation with respect to λ increasing by unity both indices m and l.

2. Physical dimension for the pressure in (9) corresponds to the energy volume density, whereas that for the dynamic compressibility being the pressure volume density, and therefore every differentiation with respect to λ increases by unity the power of the factor $1/V$.

3. There exist conditions when the pressure $P_V(q,p)$ as well as the compressibility $\Psi_V(q,p)$ are proportional to the total energy $H(q,p) = H_k(p) + H_p(q)$. Under these conditions, according to (9), the average value $<\Psi>$ is proportional to $<P>$ and/or $<H>$; thus, $<\Psi>$ is the usual thermodynamic average and its calculation does not amount to any additional problem. Clearly, these conditions can be realized only in two cases: at $m = -l$ or at $l = 0$, while m may be arbitrary.

In [15–17,19], we concentrated on the case of an *ideal* dynamic system, where the coordinate-dependent potential energy $H_p(q)$ of the inter-particle interaction vanishes, so $l = 0$. The total energy $H(q,p)$ for this system is given by the sum of the constant term E_0 and of the kinetic energy $H_k(p)$ which depends only on the particle's momentum:

$$H_p(q) = 0,\ H(\Gamma) \equiv H(q,p) = E_0 + H_k(p). \tag{10}$$

4.2. Uniform Ideal Gas

In the case when $H_k(p)$ is a uniform function (in the Euler's sense) with the exponent m, the expressions (8) obtain the following simple form

$$P_V(p) = \mu[H_k(p)/V],\ \Delta\Psi_V(p) = (1/V)\mu P_V(p) = (1/V)\mu^2[H_k(p)/V],\ \mu \equiv m/f.$$

Note that both expressions (11) contain the constant $\mu = m/f$, which is the ratio of the uniformity exponent m to the number of degrees of freedom f. The ratio μ characterizes the given dynamic system in the course of its dynamic (and also thermodynamic) description in both classic and quantum regimes; thus, μ represents some kind of 'similarity index' and specifies the whole class of dynamic systems.

For the given values of $f = 1,2,3$ typical values of index μ may vary from $\mu_{nr} = m_{nr}/f = 2/f$ up to $\mu_{ur} = m_{ur}/f = 1/f$, where the subscripts "nr" and "ur" correspond to the non- and ultra-relativistic limiting expressions for the kinetic energy $H_k(p)$

$$H_k{}^{nr}(p) \approx (cp)^2/2E_0\ (cp/E_0 \ll 1),\ H_k{}^{ur}(p) \approx cp\ (cp/E_0 \gg 1). \tag{11}$$

Note that in the particular case of massless particles (e.g., photons) with $E_0 = 0$ the expression for $H_k{}^{ur}(p)$ becomes exact. Obviously, for both limiting cases in (12) the kinetic energy has the form

$$H_k(p) = \alpha_m p^m,\ m_{ur} = 1,\ \alpha_1 \equiv \alpha_{ur} = c;\ m_{nr} = 2,\ \alpha_2 \equiv \alpha_{nr} = (\alpha_1)^2/2E_0, \tag{12}$$

which is the exponential—and thus uniform (in the Euler's sense)—function of the momentum p with the uniformity exponent m equal to 2 and 1, respectively.

In more general situations, for any possible values $1 \le f \le 3$ and $1 \le m \le 2$, one obtains $^1/_3 \le \mu \le 2$, but in some models of the 'ideal gas' (e.g., used in modern cosmology) the ranges of the parameters m, f and $\mu = m/f$ may differ in magnitude (and sometimes also in sign); nevertheless, the expressions (11) preserve the applicability for these cases too.

Note that if the energy density is positive, the pressure fluctuations are also positive for any sign of μ. This fact means that the system may be mechanically stable ($\Delta\Psi > 0$) even if the pressure is negative ($P < 0$), and this is just the case (if $\mu < 0$) due to the unusual value $m < 0$ (e.g., for the Chaplygin gas). As is easily seen, the condition $f > 0$ is always fulfilled by definition.

5. Non-Uniform and Quasi-Uniform Ideal Gas

5.1. Non-Uniform Ideal Gas

Rather general case of the ideal gas is that of the free isotropic relativistic particles with *the non-uniform* Hamilton function $H(p)$ consisting of the rest energy $E_0 \equiv H(0)$ and the kinetic energy $H_k(p)$, where $H_k(0) = 0$. Note that study of this model from the point of view of statistical mechanics was started by Jüttner [20,21] and Glaser [22] many years ago; however, the problem of pressure fluctuations was not even mentioned in these papers.

The expression for $H(p)$ is given by the Lorentz–Einstein equation

$$H(p) \equiv E_0 + H_k(p) = [E_0{}^2 + (cp)^2]^{\frac{1}{2}}, H(p) = E_0 h(p), h(p) = 1 + h_k(p); \tag{13}$$

which can be rewritten in the dimensionless form

$$h(\xi) = 1 + h_k(\xi) = (1 + \xi^2)^{\frac{1}{2}}; h_k(\xi) = h(\xi) f\mu^{(-)}(\xi),\ \xi = cp/E_0\ (E_0 \neq 0). \tag{14}$$

Here c is the velocity of light in vacuum, h and h_k being the dimensionless energies (total and kinetic). In the case $E_0 = 0$, the ultra-relativistic limit becomes an exact one: it is the uniform case with $m = 1$ (see Equation (13)).

The dynamic equations of state follow immediately from (7) but differ noticeably from (11). Using the dimensionless variable $\xi = cp/E_0$, we obtain instead of (11) the following exact dynamical equations of state

$$P_V(\xi) = (E_0/fV)\{[h^2(\xi) - 1]/h(\xi)\} = [H(\xi)/V]\nu^{(-)}(\xi) = [H_k(\xi)/V]\mu^{(+)}(\xi), \tag{15}$$

$$\Delta\Psi_V(p) = E_0(1/fV)^2\{[h^4(\xi) - 1]/h^3(\xi)\} = (1/V)P_V(\xi)\nu^{(+)}(\xi) = (1/V)[H_k(\xi)/V]\mu^{(+)}(\xi)\nu^{(+)}(\xi). \tag{16}$$

It is evident that the non-uniform expressions (14)–(16) are much more complicated as compared to their uniform counterparts (11). In particular, instead of the unique and constant 'similarity index' μ in (11) one obtains in (14)–(16) a whole family of the variable dimensionless factors $\nu^{(\pm)}(\xi)$ and $\mu^{(\pm)}(\xi)$. These factors have the meaning of the generalized 'similarity indices' and depend (though weakly enough) on ξ through the function $h(\xi)$

$$f\mu^{(\pm)}(\xi) = 1 \pm [h(\xi)]^{-1}, f\nu^{(\pm)}(\xi) = 1 \pm [h(\xi)]^{-2}, f\kappa^{(\pm)}(\xi) = 1 \pm [h(\xi)]^{-4};$$

$$f\mu^{(+)}(\xi)\mu^{(-)}(\xi) = \nu^{(-)}(\xi), f\nu^{(-)}(\xi)\nu^{(+)}(\xi) = f\kappa^{(-)}(\xi), h_k(\xi) = h(\xi)f\mu^{(-)}(\xi). \tag{17}$$

The system of exact Equations (14)–(17) is rather complicated, but in practice only their approximate forms are of real interest, namely, the two limiting cases: the non-relativistic (^{nr}) ($\xi \to 0$) and the ultra-relativistic (^{ur}) ($\xi \to \infty$) one. The lowest order corrections to the functions $h_\kappa(\xi)$ and $1/h_\kappa(\xi)$, as compared to their 'uniform' analogs (12) and (13), have the form

$$h_k(\xi) \approx h_k{}^{nr}(\xi)[1 - \frac{1}{4}\xi^2] = h_k{}^{nr}(\xi)[1 - \frac{1}{2}h^{nr}(\xi)], h_k{}^{nr}(\xi) = \frac{1}{2}\xi^2\ (\xi \to 0), \tag{18}$$

$$1/h_k(\xi) = [h_k{}^{ur}(\xi)]^{-1}\{1 - \frac{1}{2}\xi^2\} = [h_k{}^{ur}(\xi)]^{-1}\{1 - \frac{1}{2}[h_k{}^{ur}(\xi)]^{-2}\}, [h_k{}^{ur}(\xi)]^{-1} = \xi^{-1}\ (\xi \to \infty). \tag{19}$$

Note that $h_k{}^{nr}(0) = 1/h_k{}^{ur}(\infty) = 0$, this fact enabling one to consider the quantities $h_\kappa(\xi)$ and $1/h_\kappa(\xi)$ as small in corresponding ranges of the variable ξ.

In some physical problems there may be of interest to obtain the corrections to the limiting 'uniform' Equations (11) and (12), which are stipulated by the variable nature of the functions $\kappa^{(\pm)}(\xi)$ and $\mu^{(\pm)}(\xi)$ entering the dynamic equations of state (16) and (17) for $P(\xi;V)$ and $\Psi(\xi;V)$. In order to carry out some perturbation procedure at small values ξ«1 in the non-relativistic (nr) limit and at large values ξ»1 in the ultra-relativistic (ur) limit, it is convenient to use in Equations (17)–(19) as the corresponding small parameters not ξ and 1/ξ, but the quantities $h_\kappa(\xi)$ and $1/h_\kappa(\xi)$.

Omitting simple but lengthy calculations, one obtains the following approximate results

$$P_V(\xi) \approx \mu_{nr}[H_k(\xi)/V][1 - \frac{1}{2}h_k(\xi)],\ \Delta\Psi_V(\xi) \approx \mu^2{}_{nr}[H_k(\xi)/V][1 - (3/2)h_k(\xi)]\ (\xi \to 0); \quad (20)$$

$$P_V(\xi) \approx \mu_{ur}[H_k(\xi)/V]\{1 + [h_k(\xi)]^{-1}\},\ \Delta\Psi_V(\xi) \approx \mu^2{}_{ur}[H_k(\xi)/V]\ (\xi \to \infty). \quad (21)$$

These expressions reveal the tendency of 'sloping' the dependence upon ξ both for kinematical ($\kappa^{(+)}$, $\mu^{(+)}$) as well as dynamical (h_k, P, $\Delta\Psi$) quantities: at small (but finite) ξ all these quantities become smaller than their 'uniform' limits at ξ = 0, whereas at large (but finite) ξ, on the contrary, they become larger than their 'uniform' limits at 1/ξ = 0.

5.2. *Quasi-Uniform Ideal Gas*

Evidently, the most general case of ideal gas includes the Hamilton function $H(p)$ with the non-uniform dependence upon p. However, in practice only certain limiting cases (e.g., non- or ultra-relativistic ones) are of interest, where $H(p)$ (and hence also its derivatives) may be presented as an expansion in integer powers m of p with $m > 0$ or $m < 0$ (i.e., in $1/p$), where $H_0(p) = h_0 \equiv E_0$ = const, $m_0 \equiv 0$, but m_i and h_i at $i = 1, 2, \ldots$ may have both signs

$$H(p) = \sum_{i=0}^{n} H_i(p) = \sum_{i=0}^{n} h_i p^{m_i},\ P_V(p) = (1/fV)\sum_{i=1}^{n} m_i H_i(p) = (1/fV)\sum_{i=1}^{n} m_i h_i p^{m_i}$$
$$\Psi_V(p) = (1/fV)^2 \sum_{i=1}^{n} m_i^2 H_i(p) = (1/fV)^2 \sum_{i=1}^{n} m_i^2 h_i p^{m_i}. \quad (22)$$

Evidently, every term in (22) is a uniform one, whereas the whole expression (22) is not; so it can be considered as a quasi-uniform one and characterized not by the single uniformity exponent but by the whole discrete set of them. The examples can be found in [15–17]

$$\text{NR-limit: } m_1 = 2, h_1 > 0; m_2 = 4, h_2 = -\frac{1}{4}h_1 < 0; \text{ UR-limit: } m_1 = 1, h_1 > 0; m_2 = -1, h_2 = \frac{1}{2}h_1 > 0. \quad (23)$$

Obviously, the final sign of the quantities presented in (22) is determined by the non-trivial interplay of the coefficients h_i and m_i. As a rule, h_i contains some small parameter and decreases in magnitude with increasing i, whereas m_i, on the contrary, increases with i in magnitude.

Note that nowadays the Lorentz–Einstein expression (14) seems to be not the uniquely possible one and therefore in [16] the scheme outlined in that paper was carried out for this more general case. In particular, it appears, that in the Lorentz-violated case the UR-limit in (23) is supplemented by the third term with $h_3 > 0$, $m_3 = 2$, which has a typical NR-form. This term enters (22) due to the appearance in the Lorentz-violated case of the parameter $H(p)/E_{Pl}$ (here E_{Pl} is the Planck energy) which is always small—even in the extreme UR-situation when $H(p)/E_0$ is large. In other words, the ratio E_0/E_{Pl} is always very small for any reasonable choice of particles constituting the system. The analysis of relevant expressions shows the existence of some critical value p^* defined as $cp^* \sim (E_0{}^2 E_{Pl})^{1/3}$. When the particle's momentum takes the value p^*, then the usual Lorentz behavior breaks and the velocity $v(p) = \mathrm{d}H(p)/\mathrm{d}p$ exceeds the critical value c (details are given in [16]).

As it was mentioned in Section 2, the calculation of the equilibrium pressure fluctuations (3) in terms of β and V (and, may be, N) will be completed after averaging the quasi-dynamic quantities obtained in Sections 4–6. This procedure is much more traditional but far from being simple, so we give here only its general outline for the ideal system in the case (14) of the non-uniform kinetic Hamilton function $H_k(p)$. The partition function is of the multiplicative form

$$Z_N(\beta,V) = [Vz(\beta)]^N,\ z(\beta) = \exp(-\beta E_0) z_k(\beta),\ z_k(\beta) = \int \mathrm{d}\Gamma(p)\exp[-\beta H_k(p)]; \quad (24)$$

$$\rho_k(p) = [z_k(\beta)]^{-1}\exp[-\beta H_k(p)],\ d\Gamma(p) = A_f p^{f-1}dp\ (A_1 = 1, A_2 = 2\pi, A_3 = 4\pi).$$

6. Thermodynamic Equations of State—Relativistic Ideal Classical Gas

Let us turn now to the derivation of the thermodynamic equations of state for the general, i.e., non-uniform, case of the relativistic ideal classical gas with the Hamilton function $h(\xi)$, defined in (14). Here and below the dimensionless energetic ($h = H/E_0$) and momentum ($\xi = cp/E_0$) units are used, and all the extensive (i.e., proportional to the particle number N) quantities are given per particle.

6.1. Representations for the Partition Function and Some Moments

Using the definition (24) for the 'small' partition function $z(\beta)$, we express it in the dimensionless temperature units $a = \beta E_0 = T_0/T$, $a \geq 0$, putting so far $E_0 \neq 0$; where$T_0 \equiv E_0/k_B$ is the characteristic temperature and $p_0 = E_0/c = T_0(k_B/c)$ is the characteristic momentum for the given sort of particles

$$z(a) = \int d\Gamma_\xi \exp[-ah(\xi)],\ d\Gamma_\xi = d\Gamma_{p(\xi)} = A_f(p_0)^f \xi^{f-1}d\xi,\ z(a) = \zeta(\infty;a) - \zeta(0;a). \tag{25}$$

Here $A_1 = 1$, $A_2 = 2\pi$, $A_3 = 4\pi$, the integration limits on ξ in (25) (as well as on p in (24)) being equal to 0 and ∞ respectively; $\zeta(\xi;a)$ is the indefinite Riemann integral in the left part of (25).

Clearly, at any $a > 0$ the convergence of the integral (25) is ensured and improved with the growth of a, however the limiting value $a = 0$ should be excluded. Physically, the limit $a = T_0/T \to 0$ corresponds to the high-temperature approximation $T \to \infty$ or to the ultra-relativistic case $E_0 = T_0 = 0$. Therefore, the representation (25) is convenient at large values $a \gg 1$ (when $T \to 0$ and/or $T_0 \to \infty$) in order to obtain the low-temperature (LT) and/or the non-relativistic (NR) expansions, so it is natural to call it the *LT/NR-representation* of the partition function $z(a)$ for the classical relativistic gas. The inclusion of the point $a = 0$ implying the high-temperature approximation can be realized through the change of variables (see Equation (26)).

The exclusion of the point $a = 0$ for the LT/NR-representation is stipulated by the fact that the quantity $\zeta(\xi;0) = \int d\Gamma_\xi \sim \xi^f$ at any $f > 0$ diverges on the upper limit at $\xi \to \infty$; the same conclusion follows from the asymptotic behavior $z(a) \sim \int d\Gamma_\xi e^{-a\xi} \sim a^{-f}$ at $a \to 0$, where the property $h(\xi) \approx \xi$ at large values of ξ is used. For the possibility of considering small values $a \ll 1$, including $a = 0$ (when $T \to \infty$ and/or $T_0 \to 0$), i.e., to obtain the high-temperature (HT) and/or the ultra-relativistic (UR) expansions, it is necessary to go over from the *LT/NR-representation* to the *HT/UR-representation* for $z(a)$.The latter one can be of interest in the case of the hot dense quark–gluon–plasma (QGP).

To this end, one should carry out in (25) the change of variable $ah(\xi) = \eta$, where $h(\xi) = (1 + \xi^2)^{\frac{1}{2}} \geq 1$, so that $\eta \geq a$. Moreover, it is convenient to introduce the denotation $p_T = T(k_B/c)$ for the characteristic thermal momentum of gas particles, thus obtaining

$$z(a) = \int_a^\infty d\Gamma_\eta [1 - (a/\eta)^2]^{(f-2)}, dG_\eta = A_f(p_T)^f e^{-\eta}\eta^{f-1}d\eta, (a) = \zeta(\infty;a) - \zeta(0;a). \tag{26}$$

However, the structure in (26) contrasts with that in the integral (25), since the variable a enters not only into the integrand, but also into the lower limit of the integral (26). Moreover, according to (26) the quantity $z(a) \to 0$ as $a \to \infty$, whereas at $a = 0$ the quantity $z(0)/A_f(p_T)^f$ takes its finite limiting value equal to $\Gamma(f)$.

According to the results of Section 4, all the thermodynamic quantities of the relativistic ideal classical gas can be expressed through the ordinary (not central) moments of the partition function; these moments being defined in the following way (the quantities $z_\kappa(a)$ and $h_\kappa(\xi)$ all will be analogous, replaced with the $h^{(n)}(a)$ with $h_\kappa{}^{(n)}(a)$)

$$h^{(n)}(a) \equiv \int_0^\infty d\Gamma_\xi [h(\xi)]^n \exp[-ah(\xi)], h^{(0)}(a) = z(a), h^{(n)}(a) = \zeta^{(n)}(\infty;a) - \zeta^{(n)}(0;a). \tag{27}$$

After changing the variable $\xi \to \eta$ the quantities $h^{(n)}(a)$ will have the form

$$h^{(n)}(a) = (1/a)^n \int d\Gamma_\eta \eta^n \, [1 - (a/\eta)^2]^{\frac{1}{2}(f - 2)}. \tag{28}$$

It is natural to call the quantities $h^{(n)}(a)$ (or $h_K{}^{(n)}(a)$) the Jüttner integrals for the total and kinetic energies (in analogy with Maxwell, Bose, Fermi, and other similar integrals in statistical mechanics). Indeed, the definition of the canonical averages (9) reads $<[h(\xi)]^n> = h^{(n)}(a)/h^{(0)}(a)$, so for the caloric quantities—i.e., the internal energy and its fluctuations—we obtain immediately from their definitions

$$H(a) = E_0[h^{(1)}(a)/h^{(0)}(a)], <(\Delta H)^2> = E_0{}^2[h^{(2)}(a)/h^{(0)}(a)] - [H(a)]^2. \tag{29}$$

For the thermal quantities—i.e., the pressure and its fluctuations—one obtains

$$P(a,V) = (E_0/fV)[h^{(1)}(a) - h^{(-1)}(a)]/h^{(0)}(a) = E_0(1/V)(1/a), \tag{30}$$

$$<(\Delta P)^2> = (1/\beta)\Delta\Psi(a,V) = E_0{}^2(1/a)(1/fV)^2[h^{(1)}(a) - h^{(-3)}(a)]/h^{(0)}(a). \tag{31}$$

6.2. Perturbation Expansion for the HT/UR-Representation

Obviously, the exact expressions for the partition function in the representation (26) and the corresponding Jüttner integrals (28) are not available, and so we are not able to construct the corresponding asymptotic behavior as $a \to 0$. Therefore, we obtain only approximate expressions for $h^{(n)}(a)$ ($n$is any integer including zero), namely, the expansion in degrees of $h_K{}^{(m)}(a)$ with positive m. Expansions of this kind for all thermodynamic quantities arise in the limit of large values of the parameter $1/a = T/T_0 \gg 1$ (including the value $a = 0$ at $E_0 = 0$). Physically, this corresponds to the smallness of the ratio $E_0/H_K(T)$, i.e., to the high temperature case (if the rest energy E_0 is fixed) or, on the contrary, to the small values of E_0 (at fixed temperature T). As can be seen from (19), $E_0/H_K{}^{ur}(T) = \kappa^{ur}(T_0/T) = a\kappa^{ur}$, where $\kappa^{ur} = 1/f$ is the factor of the order unity.

In order to obtain the desired expansions, we use the binomial power series at $\nu \geq 0$

$$[1 - (a/\eta)^2]^{\nu-} = \sum_{m=0}^{\infty} [\nu, m] a^{2m} \eta^{-2m}, [\nu, m] = (-1)^m (2^m m!)^{-1} \prod_{l=0}^{m-1} \{2\nu - (2l - 1)\}. \tag{32}$$

The coefficients in (32) satisfy the recurrence relation $[\nu,m + 1] = -\frac{1}{2}[\nu,m]\{2\nu - (2m + 1)\}(m + 1)^{-1}$, so that $[\nu,0] \equiv 1$, $[\nu,1] = -\frac{1}{2}(2\nu - 1)$, $[\nu,2] = [\nu,1](-\frac{1}{4})(2\nu - 3) = (1/8)(2\nu - 1)(2\nu - 3)$. Furthermore, it is more convenient to designate these coefficients $[f,m]$, going over from the variable $\nu \equiv \frac{1}{2}(f - 1)$ ($\nu \geq 0$) to the variable $f = 2\nu + 1$ ($f \geq 1$).

Let us substitute the expansion (32) into the integrand of the Jüttner integral (26) and introduce the special denotation for the combined exponent $k(m)$

$$k(m) \equiv 2\nu + n - 2m + 1 = k(0) - 2m, k(0) = f + n \text{ (all } f, n, m, k \text{ being integers)} \tag{33}$$

This exponent at given values of the number of particle's degrees of freedom $f = 1, 2, 3$ as well as the order of the Jüttner integral $n = 0, \pm1, \pm2, \ldots$ depends only upon the value $m \geq 0$. Then for the $h^{(n)}(f;a)$ one obtains the infinite sum of the following integrals

$$h^{(n)}(f;a) = A_f(p_T)^f a^{-n} \sum_{m=0}^{\infty} [f, m] a^{2m} \Gamma[k(m); a], \Gamma[k(m); a] \equiv \int_a^{\infty} d\eta e^{-\eta} \eta^{k(m)-1}. \tag{34}$$

The quantity $\Gamma[k(m);a]$ is the incomplete gamma-function (related to the integral exponential function, see, e.g., [23]), and its expansion into the power series in a (at fixed value of $k(m)$) depends significantly upon the sign of $k(m)$. According to the definition (33), the quantity $k(m)$ decreases linearly with the increase of m and changes at the critical value $m = m_0$, where

$$m_0 = \frac{1}{2}k(0)\ (k(0) > 0 \text{ even}),\ m_0 = \frac{1}{2}(k(0) + 1)\ (k(0) > 0 \text{ odd}),\ m_0 = 0\ (k(0) \leq 0). \tag{35}$$

Therefore, the infinite sum (34) is appropriate to be presented in the following form

$$h^{(n)}(f;a) = A_f(p_T)^f a^{-n}\left\{\sum_{0}^{m0-1}[f,m]\,a^{2m}\Gamma[k(m) > 0;a] + \sum_{m=m0}^{\infty}[f,m]a^{2m}\Gamma[k(m) \leq 0;a]\right\}, \tag{36}$$

where the desired power expansions in a for $\Gamma[k(m);a]$ at $k(m) > 0$ and $k(m) \leq 0$ are qualitatively different and should be considered separately (all the definitions are given in Appendix A, Equations (A5)–(A7)).

Finally, the expression (36) for $h^{(n)}(f;a)$ with the account for only lowest corrections in degrees of a may be written in the following form (recall that $p_T = T(k_B/c)$, $a = T_0/T = E_0/k_BT$)

$$h^{(n)}(f;a) = A_f(k_B/c)^f T^f a^{-n}\{\Sigma(f,n;a) + S(f,n;0)a^{f+n}\}. \tag{37}$$

Clearly, however, that if the values of the parameters f and n (just their sum defines $k(0)$ in (33)) are such that $k(0) < 0$ and $m_0 = 0$, then the first summand on the right-hand side of (36) vanishes. In the second summand, pole divergences arise in of the form $a^{-|k(0)|} = (T/T_0)^{|f+n|}$ which are now not compensated, so the corresponding Jüttner integral $h^{(n)}(f;a)$ exists only at finite values of a, the same being valid for T_0.

Using this fact, let us consider qualitatively the problem of thermodynamic stability of the so-called *Wien gas*, or the ideal gas of massless particles ($E_0 = k_BT_0 = 0$, $a = 0$), in the context of its dependence upon the dimension f. In order to ensure such a stability, it is necessary that in the limit $a = 0$ the corresponding Jüttner integrals $h^{(n)}(f;a)$ should exist, since according to Section 4 they determine the main thermodynamic quantities and their fluctuations.

Recall that for the partition function the similarity index $n = 0$, for the average energy $n = 1$ and for its fluctuation (specific heat) $n = 2$. However, for the average pressure it is necessary to choose the values $n = 1$ and $n = -1$, whereas for the pressure fluctuations (compressibility)—the values $n = 1$ и $n = -3$. Note that in the structure of the perturbation theory expansions there appear two specific dependences: upon the dimensionality f (i.e., upon the particle's spatial degrees of freedom) as well as upon the order n of the moment (i.e., the average value of the n-th power of the particle's energy).

That is why in the HT/UR-representation it is impossible to write down general expressions for the coefficients of expansions in (34). Thus, one should enumerate all the terms, considering consequently different combinations of integer values of f and n.

Note that all the thermodynamic parameters and their fluctuations are determined by the dimensionless quantity $\chi^{(n)}(f;a) = h^{(n)}(f;a)/h^{(0)}(f;a)$. Indeed, we obtain for the average energy, the specific heat, the pressure and the compressibility the following expressions

$$\begin{gathered} H(f;a) = E_0\chi^{(1)}(f;a), C_V(f;a) = E_0{}^2\{\chi^{(2)}(f;a) - [\chi^{(1)}(f;a)]^2\}, \\ P(f;a) = (E_0/fV)[\chi^{(1)}(f;a) - \chi^{(-1)}(f;a)] = k_BT/V, \\ \Delta\Psi(f;a) = (E_0/fV)^2(1/a)[\chi^{(1)}(f;a) - \chi^{(-3)}(f;a)], \\ \chi^{(n)}(f;a) = a^{-n}[\Sigma(f,n;a) + S(f,n)a^{f+n}]/[\Sigma(f,0;a) + S(f,0)a^f]. \end{gathered} \tag{38}$$

The quantity $\chi^{(n)}(f;a)$ below should be approximated in the spirit of the perturbation theory with the accepted accuracy in a in the following way

$$\chi^{(n)}(f;a) - \chi^{(n\prime)}(f;a) = a^{-n}\{[\Sigma(f,n;a) + S(f,n)a^{f+n}] - a^{n-n\prime}[\Sigma(f,n';a) + S(f,n')a^{f+n\prime}]\}/[\Sigma(f,0;a) + S(f,0)a^f],$$

while for the cases $n = 1$ at $n' = -1$ and $n' = -3$ the contribution of the second summand in braces contains additional small factors a^2 and a^4. Note that for the quantities H and C_V this accuracy (within the scope of the applied here direct moments method) can be superfluous in comparison to the usual method, when the quantities H and C_V are expressed through the derivatives with respect to a of the function $\ln h^{(0)}(f;a)$. In the latter case the final accuracy is confined by that of calculating the partition function $h^{(0)}(f;a)$.

Consider now the HT/UR-expansions for the thermodynamic quantities of the ideal gas of particles with various numbers f of degrees of freedom. We start with the dimensionless moments $\widetilde{h^{(n)}}(f;a) \equiv h^{(n)}(f;a)/A_f(k_B/c)^f T^f$, which determine these thermodynamic quantities according to (38)

$n = 0$. $\tilde{h}^{(0)}(1;a) = 1 + S(1,0)a$; $\tilde{h}^{(0)}(2;a) = 1 + S(2,0)a^2$; $\tilde{h}^{(0)}(32;a) = 2 - \tfrac{1}{2}a^2 + S(3,0)a^3$.
$n = 1$. $\tilde{h}^{(1)}(1;a)a = 1 + S(1,1)a^2$; $\tilde{h}^{(1)}(2;a)a = 2 + S(2,1)a^3$; $\tilde{h}^{(1)}(3;a)a = 6 - \tfrac{1}{2}a^2 + S(3,1)a^4$.

$n = 2$. $\tilde{h}^{(2)}(1;a)a^2 = 2 + \tfrac{1}{2}a^2 + S(1,2)a^3$; $\tilde{h}^{(2)}(2;a)a^2 = 6 + S(2;2)a^4$; $\tilde{h}^{(2)}(3;a)\, a^2 = 24 - a^2 + [3,2]\, a^4 + S(3,2)a^5$.
$n = -1$. $a^{-1}\tilde{h}^{(-1)}(1;a) = S(-1;1)$; $a^{-1}\tilde{h}^{(-1)}(2;a) = 1 + S(2;-1)a$; $a^{-1}\tilde{h}^{(-1)}(3;a) = 1 + S(3;-1)a$.
$n = -3$. $\tilde{h}^{(-3)}(f;a) = S(f,-3)a^f$.

Then we write down the quantities (38), with accounting for the lowest (in a) correction terms. Average energy $H(f;a)$; $H_\kappa{}^{ur}(T) = H(f;0) = fk_BT$.

$$H(1;a) = k_BT\{1 - S(1,0) + [\, S(1,0) + S(1,-1)]\}a^2;\ H(2;a) = 2k_BT[1 + S(2,0)a^2];$$
$$H(3;a) = 3k_BT\,[1 + \tfrac{1}{6}a^2]. \quad (39)$$

Specific heat $C_V(f;a)$; $C_V{}^{ur} = C_V(f;0) = fk_B$.

$$C_V(1;a) = k_B\{1 - [3S(1,0) + 2S(1,1)\}a^2;\ C_V(2;a) = 2k_B[1 + S(2,0)a^2];\ C_V(2;a) = 3k_B[1 - \tfrac{1}{6}\, a^2] \quad (40)$$

Note that due to the multiplication of a^{-1} by the 'small' factor E_0 the quantity $H^{ur}(T) = H(f;0)$ proves to be not more 'large' and coincides with the first of the expressions (33) for the average (kinetic) energy of the UR *Wien gas* ($k = 1$, $\kappa^{ur} = 1/f$). The correction within the second order of smallness in $a = T_0/T \ll 1$ for the expression (39) is stipulated by the account for the corresponding correction in ξ, to $1/h(\xi)$ in the second of the expressions (26). This correction in (39) is positive, and physically it corresponds to the increase of the average energy with that of the rest energy.

Analogously, the correction to the specific heat in (40) at $f = 2$ and 3 is also within the second order of smallness in a and differs from the corresponding correction to the average energy only in sign. At $f = 1$ this tendency also takes place (because $S(1,0) < 0$), but the connection between the coefficients looks more intricate due to the fact that the linear in a correction to C_V disappears. One can easily see that this property always takes place and does not depend upon the specific value of the linear in a term for the average energy. Naturally, $C_V{}^{ur}$ coincides with the second expression in (23) for the specific heat of the UR Wien gas with $k = 1$ and does not depend upon the temperature T. It is worth-while to note that in this case, just as before, both $C_V(T)$ and $dC_V(T)/dT$ are positive, so the thermodynamic stability is guaranteed.

Pressure vs. temperature $P(f;a) = k_BT/V$ at all f and a.

Pressure vs. kinetic energy $P(f;H_\kappa)$; $P^{ur}(f;H_\kappa{}^{ur}) = (\kappa^{ur}/V)H_\kappa{}^{ur}$.

$$P(1;H_\kappa) = 1 - S(1,-1)[E_0/H_\kappa{}^{ur}];\ P(2;H_\kappa) = 1 - 2[E_0/H_\kappa{}^{ur}];\ P(3;H_\kappa) = 1 - (3/2)[E_0/H_\kappa{}^{ur}] \quad (41)$$

Compressibility $\Delta\Psi(f;a)$ is equal

$$\Delta\Psi(f;a) = \Delta\Psi^{ur}\{1 - S(f,-3)a^f\}. \quad (42)$$

Formally, the correction for the $\kappa^{ur} = 1/f$ can be obtained by using the second of the Equation (39), with the result of the lowest order $\widetilde{h^{(-1)}}(f;a) \approx a$. Taking into account that the small parameter reads $a = T_0/T = (1/\kappa^{ur})(E_0/H_\kappa{}^{ur}) = f(E_0/H_\kappa{}^{ue})$, one obtains (41). Finally, the corrections to the limiting

UR-value of the compressibility $\Delta\Psi^{ur} = \Delta\Psi(f;0) = (\kappa^{ur}/V)P^{ur}$ at $a = 0$ start with a^f and in full analogy with the pressure they are negative.

Therefore, it is obvious that the HT/UR-corrections do not violate the thermodynamic stability of the system because these corrections cannot change the sign of fluctuations for the energy (39) and the pressure (41).

7. Conclusions

In this paper, we have revised the long-standing problem of equilibrium pressure fluctuations and showed that its solution can be obtained on the grounds of generalizing the Bogoliubov–Zubarev theorem by using the method of quasi-averages (applied to the introduction of the volume) as well as that of scale transformation in the phase space of a physical object in question. Besides general formulation for the proof of the theorem (which can be found in Refs. [10,18]), we have presented some numerical results for the thermodynamic quantities of the relativistic gases. We hope that these results could be partly applied to the description of the hot quark-gluon plasma within the scope of thermodynamics as well as of statistical mechanics (in this connection see, e.g., papers [24,25]). However, for the moment the thermal equations of state for the pressure are formulated mostly within the phenomenological approach on the grounds of QCD thermodynamics, whereas the application of the generalized Bogoliubov–Zubarev theorem needs some dynamical description in the object's phase space (e.g., if possible, for the Mott–Hagedorn resonance gas described in [24,25]).

Author Contributions: Conceptualization, Y.G.R. and Y.P.R.; Methodology, Y.G.R. and Y.P.R.; Software, Y.G.R.; Validation, Y.P.R.; Formal Analysis Y.P.R.; Investigation, Y.G.R. and Y.P.R.; Resources, Y.G.R.; Data Curation, Y.G.R.; Writing-Original Draft Preparation, Y.G.R.; Writing-Review & Editing, Y.P.R.; Visualization, Y.P.R.; Supervision, Y.P.R.; Project Administration Y.P.R.

Funding: This research received no external funding.

Acknowledgments: The authors are grateful to D. Blaschke for invitation to the Symposium "Nonequilibrium Phenomena in Strongly Correlated Systems" held at Dubna, April 2018. We are also indebted to V.G. Morozov for the useful discussion of the manuscript. The paper is devoted to the memory of Dmitrii Nikolaevich Zubarev on the occasion of his 100th birthday.

Conflicts of Interest: The authors declare no conflict of interest.

Appendix A Details of Calculating Sum (36) in Section 6

1. Case $k(m) > 0$

At $k(m) > 0$ $(0 \leq m < m_0)$ in the expansion for $\Gamma[k(m) > 0;a]$ only positive degrees of a appear

$$\Gamma[k(m) > 0; a] = \Gamma[k(m) > 0; 0] - \int_0^a d\eta e^{-\eta}\eta^{k(m)-1} = \Gamma[k(m) > 0] - \sum_{l=0}^{\infty} (-1)^l (l!)^{-1} a^{k(m)+l} (k(m) + l)^{-1}, \quad \text{(A1)}$$

where $\Gamma[k(m)>0;0]$ is the ordinary (i.e., complete) gamma-function $\Gamma[k(m)]$ (see, e.g., [22]); for integer values $k(m) = 1, 2, \ldots$ it possesses the most simple form $[k(m) - 1]!$

In order to obtain the expansion (A1), it is sufficient to expand the exponent $e^{-\eta}$, which enters the integrand in the definition (34), in the Taylor series and then to integrate over η the relevant convergent series. In this course no singularities in (A1) in the limit $a \to 0$ arise, because they would appear in any of the terms on the right-hand side of (A1) only in the case of violating the condition $k(m) > 0$. Indeed, the function $\Gamma[k(m)]$ in this case would be not well defined and some of the denominators $k(m) + l$ might take zero values.

Taking into account the form of the product $a^{2m}a^{k(m)} = a^{k(0)}$, it can be easily seen that the first term in the braces on the right-hand side of Equation (36) contains in general case two groups of expansion terms: one running even degrees of a (starting with $a^0, a^2, \ldots$), and another running all degrees of a, starting with $a^{k(0)}$ and taking subsequent values $a^{k(0)+l}$, $l = 1, 2, \ldots$ Clearly, the lowest order contribution "surviving" in the limit $a = 0$ is of the form

$$[f,0]\Gamma[k(0) \geq 1]a^0 = [k(0) - 1]! = (f + n - 1)!,$$

with the values of f and n satisfying the aforementioned condition $k(0) \geq 1$.

If the quantity $k(0) = f + n$ has the *minimal* possible (for the case in question) value $k(0) = 1$, the lowest order contribution (linear in a) will be given by the first term of the second group $a^{k(0)}$. The next order contribution will be given by the second term of the first group, which is quadratic in a. However, if $k(0) = 2$, the terms mentioned will give the contribution of one and the same order in a, and only at $k(0) = 3$ the contributions of the second group (starting with a^3) will follow, the two first terms of the first group joining the battle.

2. **Case $k(m) \leq 0$**

At $k(m) \leq 0$ (i.e., at $m \geq m_0 \geq 0$), in contrast with the case $k(m) > 0$, only *negative* degrees of a enter into the expansion for $\Gamma[k(m) \leq 0;a]$. This fact implies the arising of the pole singularities of all orders from 1 till $|k(m)|$, as well as also the logarithmic singularity in a, the latter singularity being the only "surviving" one even in the limiting case $k(m_0) = 0$. However, as can be seen, these singularities do not become apparent in the final result for $h^{(n)}(f;a)$, since they are fully suppressed by the factor a^{2m} appearing in every order at $m \geq m_0$.

In order to obtain the expansion for $\Gamma[k(m) \leq 0;a]$ in degrees of a, it is worth-while to note that this quantity is defined by the integral in (34) and the condition of its convergence at the upper limit for any value of $k(m)$ (independently on the sign) is guaranteed by the factor $e^{-\eta}$. However, at the lower limit the convergence condition is violated already for the maximally possible in our case value $k(m) = 0$ implying the logarithmic singularity. Moreover, with the decrease of $k(m)$ (i.e., the increase of $|k(m)|$) there arise pole singularities of maximal order $|k(m)|$.

So it is appropriate to use for $\Gamma[k(m) \leq 0;a]$ the recurrence relation enabling one to increase by the unity the value $k(m)$ (and respectively to decrease the value $|k(m)|$), thus selecting the pole singularities. The relation of this kind can be easily found through the integration by parts of the original integral in (34), with the result reading

$$\Gamma[k(m) \leq 0;a] = \mathrm{e}^{-a}a^{-|k(m)|} - (1/|k(m)|)\,\Gamma[k(m) + 1 \leq 0;a]. \tag{A2}$$

Finally, the relation (A2) permits one to express $\Gamma[k(m) \leq 0;a]$ with an arbitrary value $k(m) \leq 0$ as a function of $\Gamma[k(m) = 0;a]$

$$\Gamma[k(m) \leq 0;a] = \mathrm{e}^{-a}\sum_{l=0}^{k(m)-1}(-1))^{l+1}[|k(m)|\ldots(|k(m)| - l)]^{-1}a^{-|k(\mathrm{m})|+l} + (-1)^{|k(\mathrm{m})|}(|k(m)|!)^{-1}\,\Gamma[k(m) = 0;a]. \tag{A3}$$

The finite sum entering the right-hand side of (A3) is different from zero only under the condition $k(m) < 0$. Otherwise (at $k(m) = 0$) the relation (A3) reduces to the identity. In particular, just this sum contains all the pole singularities mentioned above.

The quantity $\Gamma[k(m) = 0;a]$ is the limiting one for all possible values $k(m) \leq 0$ and coincides (up to the sign) with the integral exponent function $\mathrm{Ei}(-a)$ (see, e.g., [23])

$$\Gamma[k(m) = 0;a] = \int_a^\infty d\eta \mathrm{e}^{-\eta}\eta^{-1} \equiv -\mathrm{Ei}(-a), \mathrm{Ei}(-a) = C + \ln a + \sum_{l=0}^{\infty}(l!l)^{-1}\mathrm{a}^l, \tag{A4}$$

where $C \approx 0{,}577$ is the Euler constant. The power series on the right-hand side of (A4) converges for all finite real values of a, but the term $\ln a$ possesses an obvious singularity at the limiting value $a = 0$, corresponding to the case of massless particles with $E_0 = 0$.

It can be shown that all the singularities mentioned above of the quantity $\Gamma[k(m) \leq 0;a]$ disappear, as was expected, after its substitution into the second term in the braces on the right-hand side of Equation (36) due to its multiplication by the factor a^{2m} in every order of the infinite sum over the index $m \geq m_0 > 0$. It is quite clear for the logarithmic singularity (and also for the constant term) entering (A4). As to the pole singularities entering the finite sum in (A3) at $k(m) \equiv k(0) - 2m \leq 0$, one obtains $|k(m)| = -k(m) = 2m - k(0)$ and $-|k(m)| = -2m + k(0)$, so $a^{2\mathrm{m}}a^{-|k(m)|} = a^{k(0)}$.

Thus, the two cases 2 and 1, which look on the first glance as quite different, appear to be in sufficiently complete accordance one with another. Indeed, in the case 2 the two groups of the expansion terms in degrees of a prove to appear: those with even degrees and also with all degrees, starting with $a^{k(0)}$ and taking subsequent values $a^{k(0)+l}$ ($l = 1, 2, \ldots$). Note that the first group of terms in the case 2 starts not with a^0 (with the coefficient $\Gamma[k(0);0]$), as in the case 1, but with the term a^{m_0} (with the coefficient C), where according to Equation (35) the value m_0, in general differs from zero. Otherwise, just this term proves to be the starting one for the whole expansion (36), so that the case 1 cannot be realized.

If the case 1 is nevertheless realized, the first group of terms may be represented as

$$\Sigma(f,n;a) \equiv \sum_{m=0}^{m0-1} [f,m][k(m)-1]!a^{2\mathrm{m}} = [(f+n)-1]! + [f,1][(f+n-2)-1]!a^2 + \mathrm{O}(a^4), \quad \text{(A5)}$$

where it was taken into account that $[f,0] \equiv 1$, $k(0) = f + n(\geq 1)$ and $[f,1] = -\frac{1}{2}(f-2)$, $k(1) = k(0) - 2$. The number of terms in (A5) depends upon the value of the index m_0, which according to (33) и (35) depends in turn upon the values f and n.

As for the second groups of terms in both cases 1 and 2, it follows that they should be unified, so that the resulting contribution into the right-hand side of Equation (36) takes the form $a^{k(0)}S(f;a)$. Here $S(f,n;a) = S_<(f,n;a) + S_\geq(f,n;a)$ is the expansion in a, including all the degrees (starting with a^0), and the quantities $S_<(a)$ (with $m < m_0$) and $S_\geq(a)$ (with $m \geq m_0$) are the following double sums

$$\begin{aligned} S_<(f,n;a) &= -\Sigma_{m=0}^{m0-1}[f,m][f,m]\Sigma_{l=0}^{\infty}(-1)^l(l!)^{-1}a^l(k(m)+l)^{-1}, \\ S_\geq(f,n;a) &= \mathrm{e}^{-a}\Sigma_{m=m0}^{\infty}[f,m]\Sigma_{m=m0}^{k(m)-1}[f,m]\Sigma(-1)^{l+1}[|k(m)|\ldots(|k(m)|-l)]^{-1}a^l. \end{aligned} \quad \text{(A6)}$$

It is necessary to underline that at the point $a = 0$ in the "inner" sums over the index l only the first term with $l = 0$ remains. We do not study here the infinite sum (42), but in virtue of definitions (32) and (33) for $[f,m]$ and $k(m)$ it is seen that the general term of this sum with alternating signs is of the form $(-1)^m(2^m m!)^{-1}$ and even in the worst (in the sense of convergence) case $m_0 = 0$ the series (42) converges, with $S(0)$ taking the finite value

$$S(f,n;0) = -\sum_{m=0}^{m0-1} s(f,m) + \sum_{m=0}^{\infty} s(f,m), s(f,m) \equiv [f,m](k(m))^{-1}. \quad \text{(A7)}$$

Here the quantity $S(f,n;0) \equiv S(f,n)$, like $\Sigma(f,n;a)$, depends on n through m_0, which is determined by the relations (33) and (35).

References

1. Gibbs, J.W. *Elementary Principles in Statistical Mechanics*; Yale University Press: New Haven, CT, USA, 1902.
2. Fowler, R.H. *Statistical Mechanics*, 2nd ed.; Cambridge University Press: Cambridge, UK, 1936.
3. Hill, T.L. *Statistical Mechanics. Principles and Selected Applications*; McGraw-Hill: New York, NY, USA, 1956.
4. Kittel, C. *Thermal Physics*; Wiley: New York, NY, USA, 1969.
5. Terletzky, Y.P. *Statistical Physics*, 3rd ed.; Vysshaya Shkola: Moscow, Russia, 1994.
6. Wergeland, H. On pressure fluctuations in gases. *Det. Kgl. Norske Vidensk. Forh.* **1955**, *28*, 106–112.
7. Münster, A. Fluctuations en pression. *Physica* **1960**, *26*, 1117–1123. [CrossRef]
8. Klein, M.J. Pressure fluctuations. *Physica* **1960**, *26*, 1073–1079. [CrossRef]

9. Landau, L.D.; Lifshitz, E.M. *Statistical Physics*; Addison-Wesley: Boston, MA, USA, 1958.
10. Rudoy, Y.G.; Sukhanov, A.D. Thermodynamic fluctuations within the Gibbs and Einstein approaches. *Phys. Uspekhi* **2000**, *43*, 1169–1199. [CrossRef]
11. Bogoliubov, N.N. *Dynamical Problems in Statistical Physics*; GITTL: Moscow, Russia, 1946.
12. Zubarev, D.N. *Statistische Thermodynamic der Nichtgleigewicht*; AkademieVerlag: Berlin, Germany, 1976.
13. Bogoliubov, N.N. *Quasi-Averages in the Problems of Statistical Mechanics*; Preprint R–1451; JINR: Dubna, Russia, 1961; Phys. Abh. aus der SU, **1962**, *6*, 1–112, 113–129.
14. Vladimirov, V.S. *Generalized Functions in Mathematical Physics*; Nauka: Moscow, Russia, 1976.
15. Rudoy, Y.G.; Keita, I. Dynamic pressure and its fluctuations for the ideal gas of relativistic particles. *Bull. People's Friendsh. Univ. Russia Ser. Math. Inf. Sci. Phys.* **2007**, *1–2*, 84–93.
16. Rudoy, Y.G.; Rybakov, Y.P.; Keita, I. Thermodynamic equation of state for the ideal gas and its generalization by means of the effective parameters. *Phys. Educ. High. Sch.* **2007**, *13*, 41–56.
17. Keita, I. Thermodynamic Pressure and Its Equilibrium Fluctuations. Ph.D. Thesis, People's Friendship University of Russia (PFUR), Moscow, Russia, 2007.
18. Rudoy, Y.G. Generalization of the Bogoliubov—Zubarev theorem for the dynamic pressure to the case of compressibility. *Theor. Math. Phys.* **2018**, *194*, 114–126. [CrossRef]
19. Rudoy, Y.G.; Rybakov, Y.P.; Keita, I. Thermodynamic pressure and its fluctuations for the classical ideal gas of the relativistic particles. *J. Math. Sci.* **2011**, *172*, 870–883. [CrossRef]
20. Jüttner, F. Das Maxwellsche Gesetz der Geschwindigkeitsverteilung in der Relativitättheorie. *Ann. Phys.* **1926**, *34*, 856–882.
21. Jüttner, F. Die relativistische Quantentheorie des idealen Gases. *Ann. Phys.* **1928**, *47*, 542–566.
22. Glaser, W. Zur Theorie des idealen Gases. *Ann. Phys.* **1935**, *94*, 317–327, 677–691. [CrossRef]
23. Lebedev, N.N. *Special Functions and Their Applications*; GITTL: Moscow, Russia, 1953.
24. Turko, L.; Blaschke, D.; Prorok, D.; Bredermann, J. Effective degrees of freedom in QCD thermodynamics. *EPJ Web Conf.* **2014**, *71*, 00134. [CrossRef]
25. Blaschke, D.; Dubinin, A.; Turko, L. Mott-hadron resonance gas and lattice QCD thermodynamics. *Phys. Part. Nuclei* **2015**, *46*, 732–736. [CrossRef]

particles

MDPI

Article

Nonperturbative Kinetic Description of Electron-Hole Excitations in Graphene in a Time Dependent Electric Field of Arbitrary Polarization

Stanislav A. Smolyansky [1,2], Anatolii D. Panferov [1], David B. Blaschke [3,4,5,*] and Narine T. Gevorgyan [6]

1 Saratov State University, 410026 Saratov, Russia; smol@sgu.ru (S.A.S.); panferovad@sgu.ru (A.D.P.)
2 Department of Physics, Tomsk State University, 634050 Tomsk, Russia
3 Institute of Theoretical Physics, University of Wrocław, 50-204 Wrocław, Poland; david.blaschke@gmail.com
4 Bogoliubov Laboratory for Theoretical Physics, JINR Dubna, 141980 Dubna, Russia
5 Peoples' Friendship University of Russia (RUDN University), 117198 Moscow, Russia
6 Russian-Armenian University, 0051 Yerevan, Armenia; gevorgyan.narine@gmail.com
* Correspondence: david.blaschke@gmail.com; Tel.: +48-71-375-9252

Received: 16 December 2018; Accepted: 9 April 2019; Published: 16 April 2019

Abstract: On the basis of the well-known kinetic description of e^-e^+ vacuum pair creation in strong electromagnetic fields in $D = 3 + 1$ QED we construct a nonperturbative kinetic approach to electron-hole excitations in graphene under the action of strong, time-dependent electric fields. We start from the simplest model of low-energy excitations around the Dirac points in the Brillouin zone. The corresponding kinetic equations are analyzed by nonperturbative analytical and numerical methods that allow to avoid difficulties characteristic for the perturbation theory. We consider different models for external fields acting in both, one and two dimensions. In the latter case we discuss the nonlinear interaction of the orthogonal currents in graphene which plays the role of an active nonlinear medium. In particular, this allows to govern the current in one direction by means of the electric field acting in the orthogonal direction. Investigating the polarization current we detected the existence of high frequency damped oscillations in a constant external electric field. When the electric field is abruptly turned off residual inertial oscillations of the polarization current are obtained. Further nonlinear effects are discussed.

Keywords: graphene; dynamic critical phenomena; high-field and nonlinear effects

PACS: 81.05.Uw, 64.60.Ht, 73.50.Fq

---

1. Introduction

In recent years considerable interest has developed in a nonperturbative, dynamical description of transport phenomena in condensed matter physics inspired by the physics of strong electromagnetic fields [1]. Particular attention was devoted to graphene (see, e.g., [2,3]). In this case there is an obvious similarity with the dynamical Schwinger effect in QED, the creation of electron-positron pairs from the vacuum in strong electromagnetic fields [4–6]. In this context the nonperturbative kinetic approach has proven successful. It is based on the transition to a quasiparticle representation in the presence of an external, quasiclassical electric field facilitated by a time dependent Bogoliubov transformation [7–10]. It would be natural to adopt these methods to specific problems in condensed matter physics and, in particular, to the physics of graphene. Such an adaptation is performed in the present work. The application of these methods allows for advancement to nonperturbative investigations of nonlinear effects in graphene in the presence of strong external electric fields.

We want to give a detailed outline of the contents of the present work. In Section 2, Section 2.1 the basic kinetic equation (KE) for the simplest dynamical model of graphene [2,3,11–14] (a single layer graphene sheet with two Dirac points of the Brillouin zone and absence of the standard scattering mechanism of carriers) is obtained using nonperturbative techniques for the case of a spatially homogeneous, time-dependent external electric field of arbitrary polarization in the graphene plane. The transition to the quasiparticle representation is obtained with the help of a unitary transformation expressed in explicit form [15]. All subsequent consideration is essentially nonperturbative.

The process of electron-hole (*e-h*) pair creation in a strong electric field can be considered as a specific field-induced phase transition in a system with broken symmetry [1,10,16]. In Section 2.2 some features of this process are considered in graphene. Section 3 is devoted to the connection of observables such as the quasiparticle number and current densities with the kinetic theory. Here we discuss also the energy conservation law for a system in an external electric field. Here, in particular, an order parameter is introduced which describes the polarization properties of graphene. It is shown that after switching off the external field pulse the order parameter survives and oscillates with momentum dependent amplitude. In other words, the evolution of the order parameter is defined by the entire prehistory of the graphene evolution during the application of the external field. In particular, this effect becomes apparent in the damped oscillations of the residual polarization current on the background of a constant residual conduction current (Section 4). Here it is also shown that the polarization current dominates over the conduction current. This dominance turns out also in calculations of the currents in the framework of the standard perturbation theory. For example, in the Appendix A, we reproduce the well-known results for the polarization and conduction currents in the leading orders of the expansion with respect to $E/E_0 \ll 1$, where E_0 is the characteristic field (1).

Section 5 contains results of the numerical calculations of the distribution functions of the carriers for electric fields of different magnitude and spectral composition models both for linear and elliptic polarizations. This fact is an important hint that the similar situation is valid also in $D = 3 + 1$ QED, where analogous calculations can be very complicated [17].

In Section 6 we outline the effect of manipulating a weak signal with a current by means of generating active properties of graphene with the help of another (basic) field.

Finally, in Section 7, by analogy with Section 2, we derive the KE in the $D = 2 + 1$ tight binding model of the nearest neighbor interaction [3,11,12]. Also in this case the conduction and polarization currents are obtained. Their detailed investigation will be performed in a separate work.

The conclusions are drawn in Section 8.

We use the metric $g_{\mu\nu} = \mathrm{diag}\,(1, -1, -1)$ and the coordinates $x^\mu = (v_F t, x^1, x^2)$. We will proceed from the basic parameters of the model: $a = 2.46$ Å is the lattice spacing, $\gamma = 2.7$ eV is the hopping energy, and $v_F = 10^6$ m/s is the Fermi velocity. We define a set of scale factors for the physical quantities time (t_0), momentum (p_0), and field strength (E_0) according to

$$t_0 = \frac{a}{v_F}, \quad p_0 = \frac{\hbar}{a}, \quad E_0 = \frac{\hbar v_F}{e a^2}. \tag{1}$$

2. Kinetic Equation

In this section the basic KE for the description of electron-hole excitations in external, time-dependent electric fields will be derived for the $D = 2 + 1$ QED model of graphene in the framework of a low-energy model (for a tight-binding model, see Section 7 below). Some necessary prerequisites for such a derivation have already been obtained earlier [15] by means of the diagonalization of the initial Hamiltonian of the model. Our approach is based on the consistent usage of the occupation number representation and the adaptation of a method that is well known in $D = 3 + 1$ QED for the description of the creation of an electron-positron plasma from the vacuum in strong fields [7,8,18].

Let us assume the graphene layer is located in the plane $(x^1 = x, x^2 = y)$. A time dependent spatially homogeneous electric field acts in this plane, i.e., the corresponding vector potential in the Hamiltonian gauge is $A^k(t) = (0, A^1(t), A^2(t))$. The spatial homogeneity of the electric field can be provided, for example, in the focal spot of two coherent laser beams counter propagating along the axis perpendicular to the graphene layer. It is assumed that the field model is finite, i.e., that the field strength $\vec{E}(t) = -\frac{1}{c}\dot{\vec{A}}(t)$ vanishes before switching on and after switching off the laser fields, $\lim_{t\to\pm\infty} E(t) = 0$ (the dot above the symbol denotes its time derivative). This is necessary for the correct definition of the in- and out- states of the vacuum with $A_{\text{in}} = A(t \to -\infty)$ and $A_{\text{out}} = A(t \to \infty)$.

2.1. *The Low-Energy Approximation*

The Dirac-type equation for the low-energy excitations in graphene in a time dependent electric field described above is

$$i\hbar\dot{\Psi}(\vec{x},t) = v_F\hat{\vec{P}}\vec{\sigma}\Psi(\vec{x},t), \tag{2}$$

where $\hat{P}_k = -i\hbar\nabla_k - (e/c)A_k(t)$ is the quasi-momentum $(k = 1, 2)$ and σ_k are the Pauli matrices corresponding to the pseudospin structure of graphene.

The Hamiltonian of the theory,

$$H(t) = \frac{i\hbar}{2}\int d^2x\left[\Psi^\dagger(\vec{x},t)\dot{\Psi}(\vec{x},t) - \dot{\Psi}^\dagger(\vec{x},t)\Psi(\vec{x},t)\right], \tag{3}$$

is the 00 component of the corresponding energy-momentum tensor and it can be transformed with help of the equation of motion (2) to the form

$$H(t) = v_F\int d^2x\Psi^\dagger(\vec{x},t)\hat{\vec{P}}\vec{\sigma}\Psi(\vec{x},t). \tag{4}$$

Here we dropped the spin indices.

The wave function here is a two-component spinor permitting the decomposition

$$\Psi^T(\vec{x},t) = \frac{1}{(2\pi\hbar)^2}\int d^2p\left(\Psi^{(1)}_{\vec{p}}(t), \Psi^{(2)}_{-\vec{p}}(t)\right)e^{i\vec{p}\vec{x}/\hbar}, \tag{5}$$

which translates the Hamiltonian function (4) to the momentum representation.

For the physical interpretation of the model it is appropriate to go over to the quasiparticle representation, where the Hamiltonian of the theory is diagonal. As it was shown in the work [15], this is achieved with the unitary transformation

$$U^\dagger(t)v_F\vec{P}\vec{\sigma}U(t) = \varepsilon(\vec{p},t)\sigma_3 = H_{\vec{p}}(t), \tag{6}$$

and $\Phi = U^\dagger\Psi$ with the unitary matrix [15]

$$U(t) = \frac{1}{\sqrt{2}}\begin{pmatrix} \exp(-i\varkappa/2) & \exp(-i\varkappa/2) \\ \exp(i\varkappa/2) & -\exp(i\varkappa/2) \end{pmatrix}. \tag{7}$$

The function $\varkappa$ is defined by the condition (6) [15], corresponding to $\tan\varkappa = P^2/P^1$, where $P^k = p^k - (e/c)A^k(t)$. The quasienergy $\varepsilon(\vec{p},t)$ in (6) is determined by the dispersion relation in the vicinity of the Dirac points

$$\varepsilon(\vec{p},t) = v_F\sqrt{P^2} = v_F\sqrt{(P^1)^2 + (P^2)^2}. \tag{8}$$

Equation (2) transforms then to the form

$$i\hbar\dot{\Phi} = H_{\vec{p}}(t)\Phi + \frac{1}{2}\lambda\hbar\sigma_1\Phi, \tag{9}$$

where $H_{\vec{p}}(t)$ is defined by Equation (6) and

$$\lambda(\vec{p},t) = \dot{\varkappa} = \frac{ev_F^2[E_1P_2 - E_2P_1]}{\varepsilon^2(\vec{p},t)}. \tag{10}$$

Introducing the notation

$$\Phi(\vec{p},t) = \left[\begin{array}{c} a(\vec{p},t) \\ b^{\dagger}(-\vec{p},t) \end{array}\right], \tag{11}$$

the Hamiltonian function (4) can be rewritten in the quasiparticle form

$$\begin{aligned} H(t) &= \int [dp]\varepsilon(\vec{p},t)\Phi^{\dagger}(\vec{p},t)\,\sigma_3\Phi(\vec{p},t) \\ &= \int [dp]\varepsilon(\vec{p},t)\left[a^{\dagger}(\vec{p},t)a(\vec{p},t) - b(-\vec{p},t)b^{\dagger}(-\vec{p},t)\right], \end{aligned} \tag{12}$$

where the abbreviation $[dp] = d^2p(2\pi\hbar)^{-2}$ has been used.

Apparently, the realization of the unitary transformation in the explicit form in both the low-energy and the tight-binding (see below Section 7) models is a result of the fact that these models belong to the class of conformal-invariant field theories (see, e.g., Ref. [6]).

At this stage one can go over to the occupation number representation and replace the amplitudes $a^{\dagger}(t)$,$a(t)$ and $b^{\dagger}(t)$, $b(t)$ by the corresponding creation and annihilation operators for electrons and holes considered as quasiparticles. These operators are defined on the in-vacuum state $|\mathrm{in}\rangle$ with vector potential $\vec{A}_{\mathrm{in}}$ and satisfy the canonical anti-commutation relations

$$\left\{a(\vec{p},t),a^{\dagger}(\vec{p}',t)\right\}_{+} = \left\{b(\vec{p},t),b^{\dagger}(\vec{p}',t)\right\}_{+} = (2\pi)^2\delta(\vec{p}-\vec{p}'). \tag{13}$$

Other elementary anti-commutators are equal to zero.

From Equations (2), (6) and (11) it follows the equations of motion of the Heisenberg type for the description of the unitary evolution of the creation and annihilation operators, e.g.,

$$\dot{a}(\vec{p},t) = \frac{i}{\hbar}[H(t),a(\vec{p},t)] - \frac{i}{2}\lambda(\vec{p},t)\,b^{+}(-\vec{p},t) = \frac{i}{\hbar}[H_{tot}(t),a(\vec{p},t)], \tag{14}$$

$$\dot{b}(\vec{p},t) = \frac{i}{\hbar}[H(t),b(-\vec{p},t)] + \frac{i}{2}\lambda(\vec{p},t)\,a^{+}(\vec{p},t) = \frac{i}{\hbar}[H_{tot}(t),b(-\vec{p},t)], \tag{15}$$

where the amplitude of the transitions between states with the positive and negative energies of the quasiparticles is defined by Equation (10). From Equations (9), (14) and (15) it follows that evolution of the system is unitary. The Fock space is constructed on the time dependent vacuum state. In Equations (14) and (15) $H_{tot} = H + H_{pol}$, where

$$H_{pol}(t) = \frac{\hbar}{2}\int [dp]\lambda(\vec{p},t)[a^{+}(\vec{p},t)b^{+}(-\vec{p},t) - b(-\vec{p},t)a(\vec{p},t)] \tag{16}$$

describes the dynamics of vacuum polarization.

Now one can obtain the KE. Let us introduce the distribution functions for the electrons and the holes,

$$f^{e}(\vec{p},t) = \langle \mathrm{in}|a^{+}(\vec{p},t)a(\vec{p},t)|\mathrm{in}\rangle, \tag{17}$$

$$f^{h}(\vec{p},t) = \langle \mathrm{in}|b^{+}(-\vec{p},t)b(-\vec{p},t)|\mathrm{in}\rangle. \tag{18}$$

The averaging procedure here is carried out under the in-vacuum state $|\text{in}\rangle$. Differentiation with respect to time and taking into account Equations (14) and (15) results in

$$\dot{f}^e(\vec{p},t) = \frac{i\lambda}{2}(\vec{p},t)\left\{f^{(+)}(\vec{p},t) - f^{(-)}(\vec{p},t)\right\}, \tag{19}$$

where anomalous averages have been introduced

$$f^{(+)}(\vec{p},t) = \langle \text{in}|a^+(\vec{p},t)b^+(-\vec{p},t)|\text{in}\rangle, \tag{20}$$
$$f^{(-)}(\vec{p},t) = \langle \text{in}|b(-\vec{p},t)a(\vec{p},t)|\text{in}\rangle\,. \tag{21}$$

The equations of motion for these functions have the form

$$\dot{f}^{(+)}(\vec{p},t) = \frac{2i}{\hbar}\varepsilon(\vec{p},t)f^{(+)}(\vec{p},t) - \frac{i\lambda(\vec{p},t)}{2}[1-2f(\vec{p},t)], \tag{22}$$
$$\dot{f}^{(-)}(\vec{p},t) = \frac{-2i}{\hbar}\varepsilon(\vec{p},t)f^{(-)}(\vec{p},t) + \frac{i\lambda(\vec{p},t)}{2}[1-2f(\vec{p},t)]. \tag{23}$$

Here it was assumed that $f^e = f^h = f$ holds as a consequence of the electroneutrality condition.

Let us rewrite Equations (22) and (23) in integral form. Substitution of this result in Equation (19) leads to a KE of non-Markovian type

$$\dot{f}(\vec{p},t) = \frac{1}{2}\lambda(\vec{p},t)\int_{t_0}^{t} dt'\lambda(\vec{p},t')\left[1-2f(\vec{p},t')\right]\cos\theta(t,t'), \tag{24}$$

where

$$\theta(t,t') = \frac{2}{\hbar}\int_{t'}^{t} dt''\varepsilon(\vec{p},t'') \tag{25}$$

is the dynamical phase.

In the present work the KE (24) and its reformulation in the form of an equivalent system of ordinary differential equations (ODE), shown below in Equation (27), are considered only for zero initial conditions, $f_0 = f(t_0) = 0$. For the first time a KE of such type was obtained in the works [6,7,19] in $D = 3+1$ QED for the description of vacuum creation of electron-positron pairs under the action of a time dependent spatially homogeneous linearly polarized electric field. This method is based on the usage of unitary nonequivalent canonical transformations for the transition to the quasiparticle representation [6]. In the considered situation this approach is applicable and leads to the KE (24) that has the same mathematical structure as in the $D = 3+1$ QED case [7,8,18]. However, in the massless $D = 2+1$ QED case the transition to the quasiparticle representation is possible in the framework of a unitary transformation [15] (see, e.g., Equation (6)).

An advantage of the unitary approach is also the possibility of a generalization of this method [15] to the case of a two-dimensional electric field with the vector potential $A^k(t)(k = 1,2)$. Let us remark that the transition from the one-dimensional electric field (linear polarization) to two or three field dimensions (arbitrary polarization) in $D = 3+1$ QED is connected with the necessity to take into account a larger number of spin degrees of freedom and is accompanied with a significant increase in the number of necessary KE's [20–22].

The main feature of the KE (24) is the absence of an energy gap in the quasienergy (8). Such kind of models were considered long ago [23] (see also [6]) and have been investigated sufficiently well. In the following this feature will be investigated in the situation when the e-h-system in graphene is exposed to a time dependent electric field. In the presence of the external field the Dirac points $\varepsilon_0(p) = 0$ are transformed to a family of Dirac lines L_D which depend parametrically on time,

$$P_i^D = p_i^D - \frac{e}{c}A_i(t) = 0, \;\; i = 1, 2. \tag{26}$$

For the numerical analysis of the KE (24) for different field models it is appropriate to rewrite it in the form of an equivalent system of ODEs [6,8],

$$\dot{f} = \frac{1}{2}\lambda u, \quad \dot{u} = \lambda\,(1-2f) - \frac{2\varepsilon}{\hbar}v, \quad \dot{v} = \frac{2\varepsilon}{\hbar}u, \tag{27}$$

with the corresponding initial conditions $f(t_0) = u(t_0) = v(t_0) = 0$. The auxiliary functions $u(\vec{p},t)$ and $v(\vec{p},t)$ describe polarization effects (Section 3) and can be expressed via the anomalous averages (20) and (21)

$$u = \frac{i}{2}\left[f^{(+)} - f^{(-)}\right], v = \frac{1}{2}\left[f^{(+)} + f^{(-)}\right]. \tag{28}$$

A concrete physical interpretation of these functions will be given in Section 3.

For the system of Equation (27) one readily obtains the integral of motion

$$(1-2f)^2 + u^2 + v^2 = 1, \tag{29}$$

which is compatible with the zero initial conditions.

There is an approximate nonperturbative solution [24] of the KE (24) which is valid for small occupation numbers, $2f \ll 1$ (low density approximation),

$$f_{LD}(\vec{p},t) \;\; = \;\; J(\vec{p},t) = \frac{1}{2}\int_{t_0}^{t} dt'\lambda(\vec{p},t')\int_{t_0}^{t'} dt''\lambda(\vec{p},t'')\cos\theta(t',t''). \tag{30}$$

This integral plays an important role in the formulation of the other nonperturbative approach based on the Markovian approximation (see below).

The polarization function

$$u(\vec{p},t) = \int_{t_0}^{t} dt'\lambda(\vec{p},t')[1-2f(\vec{p},t')]\cos\theta(t,t') \tag{31}$$

is transformed in the low density approximation to the quadrature formula

$$u_{LD}(\vec{p},t) = \int_{t_0}^{t} dt'\lambda(\vec{p},t')\cos\theta(t,t'). \tag{32}$$

From the low density approximation formula (30) and Equation (10) it follows that the distribution function tends to infinity when approaching the Dirac line, $\vec{p} \to \vec{p}^D(t)$. This indicates also the non applicability of the standard perturbation theory. Thus, close by the lines L_D an essentially nonperturbative analysis of the KE (24) is required. One such nonlinear approximate solution is obtained in the Markovian approximation based on the neglect of the retardation on the r.h.s. of the KE (24), $f(\vec{p},t') \to f(\vec{p},t)$. This results in the quadrature formula

$$f_M(\vec{p},t) = \frac{1}{2}\left\{1 - \exp\left[-2J(\vec{p},t)\right]\right\}, \tag{33}$$

which has its analog in the case of D=3+1 QED [24]. From here one can see that the distribution function tends to saturation, $f_M(\vec{p},t) \to 1/2$, at $\vec{p} \to \vec{p}^D(t)$. The polarization function $u(\vec{p},t)$ can be obtained in this approximation on the basis of the first equation of the system (27) and Equation (33)

$$u_M(\vec{p},t) = \exp\left[-2J(\vec{p},t)\right] \int_{t_0}^{t} dt' \lambda(\vec{p},t') \cos\theta(t,t'). \tag{34}$$

where $J(\vec{p},t)$ is defined by Equation (30).

2.2. Order Parameter

By analogy with the standard QED [10], let us introduce the function $\Phi(t) = u(t) + iv(t)$ as an order parameter of the system that describes polarization effects in graphene by means of the anomalous averages (20), (21) and (28) which are characteristic for systems with broken symmetry (e.g. [5,6,16]). We write the corresponding equation of motion

$$\dot{\Phi} - \frac{2i\varepsilon}{\hbar}\Phi = \lambda(1-2f), \tag{35}$$

which follows from Equation (27). The formal solution of this equation with the zero initial condition is

$$\Phi(t) = \int_{t_0}^{t} dt' \lambda(t') \left[1 - 2f(t')\right] \exp\left[\frac{2i}{\hbar}\int_{t'}^{t} d\tau \varepsilon(\tau)\right]. \tag{36}$$

Let us consider now a finite electric field which is switched off at the point of time t_{off}, i.e., $E(t > t_{\text{off}}) = 0$ and hence according to Equation (10) $\lambda(t > t_{\text{off}}) = 0$. Then, for $t > t_{\text{off}}$ it follows from Equation (36) that the order parameter is different from zero and oscillates with the frequency $2\varepsilon_{\text{out}}/\hbar$, i.e.,

$$\Phi(t > t_{\text{off}}) = \Phi_{\text{out}}(\vec{p}) \exp\left[\frac{2i\varepsilon_{\text{out}}}{\hbar}(t - t_{\text{off}})\right], \tag{37}$$

where the asymptotical value of the quasienergy (8) is equal to

$$\varepsilon_{\text{out}} = \varepsilon(t \to \infty) = v_F \sqrt{(\vec{p} - \frac{e}{c}\vec{A}_{\text{out}})^2}, \tag{38}$$

$A^k_{\text{out}} = \lim_{t\to\infty} A^k(t)$. In Equation (37) the momentum dependent amplitude

$$\Phi_{\text{out}}(\vec{p}) = \int_{t_0}^{t_{\text{off}}} dt' \lambda(t') \left[1 - 2f(t')\right] \exp\left[\frac{2i}{\hbar}\int_{t'}^{t_{\text{off}}} d\tau \varepsilon(\tau)\right] \tag{39}$$

is defined by the entire prehistory of the system evolution in a given external field.

The presence of such residual oscillations of the order parameter is a prerequisite for the analogous behavior of the polarization current (see Section 5).

Thus,

$$|\Phi(t > t_{\text{off}})|^2 = |\Phi_{\text{out}}(\vec{p})|^2 = \text{const} \tag{40}$$

after switching off the external field, i.e., the long-lived order is formed.

The amplitude $\Phi_{\text{out}}(\vec{p})$ of oscillations of the order parameter in the residual state can be defined from the integral of motion (29) by rewriting it in the form

$$(1 - 2f_{\text{out}})^2 + |\Phi_{\text{out}}|^2 = 1. \tag{41}$$

The order parameter $\Phi(t)$ reflects the role of anomalous averages in the kinetics of the excitation process in graphene, that can be considered as a peculiar field induced phase transition [1,16]. Some other features of this process in graphene will be considered below.

3. Observables

It is straightforward to write expressions for the pair number density

$$n(t) = N\int [dp] f(\vec{p},t). \tag{42}$$

The factor N corresponds to number of species (or flavors) of quasiparticles in graphene [3,14,25]: $N = 4$ in the low energy model and $N = 2$ in the tight binding model.

For exact solutions of the ODE system (27) and correct nonperturbative solutions of the type (33) and (34) it follows from the normalization integral (42) that the distribution function is limited everywhere, $f(\vec{p},t) \leq 1$. Then both polarization functions $u(\vec{p},t)$ and $v(\vec{p},t)$ are limited also everywhere under the integral of motion (29). This conclusion relates to the neighborhood of the Dirac lines (26) and to the ultraviolet behavior of these functions as well.

The current density consists of two components, the conduction and polarization current densities,

$$j_k(t) = j_k^{\text{cond}}(t) + j_k^{\text{pol}}(t). \tag{43}$$

These currents are defined by the distribution function $f(\vec{p},t)$ and the polarization function $u(\vec{p},t)$, correspondingly [26].

Firstly we consider the currents in the low-energy model. On the basis of the standard definition of the current density [27] ($k = 1,2$)

$$j_k(t) = -e\frac{\delta H(t)}{\delta A_k(t)} \tag{44}$$

one can obtain for the theory with the Hamiltonian (4) taking into account the flavor number

$$j_k(t) = 4ev_F\int d^2x \Psi^*(\vec{x},t)\,\sigma_k \Psi(\vec{x},t)\,. \tag{45}$$

Going over to the quasiparticle representation with the help of the unitary operator (7) we obtain

$$j_k(t) = 4ev_F\int [dp]\Phi^\dagger(\vec{p},t)\, U^\dagger(t)\sigma_k U(t)\Phi(\vec{p},t)\,. \tag{46}$$

Taking into account the spinor (11) and the definition (43), one can separate the conduction and polarization currents,

$$\begin{aligned} j_i^{\text{cond}}(t) &= 8\int [dp] v_q^i(\vec{p},t) f(\vec{p},t), \\ j_i^{\text{pol}}(t) &= 4\int [dp]\varepsilon(\vec{p},t) l_i(\vec{p},t) u(\vec{p},t), \end{aligned} \tag{47}$$

where $v_q^i(\vec{p},t) = P_i/\varepsilon(\vec{p},t)$ and the vector $l_i(\vec{p},t) = \delta\lambda(\vec{p},t)/\delta E^i(t)$ is defined by the components

$$l_1(\vec{p},t) = \frac{ev_F^2 P_2}{\varepsilon^2}, \quad l_2(\vec{p},t) = -\frac{ev_F^2 P_1}{\varepsilon^2}. \tag{48}$$

One can see from the system (27) and its nonperturbative solutions (33) and (34), that the polarization effects dominate in the leading approximation for weak fields, $\alpha = E/E_0 \ll 1$, i.e., $f \sim \alpha^2$, $u \sim \alpha$ and so it follows that

$$|j^{\text{pol}}(t)| \gg |j^{\text{cond}}(t)|\,. \tag{49}$$

This conclusion is supported also by direct numerical calculations.

Let us note, that the conduction and polarization currents are not collinear in the general case. In the case of the linearly polarized electric field collinearity of the currents (47) rebuilds. In order to ascertain this fact, let us consider the situation when the electric field acts along the axis x_1, $\vec{E}(E_1(t), 0)$. Then $P_2 \to p_2$ and the functions $f(\vec{p}, t)$ and $u(\vec{p}, t)$ are even and odd under reflection $p_2 \to -p_2$, respectively, as it can be seen from the structure of the amplitude (10) and Equation (27). This makes the integrals for $j_2^{\text{cond}}(t)$ and $j_2^{\text{pol}}(t)$ in Equation (47) vanish. In order to investigate the theory we calculate the currents (47) in the framework of the perturbation theory in the minimal leading approximation for relatively small external field, see Appendix A.

From Equation (47) it follows that the function $u(\vec{p}, t)$ determines the vacuum polarization current. The physical meaning of the other polarization function $v(\vec{p}, t)$ is revealed if one considers the total energy density of the quasiparticles including the polarization energy. From Equations (12) and (16) one can obtain $E_{\text{tot}} = E_q + E_{\text{pol}}$, where

$$E_q(t) = 8 \int [dp] \varepsilon(\vec{p}, t) f(\vec{p}, t), \quad (50)$$

$$E_{\text{pol}}(t) = 8 \int [dp] \hbar \lambda(\vec{p}, t) v(\vec{p}, t). \quad (51)$$

Taking the time derivative of the quasiparticle energy $E_q(t)$ (50) one obtains

$$\dot{E}_q(t) = \vec{E}(t)[\vec{j}^{\text{cond}}(t) + \vec{j}^{\text{pol}}(t)] = \vec{E}(t)\vec{j}_{\text{tot}}(t), \quad (52)$$

where the currents $\vec{j}^{\text{cond}}(t)$ and $\vec{j}^{\text{pol}}(t)$ are defined by Equation (47).

On the other hand, let us write the Maxwell equation for the internal electric field $\vec{E}_{in}(t)$ generated by the motion of the eh-plasma,

$$\dot{\vec{E}}_{\text{in}}(t) = -\vec{j}_{\text{tot}}(t). \quad (53)$$

On this stage we will imply that the total electric field $\vec{E}_{tot}(t)$ is formed by an external field $\vec{E}(t)$ and an internal field $\vec{E}_{\text{in}}(t)$, i.e., $\vec{E}_{\text{tot}} = \vec{E}(t) + \vec{E}_{\text{in}}$. Let us substitute now in Equation (52) the external field $\vec{E}(t)$ by the total field $\vec{E}_{\text{tot}}(t)$. Using here Equation (53), we obtain the conservation law of the energy

$$\frac{d}{dt}\left[E_q(t) + \frac{1}{2}E_{\text{in}}^2\right] = \vec{E}\,\vec{j}_{\text{tot}}(t). \quad (54)$$

So, the work of external electric fields (r.h.s. of Equation (54)) is distributed between the energy of e-h excitation and the internal electric field.

4. Residual Currents

Here we consider some nonperturbative effects in graphene which are not sufficiently studied in the standard QED or possess some specific features. We restrict ourselves here to the case of a linearly polarized electric field directed along the axis x_1.

Let us begin by investigating the residual currents that persist in graphene after the passage of a strong electric field pulse. In the nondissipative model considered here the conduction current discontinues its evolution and remains constant while the polarization current performs damped oscillations. The character of these oscillations and their damping depends on the form of the electric field pulse, as it follows from Equations (37) and (39).

Thus, some oscillating and damped component will be present in the total residual current. In order to calculate it, we will use the formulas for the polarization currents (47) in the low energy model and their analogues in the tight binding model (below in Section 7) with the corresponding polarization function $u^{\text{out}}(t)$ for $t > t_{\text{off}}$,

$$u^{\text{out}}(t) = Re\,\Phi(t > t_{\text{out}}), \quad (55)$$

where the order parameter $\Phi(t > t_{\text{out}})$ in the out-state is defined by Equations (37)–(39).

According to Equation (37) the frequency of the order parameter is defined by the doubled quasienergy (38). However, while these oscillations are smoothed out upon integration over the momentum space in the polarization current (47), their influence remains quite appreciable, see Figure 1.

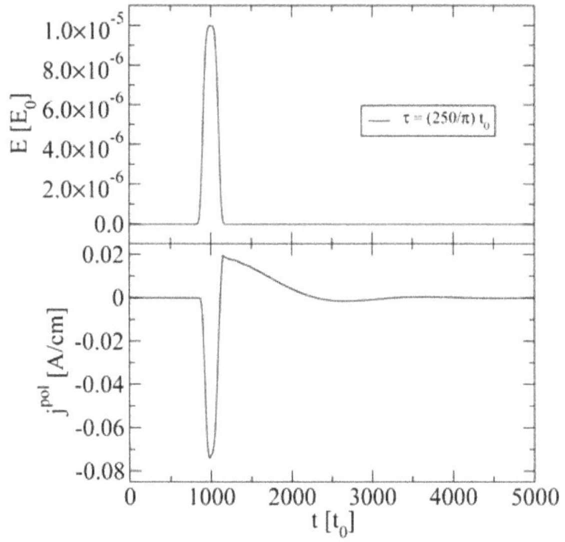

Figure 1. Upper panel: Supergaussian electric field (56) where $t_{max} = 1000\ t_0$ (2.46×10^{-13} s) and $E_a = 0.00001\ E_0$ (1.088×10^3 V/cm). **Lower panel**: The density of the polarization current.

We select the supergaussian model of the electric field

$$E(t) = -\dot{A}(t) = E_a \exp[-(t - t_{\text{max}})^4/(2\tau^4)], \tag{56}$$

where t_{max} determines the position of the maximum amplitude E_a of the field. This choice of the pulse waveform allows to realize abrupt fronts of switching on and off, see the upper panel of Figure 1, and to clearly identify the presence of a alternating polarization current, see the lower panel of Figure 1. This picture demonstrates also dominance of the polarization current.

Another feature of the polarization current becomes apparent in presence of a constant electric field

$$E(t) = E_a = \text{const}, \quad A(t) = -E_a t. \tag{57}$$

Here the oscillations of the polarization function (Figure 2) transform to damped oscillations of the polarization current (Figure 3). This damping is caused by the monotonic growth of the quasienergy (8) with time at $t \geq 0$ and, as a consequence, by the decrease of the oscillation amplitude of the polarization current. This mechanism can be traced visually in the Markovian approximation (33).

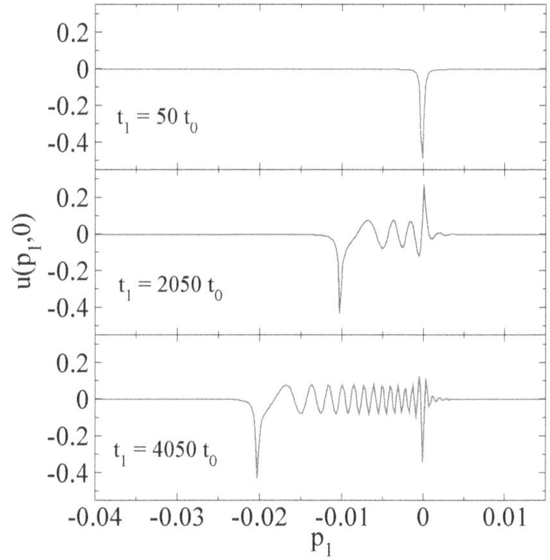

Figure 2. The polarization function $u(p_1, p_2 = 0)$ for the times: $t_1 = 50t_0$ (1.23×10^{-14} s, **upper graph**), $t_2 = 2050t_0$ (5.043×10^{-13} s, **middle graph**), $t_3 = 4050t_0$ (9.963×10^{-13} s, **lower graph**) in a constant electric field (57) $E_a = 5 \times 10^{-6}\ E_0$ (5.44×10^2 V/cm).

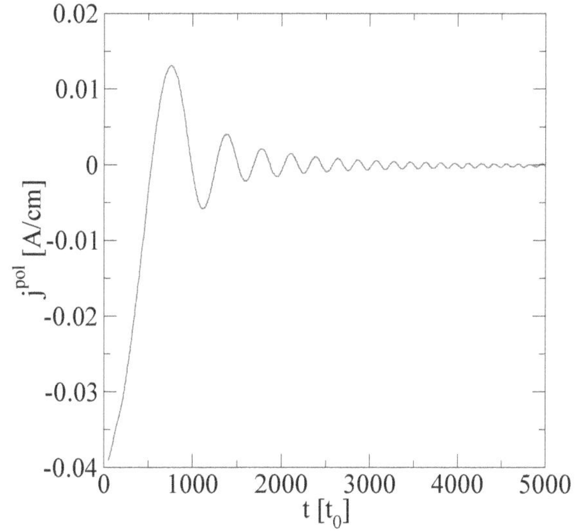

Figure 3. The density of the polarization current in a constant field (57) with parameters of Figure 2.

5. Numerical Analysis

The numerical analysis will be based on the system of ordinary differential Equation (27) rewritten in terms of the corresponding dimensionless values.

We will investigate the response of the system to four electric field models: the constant electric field (57), the Eckart - Sauter field model

$$E(t) = E_a \cosh^{-2}(t/T), \;\; A(t) = -E_a \tanh(t/T), \tag{58}$$

the harmonic function with a constant amplitude

$$E(t) = E_a \sin(\omega t), \;\; A(t) = \frac{E_a}{\omega} - \frac{E_a}{\omega}\cos(\omega t), \tag{59}$$

where ω is the angular frequency, and the "laser field" model [28]

$$\begin{aligned} E(t) &= E_a \cos(\omega t) \exp(-t^2/2\tau^2), \\ A(t) &= -\sqrt{\frac{\pi}{8}} E_a \tau \exp\left(-\sigma^2/2\right) \operatorname{erf}\left(\frac{t}{\sqrt{2}\tau} - i\frac{\sigma}{\sqrt{2}}\right) + c.c., \end{aligned} \tag{60}$$

where $\sigma = \omega\tau$. In all the cases in this section we assume that the electric field is directed along the first coordinate axis.

We start with the most convenient model of the field (58). From Equation (27) follows that the speed of the filling process of the conduction band is determined by the amplitude of the transitions (10). In the denominator of (10) the quasienergy (8) takes zero values on the Dirac line (26). This feature of the amplitude of transitions should be reflected in the behavior and properties of the distribution function. From the form of the evolution of the vector potential (58) it follows that the Dirac line in this case should be represented in the momentum space by a segment with the endpoints determined by $A(t \to -\infty)$ and $A(t \to \infty)$ in accordance with the conditions (26).

In Figure 4 we demonstrate the presence of such characteristic features of the distribution function. On the left panel the Dirac line has the end point coordinates $p_1 \mp 0.1, p_2 = 0.0$ while on the right panel the pulse duration is five times larger so that the coordinates of the end points are $p_1 \mp 0.5, p_2 = 0.0$. The Dirac line itself cuts in the distribution function a very thin canyon that is not visible in this figure owing to the selected scale of the numerical calculations.

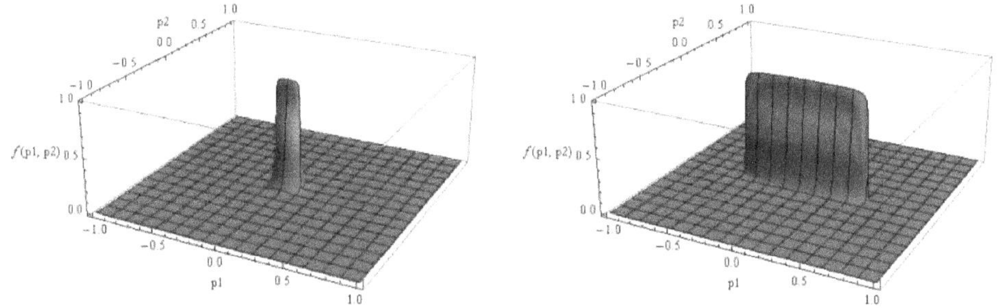

Figure 4. The distribution function in the planar momentum space after the action of the Eckart-Sauter pulse (58). **Left panel:** $E_a = 0.01\ E_0$ (1.088×10^8 V/m) and $T = 10\ t_0$ (2.46×10^{-15} s), **Right panel:** $E_a = 0.01\ E_0$ (1.088×10^8 V/m) and $T = 50\ t_0$ (1.23×10^{-14} s).

In the next step, we consider the constant field (57) at $t \geq 0$. The distribution function at the time $t = 10.0\ t_0$ of the field action is presented on the left panel of Figure 5. Results of the field action with five times longer duration are represented on the right panel of Figure 5.

Another frequently used model is the harmonic electric field (59). The procedure of switching on at $t = 0$ and off at $t_m = 2\pi m/\omega$ can be realized with sufficient accuracy in the numerical calculations. The shape of the distribution function and its change in time ($m = 1, 2, 4$ and 10) for the field (59) are presented in Figure 6.

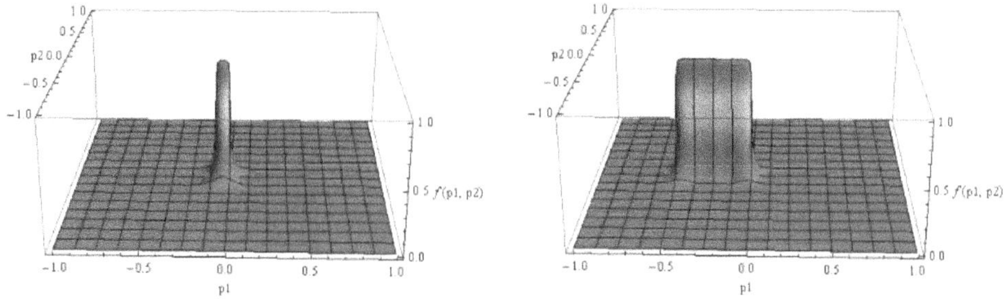

Figure 5. The distribution function in the constant electric field (57) with $E_a = 0.01\ E_0$ (1.088×10^6 V/cm) at $t = 10\ t_0$ (2.46×10^{-15} s) after switching on the field (**left panel**) and at $t = 50\ t_0$ (1.23×10^{-14} s) after switching on the field (**right panel**).

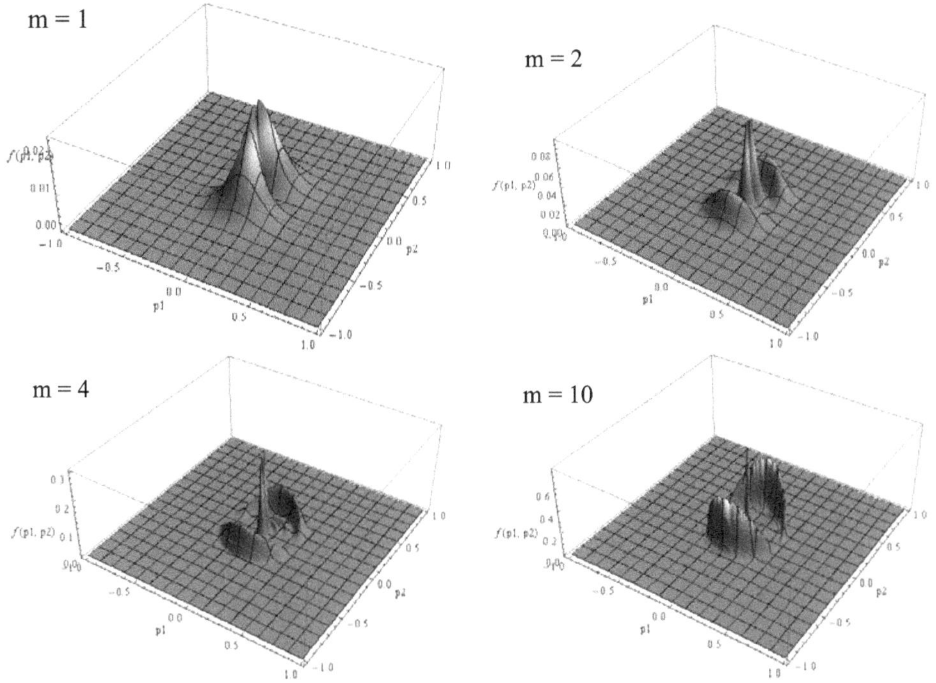

Figure 6. The stages of evolution of the distribution function under the action of the field of type (59) with the number of periods $m = 1, 2, 4$ and 10, respectively.

Finally, let us consider the more realistic model (60) of the "laser pulse". In this case the vector potential and the field strength are changed smoothly at any moment of time and do not bear any problems for the numerical calculations. The shape of the distribution function and its dependence on the pulse width determined by parameter σ are presented in Figure 7.

The above results correspond to very short time intervals from $T = 10\ t_0$ (2.46×10^{-15} s) to $T = 50\ t_0$ (1.13×10^{-14} s) of the electric field action for the models (57) and (58) and for a very high frequency of oscillations $t_0/T = 0.1(\approx 400$ THz) for the models (59) and (60). Figure 8 demonstrates the distribution function for the field model (57) and its change for the large time intervals $T =$ 406,500 t_0 (1.0×10^{-10} s) and $T =$ 1,219,500 t_0 (3.0×10^{-10} s) at the field strength $E_a = 9.19 \times 10^{-8}\ E_0$(10 V/cm). The top row shows images with a linear scale for the color code of the distribution function. This allows to demonstrate that the generated carriers are concentrated in momentum space in a very narrow area close to zero values of the momentum in the direction perpendicular to the direction of the field. The bottom row shows the same distribution function with a logarithmic scale of the color coding. In this case the complicated structure of the distribution function outside the main area of the carrier generation becomes apparent. The main area, however, is absolutely dominant. Other parameters of the electric field can change this picture. This issue requires further research.

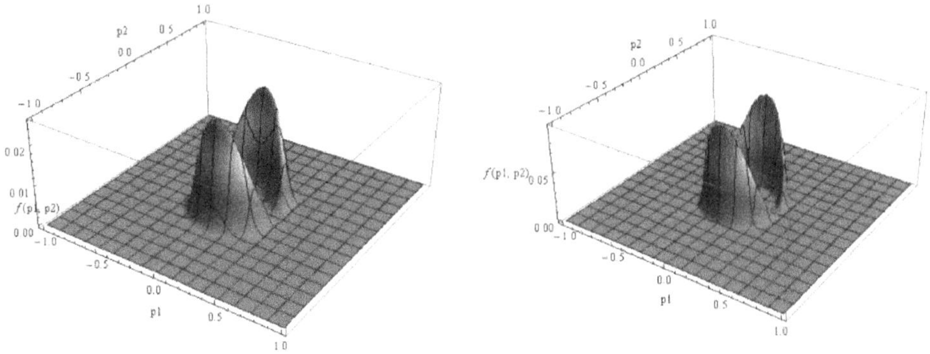

Figure 7. The residual distribution function in momentum space after the action of the electric field (60) with $E_a = 0.01\ E_0$ (1.088×10^6 V/cm), $\omega = 2\pi 0.1$. **Left**: $\sigma = 5$. **Right**: $\sigma = 10$.

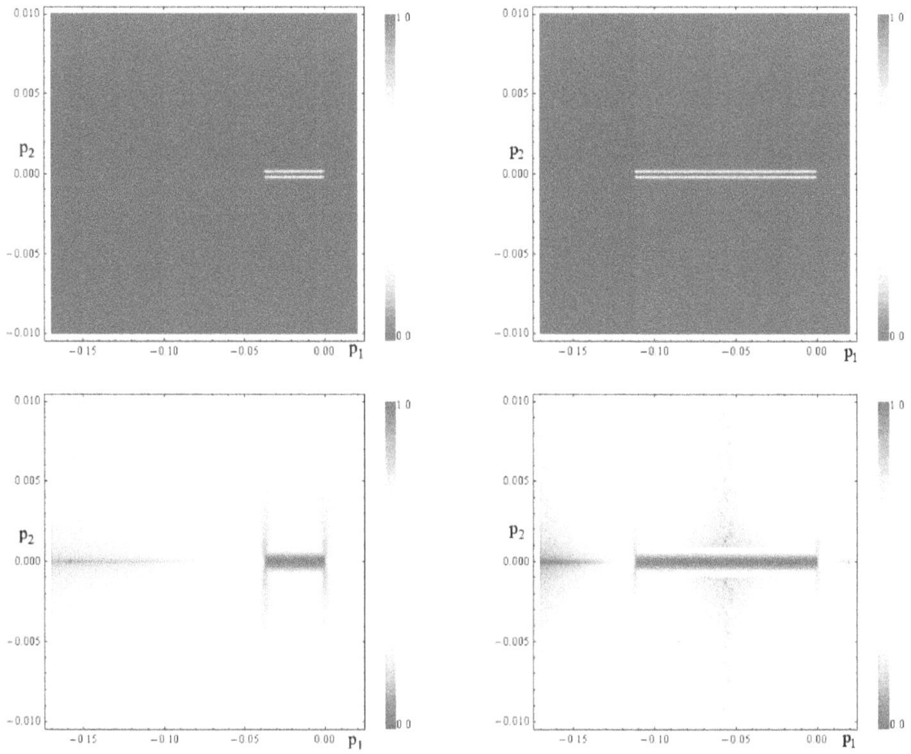

Figure 8. The residual distribution function in momentum space after the action of the field of type (57) with $E_a = 10$ V/cm for a duration of 1.0×10^{-10} s (**left column**) and 3.0×10^{-10} s (**right column**). A logarithmic color scale used for the bottom panel.

The set of parameters used here is quite realizable in the experiment. We note that the behavior of the distribution function in momentum space has not undergone fundamental changes in comparison to the ones in Figure 5. Figure 8 demonstrates agreement with the results of the work [29] where the same parameters have been used for the numerical calculations in the framework of another formalism.

The behavior of a quasiparticle plasma under the action of periodic fields (59) and (60) with increasing pulse duration is not trivial. Figure 9 shows the distribution function for the field model (60) with the parameters $\omega = 2\pi \times 2.46 \times 10^{-4}\ t_0^{-1}$ (corresponding to $2\pi \times 1.0$ THz), $E_a = 9.19 \times 10^{-6}\ E_0$ (corresponding to 1000 V/cm) for $\sigma = 3, 10, 25$, and 50.

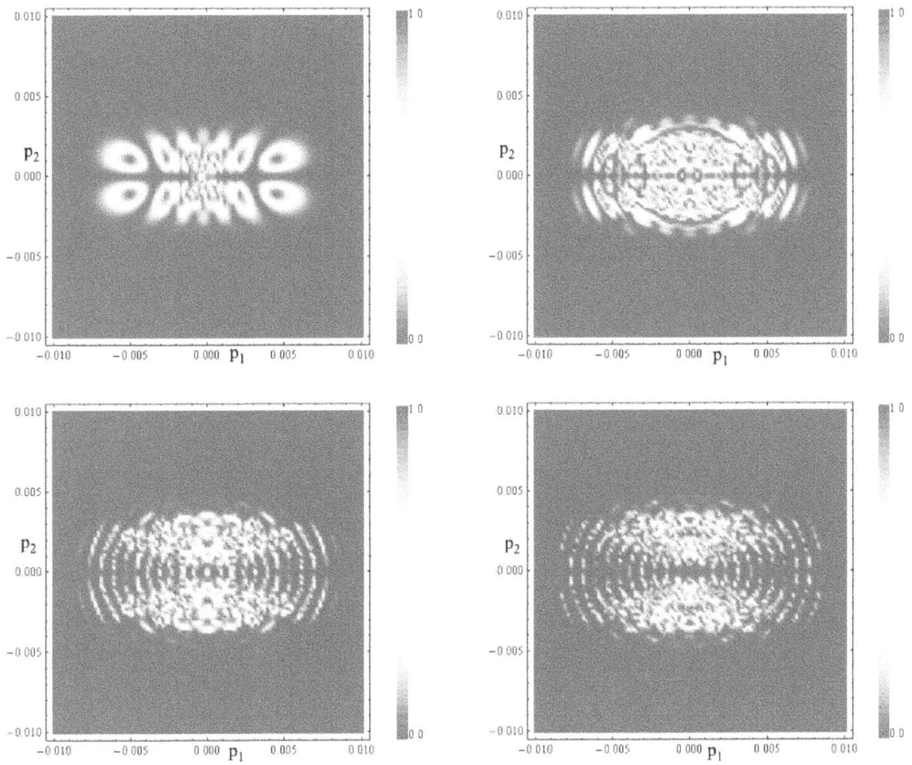

Figure 9. The residual distribution function under the action of the field of type (60) with the frequency 1.0 THz, amplitude $E_a = 1000$ V/cm and $\sigma = 3, 10, 25, 50$.

Let us now discuss the analysis of some observable values. We have studied the behavior of the density of carriers (42) in dependence on the amplitude of the electric field for the three models (57), (58) and (60). A summary of the results is presented below.

It should be noted that these results are determined solely by the filling of the conduction band due to the quasiparticle excitation by an external electric field. The presence of thermally excited carriers has not been taken into account as well as the relaxation processes since the considered times are much shorter than the relaxation time. Figure 10 demonstrates that the number of quasiparticles created during the action of the field increases quadratically with increasing electric field strength. The quadratic dependence can be traced quite rigorously in relatively weak fields $E_a \leq 0.001\ E_0$ ($\lesssim 10^5$ V/cm). The increment of the pair number density is slowing down somewhat with further increase of the electric field. This can be explained by a saturation effect.

The presented values correspond to the pulse of the constant field (57) with duration $20t_0$, the Eckart-Sauter pulse (58) with duration parameter $T = 10\ t_0$ and a "laser" pulse (60) with a period of the carrier frequency equal to $2\pi/\omega = 10\ t_0$. Such a proximity of the characteristics of the compared field pulses provides very similar values for the surface density of the charge carriers. However, it should be noted that above it has been demonstrated that there is a strong difference between the quasiparticle spectrum in the field of type (60) and the quasiparticle spectrum produced by fields of the type (57) or (58). Nevertheless, the density of carriers and their dependence on the amplitude of the electric field are very similar, see Figure 10.

The dotted line in Figure 10 indicates the approximate level of the thermal carrier density at room temperature. For short pulses their contribution to the total number of carriers will be noticeable only at high electric fields. On the other hand, the spectrum of thermal quasiparticles and quasiparticles generated by the field pulse are different. These differences appear at any electric field strength.

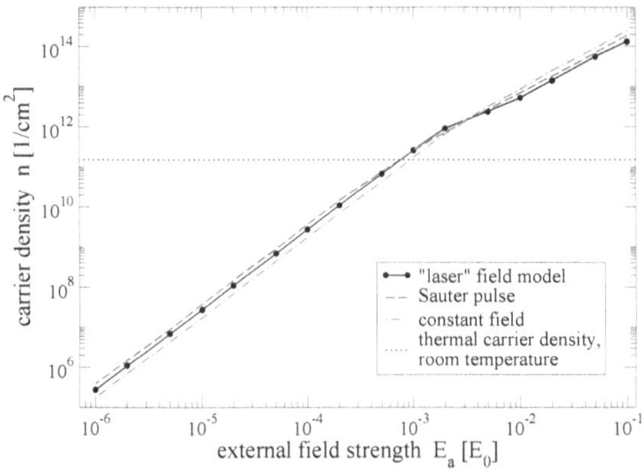

Figure 10. The dependence of the carrier density for the electric field models (57), (58) and (60).

Now we come back to the constant field and look at the dynamics of the process of creation of the quasiparticles in the period of the field action. We consider a weak field strength of about 1 V/cm and a field action time of $5 \times 10^5 t_0$ (corresponding to 1.23×10^{-10} s). The left panel of Figure 11 shows the evolution of the distribution function along the direction of the electric field (for $p_2 \simeq 0$). The sections of the distribution function along the p_1 axis are presented for six time points from $t_1 = 25{,}000\ t_0$ to $t_6 = 500{,}000\ t_0$. This figure shows in more detail the dynamics that we have already seen in Figures 5 and 8. The complete picture is presented in the right panel of Figure 11. It shows the evolution of a slice of the distribution function for the value of $p_1 = -0.002002\ p_0$ in which the distribution function at the initial period ($t_1 = 2.5 \times 10^4 t_0$, $t_2 = 1 \times 10^5 t_0$) is not large. At the time $t_3 = 2 \times 10^5 t_0$ there is a transition in the state of saturation and then the picture becomes almost stationary.

Figure 12 shows the evolution of three observables under the action of a constant electric field with the same parameters as in Figure 11. The left panel shows the time dependence of the density of the charge carriers (42). The dashed line shows the linear extrapolation of the initial values. The middle panel shows the time dependence of the density of the conduction current in the direction of the field. The dashed line also shows a linear extrapolation. It can be concluded that the creation of charge carriers in a weak constant field proceeds at a constant rate. The energy of the carriers is proportional to their momentum. The number of carriers and the average value of their momentum increase under the influence of the field. As a result, the energy density of the carriers in graphene increases quadratically. This is shown in the right panel of Figure 11 (the dashed line shows the quadratic extrapolation of the initial values).

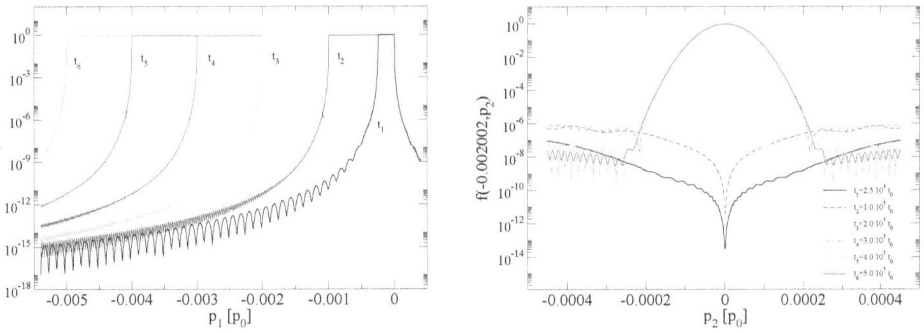

Figure 11. The distribution function in momentum space for the range of time: $t_1 = 2.5 \times 10^4\ t_0$ (6.15×10^{-12} s), $t_2 = 1 \times 10^5\ t_0$ (2.46×10^{-11} s), $t_3 = 2 \times 10^5\ t_0$ (4.92×10^{-11} s), $t_4 = 3 \times 10^5\ t_0$ (7.38×10^{-11} s), $t_5 = 4 \times 10^5\ t_0$ (9.84×10^{-11} s), $t_6 = 5 \times 10^5\ t_0$ (1.23×10^{-10} s). The electric field strength $E_a = 1 \times 10^{-8}\ E_0$ (1.088 V/cm). The dependence of the distribution function on p_1 for $p_2 = 0$ is shown on the left panel while the dependence on p_2 for $p_1 = -0.002002\ p_0$ is shown on the right panel.

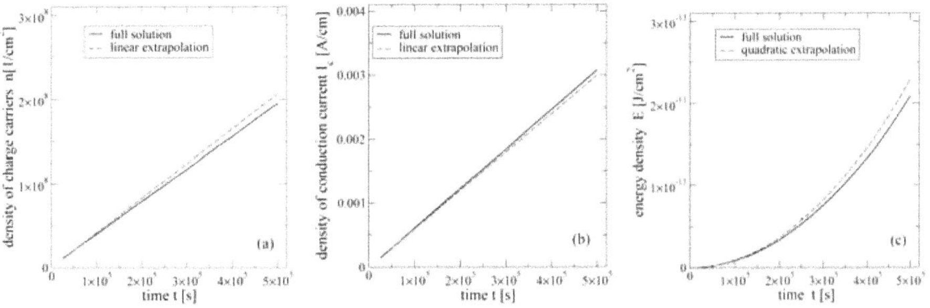

Figure 12. From left to right: density of charge carriers (42), density of conduction current and energy density the carriers for range of the time 25,000 t_0– 500,000 t_0 (6.15×10^{-12}s $- 1.23 \times 10^{-10}$s). The constant electric field strength $E_a = 1 \times 10^{-8}\ E_0$ (1.088 V/cm).

6. Graphene as Active Medium

The nonlinear properties of graphene allow to activate it by some basic electric field for driving by the current of another weak signal. Below we will consider an example when a rather strong basic field is aligned with the x_1—axis while the probe field aligned with the x_2—axis allows the application of perturbation theory.

The corresponding perturbation theory can be constructed both on the system of Equation (27) and in the framework of the Markovian approximation (33). The latter variant allows to proceed with analytical calculations.

In the framework of such an approximation we can limit ourselves in the weak field approximation to the Markovian solution (33) and (34). The distribution function in this approximation is $f_M \approx f^{(0)} + f^{(1)}$,

$$f^{(0)} = \frac{1}{2}(1 - e^{-J^{(0)}}), \quad f^{(1)} = J^{(1)} e^{-J^{(0)}}, \tag{61}$$

where labels (0) and (1) correspond to the "basic" field $A_1(t)$ (nonperturbative solutions) and to the perturbing field $A_2(t)$, respectively. The function $J(\vec{p}, t)$ is defined by Equation (33), so that

$$J^{(1)}(\vec{p}, t) = 8 \int_{t_0}^{t} dt' \lambda^{(1)}(\vec{p}, t') \int_{t_0}^{t'} dt'' \lambda^{(0)}(\vec{p}, t'') \cos\theta^{(0)}(t', t''), \tag{62}$$

where according to Equation (10)

$$\lambda^{(0)}(\vec{p},t) = \frac{ev_F^2 E_1(t) p_2}{2[\varepsilon^{(0)}(\vec{p},t)]^2}, \ \lambda^{(1)}(\vec{p},t) = \frac{ev_F^2 E_2(t) P_1}{2[\varepsilon^{(0)}(\vec{p},t)]^2}. \tag{63}$$

In Equation (62) we have neglected in the phase (25) the frequency shift under the influence of the weak field $A^2(t)$, i.e., $\theta \to \theta^{(0)}$. An analogous decomposition of the polarization function (34) leads to the result: $u_M \simeq u^{(0)} + u^{(1)}$, where

$$u^{(1)}(\vec{p},t) = J^{(0)}(\vec{p},t)\Big\{ \int_{t_0}^{t} dt' \lambda^{(1)}(\vec{p},t') \cos\theta^{(0)}(t,t') - J^{(1)}(\vec{p},t) \int_{t_0}^{t} dt' \lambda^{(0)}(\vec{p},t') \cos\theta^{(0)}(t,t') \Big\}. \tag{64}$$

Substitution of Equations (61)–(64) into Equation (47) results in the perturbed current calculated in the first order of perturbation theory under the weak field,

$$j_1^{(1)}(t) = 0, \ j_2^{(1)}(t) = \int_{t_0}^{t} dt' \sigma(t,t') E_2(t'), \tag{65}$$

where $\sigma(t,t')$ is the linear induced conductivity of graphene controlled by the external field $A_2(t)$,

$$\begin{aligned} \sigma(t,t') = -8ev_F^2 \int \frac{[dp]}{\varepsilon^{(0)}(\vec{p},t)} \Big\{ & \frac{\delta f^{(1)}(\vec{p},t)}{\delta E_2(t')} + f^{(2)}(\vec{p},t) \frac{ev_F^2 P_1^2(t)}{[\varepsilon^{(0)}(\vec{p},t)]^2} \\ & + P_1(t) \frac{\delta u^{(1)}(\vec{p},t)}{\delta E_2(t')} - u^{(0)}(\vec{p},t) \frac{ev_F^2 p_2}{[\varepsilon^{(0)}(\vec{p},t)]^2} \Big\}. \end{aligned} \tag{66}$$

Here the first and second groups of terms correspond to the contributions of the conduction and polarization currents.

The dependence of the conductivity (66) on the magnitude and spectral decomposition of the basic field will be considered separately.

7. Tight Binding Model

It is not difficult to obtain now the analogous KE in the $D = 2+1$ tight binding model of the nearest neighbor interaction [3,11,12]. The Hamiltonian function in the momentum representation in this case is

$$H_{\vec{p}}(t) = \begin{pmatrix} 0 & h_{\vec{p}}(t) \\ h^*_{\vec{p}}(t) & 0 \end{pmatrix} = h'_{\vec{p}}(t)\sigma_1 - h''_{\vec{p}}(t)\sigma_2, \tag{67}$$

where

$$h_{\vec{p}}(t) = h'_{\vec{p}}(t) + ih''_{\vec{p}}(t) = -\gamma \sum_{\alpha} \exp\left(\frac{i}{\hbar} \vec{P}\vec{\delta}_\alpha \right) , \tag{68}$$

with $\gamma \approx 2.7$ eV being the hopping energy, and

$$\vec{\delta}_1 = \frac{a}{3}(0, \sqrt{3}), \ \vec{\delta}_2 = \frac{a}{3}(\pm 3/2, -\sqrt{3}/2) \tag{69}$$

are the locations of the nearest neighbors, $a \approx 3$.

An external electric field is introduced here according to the rule $\vec{p} \to \vec{P} = \vec{p} - e/c\vec{A}(t)$. Such a method was used in the work [3] in the case of a constant electric field $A_2(t) = -eEt$ and resulted immediately in a nonlinear interaction with external field. Such a theory belongs to the class of theories with the highest derivatives.

The Hamiltonian functions (4) and (67) have the same pseudospin structure. Therefore one can follow the way of derivation of KE (24) in the theory with the Hamiltonian function (67). The quasienergy (8) and the amplitude (10) are changed only by the following formal substitutions

$$v_F P_1 \to h'_{\vec{p}}(t),\ v_F P_2 \to -h''_{\vec{p}}(t). \tag{70}$$

This results in

$$\varepsilon(\vec{p},t) = \sqrt{h^*_{\vec{p}}(t) h_{\vec{p}}(t)} = |h_{\vec{p}}(t)|, \tag{71}$$

$$\lambda(\vec{p},t) = \frac{1}{|h_{\vec{p}}(t)|^2} \left\{ \dot{h}''_{\vec{p}}(t) h'_{\vec{p}}(t) - \dot{h}'_{\vec{p}}(t) h''_{\vec{p}}(t) \right\}. \tag{72}$$

An analogous KE can be obtained also for the case of the multilayer graphene model [30].

The conduction and polarization currents have the following form (the flavor number in the given model is equal to 2 [3])

$$j_k^{\rm cond}(t) = -4e\gamma \int [dp] f(\vec{p},t) [F_k^{(1)}(\vec{p},t) \cos\chi + F_k^{(2)}(\vec{p},t) \sin\chi], \tag{73}$$

$$j_k^{\rm pol}(t) = -4e\gamma \int [dp] f(\vec{p},t) [-F_k^{(1)}(\vec{p},t) \sin\chi + F_k^{(2)}(\vec{p},t) \cos\chi], \tag{74}$$

with the vector formfactors

$$F_k^{(1)}(\vec{p},t) = \sum_\alpha \delta_\alpha^{(k)} \sin\left(\frac{1}{\hbar}\vec{P}\vec{\delta}_\alpha\right), \tag{75}$$

$$F_k^{(2)}(\vec{p},t) = \sum_\alpha \delta_\alpha^{(k)} \cos\left(\frac{1}{\hbar}\vec{P}\vec{\delta}_\alpha\right) \tag{76}$$

and χ being the angle of the unitary rotation in the matrix of the type (7),

$$\chi = -h''_{\vec{p}}(t)/h'_{\vec{p}}(t). \tag{77}$$

Let us rewrite Equations (73) and (74) for the currents to obtain

$$j_k^{\rm cond}(t) = -4e\gamma \int [dp] f(\vec{p},t) \sum_\alpha \delta_\alpha^{(k)} \sin\left(\chi + \frac{1}{\hbar}\vec{P}\vec{\delta}_\alpha\right), \tag{78}$$

$$j_k^{\rm pol}(t) = -4e\gamma \int [dp] u(\vec{p},t) \sum_\alpha \delta_\alpha^{(k)} \cos\left(\chi + \frac{1}{\hbar}\vec{P}\vec{\delta}_\alpha\right) \tag{79}$$

as the final result of this section. The numerical evaluation of the currents for particular external field models is delegated to future work.

8. Conclusions

We have obtained on a nonperturbative basis the KE for describing electron-hole excitations in graphene under the action of a spatially homogeneous time dependent electric field. To this end the analogy with the well-developed case of kinetic theory of vacuum e^+e^- plasma generation in strong fields [8,10] in $D = 3+1$ QED has been used. As a rule, we used the simplest low energy model. However, the used method admits a straightforward generalization to other realistic models of the carrier dynamics as, e.g., the tight binding model of nearest neighbour interaction. The derivation of the KE is based on the transition to the quasiparticle representation [6]. As shown in Section 2, in the $D = 2+1$ QED model of graphene such a derivation can be given in an explicit form with the help of a unitary transformation first introduced in the work [15] for the linearly polarized electric field. It is important that the final KE is valid in the general case of an arbitrarily polarized electric field. Some features of the obtained KE are discussed in that Section. In particular, the non applicability of the standard perturbation theory in vicinity of the Dirac lines has been demonstrated. However, the corresponding approximate analytical and numerical nonperturbative solutions (e.g., the Markovian approximation) of the KE provide a correct description in physical terms in the entire momentum space. In Section 2.2 we consider also some general properties of the evolution of the excited electron-hole plasma that allow to interpret this phenomenon as a specific field induced phase transition [10,16]. An important characteristics of this process is an order parameter that continues to oscillate in the out-state after the external field pulse ceases. The connection of the observables with both, the distribution function and the polarization functions has been discussed in Section 3. The damped oscillations of the residual polarization current on the background of a conduction current were considered in Section 4. The character of these oscillations is related to features of the external field pulse. The damped oscillations of the polarization current in a constant electric field have demonstrated a similar nature. Apparently, these effects are accessible to experimental observation. It can be assumed that similar phenomena occur in $D = 3 + 1$ QED. Here too it was shown that the polarization current dominates over the conduction current. We have performed a systematic numerical investigation based on the KE for the distribution function of quasiparticle excitations and the corresponding observable values for various models of the external electric field.

We have discussed the possibility of using graphene as an active medium excited by the basic electric field to be probed by another signal current ("pump-and-probe").

Finally, we have derived an analogous KE for the tight binding model that is substantially nonperturbative. In the framework of this model we have obtained and discussed the conduction and polarization currents.

A verification of the developed theory was obtained in the work [31], where good agreement with experiment has been shown for the case of a constant electric field [32].

Let us note that both models considered here led KE's of identical form. Moreover, this form invariance is conserved also in the standard QED in the case of a linearly polarized electric field when the spin degrees of freedom are frozen.

Author Contributions: Conceptualization, S.A.S. and A.D.P.; Validation, all authors; Data Curation, A.D.P. and N.T.G.; Writing—Original Draft Preparation, S.A.S. and A.D.P.; Writing—Review & Editing, D.B.B. and N.T.G.; Visualization, A.D.P. and N.T.G.; Funding Acquisition, S.A.S. and D.B.B.

Funding: This research was supported in part by the "RUDN University Program 5-100", by RFBR according to the research project No 17-02-00375 A, and by the Polish NCN under grant number UMO-2014/15/B/ST2/03752.

Acknowledgments: The authors thank V.V. Dmitriev, B. Dora, D.M. Gitman and R. Moessner for useful discussions. D.B. is grateful to Hayk Sarkisyan for inspiring discussions on low-dimensional quantum systems and for the hospitality extended to him at the Russian-Armenian University.

Conflicts of Interest: The authors declare no conflict of interest.

Appendix A. Perturbation Theory

In order to demonstrate the effectiveness of the introduced approach, we will reproduce some well known results in the framework of perturbation theory for relatively small external fields, $E < E_0$.

We begin with the analysis of currents in the low density approximation (30) and (32) which corresponds to the one-photon excitation mechanism [33]. In the minimal leading approximation $\varepsilon(\vec{p},t) \to \varepsilon_0(\vec{p}) = v_F|\vec{p}|$ we have

$$f^{(2)}_{LD}(\vec{p},t) = \frac{1}{2}\int^t dt' \lambda^{(1)}(\vec{p},t') \, , u^{(1)}_{LD}(\vec{p},t') \tag{A1}$$

$$u^{(1)}_{LD}(\vec{p},t) = \int^t dt'' \lambda^{(1)}(\vec{p},t'') \cos[\eta p(t-t'')], \tag{A2}$$

with

$$\lambda^{(1)}(\vec{p},t) = \lambda_0(\vec{p}) \left[E_1(t)P_2 - E_2(t)P_1\right] , \tag{A3}$$

where $\lambda_0(\vec{p}) = ev_F^2/2\varepsilon_0^2(p) = e/2p_2$ and $\eta = 2v_F/\hbar$. The upper indices at the functions $f^{(2)}$ and $u^{(1)}$ indicate the order of perturbation theory.

The relations (A1) and (A2) indicate the dominant role of polarization effects in the considered approximation, $|j^{(1)\mathrm{pol}}(t)| \gg |j^{(2)\mathrm{cond}}(t)|$.

Let us consider the case of linear polarization $\vec{E}(t) = (E(t), 0)$ with arbitrary time dependence of the electric field.

The polarization current in lowest order perturbation theory according to Equation (47) is

$$\begin{aligned} j_1^{(1)\mathrm{pol}}(t) &= 8ev_F \int [dp] u \sin \varkappa, \\ j_2^{(1)\mathrm{pol}}(t) &= -8ev_F \int [dp] u \cos \varkappa, \end{aligned} \tag{A4}$$

where $\varkappa$ is defined in explanation to Equation (7),

$$\varkappa = \arctan(P_2/P_1) \approx \arctan(p_2/p_1), \tag{A5}$$

where the last step corresponds to the leading approximation. From Equation (A5) follows

$$\sin \varkappa \approx p_2/p = \sin \Phi, \quad \cos \varkappa \approx p_1/p = \cos \Phi, \tag{A6}$$

where Φ is the polar angle in the polar representation of the momentum space. Integration over the momentum p in the neighborhood of the Dirac points is limited by the cutoff parameter Λ. It is implied that it can be defined by the limits of the validity range of the linear dispersion law $\varepsilon_0(p) = v_F p$. However, the results obtained below are universal and do not depend on the choice of Λ.

Taking these remarks into account, one can thus write the polarization current after integration over the angle (here $t_0 \to -\infty$),

$$\begin{aligned} j_1^{(1)\mathrm{pol}}(t) &= \frac{e^2 v_F}{\pi \hbar^2} \int_{-\infty}^{t} dt' E(t') \int_0^{\Lambda} dp \cos[\eta p (t - t')], \\ j_2^{(1)\mathrm{pol}}(t) &= 0\,. \end{aligned} \tag{A7}$$

Let us now perform a Fourier transformation of the function $E(t)$ and after that integrate over the momentum p,

$$\begin{aligned} j_1^{(1)\mathrm{pol}}(t) &= \frac{e^2}{\pi \hbar} \int d\omega E(\omega) \int_{-\infty}^{t} dt' \frac{\sin[\Lambda \eta (t - t')]}{t - t'} e^{i\omega t'} \\ &= \frac{e^2}{\pi \hbar} \int d\omega E(\omega) e^{i\omega t} \int_{-\infty}^{0} \frac{dx}{x} \sin(\gamma x) \cos x. \end{aligned} \tag{A8}$$

The last integral does not depend on the parameter $\gamma = 2v_F \Lambda / \hbar \omega$,

$$\int_{-\infty}^{0} \frac{dx}{x} \sin \gamma x \cos x = \int_{-\infty}^{0} \frac{dx}{x} = \frac{\pi}{2}, \tag{A9}$$

so that

$$j_1^{(1)\mathrm{pol}}(t) = \frac{e^2}{4\hbar} E(t). \tag{A10}$$

This result does not depend on the choice of the field model.

In order to calculate the conduction current, it is necessary to find the distribution function. To this end we use perturbation theory as a first step and consider the case of a constant electric field (57) switched on at the time $t_0 = 0$. In the leading approximation from Equation (30) follows the known result [15,34]

$$f_{LD}^{(2)}(\vec{p},t) = \frac{e^2\hbar^2 E^2 p_2^2}{4v_F^2 p^6} \sin^2 \Omega t\,, \tag{A11}$$

where $\Omega = v_F p/\hbar$ is the frequency of the vacuum oscillations.

The anisotropic distribution (A11) and the corresponding nonperturbative Markovian distribution (33) have the center symmetry relative to the Dirac point $p_i \to -p_i$ whereby the conductivity current (see Equation (47)) vanishes.

In order to break this symmetry, it is necessary to go beyond the leading approximation. However, the next correction leads to secular terms that indicate a problem with perturbation theory. For further details on the transport properties of graphene see, e.g., Refs. [35–39].

References

1. Oka, T. Nonlinear doublon production in a Mott insulator: Landau-Dykhne method applied to an integrable model. *Phys. Rev.* **2012**, *B86*, 075148. [CrossRef]
2. Yokomizo, N. Radiation from electrons in graphene in strong electric field. *Ann. Phys.* **2014**, *351*, 166. [CrossRef]
3. Kao, H.C.; Lewkowicz, M.; Rosenstein, B. Ballistic transport, chiral anomaly and emergence of the neutral electron - hole plasma in graphene. *Phys. Rev.* **2010**, *B82*, 035406. [CrossRef]
4. Schwinger, J.S. On gauge invariance and vacuum polarization. *Phys. Rev.* **1951**, *82*, 664. [CrossRef]
5. Fradkin, E.S.; Gitman, D.M.; Shvartsman, S.M. *Quantum Electrodynamics with Unstable Vacuum*; Springer: Berlin, Germany, 1991.
6. Grib, A.A.; Mamaev, S.G.; Mostepanenko, V.M. *Vacuum Quantum Effects in Strong External Fields*; Friedmann Laboratory Publishing: St. Petersburg, Russia, 1994.
7. Schmidt, S.M.; Blaschke, D.; Röpke, G.; Smolyansky, S.A.; Prozorkevich, A.V.; Toneev, V.D. A Quantum kinetic equation for particle production in the Schwinger mechanism. *Int. J. Mod. Phys.* **1998**, *E7*, 709. [CrossRef]
8. Blaschke, D.B.; Prozorkevich, A.V.; Röpke, G.; Roberts, C.D.; Schmidt, S.M.; Shkirmanov, D.S.; Smolyansky, S.A. Dynamical Schwinger effect and high-intensity lasers. realising nonperturbative QED. *Eur. Phys. J.* **2009**, *D55*, 341. [CrossRef]
9. Otto, A.; Nousch, T.; Seipt, D.; Kämpfer, B.; Blaschke, D.; Panferov, A.D.; Smolyansky, S.A.; Titov, A.I. Pair production by Schwinger and Breit? Wheeler processes in bi-frequent fields. *J. Plasma Phys.* **2016**, *82*, 655820301 [CrossRef]
10. Blaschke, D.; Smolyansky, S.A.; Panferov, A.D.; Juchnowski, L. Particle Production in Strong Time-dependent Fields. In Proceedings of the Helmholtz International Summer School on Quantum Field Theory at the Limits: From Strong Fields to Heavy Quarks, Dubna, Russia, 18–30 July 2016.
11. Castro Neto, A.H.; Guinea, F.; Peres, N.M.R.; Novoselov, K.S.; Geim, A.K. The electronic properties of graphene. *Rev. Mod. Phys.* **2009**, *81*, 109. [CrossRef]
12. Gusynin, V.P.; Sharapov, S.G.; Carbotte, J.P. AC conductivity of graphene: from tight-binding model to 2+1-dimensional quantum electrodynamics. *Int. J. Mod. Phys.* **2007**, *B21*, 4611. [CrossRef]
13. Gavrilov, S.P.; Gitman, D.M.; Yokomizo, N. Dirac fermions in strong electric field and quantum transport in graphene. *Phys. Rev.* **2012**, *D86*, 125022. [CrossRef]
14. Klemchitskaya, G.L.; Mostepanenko, V.M. Creation of quasiparticles in graphene by a time-dependent electric field. *Phys. Rev.* **2013**, *D87*, 125011.
15. Dora, B.; Moessner, R. Nonlinear electric transport in graphene: Quantum quench dynamics and the Schwinger mechanism. *Phys. Rev.* **2010**, *B81*, 165431. [CrossRef]

16. Smolyansky, S.A.; Panferov, A.D.; Blaschke, D.; Juchnowski, L.; Kämpfer, B.; Otto, A. Vacuum particle-antiparticle creation in strong fields as a field induced phase transition. *Russ. Phys. J.* **2017**, *59*, 1731–1738. [CrossRef]
17. Fedotov, A.M.; Dmitriev, V.V.; Panferov, A.D.; Smolyansky, S.A. Spin Effects in Schwinger Pair Production: Quantum Kinetics vs. Imaginary Time. Paper Presented at the 27th Annual International Laser Physics Workshop (LPHYS'18), Nottingham, UK, 16–20 July 2018.
18. Kluger, Y.; Mottola, E.; Eisenberg, J.M. The Quantum Vlasov equation and its Markov limit. *Phys. Rev.* **1998**, *D58*, 125015. [CrossRef]
19. Bialynicky-Birula, I.; Gornicki, P.; Rafelski, J. Phase space structure of the Dirac vacuum. *Phys. Rev.* **1991**, *D44*, 1825. [CrossRef]
20. Pervushin, V.N.; Skokov, V.V. Kinetic description of fermion production in the oscillator representation. *Acta Phys. Polon.* **2006**, *B37*, 2587.
21. Filatov, A.V.; Prozorkevich, A.V.; Smolyansky, S.A. Pair creation by electromagnetic wave in a collisionless plasma. *Proc. SPIE Int. Soc. Opt. Eng.* **2006**, *6165*, 616509.
22. Filatov, A.V.; Smolyansky, S.A.; Tarakanov, A.V. Kinetics of parton-antiparton plasma vacuum creation in the time—Dependent chromo—Electric fields of arbitrary polarization. *arXiv* **2009**, arXiv:0901.0522.
23. Zeldovich, Y.B.; Starobinsky, A.A. Rate of particle production in gravitational fields. *JETP Lett.* **1977**, *26*, 252.
24. Schmidt, S.M.; Blaschke, D.; Röpke, G.; Prozorkevich, A.V.; Smolyansky, S.A.; Toneev, V.D. NonMarkovian effects in strong field pair creation. *Phys. Rev.* **1999**, *D59*, 094005.
25. Beneventano, C.J.; Giacconi, P.; Santangelo, E.M.; Soldati, R. Planar QED at finite temperature and density: Hall conductivity, Berry's phases and minimal conductivity of graphene. *J. Phys. A Math. Theor.* **2009**, *42*, 275401. [CrossRef]
26. Bloch, J.C.; Mizerny, V.A.; Prozorkevich, A.V.; Roberts, C.D.; Schmidt, S.M.; Smolyansky, S.A.; Vinnik, D.V. Pair creation: Back reactions and damping. *Phys. Rev.* **1999**, *D60*, 1160011. [CrossRef]
27. Martin, P.; Schwinger, J. Theory of many particle systems. 1. *Phys. Rev.* **1959**, *115*, 1342. [CrossRef]
28. Hebenstreit, F.; Alkofer, R.; Dunne, G.; Gies, H. Momentum signatures for Schwinger pair production in short laser pulses with sub-cycle structure. *Phys. Rev. Lett.* **2009**, *102*, 150404. [CrossRef]
29. Fillion-Gourdeau, F.; MacLean, S. Time-dependent pair creation and the Schwinger mechanism in graphene. *Phys. Rev.* **2015**, *B92*, 035401. [CrossRef]
30. Zubkov, M.A. Schwinger pair creation in multilayer graphene. *JETP Lett.* **2012**, *95*, 476. [CrossRef]
31. Panferov, A.; Smolyansky, S.; Blaschke, D.; Gevorgyan, N. Comparing two different descriptions of the I-V characteristic of graphene: theory and experiment. *EPJ Web Conf.* **2019**, *204*, 06008. [CrossRef]
32. Vandecasteele, N.; Barreiro, A.; Lazzeri, M.; Bachtold, A.; Mauri, F. Current-voltage characteristics of graphene devices: Interplay between Zener-Klein tunneling and defects. *Phys. Rev.* **2010**, *B82*, 045416. [CrossRef]
33. Blaschke, D.B.; Kämpfer, B.; Schmidt, S.M.; Panferov, A.D.; Prozorkevich, A.V.; Smolyansky, S.A. Properties of the electron-positron plasma created from a vacuum in a strong laser field: Quasiparticle excitations. *Phys. Rev.* **2013**, *D88*, 045017. [CrossRef]
34. Vajna, S.; Dora, B.; Moessner, R. Nonequilibrium transport and statistics of Schwinger pair production in Weyl semimetals. *Phys. Rev.* **2015**, *B92*, 085122. [CrossRef]
35. Ludwig, A. W. W.; Fisher, M. P. A.; Shankar, R.; Grinstein, G. Integer quantum Hall transition: An alternative approach and exact results. *Phys. Rev.* **1994**, *B50*, 7526. [CrossRef]
36. Ziegler, K. Robust Transport Properties in Graphene. *Phys. Rev. Lett.* **2006**, *97*, 266802. [CrossRef]
37. Ziegler, K. Minimal conductivity of graphene: Nonuniversal values from the Kubo formula. *Phys. Rev.* **2007**, *B75*, 233407. [CrossRef]
38. Ryu, S.; Mudry, C.; Furusaki, A.; Ludwig, A. W. W. Landauer conductance and twisted boundary conditions for Dirac fermions in two space dimensions. *Phys. Rev.* **2007**, *B75*, 205344. [CrossRef]
39. Cserti, J. Minimal longitudinal dc conductivity of perfect bilayer graphene. *Phys. Rev.* **2007**, *B75*, 033405 [CrossRef]

particles

MDPI

Article

Kinetic Approach to Pair Production in Strong Fields—Two Lessons for Applications to Heavy-Ion Collisions

David B. Blaschke [1,2,3,*], **Lukasz Juchnowski** [1] **and Andreas Otto** [4,5]

[1] Institute of Theoretical Physics, University of Wrocław, 50–204 Wrocław, Poland; lukasz.juchnowski@ift.uni.wroc.pl
[2] Bogoliubov Laboratory for Theoretical Physics, JINR Dubna, 141980 Dubna, Russia
[3] Department of Theoretical Nuclear Physics, National Research Nuclear University (MEPhI), 115409 Moscow, Russia
[4] Helmholtz–Zentrum Dresden–Rossendorf, D-01314 Dresden, Germany; a.otto@hzdr.de
[5] Institut für Theoretische Physik, TU Dresden, D-01062 Dresden, Germany
* Correspondence: david.blaschke@gmail.com

Received: 19 December 2018; Accepted: 18 March 2019; Published: 1 April 2019

Abstract: The kinetic-equation approach to particle production in strong, time-dependent external fields is revisited and three limiting cases are discussed for different field patterns: the Sauter pulse, a harmonic pulse with a Gaussian envelope, and a Poisson-distributed stochastic field. It is shown that for transient subcritical electric fields $E(t)$ a finite residual particle number density $n(\infty)$ would be absent if the field-dependence of the dynamical phase in the Schwinger source term would be neglected. In this case the distribution function of created particles follows the law $f(t) \sim E^2(t)$. Two lessons for particle production in heavy-ion collisions are derived from this exercise. First: the shorter the (Sauter-type) pulse, the higher the residual density of produced particles. Second: although the Schwinger process in a string-type field produces a non-thermal particle spectrum, a Poissonian distribution of the (fluctuating) strings produces a thermal spectrum with an apparent temperature that coincides with the Hawking–Unruh temperature for the mean value of the string tension.

Keywords: kinetic theory; particle production; Schwinger effect; Zitterbewegung; low density approximation

1. Introduction

The kinetic equation (KE) approach to particle production in strong, time-dependent external fields by the dynamical or dynamically assisted Schwinger mechanism (see, e.g., reference [1] for a recent review) has a broad spectrum of applications in different fields of Physics, ranging from high-intensity laser colliders to nuclear collisions and graphene in an external (laser) field. Even in the case when spatially homogeneous fields are considered the momentum distribution of the produced particles shows a complex pattern, reminding of interference fringes [2,3]. Therefore, it is instructive to consider limiting cases which may already provide valuable insights for phenomenological applications. In this spirit we shall consider in the present work the case of spatially homogeneous fields with three approximations to the Schwinger source term in the KE and three examples for the temporal pulse shape of the external field in order to draw conclusions for the systematics of particle production in relativistic heavy-ion collisions. Hereby we focus on the questions of how to maximize the yield of produced particles and how to explain their thermal-like spectra when they would be produced by a Schwinger mechanism.

This work is organized in the following way. In Section 2, the KE approach to particle production is shortly summarized, the differential form of the KE is given and three approximations are derived: the Markovian limit, the low-density approximation (LDA) and the low-field limit. In Section 3, the full solutions of the KE for two temporal pulse shapes are given (Sauter and Gaussian envelope harmonic (GEH) pulse) and compared with the results for the three approximations. In Sections 4 and 5 the two lessons for the phenomenology of particle production in heavy-ion collisions are presented and in Section 6 we draw the conclusions.

2. Kinetic Approach to Particle Production

Our investigation is based on a KE which is a nonperturbative consequence of the fundamental equations of motion of QED. The KE for the (quasi-)particle distribution function can be derived from the Dirac equation by a canonical time-dependent Bogoliubov transformation [4]. This method is valid only in a spatially-uniform time-dependent field. In the case of a linearly polarized electric field with the vector potential $A^{\mu}(t) = (0,0,0,A(t))$ (Hamiltonian gauge) we obtain a non-Markovian integro-differential collisionless KE [5]

$$\frac{df(\bar{p},t)}{dt} = \frac{1}{2}\lambda(\bar{p},t)\int_{t_0}^{t} dt'\lambda(\bar{p},t')\left[1-2f(\bar{p},t')\right]\cos\left(2[\Theta(\bar{p},t)-\Theta(\bar{p},t')]\right), \tag{1}$$

where

$$\lambda(\bar{p},t) = \frac{eE(t)\varepsilon_{\perp}}{\omega^2(\bar{p},t)} \tag{2}$$

is the amplitude of vacuum transitions governing the rate of particle production. The dynamical phase,

$$\Theta(\bar{p},t) = \int_{t_0}^{t} dt'\omega(\bar{p},t'), \tag{3}$$

describes the vacuum oscillations (Zitterbewegung) with a frequency of the energy gap $2\omega(\bar{p},t)$ between lower ($\omega < -m$) and upper ($\omega > m$) continua (one can regard particle creation as an excitation of massive field quanta from lower to upper continua just like electrons and holes in the solid state physics models). Due to the fact that our calculations are performed in Hamiltonian gauge it is convenient to use a cylindrical system of coordinates, so it is natural to express the dispersion relation,

$$\omega(\bar{p},t) = \sqrt{\varepsilon_{\perp}^2(\bar{p}_{\perp}) + P^2(\bar{p}_{\parallel},t)}, \tag{4}$$

in terms of the transverse energy and the parallel canonical momentum,

$$\varepsilon_{\perp}(\bar{p}_{\perp}) = \sqrt{m^2+\bar{p}_{\perp}^2}, \tag{5}$$

$$P(\bar{p}_{\parallel},t) = \bar{p}_{\parallel} - eA(t). \tag{6}$$

Here m is the electron mass, e is the charge, $\bar{p}_{\perp}$ is the momentum component perpendicular to the field vector, whereas $\bar{p}_{\parallel}$ is the momentum component parallel to the field.

For the initial condition we choose

$$f(\bar{p},t)\Big|_{t=t_0} = 0. \tag{7}$$

2.1. *Differential Form*

The numerical evaluation of the integro-differential Equation (1) through straightforward double time integration is highly ineffective. First of all, one needs to deal with the rapidly oscillating term $\cos(2[\Theta(\bar{p},t)-\Theta(\bar{p},t')])$. To address this problem we can take the integration step small enough. Second, due to the non-Markovian character of the equation, it is required to store the whole pre-history of $f(t)$ in the computer memory. Luckily, one can avoid these complications by transforming (1) to a time local system of differential equations [6,7]. In order to perform the transformation we introduce two auxiliary functions

$$u(t) = \int_{t_0}^{t} dt' \lambda(\bar{p},t') \Big[1 - 2f(\bar{p},t')\Big] \cos\Big(2[\Theta(\bar{p},t) - \Theta(\bar{p},t')]\Big), \tag{8}$$

$$v(t) = \int_{t_0}^{t} dt' \lambda(\bar{p},t') \Big[1 - 2f(\bar{p},t')\Big] \sin\Big(2[\Theta(\bar{p},t) - \Theta(\bar{p},t')]\Big). \tag{9}$$

The auxiliary functions $u(\bar{p},t)$ and $v(\bar{p},t)$ describe vacuum polarization effects [8]. The differentiation of these functions with respect to t together with

$$\partial_t\Big([\Theta(\bar{p},t) - \Theta(\bar{p},t')]\Big) = \partial_t \int_{t'}^{t} \omega(\bar{p},t'')dt'' = \omega(\bar{p},t) \tag{10}$$

and Equation (1) leads to a coupled system of first order differential equations [7]

$$\dot{f} = \frac{1}{2}\lambda(\bar{p},t)u(t), \tag{11}$$

$$\dot{u} = \lambda(\bar{p},t)\Big[1 - 2f(\bar{p},t)\Big] - 2\omega(\bar{p},t)v(t), \tag{12}$$

$$\dot{v} = 2\omega(\bar{p},t)u(t), \tag{13}$$

with the initial conditions

$$f(t_0) = u(t_0) = v(t_0) = 0. \tag{14}$$

The above system of Equations (11)–(13) is much simpler to solve numerically.

2.2. Three Approximations to the Schwinger Source Term

In this section, we discuss three related approximations which can be obtained when the applied external electric field, $E \ll E_c$, is considerably smaller than the critical field strength [6,9].

$$E_c = \frac{m^2c^3}{e\hbar} \simeq 1.32 \times 10^{18}\,\mathrm{V/m}. \tag{15}$$

The first approximation is the low density limit. When the electric field E is small we expect the probability of pair creation to be small $f(\bar{p},t) \ll 1$, hence $1 - 2f(\bar{p},t) \approx 1$. Consequently, the source term (r.h.s. of (1)) in LDA assumes the following form

$$\mathcal{S}^{\mathrm{LDA}}(t) = \frac{1}{2}\lambda(\bar{p},t) \int_{t_0}^{t} dt' \lambda(\bar{p},t') \cos\Big(2[\Theta(\bar{p},t) - \Theta(\bar{p},t')]\Big). \tag{16}$$

2.2.1. Markovian Limit

In the Markovian limit, one replaces the time argument t' in the statistical factor of (1) by the actual time t thus neglecting dependence on pre-history of the process [10],

$$\frac{df^M(t)}{dt} = [1 - 2f^M(t)]\mathcal{S}^{\mathrm{LDA}}(t) = \mathcal{S}^M(t). \tag{17}$$

Then, for the initial condition $f(t_0) = 0$, the solution of (17) is given by

$$f^M(t) = \frac{1}{2}\Big(1 - \exp\Big[-2\int_{t_0}^{t} dt' \mathcal{S}^{\mathrm{LDA}}(t')\Big]\Big). \tag{18}$$

2.2.2. Low-Density Approximation (LDA)

The expansion of f^M in powers of the argument of the exponential function leads to

$$f^M(t) = \int_{t_0}^{t} dt' \mathcal{S}^{\mathrm{LDA}}(t') - \left(\int_{t_0}^{t} dt' \mathcal{S}^{\mathrm{LDA}}(t') \right)^2 + \mathcal{O}\left[\left(\int_{t_0}^{t} dt' \mathcal{S}^{\mathrm{LDA}}(t') \right)^3 \right] . \tag{19}$$

Provided that the integral in (18) is small we can keep only the leading term and get the low-density solution

$$f^{\mathrm{LDA}}(t) = \int_{t_0}^{t} dt' \mathcal{S}^{\mathrm{LDA}}(t') . \tag{20}$$

The low-density limit gives us a tool to demonstrate the positive definiteness of the distribution function. Using the trigonometric identity $\cos(\alpha - \beta) = \cos\alpha \cdot \cos\beta + \sin\alpha \cdot \sin\beta$, we rewrite (20) as

$$f^{\mathrm{LDA}}(t) = \frac{1}{2} \int_{t_0}^{t} dt' g_1(t') \int_{t_0}^{t'} dt'' g_1(t'') + \frac{1}{2} \int_{t_0}^{t} dt' g_2(t') \int_{t_0}^{t'} dt'' g_2(t'') , \tag{21}$$

$$g_{1,2}(\tau) = \lambda(\tau) \left\{ \begin{array}{c} \cos[2\Theta(\tau)] \\ \sin[2\Theta(\tau)] \end{array} \right\} .$$

The application of the mathematical identity

$$\int_{t_0}^{t} dt' A(t') \int_{t_0}^{t'} dt'' B(t'') = \frac{1}{2} \int_{t_0}^{t} dt' A(t') \int_{t_0}^{t} dt'' B(t'') \tag{22}$$

to (21) leads to the quadratic form

$$f^{\mathrm{LDA}}(t) = \frac{1}{4} \left(\int_{t_0}^{t} dt' g_1(t') \right)^2 + \frac{1}{4} \left(\int_{t_0}^{t} dt' g_2(t') \right)^2 . \tag{23}$$

Now it is straightforward to see that the distribution function in the LDA is positive definite as is required by the interpretation of the distribution function as a probability

$$f^{\mathrm{LDA}}(t) \geq 0 . \tag{24}$$

2.2.3. Low-Field Limit

A further simplification of (23) can be obtained by expanding the dispersion relation with respect to a small external field $A \approx 0$,

$$\omega(\bar{p}, t) = \sqrt{m^2 + \bar{p}_\perp^2 + \bar{p}_\parallel^2} - \frac{\bar{p}_\parallel e A}{\sqrt{m^2 + \bar{p}_\perp^2 + \bar{p}_\parallel^2}} + \mathcal{O}\left(A^2\right) , \tag{25}$$

and keeping only the leading order by assuming the smallness of the vector potential

$$\omega(\bar{p}, t) \approx \sqrt{m^2 + \bar{p}_\perp^2 + \bar{p}_\parallel^2} \equiv a . \tag{26}$$

Immediately one gets

$$\Theta(\bar{p}, t) = \int_{t_0}^{t} dt' \omega(\bar{p}, t') = a(t - t_0) . \tag{27}$$

Then, we have to move out λ in front of the integrals in (23),

$$\int_{t_0}^{t} dt' g_1(t') = \lambda(t) \int_{t_0}^{t} dt' \cos[2a(t'-t_0)] = \lambda(t)\frac{\sin[2a(t-t_0)]}{2a}, \tag{28}$$

$$\int_{t_0}^{t} dt' g_1(t') = \lambda(t) \int_{t_0}^{t} dt' \sin[2a(t'-t_0)] = -\lambda(t)\frac{\cos[2a(t-t_0)]}{2a}, \tag{29}$$

to obtain

$$f^0(\bar{p},t) = \lambda^2(t)\frac{1}{16a^2}. \tag{30}$$

Applying a system of units such that $m = 1$ leads to

$$f^0(\bar{p}=0,t) = \frac{E^2(t)}{16}. \tag{31}$$

3. Results for Sauter Pulse and Gaussian-Envelope Harmonic (GEH) Pulse

In this work we consider the simplest model of the external laser-like field, namely the linearly polarized, time-dependent and spatially homogeneous electric pulse. We solved the KE (1) numerically for the two field shapes. The first one, the so-called Sauter pulse [11] is defined by

$$A(t) = -E_0\tau \tanh\frac{t}{\tau}, \quad E(t) = \frac{E_0}{\cosh^2\frac{t}{\tau}}, \tag{32}$$

with τ being the characteristic duration of action. The second one, called the GEH pulse, is given by

$$E(t) = E_0 \cos(\omega t + \varphi)\exp(-\frac{t^2}{2\tau^2}), \tag{33}$$

$$A(t) = -\sqrt{\frac{\pi}{8}}E_0\tau\exp(-\frac{1}{2}\sigma^2 + i\varphi) \times \mathrm{erf}\left(\frac{t}{\sqrt{2}\tau} - i\frac{\sigma}{\sqrt{2}}\right) + c.c., \tag{34}$$

where $\sigma = \omega\tau$ is a dimensionless measure for the characteristic duration of the pulse τ connected with the number of periods of the carrier field [12].

The impact of the above mentioned approximations on the fermionic distribution function for case of the Sauter have been presented on Figure 1. The analysis of these graphs shows:

1. In case of a critical field strength $E_0 \sim E_c$ and $t > 0 > t_0$ one gets $f^{\mathrm{LDA}}(t) > f^{M}(t) > f(t)$. This happens due to the presence of the factor $(1-2f)$ in (1) and its absence in (16).
2. When $E_0 \sim 10^{-1}E_c$, the Markovian and the low-density approximation give similar values for the distribution functions so that $f^{\mathrm{LDA}}(t) \approx f^{M}(t) > f(t)$.
3. In the case when $E_0 \sim 10^{-2}E_c$ we obtain $f^{\mathrm{LDA}}(t) \approx f^{M}(t) \approx f(t)$.
4. When the external field is $E_0 \sim 10^{-2}E_c$, the distribution function is given by $f(t) \sim f^{(0)}(t) = E(t)^2/16$ at least for some finite period of time. For higher field strength, such an equality may not hold.
5. When distribution function $f(t)$ follows the trend of $E(t)^2/16$ we are dealing with the quasi-particle electron-positron plasma (QEPP). However, when the distribution function reaches its asymptotic (residual) value $f(t) = const$, the state of the residual electron-positron plasma (REPP) is attained. In-between, there is a transition region characterized by fast oscillations which divides the system evolution into QEPP and REPP domains.
6. For high field strengths, it is more difficult to distinguish the QEPP and REPP domains (see bottom panel of Figure 1).
7. The higher the external field strength E_0, the faster $f(t)$ reaches the residual value.
8. For shorter pulse duration the residual value $f(t \to \infty)$ is closer to maximal one.

9. The approximation given by (31) assumes time-independence of the dispersion relation (26). In such circumstances $f(t)$ goes to zero when $E(t) \to 0$. No real particles are created, only virtual ones which disappear with the disappearance of the external electric field [7].

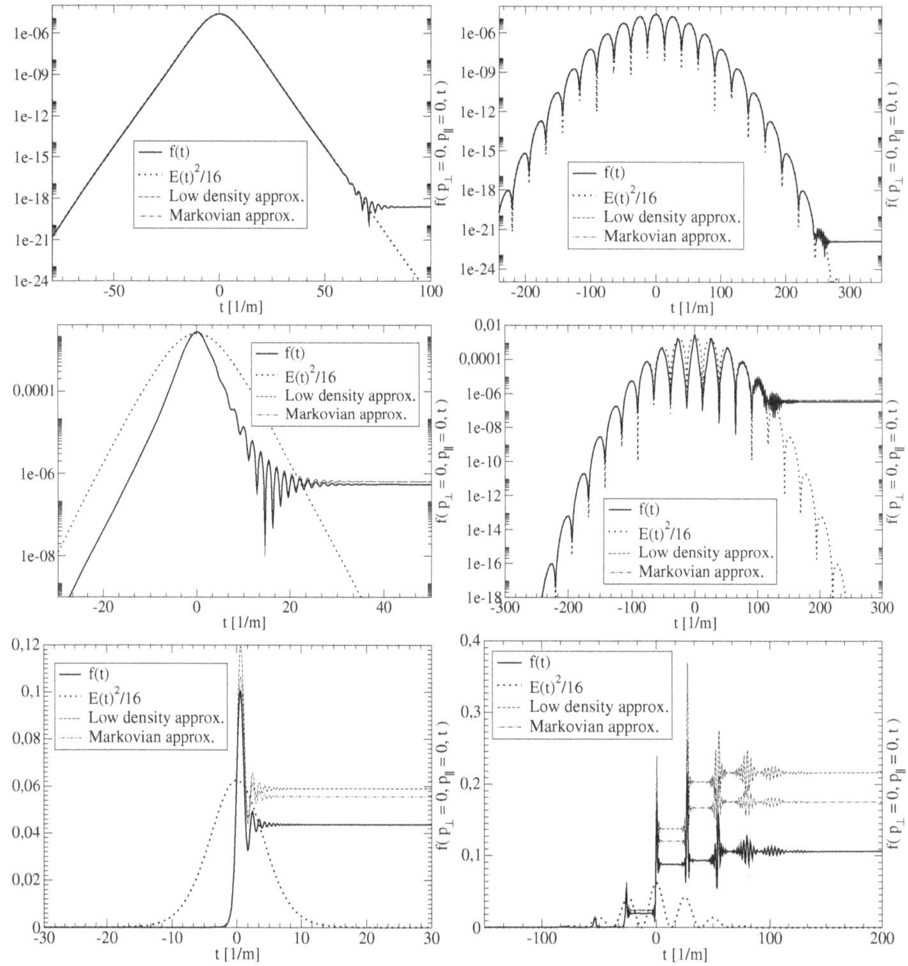

Figure 1. Time evolution of the fermionic distribution function $f(p_\perp = 0,\ p_\parallel = 0, t)$. **Left panels:** for the Sauter pulse (32) with $\tau = 8$. **Right panels:** for the Gaussian envelope harmonic (GEH) pulse (33) with $\sigma = 5$, $\varphi = 0$ and $\omega = 0.02$ nm. From the upper to the lower panel the electric field increases as $E_0/E_c = 0.02,\ 0.2,\ 1$. Time is scaled with the electron mass. Solid curve: full solution $f(t)$, dotted curve: $E(t)^2/16$, dashed curve: low density approximation $f^0(t)$ given by (23), dot-dashed curve: Markovian limit $f^M(t)$ given by (18).

4. Lesson 1: Sauter Pulse Asymptotics

Now we are going to discuss the case of the Sauter pulse more in detail. We set $\vec{p} = 0$ throughout. Its low-density approximation (LDA) [3] is denoted $f^{\rm LDA}$ and is given by

$$f^{\rm LDA}(t) = \frac{1}{2}|I(t)|^2, \quad I(t) = \int_{-\infty}^{t} \mathrm{d}t' J(t'), \tag{35}$$

$$J(t) = \frac{eE(t)m}{m^2 + e^2A(t)^2}\, e^{2i\Theta(t)}, \quad \Theta(t) = \int_0^t \mathrm{d}t' \sqrt{m^2 + e^2A(t)^2}. \tag{36}$$

Following Equations (35) and (32), it is easy to see that for $t \ll -\tau$

$$A(t) \sim E_0\tau, \quad E(t) \sim 4E_0\, e^{2t/\tau}, \quad \Theta(t) \sim \sqrt{m^2 + (eE_0\tau)^2}\, t, \tag{37}$$

$$J(t) \sim \frac{4eE_0 m}{m^2 + (eE_0\tau)^2}\, e^{2t/\tau + 2i\sqrt{m^2+(eE_0\tau)^2}\, t}. \tag{38}$$

From these relations follows

$$I(t) \sim \frac{2eE_0 m}{m^2 + (eE_0\tau)^2} \cdot \frac{e^{2t/\tau + 2i\sqrt{m^2+(eE_0\tau)^2}\, t}}{1/\tau + i\sqrt{m^2 + (eE_0\tau)^2}} =: I_{\rm asy}(t)\,. \tag{39}$$

This allows us to define the small-t asymptotics of $f^{\rm LDA}$, denoted $f_{-\infty}$ as

$$f_{-\infty}(t) = \frac{1}{2}\left|I_{\rm asy}(t)\right|^2 = \frac{2(eE_0 m)^2}{[m^2 + (eE_0\tau)^2]^2\,[1/\tau^2 + m^2 + (eE_0\tau)^2]}\, e^{4t/\tau}\,. \tag{40}$$

For $t \gg \tau$, we need the following symmetries

$$A(-t) = -A(t), \quad E(-t) = E(t), \quad \Theta(-t) = -\Theta(t), \quad J(-t) = J(t)^* \tag{41}$$

and therefore

$$I(t) = I(\infty) - \int_t^{\infty} \mathrm{d}t' J(t') = I(\infty) - \int_{-\infty}^{-t} \mathrm{d}t' J(-t') = I(\infty) - \int_{-\infty}^{-t} \mathrm{d}t' J(t')^* = I(\infty) - I(-t)^*\,. \tag{42}$$

The large-t asymptotic can thus be reduced to the small-t asymptotic and the constant $I(\infty)$. We denote it as f_∞ and it is given by

$$f_\infty(t) = \frac{1}{2}\left|I(\infty) - I_{\rm asy}(-t)^*\right|^2. \tag{43}$$

In Figures 2 and 3, we present the behavior of the Sauter pulse case together with the asymptotics introduced above. This comparison shows

1. The shorter the Sauter-type pulse (smaller τ), the higher the residual value of $f^{\rm LDA}$, f_∞ and f.
2. The difference between the maximal value of f and its residual value grows with τ. The same situation concerns $f^{\rm LDA}$. This feature is not observed in the case of f_∞ and $f_{-\infty}$.
3. Differences in the asymptotic values of $f^{\rm LDA}(t)$ and $f(t)$ grow with E_0 and with τ.
4. The curve f_∞ exhibits a much weaker oscillatory behavior than f and $f^{\rm LDA}$.

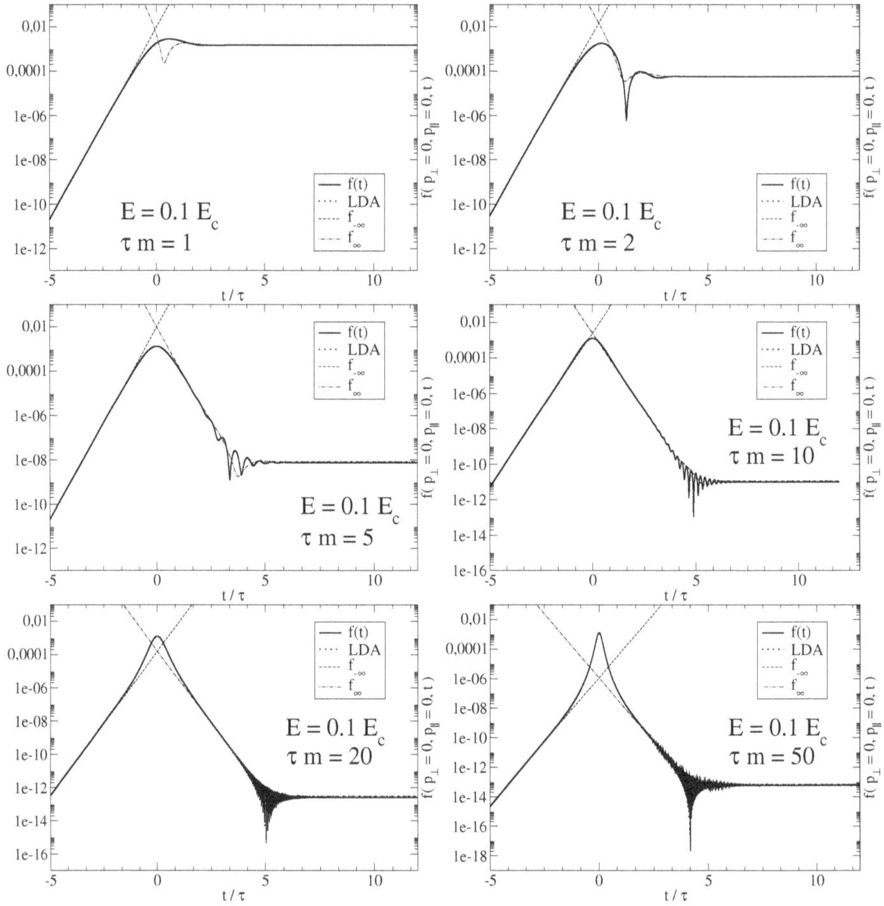

Figure 2. Time evolution of the fermionic distribution function $f(p_\perp = 0,\ p_\parallel = 0, t)$ in the case of Sauter pulse for $E_0 = 0.1E_c$. From the upper left to the lower right panel the pulse duration increases as $\tau m = 1, 2, 5, 10, 20, 50$. The solid curve is for the full solution $f(t)$. The dotted curve shows the low density approximation, the dashed curve depicts the small-t asymptotics $f_{-\infty}$, while the dot-dashed curve stands for the large-t asymptotics f_∞.

The features of $f(t)$ can be useful in explaining phenomena related to heavy-ion collisions (HIC). Lorentz-contracted pancake-like nuclei at high energies are better sources for producing high parton densities than spherically-shaped nuclei at lower ones. This fact can be explained on the basis of Schwinger mechanism. After the collision of two ions, the color glass condensate (CGC) is likely formed, creating a strong longitudinal color electric field, called a flux tube. In this circumstance, the decay of the color electric field due to the Schwinger mechanism takes place. As shown in Figures 2 and 3, particle creation is greatly enhanced when the external field duration is short. Then, the residual value of the distribution $f(t \to \infty)$ is higher and closer to the maximal value. Similarly, in HIC the number of created partons increases when nuclei collide rapidly.

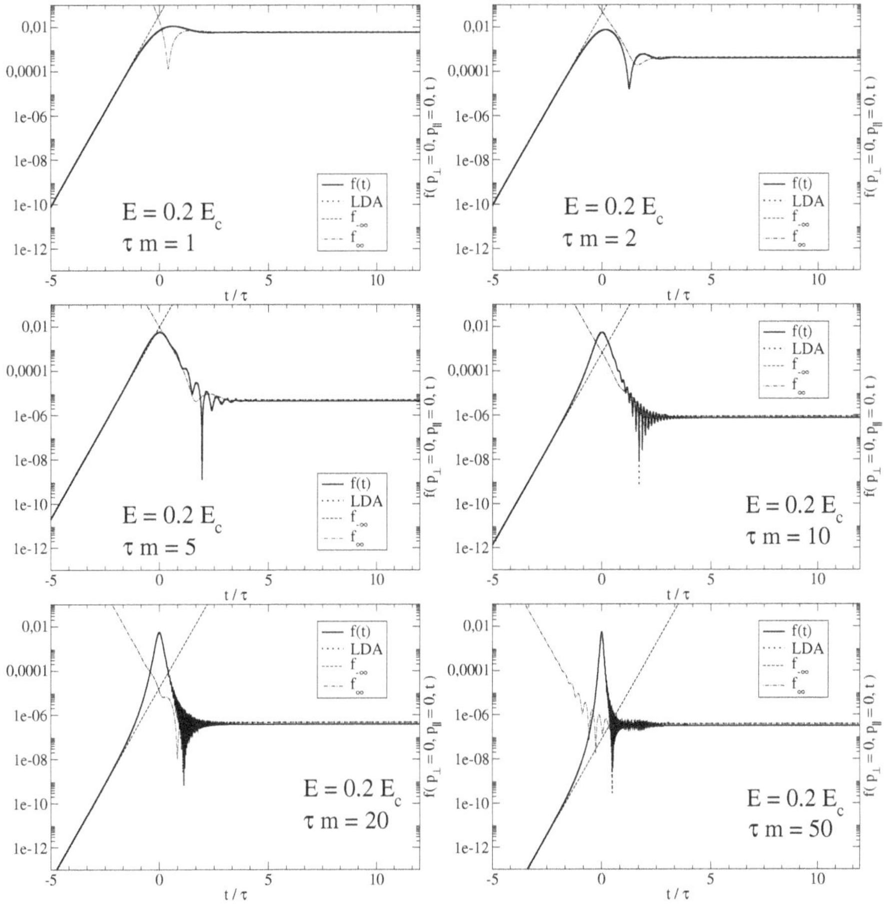

Figure 3. Time evolution of the fermionic distribution function as in Figure 2, but for $E_0 = 0.2E_c$.

Although the individual process of a particle-antiparticle pair creation leads to a non thermal spectrum, a statistical ensemble of the (fluctuating) color fields produces an apparently thermal spectrum with a temperature that is surprisingly given by the mean string tension in exactly the same functional form as the temperature of Hawking–Unruh radiation in a confining field. This observation can also be explained by the dynamical Schwinger mechanism.

Lesson 1: the shorter the Sauter-type pulse, the higher the residual density of produced particles. Therefore, Lorentz-contracted pancake-like nuclei at high energies are better sources for producing high parton densities than sphere-shaped nuclei at lower ones. Note, that we are speaking here not about the particle production in binary collisions, but rather by the vacuum decay in strong color-electric fields.

5. Lesson 2: Thermalization and Hawking Radiation

As an application of the Schwinger process the particle production in heavy-ion collisions has been considered which may proceed by the decay of color electric flux tubes [13–16]. The flux tubes are characterized by a linear, stringlike potential between color charges, analogous to the case of a homogeneous electric field considered by Schwinger. Using this analogy that $|eE| = \sigma$

with $\sigma \sim 0.19$ GeV^2 being the string tension, the transverse energy spectrum of produced particles according to the Schwinger mechanism would be

$$\frac{dN_{\text{Schwinger}}}{d^2p_\perp} \sim \exp\left(-\frac{\pi\varepsilon_\perp^2}{\sigma}\right), \tag{44}$$

with $\varepsilon_\perp = \sqrt{m^2 + p_\perp^2}$ being the transverse energy (5), often also denoted as "transverse mass" $m_\perp$. This spectrum of produced particles is Gaussian and thus would contradict the general observation of exponential particle spectra in heavy-ion collision experiments

$$\frac{dN_{\text{exp}}}{d^2p_\perp} \sim \exp\left(-\frac{\varepsilon_\perp}{T_{\text{eff}}}\right), \tag{45}$$

with an inverse slope parameter $T_{\text{eff}} \sim 160$ MeV that can be considered as an effective temperature at the freeze-out (see, e.g., reference [17]). Thus the question arises how this transformation from a Gaussian to an exponential behavior of the spectrum (or the "thermalization") could occur. It has been suggested that it proceeds via collisions described by a kinetic equation [18,19]. For a most recent discussion of the issue, see [20–24]. It has been questioned whether in high-energy nuclear collisions there is enough time for the thermal equilibration and the isotropization [25] of the system by collisions, after the particle production in a Schwinger process.

As an alternative picture for the emergence of a thermal particle spectrum in ultrarelativistic particle collisions the analogue of the Hawking–Unruh radiation has been discussed [26–28]. This reasoning predicts thermal spectra of hadrons with the Hawking–Unruh temperature

$$T_H(\sigma) = \sqrt{\frac{\sigma}{2\pi}} \sim 173 \text{ MeV}, \tag{46}$$

where for the string tension, $\sigma = 1$ GeV/fm has been taken.

In this context it is interesting to note a possible synthesis of both pictures as provided by the argument elucidated by Bialas [29]. If the string tension in the Schwinger process for flux tube decay would fluctuate and follow, e.g., a Poissonian distribution

$$P(\sigma) = \exp(-\sigma/\sigma_0)/\sqrt{\pi\sigma\sigma_0}, \tag{47}$$

which is normalized $\int d\sigma P(\sigma) = 1$ and has a mean value $\langle\sigma\rangle = \int d\sigma\sigma P(\sigma) = \sigma_0/2$, then the initial Gaussian transverse energy spectrum (44) after averaging with the string tension fluctuations becomes exponential, i.e., thermal with the temperature parameter $T_{\text{eff}} = \sqrt{\langle\sigma\rangle/(2\pi)}$,

$$\int d\sigma P(\sigma) \exp\left(-\frac{\pi\varepsilon_\perp^2}{\sigma}\right) = \exp\left(-\frac{\varepsilon_\perp}{T}\right). \tag{48}$$

Here the integral $\int_0^\infty dt \exp[-t - k^2/(4t)]/\sqrt{\pi t} = \exp(-k)$ has been used [30].

This coincides with the Hawking–Unruh picture of thermal hadron production, where in the case of fluctuating strings the string tension of Equation (46) is now replaced by its mean value. We would like to note at this point that a largely thermal spectrum would arise also from the solution of a kinetic equation with the Schwinger source term, as has been demonstrated by Florkowski in reference [31] for the case of parton creation (a more detailed calculation has recently been done in [20]). This demonstrates the dynamical origin of thermal spectra.

A recent study of the thermalization and isotropization question in the early stages of heavy-ion collisions [32] by solving a relativistic Boltzmann transport equation with a Schwinger source term for particle production from flux-tube decay goes beyond reference [20] by taking into account viscosity effects and $2 \to 2$ collisions in the gluon sector. This study finds that for ideal fluid conditions with a minimal viscosity at the KSS bound $\eta = s/(4\pi)$ [33] already at a timescale below 1 fm/c the ratio of longitudinal to transverse pressure approaches unity with oscillations being damped out and the transverse momentum spectrum shows thermal behavior $dN/(p_T^2\, dp_T\, dy) \propto \exp(-\beta p_T)$ with an inverse slope parameter fulfilling the ideal gas relationship $\beta^{-1} = T_{\rm eff} \propto \varepsilon_{\rm kin}^{1/4}$, where $\varepsilon_{\rm kin}$ is the kinetic energy density. It is interesting to note that this feature is reproduced by the much simpler model considered here which neglects collisions, spatial evolution and finite size as well as the backreaction of the produced particles on the field. It has, however, the advantage of being particularly suitable for discussing the temporal evolution (pulse shape) of the flux-tube field with special emphasis on subcritical field strengths (we remind that the account for confining boundary conditions in a flux tube of finite radial extension r_0 gives rise to an r_0-dependent suppression of the Schwinger pair production rate [34]).

In order to draw the link to the observed hadron spectra in heavy-ion collision experiments, it remains to consider also the hadronization process when starting from the parton level of description. For this purpose one could employ, e.g., kinetic theory approaches built on the basis of the Nambu–Jona–Lasinio model Lagrangian, see [35–38]. In this context, the dynamical chiral symmetry breaking in the quark sector plays an essential role as it triggers the binding of quarks into hadrons (inverse Mott effect). The increase in the sigma meson mass that accompanies the dynamical chiral symmetry breaking gives rise to additional sigma meson production by the inertial mechanism (see [39] and references therein). By the dominant decay $\sigma \to \pi\pi$ this leads to an additional population of low-momentum pion states and can contribute to the observed effect that s also discussed as a precursor of pion Bose condensation and may simultaneously resolve the Large Hadron Collider (LHC) proton puzzle [40] within a non-equilibrium model.

Lesson 2: although the individual Schwinger process of for creating a particle-antiparticle pair from flux-tube decay has a Gaussian transverse energy spectrum, a statistical distribution of the (fluctuating) color fields produces an apparently thermal (exponential) spectrum with an inverse slope parameter (effective temperature) $T_{\rm eff} = T_H(\langle\sigma\rangle)$ that surprisingly is given by the mean string tension in exactly the same functional form as the temperature of Hawking–Unruh radiation in a confining field.

6. Conclusions

In the present work, we have revisited the KE approach to particle production by the dynamical Schwinger effect. We have shown that in the case of subcritical external fields both, the LDA and the Markovian approximation to the source term give quite accurate estimations for the residual particle densities, to be observed after the field is switched off. It is an elucidating exercise to retain only the lowest order term in a low-field expansion of the dynamical phase of the Schwinger source term. In this case, the time-dependence of the distribution function of produced particles follows the temporal shape of the external field according to $f(t) \sim E^2(t)$ with the consequence that there are no produced particles in the final state where the field is absent. Thus the origin of particle production in subcritical fields can be traced to the self-interference (decoherence) of the virtual fields in the transient stage, formally accounted for by the time-dependent dynamical phase in the source term.

Two lessons for particle production in heavy-ion collisions are drawn from our exercise.

Lesson 1: The shorter the Sauter-type pulse, the higher the residual density of produced particles. Therefore, Lorentz-contracted pancake-nuclei at high energies are better sources for producing high parton densities than sphere-shaped nuclei at lower energies. Note, that in this argument we are considering only particle production from the vacuum decay in strong color fields as if particle production by collisions were absent.

Lesson 2: Although the individual Schwinger process of a particle-antiparticle pair has a non thermal (Gaussian) spectrum, a statistical distribution of the (fluctuating) color fields produces an apparently thermal (exponential) spectrum with a temperature (inverse slope parameter) that surprisingly is given by the mean string tension in exactly the same functional form as the temperature of Hawking–Unruh radiation in a confining field.

In a more complete kinetic description of particle production in a complex process like a heavy-ion collision, the subsequent stages following the creation of particles in the initial phase of the process should be included by adding elastic and inelastic scattering processes in the collision integrals of the system of kinetic equations for all relevant particle species. Thus, one can address the process of hadron production in heavy-ion collisions starting from parton production in strong field decay, their rescattering and conversion to hadrons (hadronization) with chemical equilibration and rescattering in the hadronic final state.

Author Contributions: conceptualization, D.B.; software, L.J. and A.O.; investigation, L.J., A.O.; writing, D.B., L.J. and A.O.; funding acquisition, D.B.

Funding: This research was supported by the NCN grant No. UMO-2014/15/B/ST2/03752.

Acknowledgments: It is our pleasure to acknowledge the long-standing collaboration with Burkhard Kämpfer, Anatolii Panferov and Stanislav Smolyansky on the kinetic approach to particle production in strong fields from which the discussion of the two lessons emerged that is presented here.

Conflicts of Interest: The authors declare no conflict of interest.

Abbreviations

LDA	Low density approximation
KE	Kinetic equation
QEPP	Quasi-particles electron-positron plasma
REPP	Real particles electron-positron plasma
CGC	Color-glass condensate
GEH	Gaussian-envelope harmonic

References

1. Blaschke, D.B.; Smolyansky, S.A.; Panferov, A.; Juchnowski, L. Particle production in strong time-dependent fields. In Proceedings of the Quantum Field Theory at the Limits: From Strong Fields to Heavy Quarks (HQ 2016), Dubna, Russia, 18–30 July 2016; pp. 1–23. [CrossRef]
2. Otto, A.; Seipt, D.; Blaschke, D.; Kämpfer, B.; Smolyansky, S.A. Lifting shell structures in the dynamically assisted Schwinger effect in periodic fields. *Phys. Lett. B* **2015**, *740*, 335–340. [CrossRef]
3. Otto, A. The Dynamically Assisted Schwinger Process: Primary and Secondary Effects. Ph.D. Thesis, Technischen Universität Dresden, Dresden, Germany, 2017.
4. Blaschke, D.B.; Prozorkevich, A.V.; Ropke, G.; Roberts, C.D.; Schmidt, S.M.; Shkirmanov, D.S.; Smolyansky, S.A. Dynamical Schwinger effect and high-intensity lasers. Realising nonperturbative QED. *Eur. Phys. J. D* **2009**, *55*, 341–358. [CrossRef]
5. Blaschke, D.; Juchnowski, L.; Panferov, A.; Smolyansky, S. Dynamical Schwinger effect: Properties of the e+ e− plasma created from vacuum in strong laser fields. *Phys. Part. Nucl.* **2015**, *46*, 797–800. [CrossRef]
6. Juchnowski, L. Quantum Kinetic Approach to Particle Production in Time Dependent External Fields. Ph.D. Thesis, University of Wroclaw, Wroclaw, Poland, 2018; in preparation.
7. Bloch, J.C.R.; Mizerny, V.A.; Prozorkevich, A.V.; Roberts, C.D.; Schmidt, S.M.; Smolyansky, S.A.; Vinnik, D.V. Pair creation: Back reactions and damping. *Phys. Rev. D* **1999**, *60*, 116011. [CrossRef]
8. Calzetta, E.A.; Hu, B.L.B. *Nonequilibrium Quantum Field Theory*; Cambridge University Press: Cambridge, UK, 2008.
9. Schwinger, J.S. On gauge invariance and vacuum polarization. *Phys. Rev.* **1951**, *82*, 664–679. [CrossRef]
10. Schmidt, S.M.; Blaschke, D.; Ropke, G.; Prozorkevich, A.V.; Smolyansky, S.A.; Toneev, V.D. NonMarkovian effects in strong field pair creation. *Phys. Rev. D* **1999**, *59*, 094005. [CrossRef]
11. Sauter, F. Uber das verhalten eines elektrons im homogenen elektrischen feld nach der relativistischen theorie diracs. *Z. Phys.* **1931**, *69*, 742–764. [CrossRef]

12. Panferov, A.D.; Smolyansky, S.A.; Otto, A.; Kämpfer, B.; Blaschke, D.B.; Juchnowski, L. Assisted dynamical Schwinger effect: Pair production in a pulsed bifrequent field. *Eur. Phys. J. D* **2016**, *70*, 56. [CrossRef]
13. Casher, A.; Neuberger, H.; Nussinov, S. Chromoelectric flux tube model of particle production. *Phys. Rev. D* **1979**, *20*, 179–188. [CrossRef]
14. Bialas, A.; Czyz, W. Chromoelectric flux tubes and the transverse momentum distribution in high-energy nucleus-nucleus collisions. *Phys. Rev. D* **1985**, *31*, 198. [CrossRef]
15. Gatoff, G.; Kerman, A.K.; Matsui, T. The flux tube model for ultrarelativistic heavy ion collisions: Electrohydrodynamics of a quark gluon plasma. *Phys. Rev. D* **1987**, *36*, 114. [CrossRef]
16. Braun, M.A.; Pajares, C. Particle production in nuclear collisions and string interactions. *Phys. Lett. B* **1992**, *287*, 154–158. [CrossRef]
17. Broniowski, W.; Florkowski, W. Explanation of the RHIC p(T) spectra in a thermal model with expansion. *Phys. Rev. Lett.* **2001**, *87*, 272302. [CrossRef] [PubMed]
18. Bialas, A.; Czyz, W. Boost invariant Boltzmann-vlasov equations for relativistic quark—Anti-quark plasma. *Phys. Rev. D* **1984**, *30*, 2371. [CrossRef]
19. Kajantie, K.; Matsui, T. Decay of strong color electric field and thermalization in ultrarelativistic nucleus-nucleus collisions. *Phys. Lett. B* **1985**, *164*, 373–378. [CrossRef]
20. Ryblewski, R.; Florkowski, W. Equilibration of anisotropic quark-gluon plasma produced by decays of color flux tubes. *Phys. Rev. D* **2013**, *88*, 034028. [CrossRef]
21. Gelis, F.; Tanji, N. Schwinger mechanism revisited. *Prog. Part. Nucl. Phys.* **2016**, *87*, 1–49. [CrossRef]
22. Gelis, F. Initial state and thermalization in the color glass condensate framework. In *Quark-Gluon Plasma 5*; Wang, X.N., Ed.; World Scientific: Singapore, 2016; pp. 67–129. [CrossRef]
23. Blaizot, J.P.; Liao, J.; Mehtar-Tani, Y. The thermalization of soft modes in non-expanding isotropic quark gluon plasmas. *Nucl. Phys. A* **2017**, *961*, 37–67. [CrossRef]
24. Boguslavski, K.; Kurkela, A.; Lappi, T.; Peuron, J. Spectral function for overoccupied gluodynamics from real-time lattice simulations. *Phys. Rev. D* **2018**, *98*, 014006. [CrossRef]
25. Attems, M.; Rebhan, A.; Strickland, M. Instabilities of an anisotropically expanding non-Abelian plasma: 3D + 3V discretized hard-loop simulations. *Phys. Rev. D* **2013**, *87*, 025010. [CrossRef]
26. Castorina, P.; Kharzeev, D.; Satz, H. Thermal hadronization and Hawking–Unruh radiation in QCD. *Eur. Phys. J. C* **2007**, *52*, 187–201. [CrossRef]
27. Castorina, P.; Satz, H. Hawking-Unruh hadronization and strangeness production in high energy collisions. *Adv. High Energy Phys.* **2014**, *2014*, 376982. [CrossRef]
28. Castorina, P.; Iorio, A.; Satz, H. Hadron freeze-out and unruh radiation. *Int. J. Mod. Phys. E* **2015**, *24*, 1550056. [CrossRef]
29. Bialas, A. Fluctuations of string tension and transverse mass distribution. *Phys. Lett. B* **1999**, *466*, 301–304. [CrossRef]
30. Abramowitz, M.; Stegun, I. *Handbook of Mathematical Functions*; Dover: New York, NY, USA, 1964; p. 1026.
31. Florkowski, W. Schwinger tunneling and thermal character of hadron spectra. *Acta Phys. Polon. B* **2004**, *35*, 799–808.
32. Ruggieri, M.; Puglisi, A.; Oliva, L.; Plumari, S.; Scardina, F.; Greco, V. Modelling early stages of relativistic heavy ion collisions: Coupling relativistic transport theory to decaying color-electric flux tubes. *Phys. Rev. C* **2015**, *92*, 064904. [CrossRef]
33. Kovtun, P.; Son, D.T.; Starinets, A.O. Viscosity in strongly interacting quantum field theories from black hole physics. *Phys. Rev. Lett.* **2005**, *94*, 111601. [CrossRef] [PubMed]
34. Pavel, H.P.; Brink, D.M. q anti-q pair creation in a flux tube with confinement. *Z. Phys. C* **1991**, *51*, 119–125. [CrossRef]
35. Rehberg, P.; Klevansky, S.P.; Hufner, J. Hadronization in the SU(3) Nambu-Jona-Lasinio model. *Phys. Rev. C* **1996**, *53*, 410–429. [CrossRef]
36. Rehberg, P.; Bot, L.; Aichelin, J. Expansion and hadronization of a chirally symmetric quark—Meson plasma. *Nucl. Phys. A* **1999**, *653*, 415–435. [CrossRef]
37. Friesen, A.V.; Kalinovsky, Y.V.; Toneev, V.D. Quark scattering off quarks and hadrons. *Nucl. Phys. A* **2014**, *923*, 1–18. [CrossRef]
38. Marty, R.; Torres-Rincon, J.M.; Bratkovskaya, E.; Aichelin, J. Transport theory from the Nambu-Jona-Lasinio lagrangian. *J. Phys. Conf. Ser.* **2016**, *668*, 012001. [CrossRef]

39. Juchnowski, L.; Blaschke, D.; Fischer, T.; Smolyansky, S.A. Nonequilibrium meson production in strong fields. *J. Phys. Conf. Ser.* **2016**, *673*, 012009. [CrossRef]
40. Begun, V.; Florkowski, W.; Rybczynski, M. Explanation of hadron transverse-momentum spectra in heavy-ion collisions at $\sqrt{s_{NN}} = 2.76$ TeV within chemical non-equilibrium statistical hadronization model. *Phys. Rev. C* **2014**, *90*, 014906. [CrossRef]

particles

MDPI

Communication

Bose-Einstein Condensation from the QCD Boltzmann Equation

Brent Harrison * and Andre Peshier

Department of Physics, University of Cape Town, Cape Town 7700, South Africa; andre.peshier@uct.ac.za
* Correspondence: brent.harrison@alumni.uct.ac.za or brent.andrew.harrison@gmail.com

Received: 28 February 2019; Accepted: 12 April 2019; Published: 22 April 2019

Abstract: We present a novel numerical scheme to solve the QCD Boltzmann equation in the soft scattering approximation, for the quenched limit of QCD. Using this we can readily investigate the evolution of spatially homogeneous systems of gluons distributed isotropically in momentum space. We numerically confirm that for so-called "overpopulated" initial conditions, a (transient) Bose-Einstein condensate could emerge in a finite time. Going beyond existing results, we analyze the formation dynamics of this condensate. The scheme is extended to systems with cylindrically symmetric momentum distributions, in order to investigate the effects of anisotropy. In particular, we compare the rates at which isotropization and equilibration occur. We also compare our results from the soft scattering scheme to the relaxation time approximation.

Keywords: QCD; Boltzmann equation; gluons; Bose-Einstein condensate; Fokker-Planck equation; relaxation time approximation; thermalization

---

1. Introduction

The study of quark-gluon plasma (QGP), the phase of strongly interacting matter formed in relativistic nuclear collisions and consisting of quasi-free quarks and gluons, is of increasing relevance in modern physics [1]. It represents a testing ground for the Standard Model, as well as for finite temperature field theory and possible grand unification theories. It is also of cosmological significance, as the early universe was dominated by this phase of matter.

Experiments at the Super Proton Synchrotron (SPS), Relativistic Heavy Ion Collider (RHIC) and Large Hadron Collider (LHC) allow us to probe the energy scales at which the QGP is produced. Inferring its properties and phenomenological behaviour is a central goal of the heavy ion programs at these facilities. The theoretical tools that have been developed to describe it are manifold, as the various stages of a heavy ion collision represent very different physical regimes that demand similarly diverse mathematical formalisms to describe (see Figure 1).

Prior to the collision, the nuclei are accelerated to near-light speed, with a Lorentz factor on the order of 100. They are therefore subject to strong Lorentz contraction along the beam axis. At these energies, the lifetime of gluons emitted from the valence quarks or other gluons is long enough to allow additional emissions of soft gluons from themselves. This process keeps increasing the number density of gluons until saturation occurs as recombination of gluons becomes non-negligible, forming the state of matter called the Color Glass Condensate (CGC) [2–4]. This regime of large gluon number can be approximated by classical dynamics.

In the first stage of a collision, a large number of gluons are liberated from the CGC. These gluons form a dense, off-equilibrium state called the glasma. Extensive hydrodynamic analyses of HIC indicate that as the medium expands, rapid thermalization occurs (characteristic time on the order of 1 fm) and a QGP in local equilibrium forms [5–8]. This rapid thermalization is indicative of strong interactions. As the medium continues to expand and decrease in temperature, it eventually drops below the deconfinement temperature ($T_c \approx 170\,\mathrm{MeV}$) and hadronization occurs.

Despite longstanding efforts and various approaches to describe the dynamics of heavy ion collisions (see e.g., [9,10]), the rapid equilibration of the QGP remains to be thoroughly understood. Another question that has received a lot of recent attention is the possible formation of a gluon condensate in heavy ion collisions [11,12]. We will address these two questions by adapting and numerically solving the QCD Boltzmann equation assuming the dominance of soft gluon exchange in binary collisions. In this framework we can describe the evolution of the QGP from the early pre-equilibrium stages through thermalization towards freeze-out.

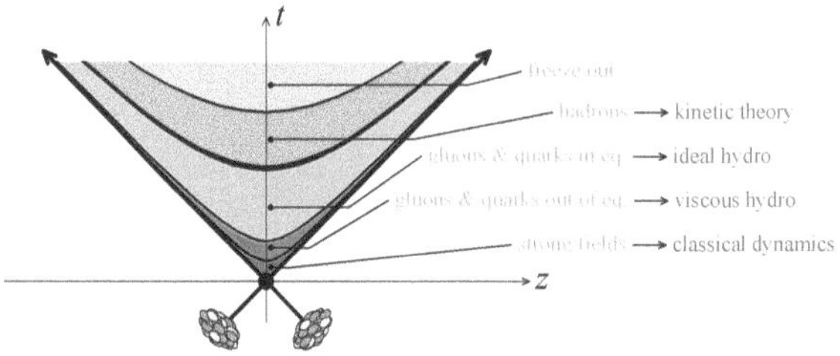

Figure 1. The stages of a heavy ion collision (from [1]).

2. The Boltzmann Transport Equation

The fundamental equation of kinetic theory is the Boltzmann transport equation. It is a non-linear integro-differential equation describing the evolution of a distribution function of particles, for our purposes a dilute gas of gluons "in a box". (Quarks are omitted for conceptual simplicity and also motivated for systems which are gluon-dominated). For a spatially homogeneous system under the assumption that $2 \to 2$ processes dominate, it can be written as

$$\partial_t f = \frac{1}{2}\int \frac{d^3p_2}{(2\pi)^3 2E_2}\frac{d^3p_3}{(2\pi)^3 2E_3}\frac{d^3p_4}{(2\pi)^3 2E_4}\frac{|\mathcal{M}_{12\to 34}|^2}{2E_1}(2\pi)^4\delta(p_1+p_2-p_3-p_4)(f_3f_4\tilde{f}_1\tilde{f}_2 - f_1f_2\tilde{f}_3\tilde{f}_4)\,. \quad (1)$$

Here f_i is the distribution function of particle i with 4-momentum $p_i = (E_i, \boldsymbol{p}_i)$. As shorthand, we write $\tilde{f}_i \equiv 1 + f_i$.

The transition amplitude $\mathcal{M}$ of binary gluon scattering reads at tree level

$$|\mathcal{M}_{12\to 34}|^2 = 72g^4\left[3 - \tfrac{tu}{s^2} - \tfrac{su}{t^2} - \tfrac{st}{u^2}\right], \quad (2)$$

where s, t and u are the familiar Mandelstam variables and g is related to the QCD coupling constant α by $g^2 = 4\pi\alpha$.

For small scattering angles, $|t| \ll s$ and expression (2) simplifies to

$$|\mathcal{M}_{12\to 34}|^2 \approx 144g^4\tfrac{s^2}{t^2}, \quad (3)$$

which is to be regulated, e.g., by making the substitution

$$\frac{1}{t^2} \to \frac{1}{(t-\mu^2)^2}, \quad (4)$$

where μ is the screening mass.

While this equation is a challenge to solve, Boltzmann's H-Theorem guarantees that regardless of the initial condition, the equilibrium distribution function will be a Bose-Jüttner function [13],

$$f_{eq}(x,p) = \left[e^{\frac{p^\alpha u_\alpha(x) - \mu(x)}{T(x)}} - 1\right]^{-1}. \quad (5)$$

Here T, u and μ parameterize the temperature, collective flow velocity and chemical potential, respectively.

There is one caveat; there exist "overpopulated" initial distributions (see Figure 2) which contain more gluons than can be "accommodated" in a Bose-Jüttner distribution while maintaining particle number and energy conservation. It has been argued [11] that under the assumption of approximate gluon number conservation, a transient state close to equilibrium may form with a Bose-Einstein condensate.

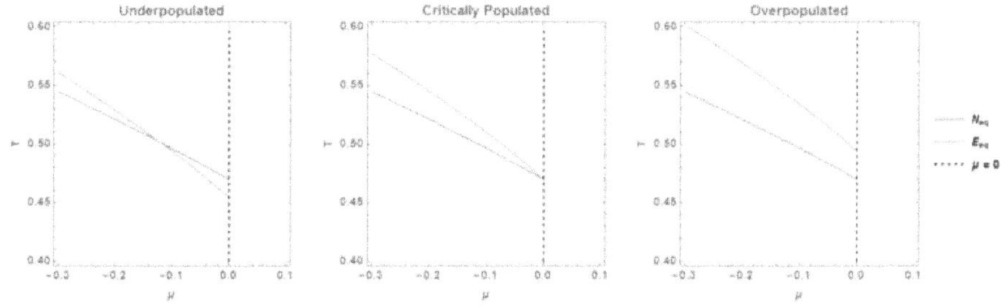

Figure 2. Contours of constant particle number and energy density at equilibrium. The values of the equilibrium parameters T and μ are found where the lines intersect. In the critically populated case, the intersection occurs at the maximum possible value of $\mu = 0$. In the overpopulated case, no real solution for $\mu < 0$ exists and a condensate is necessary to contain the excess particles.

3. The Fokker-Planck and Relaxation Time Approximations

Under the assumption that small-angle scattering dominates, the RHS of Equation (1) can be approximated as the divergence of a current in momentum space [11],

$$D_t f = -\boldsymbol{\nabla}_p \cdot \boldsymbol{\mathcal{J}}(\boldsymbol{p}) \,, \tag{6}$$

which is a Fokker-Planck type equation. Here the components of the current $\boldsymbol{\mathcal{J}}$ read

$$\mathcal{J}_i(\boldsymbol{p}) = \tfrac{9}{4\pi} g^4 \mathcal{L} \int_{\boldsymbol{k}} \mathcal{V}_{ij}(\boldsymbol{p},\boldsymbol{k}) \left\{ f_p \bar{f}_p \nabla^j_k f_k - f_k \bar{f}_k \nabla^j_p f_p \right\} \,, \tag{7}$$

where

$$\mathcal{V}^{ij} = (1 - \boldsymbol{v}\cdot\boldsymbol{w})\,\delta^{ij} + \left(v^i w^j + v^j w^i\right) \,, \tag{8}$$

and we define $\boldsymbol{p} \equiv \boldsymbol{p}_1$, $\boldsymbol{k} \equiv \boldsymbol{p}_2$ and denote the corresponding unit vectors by $\boldsymbol{w} \equiv \boldsymbol{p}/p$ and $\boldsymbol{v} \equiv \boldsymbol{k}/k$.

In Equation (7), $\mathcal{L}$ is the so-called Coulomb logarithm emerging for screened interactions with vector boson exchange, $\mathcal{L} = \int_{q_{min}}^{q_{max}} \frac{dq}{q} = \ln\frac{q_{max}}{q_{min}}$ where q_{max} and q_{min} are cutoffs of the order of the equilibrium temperature T and the screening mass μ introduced in expression (4), respectively [11]. We take $\mathcal{L}$ to be a constant of order 1 in our analysis.

It is convenient to rescale the time variable in Equation (6) as $\tau = \frac{9}{4\pi} g^4 \mathcal{L}\, t$ to eliminate the constant factor in Equation (7). The integral in (7) can then be performed (see Appendix A), yielding

$$\boldsymbol{\mathcal{J}}(\boldsymbol{p}) = I_a \boldsymbol{\nabla}_p f + I_b f \bar{f} \hat{\boldsymbol{p}} + (\boldsymbol{\nabla}_p f \cdot \hat{\boldsymbol{p}})\boldsymbol{\mathcal{I}} + (\boldsymbol{\nabla}_p f \times \hat{\boldsymbol{p}}) \times \boldsymbol{\mathcal{I}} \,, \tag{9}$$

where $I_a = \int f\bar{f}$, $I_b = \int \frac{2f}{p}$ and $\boldsymbol{\mathcal{I}} \equiv (\mathcal{I}_x, \mathcal{I}_y, \mathcal{I}_z) = \int \boldsymbol{w} f \bar{f}$ are functionals of the distribution function f.

It will be interesting to compare the Fokker-Planck approximation of the Boltzmann equation to the well-known Relaxation Time Approximation (RTA),

$$\partial_t f = \frac{p^\mu u_\mu}{p_0} \frac{f_\infty - f}{\tau} \,. \tag{10}$$

The RTA is easily solvable (and convergences to the same equilibrium distribution); however it lacks QCD-specific features and, as we will see, yields qualitatively different behavior to the Fokker-Planck approximation, which we argue is more physically motivated.

4. The Method of 'B-Lines'

We have developed a flux-conservative numerical scheme that allows us to readily solve the Boltzmann equation in the Fokker-Planck approximation, (6) + (9), which we call the method of 'B-lines'. The name is given in analogy to splines, with the 'B' referring to an efficient parameterization of the distribution function in terms of piecewise Bose functions. We have implemented it for distribution functions spherically and cylindrically symmetric in momentum space; here we will discuss the scheme for the simpler isotropic case.

For spherically symmetric distribution functions, we discretize the momentum grid into bins of width Δ and construct a piecewise Bose interpolation of f,

$$f^{(i)}(p) = \frac{1}{e^{a_i p + b_i} - 1} \, . \tag{11}$$

The domain of $f^{(i)}$ is $p \in [i, (i+1)]\Delta$ for $0 \leq i < M-1$ and $[\Delta(M-1), \infty)$ for $i = M-1$.

A couple of points are in order. Firstly, it should be noted that this approach is equivalent to a linear interpolation of an expedient transformation of the distribution function, $g \equiv \ln(\bar{f}/f)$, i.e., $g^{(i)}(p) = a_i p + b_i$. One of the reasons that we choose to make this transformation is that a piecewise linear interpolation directly in terms of f would not allow us to describe the formation of the Bose-Einstein condensate. Secondly, for equilibrium distribution functions approaching equilibrium our interpolation scheme becomes exact, which is a nice property. An equilibrium distribution in g-space of course is simply a straight line.

Physically, the a_i correspond to local (in momentum space) inverse temperature parameters, and the b_i correspond to the chemical potential. We determine them by sampling the distribution function at the gridpoints,

$$\begin{aligned} f_0 &\equiv f(\delta) \, , \\ f_i &\equiv f(\Delta i), \;\; 0 < i < M \, . \end{aligned} \tag{12}$$

Here δ is small relative to Δ but non-zero in order to avoid singularities at the origin.

Having established the details of the initial interpolation, we now consider the process by which we evolve the distribution function in time. We separate our $M+1$ cells on the p-axis at the momenta

$$\begin{aligned} p_0 &= \delta \, , \\ p_i &= \left(i + \frac{1}{2}\right)\Delta, \;\; 0 < i < M \, , \end{aligned} \tag{13}$$

such that cell 0 is $[0, \delta]$, cell M is $[(M - \frac{1}{2})\Delta, \infty)$ and intermediate cells with index $0 < i < M$ are $[p_{i-1}, p_i]$. These cell boundaries are "staggered" with respect to the grid used for the interpolation, with the distribution function in each cell being interpolated by two B-lines. This is because as we will see shortly, the first derivative of our interpolation of the distribution function is required to be continuous at our cell boundaries, which is not in general the case at B-line boundaries.

From the B-lines we can easily calculate the particle number (per volume) in each cell,

$$\begin{aligned} n_0 &= \frac{4\pi}{(2\pi)^3} \int_0^{\delta} \mathrm{d}p \; p^2 f^{(0)}(p) \, , \\ n_i &= \frac{4\pi}{(2\pi)^3} \int_{p_{i-1}}^{\Delta i} \mathrm{d}p \; p^2 f^{(i-1)}(p) + \frac{4\pi}{(2\pi)^3} \int_{\Delta i}^{p_i} \mathrm{d}p \; p^2 f^{(i)}(p), \;\; 0 < i < M \, , \\ n_M &= \frac{4\pi}{(2\pi)^3} \int_{p_{M-1}}^{\infty} \mathrm{d}p \; p^2 f^{(M-1)}(p) \, . \end{aligned} \tag{14}$$

These integrals are combinations of polylogarithm functions depending on the B-line parameters a_i, b_i. For convenience we have set the gluon degeneracy to 1; $d_g = 16$ can be reinstated as needed.

Now, recall that the Fokker-Planck equation (6) can be written as a continuity equation (conserving both particle number and energy). Thus the rate of change of particle number in cell i,

$$\partial_\tau n_i = \frac{4\pi}{(2\pi)^3}\int_{p_i}^{p_{i+1}} \mathrm{d}p p^2 \partial_\tau f(p,\tau) = \frac{4\pi}{(2\pi)^3} p^2 \mathcal{J}(p)\bigg|_{p_i}^{p_{i+1}} , \tag{15}$$

is given by $\phi_{i+1} - \phi_i$, the net radial flux into cell i, where

$$\phi_i \equiv \frac{4\pi}{(2\pi)^3} p^2 \mathcal{J}(p_i) = \frac{4\pi}{(2\pi)^3} p^2 (I_a \partial_p f + I_b f(1+f))\bigg|_{p=p_i} . \tag{16}$$

For the zeroth cell, the flux ϕ_0 at $p = 0$ is zero by definition. Similarly, the last cell's rightmost boundary is at infinity, with zero flux through it.

We thus arrive at the following non-linear system of ODEs,

$$\begin{aligned} \dot{n}_0 &= \phi(\delta) , \\ \dot{n}_i &= \phi_{i+1} - \phi_i, \quad 0 < i < M , \\ \dot{n}_M &= -\phi_M . \end{aligned} \tag{17}$$

Note that the integrals I_a and I_b ($\mathcal{I}$ vanishes in the spherically symmetric case), which determine the flux (16) depend non-linearly on all of the f_i and must be updated at each time step. We can readily solve these ODEs using the forward Euler method. Having updated the particle number in each cell, it is straightforward to find the evolved set of B-line parameters.

One advantage of the modified scheme is that it allows us to compute the number of particles in the condensate. Analysis shows that the flux into the zeroth cell becomes non-zero after finite time for overpopulated systems approaching the equilibrium Bose-Einstein distribution. Note that this flux remains well-defined as we take the limit $\delta \to 0$. For large t, the flux becomes proportional to $I_b - I_a/T$, which vanishes for an equilibrium distribution. The particle number in cell 0 has a "regular" contribution, which vanishes for $\delta \to 0$, as well as the condensate contribution.

5. Results

Figures 3–6 show the evolution in the special case of spherically symmetric, CGC-inspired initial conditions of the form

$$f(p) = f_0 \frac{1}{e^{(p-Q)/C}+1} , \tag{18}$$

where f_0 and C are constants and Q sets the overall momentum scale. For these figures, we have chosen $f_0 = 0.225$ and $C = 0.05Q$ (and $Q \to 1$), which is a moderately overpopulated initial condition where some 8% of the particles asymptotically condense. We point out the qualitative difference between the Fokker-Planck and Relaxation Time Approximations; in the latter the condensate begins to form immediately, whereas the Fokker-Planck scheme exhibits a characteristic "lag". The onset time t_c is fairly short, assuming $\mathcal{L} \approx 1$, $\alpha \approx 0.4$ and $Q \approx 2$ GeV we find $t_c \approx 0.2$ fm/c.

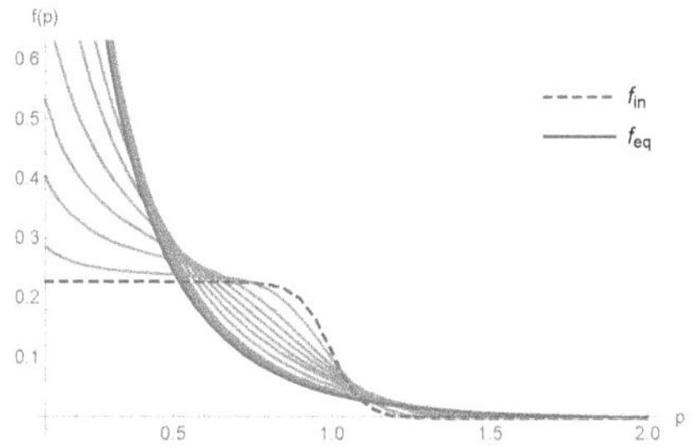

Figure 3. Evolution of the initial condition according to the Fokker-Planck scheme. The intermediate distribution functions shown are for times $\tau \in \{1, 3, 5, 7.5, 11, 15.5, 25.5, 50, 70, 100\}$.

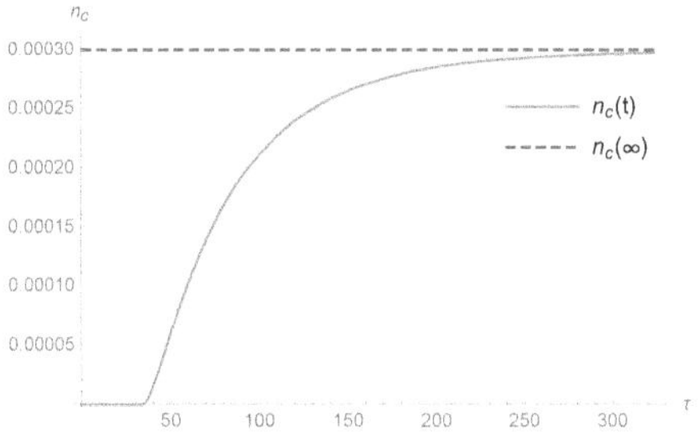

Figure 4. Corresponding evolution of the condensate for the system in Figure 3.

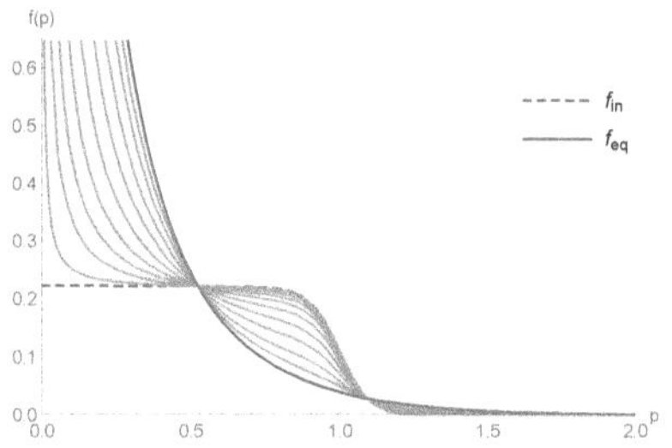

Figure 5. Evolution of the initial condition using the Relaxation Time Approximation. The relaxation time parameter is taken to be 40 in order to match the Fokker-Planck timescale; the intermediate distribution functions shown are for times $t \in \{0.5, 2, 4, 7, 12, 20, 32, 52, 80\}$.

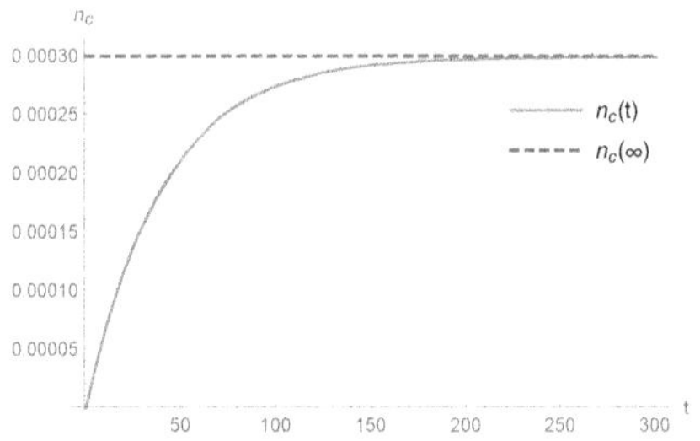

Figure 6. Corresponding evolution of the condensate for the system in Figure 5.

Generalizing from spherically symmetric to cylindrically symmetric initial conditions, we are able to explore the effects on anisotropy on the evolution of the distribution function. It is important to differentiate between isotropic distribution functions just boosted out of their rest frame and distribution functions that are "genuinely" anisotropic, i.e., even in their rest frame.

"Genuinely" anisotropic distributions are often parameterized in the form [14,15]

$$f_{\text{iso}}\left(\sqrt{\omega^2 + \xi p_z^2}\right) , \tag{19}$$

where $\xi > -1$ specifies the anisotropy. Similarly, we consider as a generalization of (18) initial conditions of the form

$$f(\omega, p_z) = f_0 \frac{\sqrt{1+\xi}}{e^{\left(\sqrt{\omega^2+\xi p_z^2}+bp_z-Q\right)/C}+1} , \tag{20}$$

where $\omega = |p|$, b is a boost parameter and the numerator is a normalization that is convenient with regard to the particle number density.

We extract the equilibration time by studying the entropy, evaluated towards final equilibrium. In particular we would like to compare it to the time taken for the initially anisotropic distribution function to isotropize. To this end, as a measure of the anisotropy of a distribution function, we define the "anisotropy parameter"

$$\alpha = \frac{T^{22}_{LRF}}{T^{33}_{LRF}} , \tag{21}$$

where $T^{\mu\nu}_{LRF}$ is the energy-momentum tensor in the local rest frame. In the rest frame, for a cylindrically symmetric distribution function with some anisotropy, $T^{11} = T^{22} = P_\perp$ is the transverse pressure of the fluid, while $T^{33} = P_z$ is the longitudinal pressure. For an isotropic distribution they are equal; thus the ratio α must also approach 1 as the system isotropizes.

In Figure 7 we plot the evolution of the normalized entropy and anisotropy parameters associated with an initial condition of form (20), with parameters $f_0 = 0.1, C = 0.05, \xi = b = 0.2$ and $Q = 1$. Figure 8 shows a log plot of this evolution.

From a fit, the gradients of the lines in Figure 7 are identical within the uncertainties, which corroborates that the rates of isotropization and equilibration are strongly correlated.

6. Discussion

In summary, we have developed an efficient numerical scheme to solve the relativistic Boltzmann equation for gluons in the small-scattering approximation under the assumption of spherically/cylindrically symmetric initial conditions and spatial homogeneity. Among our findings, we have reproduced results from [11] regarding the formation of a transient Bose-Einstein condensate state for overpopulated, spherically symmetric initial conditions. We have investigated the rate at which an anisotropic distribution function becomes isotropic and compared it to the rate of thermalization. Further, we have compared these results to the relaxation-time approximation to the Boltzmann equation.

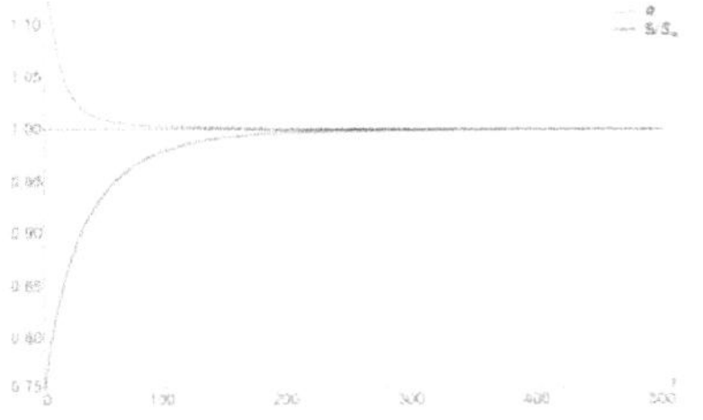

Figure 7. .Evolution of the normalized entropy and anisotropy parameters.

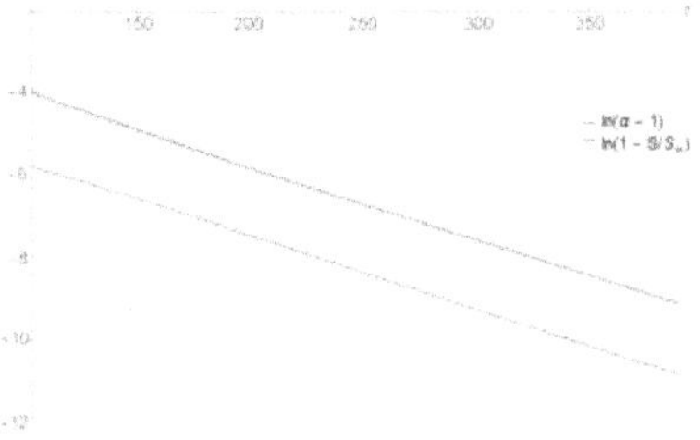

Figure 8. Linearized evolution of the normalized entropy and anisotropy parameters.

Possible directions for future work might include investigating the timescale of hydrodynamization (i.e., the time at which hydrodynamics becomes applicable). Following [16], it would be interesting to explore the relation between Bose-Einstein condensation and Kolmogorov turbulence in the relativistic case. Another follow-up would be to study the non-equilibrium attractor described by [17] for the relaxation-time approximation, and see if a similar phenomenon can be observed in the Fokker-Planck approximation.

Scope for further extension of our scheme exists, and such an extension is planned. In particular, it is desirable to extend the scheme to remove the assumption of spatial homogeneity and describe systems without symmetry assumptions in which the above scheme would essentially represent a single spatial cell. A challenge is the fact that the computational complexity scales geometrically with each additional degree of freedom - the so-called "curse of dimensionality". (Boltzmann equation solvers as well as hydro-codes typically rely on assumptions of symmetry, and for good reason).

Author Contributions: This work is based on the M.Sc. thesis written by B.H. and supervised by A.P.

Funding: This research was funded by NiTheP.

Acknowledgments: The authors are grateful for conversations and coding assistance provided by Nicole Moodley, Will Grunow and Greg Jackson.

Conflicts of Interest: The authors declare no conflict of interest.

Appendix A. Derivation of the Current

Here we present a derivation of the Fokker-Planck current $\mathcal{J}$ given in Equation (9). Recall expression (7) for the current, where the constant prefactor is absorbed into τ,

$$\mathcal{J}_i(\boldsymbol{p}) = f_p \bar{f}_p \int \mathcal{V}_{ij} \nabla^j_k f_k - \nabla^j_p f_p \int \mathcal{V}_{ij} f_k \bar{f}_k \,. \tag{A1}$$

These two integrals correspond to a vector quantity

$$J_i \equiv \int \mathcal{V}_{ij} \nabla^j_k f_k \tag{A2}$$

and a tensor quantity

$$\mathbb{J}_{ij} = \int \mathcal{V}_{ij} f_k \bar{f}_k \,, \tag{A3}$$

each being a functional of the distribution function f. The current (A1) is defined for a specific momentum $\boldsymbol{p}$. For this $\boldsymbol{p}$ we then integrate over all possible values of $\boldsymbol{k}$. We can represent the $\mathcal{V}_{ij}$ tensor (8) as a matrix,

$$\mathcal{V}_{ij} = \begin{pmatrix} 1 + v_x w_x - v_y w_y - v_z w_z & v_y w_x + v_x w_y & v_z w_x + v_x w_z \\ v_y w_x + v_x w_y & 1 - v_x w_x + v_y w_y - v_z w_z & v_z w_y + v_y w_z \\ v_z w_x + v_x w_z & v_z w_y + v_y w_z & 1 - v_x w_x - v_y w_y + v_z w_z \end{pmatrix} . \tag{A4}$$

Thus we find for the components of the first integral in (A1),

$$
\begin{aligned}
\mathcal{V}_{1j}\nabla_k^j f_k &= \begin{pmatrix} 1+v_xw_x-v_yw_y-v_zw_z, & v_yw_x+v_xw_y, & v_zw_x+v_xw_z \end{pmatrix} \begin{pmatrix} \frac{\partial f_k}{\partial k_x} \\ \frac{\partial f_k}{\partial k_y} \\ \frac{\partial f_k}{\partial k_z} \end{pmatrix} \\
&= (1+v_xw_x-v_yw_y-v_zw_z)\frac{\partial f_k}{\partial k_x} + (v_yw_x+v_xw_y)\frac{\partial f_k}{\partial k_y} + (v_zw_x+v_xw_z)\frac{\partial f_k}{\partial k_z}\,, \\
\mathcal{V}_{2j}\nabla_k^j f_k &= \begin{pmatrix} v_yw_x+v_xw_y, & 1-v_xw_x+v_yw_y-v_zw_z, & v_zw_y+v_yw_z \end{pmatrix} \begin{pmatrix} \frac{\partial f_k}{\partial k_x} \\ \frac{\partial f_k}{\partial k_y} \\ \frac{\partial f_k}{\partial k_z} \end{pmatrix} \\
&= (v_yw_x+v_xw_y)\frac{\partial f_k}{\partial k_x} + (1-v_xw_x+v_yw_y-v_zw_z)\frac{\partial f_k}{\partial k_y} + (v_zw_y+v_yw_z)\frac{\partial f_k}{\partial k_z}\,, \\
\mathcal{V}_{3j}\nabla_k^j f_k &= \begin{pmatrix} v_zw_x+v_xw_z, & v_zw_y+v_yw_z, & 1-v_xw_x-v_yw_y+v_zw_z \end{pmatrix} \begin{pmatrix} \frac{\partial f_k}{\partial k_x} \\ \frac{\partial f_k}{\partial k_y} \\ \frac{\partial f_k}{\partial k_z} \end{pmatrix} \\
&= (v_zw_x+v_xw_z)\frac{\partial f_k}{\partial k_x} + (v_zw_y+v_yw_z)\frac{\partial f_k}{\partial k_y} + (1-v_xw_x-v_yw_y+v_zw_z)\frac{\partial f_k}{\partial k_z}
\end{aligned}
\tag{A5}
$$

Note that $\int_{-\infty}^{\infty} dk_i \frac{\partial f_k}{\partial k_i} = f_k|_{-\infty}^{\infty} = 0$ since the distribution function vanishes for large momenta. Thus only terms of $\int \frac{k_i}{k}\frac{\partial f_k}{\partial k_i}$ survive. Integrating by parts we have

$$
\begin{aligned}
\int_{-\infty}^{\infty} dk_x \frac{k_x}{\sqrt{k_x^2+k_y^2+k_z^2}}\frac{\partial f_k}{\partial k_x} &= \frac{k_x}{k} f_k|_{-\infty}^{\infty} - \int_{-\infty}^{\infty} dk_x \left(-\frac{k_x^2}{k^3}+\frac{1}{k}\right) f_k \\
&= \int_{-\infty}^{\infty} dk_x \left(\frac{k_x^2}{k^3}-\frac{1}{k}\right) f_k\,,
\end{aligned}
\tag{A6}
$$

with corresponding expressions for k_y and k_z.

Altogether, the non-vanishing terms of J_x are

$$
\begin{aligned}
J_x &= w_x \int v_x\frac{\partial f_k}{\partial k_x} + v_y\frac{\partial f_k}{\partial k_y} + v_z\frac{\partial f_k}{\partial k_z} \\
&= w_x \int \left(\frac{k_x^2+k_y^2+k_z^2}{k^3} - \frac{3}{k}\right) f_k \\
&= -w_x \int \frac{2}{k} f_k\,.
\end{aligned}
\tag{A7}
$$

Similarly

$$
\begin{aligned}
J_y &= -w_y \int \frac{2}{k} f_k\,, \\
J_z &= -w_z \int \frac{2}{k} f_k\,.
\end{aligned}
\tag{A8}
$$

Defining

$$
I_b \equiv \int \frac{2}{k} f_k\,, \tag{A9}
$$

we can simply write

$$
J = \frac{\boldsymbol{p}}{p} I_b\,. \tag{A10}
$$

Now consider the tensor term $\mathbb{J}_{ij}$ (A3). Expanding $\mathbb{J}_{ij}\nabla^j_p f_p$ we have

$$\begin{aligned}
\mathbb{J}_{1j}\nabla^j_p f_p &= \int \begin{pmatrix} 1+v_x w_x - v_y w_y - v_z w_z, & v_y w_x + v_x w_y, & v_z w_x + v_x w_z \end{pmatrix} \begin{pmatrix} \frac{\partial f_p}{\partial p_x} \\ \frac{\partial f_p}{\partial p_y} \\ \frac{\partial f_p}{\partial p_z} \end{pmatrix} f_k \bar{f}_k \\
&= \frac{\partial f_p}{\partial p_x}\int (1+v_x w_x - v_y w_y - v_z w_z) f_k \bar{f}_k + \frac{\partial f_p}{\partial p_y}\int (v_y w_x + v_x w_y) f_k \bar{f}_k \\
&+ \frac{\partial f_p}{\partial p_z}\int (v_z w_x + v_x w_z) f_k \bar{f}_k \,.
\end{aligned} \tag{A11}$$

We can tidy this expression by defining

$$\begin{aligned}
I_a &\equiv \int f_k \bar{f}_k \,, \\
\mathcal{I}_i &\equiv \int v_i f_k \bar{f}_k \,,
\end{aligned} \tag{A12}$$

and writing $w_i = p_i/p$. As it is no longer necessary to differentiate between f_p and f_k, we drop the subscript. Then

$$\begin{aligned}
\mathbb{J}_{1j}\nabla^j_p f_p &= \frac{\partial f_p}{\partial p_x}\left(I_a + \frac{p_x}{p}\mathcal{I}_x - \frac{p_y}{p}\mathcal{I}_y - \frac{p_z}{p}\mathcal{I}_z\right) + \frac{\partial f_p}{\partial p_y}\left(\frac{p_x}{p}\mathcal{I}_y + \frac{p_y}{p}\mathcal{I}_x\right) \\
&+ \frac{\partial f_p}{\partial p_z}\left(\frac{p_z}{p}\mathcal{I}_x + \frac{p_x}{p}\mathcal{I}_z\right) \\
&= \frac{\partial f_p}{\partial p_x} I_a + \left(\frac{p_x}{p}\frac{\partial f_p}{\partial p_x} + \frac{p_y}{p}\frac{\partial f_p}{\partial p_y} + \frac{p_z}{p}\frac{\partial f_p}{\partial p_z}\right)\mathcal{I}_x + \left(\frac{p_x}{p}\frac{\partial f_p}{\partial p_y} - \frac{p_y}{p}\frac{\partial f_p}{\partial p_x}\right)\mathcal{I}_y \\
&+ \left(\frac{p_x}{p}\frac{\partial f_p}{\partial p_z} - \frac{p_z}{p}\frac{\partial f_p}{\partial p_x}\right)\mathcal{I}_z \,,
\end{aligned} \tag{A13}$$

and similarly

$$\begin{aligned}
\mathbb{J}_{2j}\nabla^j_p f_p &= \frac{\partial f_p}{\partial p_y} I_a + \left(\frac{p_y}{p}\frac{\partial f_p}{\partial p_x} - \frac{p_x}{p}\frac{\partial f_p}{\partial p_y}\right)\mathcal{I}_x + \left(\frac{p_x}{p}\frac{\partial f_p}{\partial p_x} + \frac{p_y}{p}\frac{\partial f_p}{\partial p_y} + \frac{p_z}{p}\frac{\partial f_p}{\partial p_z}\right)\mathcal{I}_y \\
&+ \left(\frac{p_y}{p}\frac{\partial f_p}{\partial p_z} - \frac{p_z}{p}\frac{\partial f_p}{\partial p_y}\right)\mathcal{I}_z \,,
\end{aligned} \tag{A14}$$

and

$$\begin{aligned}
\mathbb{J}_{3j}\nabla^j_p f_p &= \frac{\partial f_p}{\partial p_z} I_a + \left(\frac{p_z}{p}\frac{\partial f_p}{\partial p_x} - \frac{p_x}{p}\frac{\partial f_p}{\partial p_z}\right)\mathcal{I}_x + \left(\frac{p_z}{p}\frac{\partial f_p}{\partial p_y} - \frac{p_y}{p}\frac{\partial f_p}{\partial p_z}\right)\mathcal{I}_y \\
&+ \left(\frac{p_x}{p}\frac{\partial f_p}{\partial p_x} + \frac{p_y}{p}\frac{\partial f_p}{\partial p_y} + \frac{p_z}{p}\frac{\partial f_p}{\partial p_z}\right)\mathcal{I}_z \,.
\end{aligned} \tag{A15}$$

We can write down a vector expression for $\mathbb{J}_{ij}\nabla^j_p f_p$ by inspection as $I_a \boldsymbol{\nabla}_p f + (\boldsymbol{\nabla}_p f \cdot \hat{\boldsymbol{p}})\boldsymbol{\mathcal{I}} + (\boldsymbol{\nabla}_p f \times \hat{\boldsymbol{p}}) \times \boldsymbol{\mathcal{I}}$.

Altogether we have the complete expression for the current,

$$\boldsymbol{\mathcal{J}}(\boldsymbol{p}) = I_a \boldsymbol{\nabla}_p f + I_b f \bar{f} \hat{\boldsymbol{p}} + (\boldsymbol{\nabla}_p f \cdot \hat{\boldsymbol{p}})\boldsymbol{\mathcal{I}} + (\boldsymbol{\nabla}_p f \times \hat{\boldsymbol{p}}) \times \boldsymbol{\mathcal{I}} \,. \tag{A16}$$

References

1. Gelis, F. The early stages of a high energy heavy ion collision. *J. Phys. Conf. Ser.* **2012**, *381*, 012021. [CrossRef]
2. McLerran, L.; Venugopalan, R. Computing Quark and Gluon Distribution Functions for Very Large Nuclei. *Phys. Rev. D* **1994**, *49*, 2233–2241. [CrossRef]
3. Weigert, H. Evolution at small x_bj: The Color Glass Condensate. *Prog. Part. Nucl. Phys.* **2005**, *55*, 461–565.

4. Gelis, F. Initial State and Thermalization in the Color Glass Condensate Framework. In *Quark–Gluon Plasma 5*; World Scientific: Singapore, 2016; pp. 67–129, ISBN 9789814663700.
5. Heinz, U.W.; Kolb, P.F. Early thermalization at RHIC. *Nucl. Phys. A* **2002**, 702, 269–280. [CrossRef]
6. Romatschke, P.; Romatschke, U. Viscosity Information from Relativistic Nuclear Collisions: How Perfect is the Fluid Observed at RHIC? *Phys. Rev. Lett.* **2007**, 99, 172301. [CrossRef] [PubMed]
7. Ollitrault, J.-Y. Relativistic hydrodynamics for heavy-ion collisions. *Eur. J. Phys.* **2008**, *29*, 275–302. [CrossRef]
8. Romatschke, P.; Romatschke, U. Relativistic Fluid Dynamics In and Out of Equilibrium—Ten Years of Progress in Theory and Numerical Simulations of Nuclear Collisions. *arXiv* **2017**, arXiv:1712.05815.
9. Biro, T.S.; van Doorn, E.; Mueller, B.; Thoma, M.H.; Wang, X.N. Parton Equilibration in Relativistic Heavy Ion Collisions. *Phys. Rev. C* **1993**, 48, 1275–1284. [CrossRef]
10. van der Schee, W. Equilibration and hydrodynamics at strong and weak coupling. *Nucl. Phys. A* **2017**, 967, 74–80.
11. Blaizot, J.-P.; Liao, J.; McLerran, L. Gluon transport equation in the small angle approximation and the onset of Bose–Einstein condensation. *Nucl. Phys. A* **2013**, *920*, 58–77. [CrossRef]
12. Blaizot, J.-P.; Liao, J.; Mehtar-Tani, Y. The thermalization of soft modes in non-expanding isotropic quark gluon plasmas. *Nucl. Phys. A* **2017**, *961*, 37–67. [CrossRef]
13. Giulini, D. *Luciano Rezzolla and Olindo Zanotti: Relativistic Hydrodynamics*; Oxford University Press: Oxford, UK, 2013; 752p, ISBN 978-0-19-852890-6.
14. Romatschke, P.; Strickland, M. Collective Modes of an Anisotropic Quark-Gluon Plasma. *Phys. Rev. D* **2003**, *68*, 036004. [CrossRef]
15. Romatschke, P.; Strickland, M. Collective modes of an Anisotropic Quark-Gluon Plasma II. *Phys. Rev. D* **2004**, *70*, 116006. [CrossRef]
16. Semikoz, D.V.; Tkachev, I.I. Condensation of bosons in kinetic regime. *Phys. Rev. D* **1997**, 55, 489–502. [CrossRef]
17. Strickland, M. The non-equilibrium attractor for kinetic theory in relaxation time approximation. *J. High Energy Phys.* **2018**, *2018*, 128. [CrossRef]

particles

MDPI

Communication

Low-Momentum Pion Enhancement from Schematic Hadronization of a Gluon-Saturated Initial State

Elizaveta Nazarova [1,2], Łukasz Juchnowski [2], David Blaschke [2,3,4,*] and Tobias Fischer [2]

1 Skobeltsyn Institute of Nuclear Physics, Lomonosov Moscow State University, RU-119991 Moscow, Russia; elizaveta.nazarova@cern.ch
2 Institute of Theoretical Physics, University of Wrocław, 50-204 Wrocław, Poland; lukasz.juchnowski@gmail.com (Ł.J.); tobias.fischer@ift.uni.wroc.pl (T.F.)
3 Bogoliubov Laboratory for Theoretical Physics, JINR Dubna, 141980 Dubna, Russia
4 Department of Theoretical Nuclear Physics, National Research Nuclear University (MEPhI), 115409 Moscow, Russia
* Correspondence: david.blaschke@gmail.com

Received: 18 December 2018; Accepted: 6 March 2019; Published: 11 March 2019

Abstract: We study the particle production in the early stage of the ultrarelativistic heavy-ion collisions. To this end the Boltzmann kinetic equations for gluons and pions with elastic rescattering are considered together with a simple model for the parton-hadron conversion process (hadronisation). It is shown that the overpopulation of the gluon phase space in the initial state leads to an intermediate stage of Bose enhancement in the low-momentum gluon sector which due to the gluon-pion conversion process is then reflected in the final distribution function of pions. This pattern is very similar to the experimental finding of a low-momentum pion enhancement in the ALICE experiment at the CERN Large Hadron Collider (LHC). Relations to the thermal statistical model of hadron production and the phenomenon of thermal and chemical freeze-out are discussed in this context.

Keywords: Boltzmann equation; gluon saturation; pion enhancement; ALICE; LHC; thermalization; hadronization

1. Introduction

One of the issues which can be addressed by the kinetic approach is the question of a low-momentum pion enhancement in heavy ion collisions [1]. There are several solutions proposed to explain this effect as, e.g., the hadronization and freeze-out in a chemical non-equilibrium [2–4], the separate freeze-out for strange particles [5], Bose-Einstein condensate (BEC) of pions [6–10], established by elastic rescattering in the final stage [10,11]. However, none of them are commonly accepted yet [8]. We believe, an explanation linked to the presence of non-equilibrium physics and a precursor of pion condensation in heavy ion collisions should be the favorable one, especially after the recent analysis of particle correlations performed by the ALICE collaboration is showing a coherent fraction of charged π-meson emission that is reaching 23% [1,9]. Such formation of a Bose condensate is usually described by the introduction of additional non-equilibrium parameters to the statistical approach [10,12], see also [2,8,13].

An alternative scheme may rely on the Boltzmann kinetic equation for gluons and pions with elastic rescattering and a simple model for the parton-hadron conversion process (hadronisation). There are deep physical reasons for the non-equilibrium and pion condensation at the Large Hadron Collider (LHC). It can be due to fast expansion and overcooling of the quark-gluon plasma (QGP), or due to gluon condensation in the color glass condensate (CGC) initial state preceeding subsequent hadronization of the low-momentum gluons into low-momentum pions [8]. A scenario with an initial state dominated by gluons which subsequently hadronize, eventually via a quarkless evolution through a first order phase transition, has recently been considered in Ref. [14].

In this short communication we investigate the idea that a certain oversaturation of the purely gluonic initial state could lead by elastic rescattering to a precursor of Bose condensation in the gluon sector in the form of a low-momentum gluon enhancement which, however, should be depopulated by the gluon-pion conversion process and thus appear as low-p pion enhancement in the pion sector. The gluon-pion conversion process is assumed with a constant matrix element which may be pictured as the local limit of a quark one-loop diagram for the case of large quark mass (quark confinement). We demonstrate the evolution of the coupled gluon and pion distribution functions in this case within a schematic model of coupled kinetic equations.

2. Kinetic Equation Approach to Thermalization and Hadronization

We start with the kinetic equation in the form of a Boltzmann-Nordheim equation, which for a single particle distribution function $f = f(\vec{x}, \vec{p}, t)$ can be written as

$$\frac{\mathrm{d}f}{\mathrm{d}t} = C[f], \tag{1}$$

where

$$\frac{\mathrm{d}f}{\mathrm{d}t} = \frac{\partial f}{\partial \vec{x}}\frac{\mathrm{d}\vec{x}}{\mathrm{d}t} + \frac{\partial f}{\partial \vec{p}}\frac{\mathrm{d}\vec{p}}{\mathrm{d}t} + \frac{\partial f}{\partial t} \tag{2}$$

and $C[f]$ represents the collision integral. In this study we restrict ourselves to the case of a uniform ($\partial f/\partial \vec{x} = 0$) system in a non-expanding box ($\vec{F} = \mathrm{d}\vec{p}/\mathrm{d}t = 0$), therefore only the explicit time-dependence remains: $\mathrm{d}f/\mathrm{d}t = \partial f/\partial t \equiv \partial_t f$.

On the other hand, the collision integral for the $1+2 \to 3+4$ process is defined as:

$$C[f(t, \vec{p}_1)] = \frac{(2\pi)^4}{2E_1} \int \delta^4(\sum_i P_i)|M|^2 F[f] \prod_{k=2}^{4} \frac{\mathrm{d}^3\vec{p}_k}{(2\pi)^3 2E_k}, \tag{3}$$

so that the Equation (1) will take the following form:

$$\partial_t f(t, \vec{p}_1) = \frac{(2\pi)^4}{2E_1} \int \delta^4(\sum_i P_i)|M|^2 F[f] \prod_{k=2}^{4} \frac{\mathrm{d}^3\vec{p}_k}{(2\pi)^3 2E_k}, \tag{4}$$

describing elastic scattering of the system of particles of one type, e.g., gluons. Here for the process $1+2 \to 3+4$ we define as f_i the distribution function of particle i with 4-momentum $P_i = (E_i, \vec{p}_i)$, $|M|$ as the transition amplitude of the process, and $F[f] = (1+f_1)(1+f_2)f_3 f_4 - f_1 f_2 (1+f_3)(1+f_4)$ represents the gain and loss terms in the collision integral. In the current study we consider the distribution function to be isotropic through the whole evolution. Moreover, the matrix elements of all the processes involved are taken to be constant:

$$|M|_{12\to 34} = \mathrm{const}, \tag{5}$$

following [11], where the case of a system of pions was considered. Albeit this work describes the academic study with only constant matrix elements, the ongoing project involving momentum- and angle-dependent transition amplitudes is discussed in the Section 4.

As we consider an isotropic, uniform, non-expanding system and constant matrix elements for the processes, and taking into account the 4-momentum conservation ($P_1 + P_2 = P_3 + P_4$), the Equation (4) takes the form

$$\partial_t f(\varepsilon_1) = \frac{|M|^2}{64\pi^3\varepsilon_1} \int\int d\varepsilon_3 d\varepsilon_4 DF[f], \tag{6}$$

where $D = \min\{p_1, p_2, p_3, p_4\}$ and p_i are now the radial components of the three-momenta. Details of the derivation are shown in the Appendix A. For future investigations it is helpful to rewrite the Equation (6) in terms of a momentum integration, as we would like to extend the approach to the angle-dependent collision integral, as well as to non-uniform systems. Therefore, in the current work we use the following formula:

$$\partial_t f(p_1) = \frac{|M|^2}{64\pi^3\varepsilon_1} \int\int \frac{p_3 p_4}{\varepsilon_3\varepsilon_4} dp_3 dp_4 DF[f]. \tag{7}$$

Obviously, elastic scattering is necessary but not sufficient to achieve low-p pion enhancement. The second required process which needs to be accounted for is hadronization. In this exploratory work we connect the gluon sector directly with the pion one. For such system there are three contributing channels: $\pi\pi \to \pi\pi$, $gg \to gg$, and $gg \leftrightarrow \pi\pi$. Therefore at the end we have a coupled system of equations:

$$\begin{aligned}\frac{\partial f_\pi}{\partial t}(t, \vec{p}_1) &= \int\int \frac{|M_{\pi\pi\to\pi\pi}|^2}{64\pi^3\varepsilon_1} \frac{p_3 p_4}{\varepsilon_3\varepsilon_4} dp_3 dp_4 DF[f_\pi] \\ &+ (1 + f_\pi(t, p_1)) \int\int \frac{|M_{gg\to\pi\pi}|^2}{64\pi^3\varepsilon_1} \frac{p_3 p_4}{\varepsilon_3\varepsilon_4} dp_3 dp_4 D\,(1 + f_\pi(t, p_2))\, f_g(t, p_3) f_g(t, p_4) \\ &- f_\pi(t, p_1) \int\int \frac{|M_{\pi\pi\to gg}|^2}{64\pi^3\varepsilon_1} \frac{p_3 p_4}{\varepsilon_3\varepsilon_4} dp_3 dp_4 D f_\pi(t, p_2)\,(1 + f_g(t, p_3))\,(1 + f_g(t, p_4))\end{aligned} \tag{8a}$$

$$\begin{aligned}\frac{\partial f_g}{\partial t}(t, \vec{p}_1) &= \int\int \frac{|M_{gg\to gg}|^2}{64\pi^3\varepsilon_1} \frac{p_3 p_4}{\varepsilon_3\varepsilon_4} dp_3 dp_4 DF[f_g] \\ &+ (1 + f_g(t, p_1)) \int\int \frac{|M_{\pi\pi\to gg}|^2}{64\pi^3\varepsilon_1} \frac{p_3 p_4}{\varepsilon_3\varepsilon_4} dp_3 dp_4 D\,(1 + f_g(t, p_2))\, f_\pi(t, p_3) f_\pi(t, p_4) \\ &- f_g(t, p_1) \int\int \frac{|M_{gg\to\pi\pi}|^2}{64\pi^3\varepsilon_1} \frac{p_3 p_4}{\varepsilon_3\varepsilon_4} dp_3 dp_4 D f_g(t, p_2)\,(1 + f_\pi(t, p_3))\,(1 + f_\pi(t, p_4))\end{aligned} \tag{8b}$$

where $M_{gg\to\pi\pi}$ and $M_{\pi\pi\to gg}$ are matrices for hadronization channels. Note, that due to the momentum conservation $p_2 = p_3 + p_4 - p_1$ in Equation (8). In this study we set $M_{\pi\pi\to gg} = 0$, which is motivated by the threshold for this process due to the large value of the gluon mass: $m_g = 0.7$ GeV. The value of $M_{gg\to\pi\pi}$ is set to be constant and should be seen as an academic example.

As the initial condition of the system we take an oversaturated gluon distribution given by a step-like function [15,16] inspired by the CGC picture of the initial state which is assumed to have no pions

$$f_\pi(t, p)\Big|_{t=0} = 0, \qquad f_g(t, p)\Big|_{t=0} = f_0\,\theta(1 - p/Q_s). \tag{9}$$

By Q_s we denote the saturation scale. However, in order to avoid numerical problems that would occur with the step-function distribution, we use instead the following smooth function [15]

$$f_g(t,p)\Big|_{t=0} = f_0\left[\theta(1-p/Q_s)+\theta(p/Q_s-1)e^{-a\,(p/Q_s-1)^2}\right], \quad a=10 \tag{10}$$

to define the initial conditions.

We keep our model simple and therefore do not introduce an extra timescale for the start of hadronization. However, we keep in mind that the underlying microphysical process is, e.g., a quark-box diagram, which consists of the Breit-Wheeler type process of $2g \rightarrow q\bar{q}$ and subsequent hadronization cross section $q\bar{q} \rightarrow \pi\pi$. In the future we plan to investigate the problem of the gluon-to-pion conversion in detail, for instance within a Nambu–Jona-Lasinio model [17–20] and/or by exploiting dynamical schemes of hadronization that would address the confinement aspect as well [21–24].

3. Results

In Figure 1 we show the evolution of the gluon distribution function from a CGC motivated initial (over-)saturated gluon state to a thermal distribution due to elastic scattering according to the $gg \rightarrow gg$ process. The timescale to reach a thermalized final state is of the order of $t_{\mathrm{final}} \sim 250$ fm/c and thus exceeds the typical duration evolution towards freeze-out of the fireball created in a heavy-ion collision. This is mainly due to the fact that the value of the matrix element taken in this example calculation as $|M| = 4.5$ is unrealistically small.

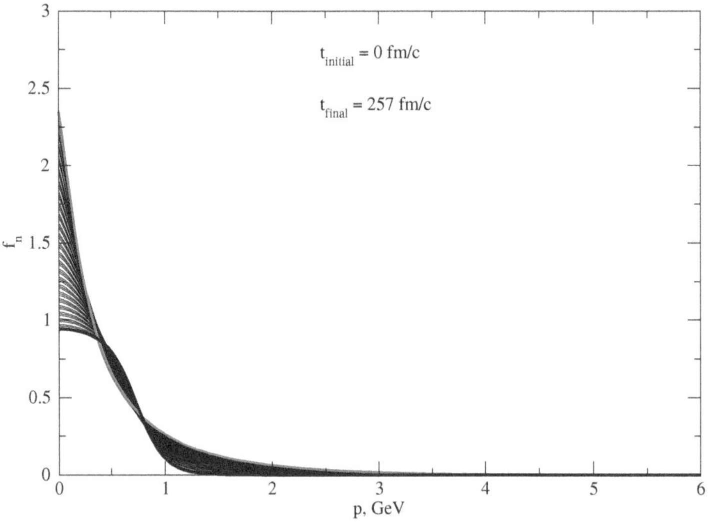

Figure 1. (Color online) The evolution of gluon distribution function $f(p)$ with time in a system of massive gluons ($m = 0.7$ GeV). The final distribution is shown as a bold red line, while the initial function is drawn as a bold black line. Thin black lines represent the intermediate stages of the gluon distribution function. The final time of the evolution represents the point when the pion distribution reaches equilibrium.

In Figure 2 we show the same evolution of the gluon distribution function for three different values of the matrix element. The value $M = 140$ leads to a thermalization time scale which nicely corresponds to the result of a calculation by Shuryak [25].

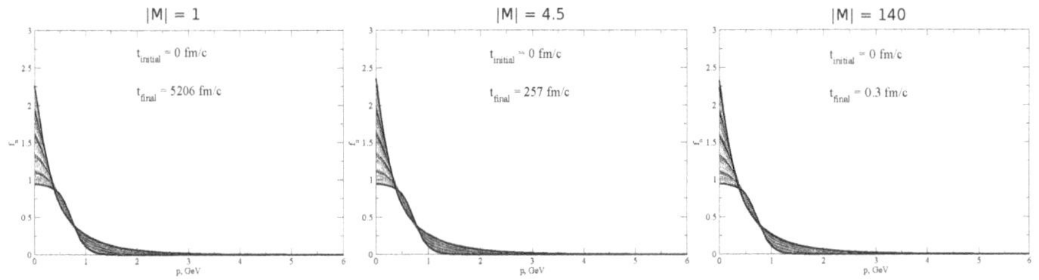

Figure 2. (Color online) Same as Figure 1 for different matrix elements $|M| = 1, 4.5, 140$.

When the coupling to the pion sector is switched on, the gluon conversion proceeds and the initially empty pion phase space gets populated at the expense of the gluon one. Due to the relation of the gluon and pion masses the reverse process (the pion annihilation to two gluons) does not practically take place. In Figure 3 the evolution from the initially pure gluon saturated state to the thermal pion state without gluons is shown. The pion distribution shows clearly the low-momentum enhancement typical for a precursor of Bose condensation. This is the fact observed in the ALICE experiment at CERN for which we wanted to give a qualitative explanation with the simple kinetic model presented here. It should be noted that here we used as a test the equal values for the three transition amplitudes: $|M_{gg\to gg}| = |M_{\pi\pi\to\pi\pi}| = |M_{gg\to\pi\pi}| = 4.5$.

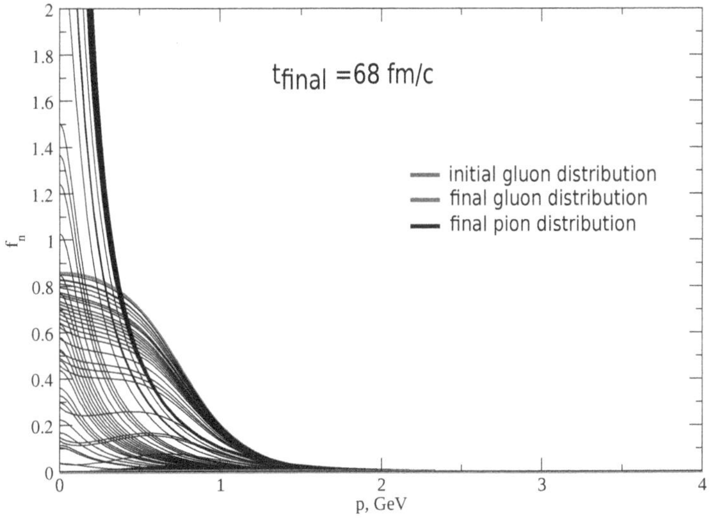

Figure 3. (Color online) The evolution of pion ($m = 0.14$ GeV) and gluon ($m = 0.7$ GeV) distribution functions $f(p)$ with time in a coupled pion-gluon system. Blue line represents the initial gluon distribution, while the final distributions are shown as bold black and red lines for pion and gluon distribution functions, respectively. Thin black lines represent the intermediate stages of the distribution functions. The final time of the evolution represents the point when the pion distribution reaches equilibrium.

Our simplified model shows, under the assumption of gluon dominance in the initial state, the quarkless evolution of the system towards a pion gas with low-momentum pion enhancement as a precursor of Bose condensation. According to (8) both particle species (gluons and pions) undergo two main processes: conversion and elastic scattering. Both of them are responsible for low-momentum (low-p) pion enhancement.

The fist process turns π-mesons to gluons and vice versa and its rate is defined by two matrix elements $M_{\pi\pi\to gg}$, $M_{gg\to\pi\pi}$, which in the simplest case considered here are constant numbers. Particle conversion can take place only when energy of incoming particles is at least equal to mass of outgoing ones. Consequently, in case of massless gluons kinematics restricts $gg \to \pi\pi$ reaction to higher energy region of a spectrum, making the whole process slow.

The impact of the second process (elastic scattering) is more subtle. It lowers momentum of particles through subsequent collisions, leading them to "pile-up" near zero momentum mode. The effect is especially strong for bosons due to the statistical factor $(1 + f_i)$ in (8) and allows pre-condensate formation even before thermalization. In normal circumstances for long enough times the distribution should become an equilibrium Bose function. However, in our model massive gluons undergo a complete conversion to pions before thermalization because $m_g > m_\pi$ ($m_g = 0.7$ GeV, while $m_\pi = 0.14$ GeV).

4. Discussion

The present model, albeit quite simple, shows the formation of the pion condensation precursor emerging from an oversaturated purely gluonic state. The process takes place before the system reaches equilibrium. The model can be improved by the use of non-constant matrix elements and thus taking into account scattering angle in collision kinematics. Such an improved model would allow us to discuss the different scales and their evolution, e.g., the Debye scale, the UV and IR scale, see Refs. [7,11,15,26].

These improved matrix elements should also bear the confining aspects of gluon-gluon interactions which ultimately should be responsible for the absence of gluons from the final state. The assumption of a constant gluon mass, exceeding the value of the pion mass is a rather schematic realization of this concept which provides ample room for improvement. Here it would be beneficial to make a comparison with the study in Ref. [15], where a system of massless gluons undergoes the evolution due to elastic scattering with similar restrictions as used in the current paper. However, the Equation (7) will no longer be valid in the case of non-constant matrix elements and angle-dependence, and thus will need to be rederived.

Another room for advancement lies in direct handling of the kinetics of Bose condensation (see, e.g., Ref. [10]). One way to do that is the separation of the distribution function into two parts:

$$\tilde{f}_\pi(p) = f_\pi(p) + (2\pi)^3 n_c^\pi \delta(p) \tag{11}$$

$$\tilde{f}_g(p) = f_g(p) + (2\pi)^3 n_c^g \delta(p) \tag{12}$$

where the first term represents the "gas" and the second describes BEC. This ansatz has been discussed for the oversaturated pion gas in Ref. [11] and recently also for the gluon plasma in Ref. [27]. We hope to achieve manifest energy and particle number conservation with such an improved formulation of the particle kinetics in the presence or precursory development of a Bose condensate in the system.

The model can be extended towards a more realistic description of a hadronizing gluon-dominated initial state in high-energy heavy-ion collisions by including more hadronic species as they are observed in those experiments in good agreement with the thermal statistical model [28]. This calls then for an extension of the collision integrals in our kinetic model to other classes of processes than just $2 \to 2$ processes as, e.g., the three-meson conversion to a baryon-antibaryon pair and its reverse [29].

Last, but not least we want to mention that the assumed absence of dynamical quarks is only a simplifying assumption. In an improved model, their kinetics shall be coupled to that of the gluons and all considered hadron species. Their absence in the final state shall be realised due to a confining mechanism. The one already tested in the framework of a kinetic theory is the Gribov-Zwanziger confinement realized by an infrared-divergent selfenergy [22–24]. We shall come back to these issues in a subsequent, more elaborate work on the subject.

Author Contributions: The original conceptualization was done by D.B. and T.F., while E.N. and L.J. are responsible for the development of methodology, software, the formal analysis and preparation of the original draft. All of the authors (E.N., L.J., D.B., T.F.) contributed to reviewing and editing of the manuscript.

Funding: This research was funded by the Polish Narodowe Centrum Nauki under grant number UMO-2014/15/B/ST2/03752 (E.N., L.J., D.B.) and grant number UMO-2016/23/B/ST2/00720 (E.N.,T.F.).

Acknowledgments: We acknowledge discussions with Viktor Begun, Marcus Bleicher, Wojciech Florkowski, Carsten Greiner, Gerd Röpke, Ludwik Turko and Dmitry Voskresensky on the topic of the nonequilibrium nature of the pion distribution emerging from an oversaturated initial state. Further we thank Niels-Uwe Friedrich Bastian for his support in numerical and algebraic questions. Brent Harrison gave a nice presentation of his ongoing work with Andre Peshier on "Bose-Einstein Condensation from a Gluon Transport Equation" at the Symposium on "Nonequilibrium Phenomena in Strongly Correlated Systems" in Dubna, 16 April 2018, which inspired us to prepare this communication.

Conflicts of Interest: The authors declare no conflict of interest.

Appendix A. Collision Integral Derivation

Here we will simplify the collision integral (3):

$$C_1[f] = \frac{(2\pi)^4}{2E_1} \int \delta^4(\sum_i P_i)|M|^2 F[f] \prod_{k=2}^{4} \frac{d^3\vec{p}_k}{(2\pi)^3 2E_k} \tag{A1}$$

Using the identity:

$$\delta^3(\sum \vec{p}_i) = \int \exp\left(i(\vec{\lambda}, \vec{p}_1 + \vec{p}_2 - \vec{p}_3 - \vec{p}_4)\right) \cdot \frac{d^3\vec{\lambda}}{(2\pi)^3}, \tag{A2}$$

and separating the angle integrations:

$$d\vec{p}_i = d\varphi_i d\cos\theta_i p_i^2 dp_i = \varepsilon_i p_i d\Omega_i d\varepsilon_i \tag{A3}$$

the integral takes the following form:

$$C_1[f] = \frac{|M|^2}{64\pi^3\varepsilon_1} \int \delta(\varepsilon_1 + \varepsilon_2 - \varepsilon_3 - \varepsilon_4) D F[f] d\varepsilon_3 d\varepsilon_4 d\varepsilon_2, \tag{A4}$$

where D is defined as follows:

$$D = \frac{p_2 p_3 p_4}{64\pi^5} \int \lambda^2 d\lambda \int e^{i(\vec{p}_1,\vec{\lambda})} d\Omega_\lambda \int e^{i(\vec{p}_2,\vec{\lambda})} d\Omega_2 \int e^{i(\vec{p}_3,\vec{\lambda})} d\Omega_3 \int e^{i(\vec{p}_4,\vec{\lambda})} d\Omega_4 . \tag{A5}$$

Taking into account that

$$\begin{aligned} \int e^{i(\vec{p}_1,\vec{\lambda})} d\Omega_\lambda &= \int e^{i(p_1\lambda\cos\theta_\lambda)} d\Omega_\lambda = \int_0^{2\pi} d\varphi \int_{-1}^{1} d\cos\theta e^{i(p_1\lambda\cos\theta_\lambda)} = \\ &= \frac{2\pi}{ip_1\lambda} e^{ip_1\lambda x}\Big|_{x=-1}^{x=1} = \frac{2\pi}{p_1\lambda}\frac{e^{ip_1\lambda} - e^{-ip_1\lambda}}{2i} \cdot 2 = \frac{4\pi}{p_1\lambda}\sin(p_1\lambda) \end{aligned} \tag{A6}$$

we can rewrite D as:

$$D = \frac{4}{\pi p_1} \int \frac{d\lambda}{\lambda^2} \sin(p_1\lambda)\sin(p_2\lambda)\sin(p_3\lambda)\sin(p_4\lambda) \tag{A7}$$

Using the Fourier transformation:

$$
\begin{aligned}
-\sqrt{\frac{\pi}{2}} w \operatorname{Sign}(w) = \frac{1}{\sqrt{2\pi}} \int_{-\infty}^{\infty} \frac{1}{x^2} e^{iwx} \mathrm{d}x = \\
\frac{1}{\sqrt{2\pi}} \left(\int_0^{\infty} \frac{1}{x^2} e^{iwx} \mathrm{d}x + \int_0^{\infty} \frac{1}{(-x)^2} e^{-iwx} \mathrm{d}x \right) = \frac{1}{\sqrt{2\pi}} \int_0^{\infty} \frac{1}{x^2} \left(e^{iwx} + e^{-iwx} \right) \mathrm{d}x,
\end{aligned} \tag{A8}
$$

we can simplify the integral in the formula for D:

$$
\begin{aligned}
\mathrm{D} &= \frac{4}{\pi p_1} \int_0^{\infty} \frac{\mathrm{d}\lambda}{\lambda^2} \frac{e^{ip_1\lambda} - e^{-ip_1\lambda}}{2i} \frac{e^{ip_2\lambda} - e^{-ip_2\lambda}}{2i} \frac{e^{ip_3\lambda} - e^{-ip_3\lambda}}{2i} \frac{e^{ip_4\lambda} - e^{-ip_4\lambda}}{2i} = \\
&= \frac{1}{4\pi p_1} \int_0^{\infty} \frac{\mathrm{d}\lambda}{\lambda^2} \Big((e^{i\lambda(p_1+p_2)} - e^{i\lambda(p_2-p_1)} - -e^{i\lambda(p_1-p_2)} + e^{i\lambda(-p_1-p_2)})(e^{i\lambda(p_3+p_4)} - \\
&- e^{i\lambda(p_4-p_3)} - e^{i\lambda(p_3-p_4)} + e^{i\lambda(-p_3-p_4)}) \Big) = \\
&= \frac{1}{4\pi p_1} \int_0^{\infty} \frac{\mathrm{d}\lambda}{\lambda^2} \Big(e^{i\lambda(p_1+p_2+p_3+p_4)} + e^{-i\lambda(p_1+p_2+p_3+p_4)} - e^{i\lambda(p_3+p_4+p_2-p_1)} \\
&- e^{-i\lambda(p_3+p_4+p_2-p_1)} - e^{i\lambda(p_3+p_4+p_1-p_2)} - e^{-i\lambda(p_3+p_4+p_1-p_2)} + e^{i\lambda(p_3+p_4-p_1-p_2)} + \\
&+ e^{-i\lambda(p_3+p_4-p_1-p_2)} - e^{i\lambda(p_1+p_2+p_4-p_3)} - e^{-i\lambda(p_1+p_2+p_4-p_3)} + e^{i\lambda(p_4-p_3+p_2-p_1)} + \\
&+ e^{-i\lambda(p_4-p_3+p_2-p_1)} + e^{i\lambda(p_4-p_3+p_1-p_2)} + e^{-i\lambda(p_4-p_3+p_1-p_2)} - e^{i\lambda(p_4-p_3-p_1-p_2)} \\
&- e^{-i\lambda(p_4-p_3-p_1-p_2)} \Big) = \\
&= \frac{1}{4\pi p_1} (-\pi)(|p_1+p_2+p_3+p_4| - |p_3+p_4+p_2-p_1| - |p_3+p_4+p_1-p_2| \\
&+ |p_3+p_4-p_1-p_2| - |p_1+p_2+p_4-p_3| + |p_4-p_3+p_2-p_1| \\
&+ |p_4-p_3+p_1-p_2| - |p_4-p_3-p_1-p_2|) = \\
&= \frac{1}{4\pi p_1} (-\pi)(-4\min\{p_1,p_2,p_3,p_4\}) = \frac{\min\{p_1,p_2,p_3,p_4\}}{p_1}
\end{aligned} \tag{A9}
$$

The last step in this Equation (A9) (changing to the minimum function between the four momenta) can be easily done by checking one of the possibilities—for example, the case when $p_1 = \min\{p_1, p_2, p_3, p_4\}$ (or $p_1 < p_2 < p_3 < p_4$). Taking into account the 4-momentum conservation: $P_1 + P_2 = P_3 + P_4$, we get the final result:

$$
\mathrm{C}[f(\varepsilon_1)] = \frac{|M|^2}{64\pi^3 \varepsilon_1} \int \int \mathrm{d}\varepsilon_3 \mathrm{d}\varepsilon_4 DF[f] \tag{A10}
$$

where $D = \frac{1}{p_1} \min\{p_1, p_2, p_3, p_4\}$. In order to change the Formula (A10) to the integration over momentum, we can use the connection between energy and momentum in the relativistic case: $\varepsilon^2 = p^2 + m^2 \rightarrow \varepsilon \mathrm{d}\varepsilon = p \mathrm{d}p$, so that the Equation (A10) takes form:

$$
\mathrm{C}[f(p_1)] = \frac{|M|^2}{64\pi^3 \varepsilon_1} \int \int \frac{p_3 p_4}{\varepsilon_3 \varepsilon_4} \mathrm{d}p_3 \mathrm{d}p_4 DF[f]. \tag{A11}
$$

References

1. Abelev, B.B.; Adam, J.; Adamová, D.; Aggarwal, M.M.; Rinella, G.A.; Agnello, M.; Agocs, A.G.; Agostinelli, A.; Agrawal, N.; Ahammed, Z.; et al. Two- and three-pion quantum statistics correlations in Pb-Pb collisions at $\sqrt{s_{NN}} = 2.76$ TeV at the CERN Large Hadron Collider. *Phys. Rev. C* **2014**, *89*, 024911. [CrossRef]
2. Kataja, M.; Ruuskanen, P.V. Nonzero Chemical Potential and the Shape of the p_T Distribution of Hadrons in Heavy Ion Collisions. *Phys. Lett. B* **1990**, *243*, 181–184. [CrossRef]

3. Gavin, S.; Ruuskanen, P.V. Low p(T) pion enhancement from partial thermalization in nuclear collisions. *Phys. Lett. B* **1991**, *262*, 326–332. [CrossRef]
4. Begun, V. Thermal model for Pb+Pb collisions at $\sqrt{s_{NN}} = 2.76$ TeV with explicit treatment of hadronic ground states. *EPJ Web Conf.* **2015**, *97*, 00003. [CrossRef]
5. Begun, V.; Florkowski, W.; Rybczynski, M. Transverse-momentum spectra of strange particles produced in Pb+Pb collisions at $\sqrt{s_{\rm NN}} = 2.76$ TeV in the chemical non-equilibrium model. *Phys. Rev. C* **2014**, *90*, 054912. [CrossRef]
6. Begun, V.; Florkowski, W.; Rybczynski, M. Explanation of hadron transverse-momentum spectra in heavy-ion collisions at $\sqrt{s_{NN}} = 2.76$ TeV within chemical non-equilibrium statistical hadronization model. *Phys. Rev. C* **2014**, *90*, 014906. [CrossRef]
7. Blaizot, J.P.; Gelis, F.; Liao, J.F.; McLerran, L.; Venugopalan, R. Bose–Einstein Condensation and Thermalization of the Quark Gluon Plasma. *Nucl. Phys. A* **2012**, *873*, 68–80. [CrossRef]
8. Begun, V.V. High temperature Bose-Einstein condensation. *EPJ Web Conf.* **2016**, *126*, 03002. [CrossRef]
9. Begun, V.; Florkowski, W. Bose-Einstein condensation of pions in heavy-ion collisions at the CERN Large Hadron Collider (LHC) energies. *Phys. Rev. C* **2015**, *91*, 054909. [CrossRef]
10. Voskresensky, D.N. Kinetic description of a pion gas in ultrarelativistic collisions of nuclei: Turbulence and Bose condensation. *Phys. Atom. Nucl.* **1996**, *59*, 2015–2023.
11. Semikoz, D.V.; Tkachev, I.I. Condensation of bosons in kinetic regime. *Phys. Rev. D* **1997**, *55*, 489–502. [CrossRef]
12. Voskresensky, D.N.; Blaschke, D.; Roepke, G.; Schulz, H. Nonequilibrium approach to dense hadronic matter. *Int. J. Mod. Phys. E* **1995**, *4*, 1–45. [CrossRef]
13. Koch, P.; Rafelski, J. Why the Hadronic Gas Description of Hadronic Reactions Works: The Example of Strange Hadrons. *S. Afr. J. Phys.* **1986**, *9*, 8–23.
14. Stoecker, H.; Zhou, K.; Schramm, S.; Senzel, F.; Greiner, C.; Beitel, M.; Gallmeister, K.; Gorenstein, M.; Mishustin, I.; Vasak, D.; et al. Glueballs amass at RHIC and LHC Colliders!—The early quarkless 1st order phase transition at $T = 270$ MeV—From pure Yang-Mills glue plasma to GlueBall-Hagedorn states. *J. Phys. G* **2016**, *43*, 015105. [CrossRef]
15. Blaizot, J.P.; Liao, J.; McLerran, L. Gluon Transport Equation in the Small Angle Approximation and the Onset of Bose-Einstein Condensation. *Nucl. Phys. A* **2013**, *920*, 58–77. [CrossRef]
16. Blaizot, J.P.; Jiang, Y.; Liao, J. Gluon transport equation with effective mass and dynamical onset of Bose–Einstein condensation. *Nucl. Phys. A* **2016**, *949*, 48–70. [CrossRef]
17. Rehberg, P.; Bot, L.; Aichelin, J. Expansion and hadronization of a chirally symmetric quark-meson plasma. *Nucl. Phys. A* **1999**, *653*, 415–435. [CrossRef]
18. Rehberg, P.; Klevansky, S.P.; Hufner, J. Hadronization in the SU(3) Nambu-Jona-Lasinio model. *Phys. Rev. C* **1996**, *53*, 410–429. [CrossRef]
19. Friesen, A.V.; Kalinovsky, Y.V.; Toneev, V.D. Quark scattering off quarks and hadrons. *Nucl. Phys. A* **2014**, *923*, 1–18. [CrossRef]
20. Marty, R.; Torres-Rincon, J.M.; Bratkovskaya, E.; Aichelin, J. Transport Theory from the Nambu-Jona-Lasinio Lagrangian. *J. Phys. Conf. Ser.* **2016**, *668*, 012001. [CrossRef]
21. Feng, B.; Xu, Z.; Greiner, C. Dynamical scheme for hadronization with first-order phase transition. *Phys. Rev. C* **2017**, *95*, 024907. [CrossRef]
22. Florkowski, W.; Maksymiuk, E.; Ryblewski, R.; Tinti, L. Anisotropic hydrodynamics for a mixture of quark and gluon fluids. *Phys. Rev. C* **2015**, *92*, 054912. [CrossRef]
23. Florkowski, W.; Ryblewski, R.; Su, N.; Tywoniuk, K. Bulk viscosity in a plasma of Gribov-Zwanziger gluons. *Acta Phys. Pol. B* **2016**, *47*, 1833. [CrossRef]
24. Florkowski, W.; Ryblewski, R.; Su, N.; Tywoniuk, K. Strong-coupling effects in a plasma of confining gluons. *Nucl. Phys. A* **2016**, *956*, 669–672. [CrossRef]
25. Shuryak, E.V. Two stage equilibration in high-energy heavy ion collisions. *Phys. Rev. Lett.* **1992**, *68*, 3270–3272. [CrossRef] [PubMed]
26. Zhou, K.; Xu, Z.; Zhuang, P.; Greiner, C. Kinetic description of Bose-Einstein condensation with test particle simulations. *Phys. Rev. D* **2017**, *96*, 014020. [CrossRef]
27. Xu, Z.; Zhou, K.; Zhuang, P.; Greiner, C. Thermalization of gluons with Bose-Einstein condensation. *Phys. Rev. Lett.* **2015**, *114*, 182301. [CrossRef] [PubMed]

28. Andronic, A.; Braun-Munzinger, P.; Redlich, K.; Stachel, J. Decoding the phase structure of QCD via particle production at high energy. *Nature* **2018**, *561*, 321–330. [CrossRef] [PubMed]
29. Seifert, E.; Cassing, W. Baryon-antibaryon annihilation and reproduction in relativistic heavy-ion collisions. *Phys. Rev. C* **2018**, *97*, 024913. [CrossRef]

particles

MDPI

Article

Causality and Renormalization in Finite-Time-Path Out-of-Equilibrium ϕ^3 QFT

Ivan Dadić [1] and Dubravko Klabučar [2,*]

1 Rudjer Bošković Institute, P.O. Box 180, 10002 Zagreb, Croatia; Ivan.Dadic@irb.hr
2 Physics Department, Faculty of Science-PMF, University of Zagreb, Bijenička c. 32, 10000 Zagreb, Croatia
* Correspondence: klabucar@phy.hr; Tel.: +385-91-5866730

Received: 30 November 2018; Accepted: 9 January 2019; Published: 18 January 2019

Abstract: Our aim is to contribute to quantum field theory (QFT) formalisms useful for descriptions of short time phenomena, dominant especially in heavy ion collisions. We formulate out-of-equilibrium QFT within the finite-time-path formalism (FTP) and renormalization theory (RT). The potential conflict of FTP and RT is investigated in $g\phi^3$ QFT, by using the retarded/advanced (R/A) basis of Green functions and dimensional renormalization (DR). For example, vertices immediately after (in time) divergent self-energy loops do not conserve energy, as integrals diverge. We "repair" them, while keeping $d < 4$, to obtain energy conservation at those vertices. Already in the S-matrix theory, the renormalized, finite part of Feynman self-energy $\Sigma_F(p_0)$ does not vanish when $|p_0| \to \infty$ and cannot be split to retarded and advanced parts. In the Glaser–Epstein approach, the causality is repaired in the composite object $G_F(p_0)\Sigma_F(p_0)$. In the FTP approach, after repairing the vertices, the corresponding composite objects are $G_R(p_0)\Sigma_R(p_0)$ and $\Sigma_A(p_0)G_A(p_0)$. In the limit $d \to 4$, one obtains causal QFT. The tadpole contribution splits into diverging and finite parts. The diverging, constant component is eliminated by the renormalization condition $\langle 0|\phi|0\rangle = 0$ of the S-matrix theory. The finite, oscillating energy-nonconserving tadpole contributions vanish in the limit $t \to \infty$.

Keywords: out-of-equilibrium quantum field theory; dimensional renormalization; finite-time-path formalism

1. Introduction and Survey

In many regions of physics, the interacting processes are embedded in a medium and require a short-time description. To respond to such demands, neither vacuum S-matrix field theory [1–5], nor equilibrium QFT [6–16] with the Keldysh-time-path [17–28] suffice. The features, a short time after the beginning of evolution, where uncertainty relations do not keep energy conserved, are to be treated with the finite-time-path method. Such an approach includes many specific features that are not yet completely understood. A particular problem, almost untreated, is handling of UV divergences of the QFT as seen at finite time. The present paper is devoted to this problem. We consider it in the simplest form of $\lambda\phi^3$ QFT, but many of the discussed features will find their analogs in more advanced QED and QCD.

Starting with perturbation expansion in the coordinate space, one performs the Wigner transform and uses the Wick theorem. The propagators, originally appearing in matrix representation, are linearly connected to the Keldysh base with R, A, and K components. For a finite-time-path, the lowest order propagators and one-loop self-energies taken at $t = \infty$ correspond to Keldysh-time-path propagators and one-loop self-energies. For simplicity, the label "∞" is systematically omitted throughout the paper, except in the Appendix with technical details.

To analyze the vertices, one further separates K-component [27,28] into its retarded (K,R) and advanced (K,A) parts:

$$G_R(p) = G_A(-p) = \frac{-i}{p^2 - m^2 + 2ip_0\epsilon},$$

$$G_K(p) = 2\pi\delta(p^2 - m^2)[1 + 2f(\omega_p)]$$

$$= G_{K,R}(p) - G_{K,A}(p),$$

$$G_{K,R}(p) = -G_{K,A}(-p) = h(p_0, \omega_p)G_R(p),$$

$$\omega_p = \sqrt{\vec{p}^2 + m^2}, \quad h(p_0, \omega_p) = -\frac{p_0}{\omega_p}[1 + 2f(\omega_p)]. \tag{1}$$

Matrix propagators are (i and j take the values $1, 2$):

$$G_{ij}(p) = \frac{1}{2}[G_K(p) + (-1)^j G_R(p) + (-1)^i G_A(p)]. \tag{2}$$

Specifically:

$$G_F(p) = G_{11}(p)_{f(\omega_p)=0} = \frac{-i}{p^2 - m^2 + 2i\epsilon}, \quad G_{\bar{F}}(p) = -G_F^*(p). \tag{3}$$

2. Results

2.1. Conservation and Non-Conservation of Energy at Vertices

Having done all this, one obtains the vertex function (for simplicity, all the four-momenta are arranged to be incoming to the vertex). For the simplicity of discussion, all the times corresponding to the external vertices (j) of the whole diagram are assumed equal ($x_{0,j,ext} = t$, all j; otherwise, some factors, oscillating with time, but inessential for our discussion, would appear), so that the vertex function becomes:

$$\frac{i}{2\pi} \frac{e^{-it\sum_i p_{0i}}}{\sum_i p_{0i} + i\epsilon}. \tag{4}$$

This expression [27–29] integrated over some $dp_{o,k}$ by closing the time-path from below gives the expected energy conserving $\delta(\sum_i p_{0i})$, with the oscillating factor reduced to one. If the integration path catches additional singularity, say the propagator's $D(p_k)$ pole at $\bar{p}_{0k}$, for this contribution, conservation of energy is "spoiled" by a finite amount $\Delta E = \sum_i' p_{0i} + \bar{p}_{0k}$, and there is an oscillating vertex function $(i/2\pi)\, e^{-it\Delta E}/(\Delta E + i\epsilon)$. Note: the fact that some time is lower or higher than another, i.e., $t_1 > t_2$ or $t_1 < t_2$, survives Wigner transform in the character of ordering (retarded or advanced) of the two-point function.

In general, we have the following possibilities:

- If the vertex time is lower than the other times of all incoming propagators, there are additional contributions, and energy is not conserved at this vertex. The oscillations are just what we would expect from the Heisenberg uncertainty relations. It is how the time dependence emerges in the finite-time-path out-of-equilibrium QFT. The ill-defined pinching singularities—products of retarded and advanced propagators with the same $(p_0, \vec{p})$, only partially eliminated for the Keldysh time-path [30]—do not appear here as the propagator energies p_0 and p_0' are different variables, so that the singularities do not coincide except at the point $p_0 = p'_0$. Thus, the pertinent mathematical expressions are well defined.

- For some vertices, at least one incoming propagator $G(p_{0k})$ is advanced (or more generally, time is lower at the other vertex of this propagator); then, integration over the p_{0k} (supposed to be UV finite) re-establishes energy conservation.
- The case of UV divergent integrals is interesting; looking at integrations done separately, one would expect energy conservation, but performing other integrals before, one notices that the result is ill-defined. The solution is in regularization: regulated quantities are finite, and (say, in the dimensional regularization) the energy conservation is re-established (as far as $d < 4$).

In the $\lambda\phi^3$ QFT, there are two divergent subdiagrams: the tadpole diagram and self-energy diagram, considered separately in the following subsections.

2.2. UV Divergence at the Tadpole Subdiagram

In the perturbation expansion, the tadpole diagram (Figure 1) appears as a propagator with both ends attached to the same vertex, which is the (lower-time) end-point vertex of the second propagator.

The tadpole subdiagram without a leg is simple. Of the three components, the loop integral vanishes for the R and A components and diverges for the K, R and K, A ones. At finite $\kappa = 4 - d$, these integrals are real constants related to the F and $\bar{F}$ components. In the limit $d = 4$, the renormalization performed on F and $\bar{F}$ makes them finite.

$$
\begin{aligned}
&ig\mu^{\kappa/2}\frac{\int d^dp}{(2\pi)^d}G_R(p) = ig\mu^{\kappa/2}\frac{\int d^dp}{(2\pi)^d}G_A(p) = 0,\\
&G_{Tad} \equiv -ig\frac{\int d^4p}{(2\pi)^4}G_{K,A}(p) = -ig\mu^{\kappa/2}\frac{\int d^dp}{(2\pi)^d}\frac{p_0}{\omega_p}\frac{1+2f(\omega_p)}{p^2-m^2-2ip_0\epsilon} = ig\mu^{\kappa/2}\frac{\int d^dp}{(2\pi)^d}G_{K,R}(p),\\
&\Longrightarrow -\frac{1}{2}G_{Tad} = -\frac{igm^2}{8\pi^2\kappa} - \frac{igm^2}{16\pi^2}[1-\gamma_E + \ln(\frac{4\pi\mu^2}{m^2})] + \mathcal{O}(\kappa) + ig\frac{\int d^3p}{(2\pi)^3}2f(\omega_p)\\
&= -\frac{igm^2}{8\pi^2(\kappa)} + finite\ vacuum\ term + finite\ f(\omega_p)\ term.
\end{aligned} \tag{5}
$$

(Above, and throughout the paper, γ_E denotes the Euler-Mascheroni constant, $\gamma_E \approx 0.5772$.)

For a tadpole subdiagram with a leg (see Figure 1), we have two vertices; higher in time (t_2), which is the connection to the rest of the diagram, and lower in time ($t_1,\ t_1 < t_2$) with the tadpole loop. The lower vertex does not conserve energy.

One has to add contributions from vertices of Type 1 and Type 2. We write it symbolically with the help of the Wigner transform, the connection between the Keldysh-time-path propagators and the finite-time-path propagators at the time $t' = \infty$ and transition to the R/A basis. The derivation given in the Appendix A shows that:

$$
G_{tad,j}(x_2) = -G_A(0,0)G_{Tad} + \int\frac{dp_{02}}{2\pi}\frac{ie^{ip_{02}x_{02}}}{p_{02}-i\epsilon}[G_A(p_{02},0) - G_A(0,0)]G_{Tad}\,. \tag{6}
$$

The contribution is split into the first, energy-conserving term, and the second term, oscillating with time, in which energy is not conserved at the vertex 1 [31].

The tadpole counterterm follows the same pattern:

$$
G^{tadpole}_{count,j}(x_2) = -G_A(0,0) + \int\frac{dp_{02}}{2\pi}\frac{ie^{ip_{02}x_{02}}}{p_{02}-i\epsilon}[G_A(p_{02},0) - G_A(0,0)]. \tag{7}
$$

Notice the similarity of the expressions (6) and (7).

An important point here is that the tadpole contribution splits into two: (1) the energy-conserving part and (2) the energy nonconserving part.

In the energy conserving part, the constant multiplying the counterterm may be adjusted to satisfy the renormalization condition $\langle 0|\phi|0\rangle = 0$ of the S-matrix theory, by which the tadpoles are completely eliminated from perturbation expansion. Nevertheless, the terms proportional to f survive. The energy nonconserving terms oscillate with time, with the frequency depending on the energy increment. In the competition with the contributions of subdiagram without tadpoles, they fade with time, thus giving the same $t \to \infty$ limit as expected from S-matrix theory.

The g^3 order tadpoles and tadpoles with the resummed loop propagator (obtainable after renormalizing the self-energy; see further in the text) do not change our conclusions.

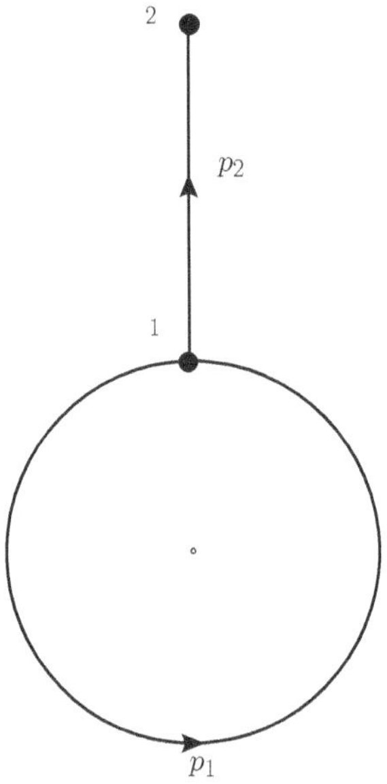

Figure 1. The tadpole diagram with a leg.

2.3. *UV Divergence at the Self-Energy Subdiagram*

While in the S-matrix theory, there is only Feynman ($\Sigma^1_F(p_0,\vec{p})$) one-loop self energy, which does not depend on the frame, in out-of-equilibrium FT, we have self-energies $\Sigma^1_R(p_0,\vec{p})$, $\Sigma^1_A(p_0,\vec{p})$, and $\Sigma^1_K(p_0,\vec{p})$, which is frame dependent through $f(\omega_p)$ (notice here that we distinguish the "true" retarded and advanced functions from those that carry index R (A), but do not vanish for $t_2 > t_1$ ($t_2 < t_1$), except at $d < 4$).

$$\Sigma^1_R(p_0,\vec{p}) = -ig^2\mu^\kappa \int \frac{d^dq}{2(2\pi)^d}[G_R(p_0-q_0,\vec{p}-\vec{q})G_{K,R}(q_0,\vec{q})$$

$$+G_{K,R}(p_0-q_0,\vec{p}-\vec{q})G_R(q_0,\vec{q})] = \Sigma^{1,*}_A(p_0,\vec{p}),$$

$$\Sigma^1_K(p_0,\vec{p}) = -\Sigma^1_{K,R}(p_0,\vec{p}) + \Sigma^1_{K,A}(p_0,\vec{p}) \tag{8}$$

$$\Sigma^1_{K,R}(p_0,\vec{p}) = -i g^2 \mu^\kappa \int \frac{d^d q}{2(2\pi)^d}[G_{K,R}(p_0-q_0,\vec{p}-\vec{q})G_{K,R}(q_0,\vec{q})$$

$$+ G_R(p_0-q_0,\vec{p}-\vec{q})q, G_R(q_0,\vec{q})] = -\Sigma^{1,*}_{K,A}(p_0,\vec{p}). \tag{9}$$

Now, all the integrals containing $f(\omega_p)$ are UV finite owing to the assumed UV cut-off in the definition of f. Vacuum contributions to $\Sigma^1_{K,R}$ are finite separately at $d \to 4$; at $d \to 6$, this is no longer the case, but their sum is finite.

For retarded and advanced self-energies, imaginary parts and parts proportional to $f(\omega_p)$ are UV finite and could be calculated directly from (8). Real, vacuum parts of Σ^1_R are connected to Σ^1_F, and we use the results already available from S-matrix renormalization. The connection is:

$$\Sigma^1_{j,k} = \frac{1}{2}[-\Sigma^1_{K,R} + \Sigma^1_{K,A} - (-1)^k\Sigma^1_R - (-1)^j\Sigma^1_A],$$

$$Re\Sigma^1_{R,f=0} = Re\Sigma^1_{11} + \Sigma^1_{K,R,f=0} = \Sigma^1_F + \Sigma^1_{K,R,f=0}. \tag{10}$$

The regularization procedure (either by making $d < 4$ or by introducing fictive massive particles as in Pauli–Villars regularization) is usually considered artificial. Nevertheless, there are efforts to generate necessary massive particles (virtual wormholes) dynamically [32].

For $\Sigma^1_F(p)$, we find in the literature [33]:

$$\Sigma^1_F(p) = \frac{1}{2}i^2 g^2 \frac{\int d^4q_1 d^4q_2}{(2\pi)^8} G_F(q_1)G_F(q_2)(2\pi)^4\delta^{(4)}(q_1-q_2-p),$$

$$= \frac{1}{2}g^2 \frac{\int d^4q_1 d^4q_2}{(2\pi)^8} \frac{(2\pi)^4\delta^{(4)}(q_1-q_2-p)}{(q_1^2-m^2+i\epsilon)(q_2^2-m^2+i\epsilon)},$$

$$\Longrightarrow \frac{1}{2}g^2(\mu)^\kappa \int_0^1 dz \int \frac{d^d q'}{(2\pi)^d} \frac{1}{[q'^2-m^2+p^2z(1-z)+i\epsilon]^2},$$

$$= \frac{ig^2}{32\pi^2}(\mu^2)^{\kappa/2}\Gamma(\kappa/2)\int_0^1 dz[\frac{p^2z(1-z)-m^2+i\epsilon}{4\pi\mu^2}]^{-\kappa/2}. \tag{11}$$

The last relation above is still causal. It is UV finite, and it allows the separation into the sum of the retarded and advanced term. However, the expansion of $[p^2z(1-z)-m^2+i\epsilon/4\pi\mu^2]^{-\kappa/2}$ in power series of $|\kappa|$ is allowed only when $\kappa\ln[p^2/(4\pi\mu)] << 1$; thus, it is a "low energy" expansion, and in spite of the fact that κ may be taken arbitrarily small, the limit $|p_0| \to \infty$ is never allowed.

$$\Sigma^1_F(p) \approx \frac{ig^2\mu^\kappa}{16\pi^2(\kappa)} - \frac{ig^2\mu^\kappa}{32\pi^2}[\gamma_E + \int_0^1 dz\ln[\frac{p^2z(1-z)-m^2+i\epsilon}{4\pi\mu^2}]]$$

$$= \frac{ig^2\mu^\kappa}{16\pi^2(\kappa)} + finite. \tag{12}$$

This expression is no longer causal; it is valid only if $\kappa\ln[p^2/(4\pi\mu)] << 1$. One needs the vanishing of self-energy for $|p_0| \to \infty$, i.e., the region where the opposite condition $\kappa\ln[p^2/(4\pi\mu)] >> 1$ is fulfilled. Then, $|\Sigma^1_{\infty,F}(p)| \to 0$ as $|p_0| \to \infty$ as far as $\kappa \neq 0$.

The integration over z gives:

$$\Sigma^1_F(p) = -\frac{g^2}{16\pi^2}\left\{\frac{1}{\kappa} - \frac{\gamma_E}{2} + 1 + \frac{1}{2}\ln(4\pi\frac{\mu^2}{m^2}) - \frac{1}{2}\sqrt{1-\frac{4m^2}{p^2+i\epsilon}}\ln\left[\frac{\sqrt{1-\frac{4m^2}{p^2+i\epsilon}}+1}{\sqrt{1-\frac{4m^2}{p^2+i\epsilon}}-1}\right]\right\} \tag{13}$$

with a high p_0 limit:

$$\Sigma_F(p^2, m^2)_{p^2 \to \infty} \approx -\frac{g^2}{16\pi^2}\left\{\frac{1}{\kappa} - \frac{\gamma_E}{2} + 1 + \frac{1}{2}\ln(4\pi\frac{\mu^2}{m^2}) - \frac{1}{2}\ln\left[-\frac{m^2}{p^2}\right]\right\}. \tag{14}$$

To verify the causality of the two-point function, one may try to project out the retarded part of the finite (subtracted) part of $\Sigma^1_F(p)$, namely $-i\int \frac{dp'_0}{2\pi}\Sigma^1_{F,finite}(p)/(p_0 - p'_0 - i\epsilon)$, by integration $\int dp_0$ over a large semicircle. However, the contribution over a very large semicircle does not vanish, and the integral is ill defined.

Indeed, we have started from the expressions for G_F (Σ_F) containing only retarded and advanced functions, and in the absence of divergence, we expect this to be the truth at the end of calculation. Instead, the function in the last two lines of Expression (12) is not a combination of the R and A functions, otherwise it should vanish when $|p_0| \to \infty$ and κ are chosen as arbitrarily small; such a behavior can be shifted to an arbitrarily high scale. However, the limit $\kappa \to 0$ remains always out of reach. To preserve causality, we should keep the whole p_0 complex plane. Specifically, we need the region with large $|p_0|$, to be able to integrate over a large semicircle in the complex p_0 plane, at least to get $\int dp_0 \Sigma^1_R(p) G_{K,A}(p_0) = 0$. Thus, we have obtained a result correct at $\kappa \neq 0$ and problematic at $d = 4$.

Fortunately enough, there is a way to "repair" causality: the composite object $G_F(p)\Sigma^1_F(p)$ is vanishing when $|p_0| \to \infty$; it can be split into its retarded and advanced parts; thus, it is causal. This sort of reparation of causality is possible in other QFT in which logarithmic UV divergence appears. It is similar to the Glaser–Epstein [34–36] approach, where not just Σ, but $G\Sigma$ are the subjects of expansion.

In this spirit, we agree with the conclusion of [37–39]: "Our amplitudes are manifestly causal, by which we mean that the source and detector are always linked by a connected chain of retarded propagators."

Similar is the problem we can see by considering $\lambda\phi^4$ theory. In this theory, the loop of Figure 2 is a vertex diagram, and the above Glaser–Epstein philosophy does not apply. Nevertheless, the propagator attached to the vertex depends on p_0 and "improves" the convergence of dp_0 integration.

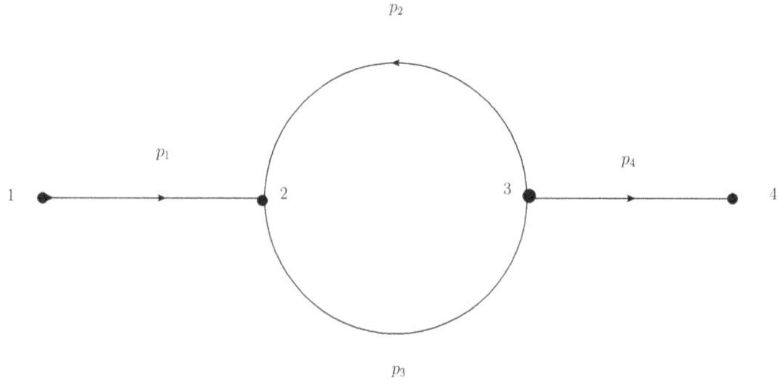

Figure 2. The vertex diagram.

2.4. Self-Energy Diagram with Legs

To be able to introduce composite objects with $\Sigma_{R(A)}$, we need one of $\Sigma_{R(A)}$'s vertices to conserve energy. The lower in time vertex may be the minimal time vertex, so it does not help in all cases. However, the higher in time vertex would do it, if both the integrals dq_0 and dp_0 converge.

The Σ_{ij} self-energy contributions with legs (see Figure 2) are:

$$G_R\Sigma^1_{K,R} * G_A,\ G_R * \Sigma^1_{K,A}G_A,\ G_R\Sigma^1_R * G_{K,A},\ G_{K,R} * \Sigma^1_A G_A,$$

$$G_R\Sigma^1_R * G_A,\ G_A\Sigma^1_A G_A,\ G_R\Sigma^1_R G_{K,R},\ G_{K,A}\Sigma^1_A G_A. \tag{15}$$

In the above expression, Σs are introduced in Equation (8). "$*$" indicates the convolution product, which includes the energy nonconserving vertex. Terms containing $\Sigma^1_{K,R}$ and $\Sigma^1_{K,A}$ are UV-finite, creating no problems. The other terms, containing Σ^1_R and Σ^1_A, are finite as long as $d < 4$, and we may obtain their real part through (11).

Two features seem potentially suspicious: (1) UV divergence in the loop defining $\Sigma^1_{R(A)}$, (2) the ill-defined vertex function between G_R and Σ^1_R and between Σ^1_A and G_A.

Nevertheless, both problems are resolved at $d < 4$: "to be" UV divergence is subtracted and energy conservation is recovered in the above-mentioned vertices. The composite objects $G_R(p)\Sigma^1_R(p)$ and $\Sigma^1_A(p)G_{FA}(p)$ are now well defined.

3. Discussion and Conclusions

We examined renormalization prescriptions for the finite-time-path out-of-equilibrium $\lambda\phi^3$ QFT in the basis of $G_R, G_A, G_{K,R}$, and $G_{K,A}$ propagators.

As expected, the number of counterterms did not change, and the formalism enables term by term finite perturbation calculation.

There are some interesting features:

1. The integrals ensuring the energy conservation at the vertices above Σ_R and Σ_A should have been done before taking the limit $d = 4$.
2. The renormalized self-energies (Σ_F, Σ_R, and Σ_A) are not a linear combination of true retarded and advanced components. This is directly readable from the final result, which does not vanish as $|p_0| \to \infty$ in all directions in a complex plane p_0. This problem is present already in S-matrix theory, and we only recognize it properly as a causality problem, in the sense that the expected properties of the theta-function fail: $\Theta(t)\Theta(-t) \neq 0$ or $\Theta(t)\Theta(t) \neq \Theta(t)$. While it is not clear what harm it does to the theory, one may introduce "composite objects" $G_F(p)\Sigma^1_F(p)$, $G_R(p)\Sigma^1_R(p)$, and $\Sigma^1_A(p)G_A(p)$ to improve convergence, and the causality is "repaired". Indeed in the Glaser–Epstein approach, they consider the perturbation expansion, in which only self-energy with a leg appears.
3. The tadpole contribution splits into the energy-conserving, constant component, which is eliminated by renormalization condition, and the other energy nonconserving, time-dependent component, is finite after subtraction. These tadpole contributions are strongly oscillating with time and vanish as $t \to \infty$, in good agreement with the renormalization condition $< 0|\phi|0 >= 0$ of the S-matrix theory.
4. The regularization ($d \neq 4$) is extended till the late phase of calculation.

The procedure is therefore generalized for application to more realistic theories (QED and QCD, electro-weak QFT, etc.) by the following:

(A) regularize; (B) do energy-conserving integrals; (C) subtract "to be" UV infinities; (D) deregularize (do limit $d \to 4$).

Again, the above described Features (1) and (2) will emerge.

This work contains many of the features [40] arising in the more realistic theories like QED or QCD. Such finite-time-path renormalization is a necessary prerequisite for the calculation of damping rates, and other transition coefficients under the more realistic conditions truly away from equilibrium as opposed to the results obtained within the linear response approximation.

Our plan is to extend the exposed methods to the case of QED. Specifically, we resolve the controversy of the UV diverging number of direct photons in the lowest order of quark QED, as calculated by Boyanovsky and collaborators [41,42] and criticized by [43]. We find that, at the considered one-loop order of perturbation, it is only the vacuum-polarization diagram contributing. The renormalization leaves only finite contributions to the photon production [44].

Author Contributions: Conceptualization, I.D. and D.K.; Formal analysis, I.D.; Investigation, I.D. and D.K.; Methodology, I.D. and D.K.; Validation, I.D. and D.K.; Visualization, D.K.; Writing—original draft, I.D.; Writing—review & editing, I.D. and D.K.

Funding: This work was supported in part by the Croatian Science Foundation under Project Number 8799 and by STSMgrants from COST Actions CA15213 THORand CA16214 PHAROS.

Conflicts of Interest: The authors declare no conflict of interest.

Abbreviations

The following abbreviations are used in this manuscript:

QFT	quantum field theory
FTP	finite-time-path
RT	renormalization theory
DR	dimensional regularization
UV	ultra-violet
QED	quantum electrodynamics
QCD	quantum chromodynamics

Appendix

This Appendix provides the derivation of Equation (6).

The tadpole diagram, Figure 1, appears as a propagator with both ends attached to the same vertex. We start in coordinate representation. To sum contributions from the vertices of Types 1 and 2, we write the propagators with the help of the Wigner transform. Keldysh-time-path propagators and the finite-time propagators become identical in the limit $t' \to \infty$. To translate to the R/A basis, we use $G_{i,j} = \frac{1}{2}[G_K + (-1)^j G_R + (-1)^i G_A]$.

$$\begin{aligned}
G_{tad,j}(x_2) &= ig\mu^{\kappa/2} \int d^d x_1 \\
&\times [G_{1,1}(x_1, x_1) G_{1,j}(x_1, x_2) - G_{2,2}(x_1, x_1) G_{2,j}(x_1, x_2)], \\
&= ig\mu^{\kappa/2} \int d^{d-1} x_1 \int_0^\infty dx_{01} e^{-ip_2(x_1 - x_2)} \frac{d^d p_1}{(2\pi)^d} \frac{d^d p_2}{(2\pi)^d} \\
&\times [G_{1,1,x_{01}}(p_1) G_{1,j,t}(p_2) - G_{2,2,x_{01}}(p_1) G_{2,j,t}(p_2)], \; t = \frac{x_{01} + x_{02}}{2}, \\
&= ig\mu^{\kappa/2} \int d^{d-1} x_1 \int_0^\infty dx_{01} \frac{d^d p_1}{(2\pi)^d} \frac{d^d p_2}{(2\pi)^d} \\
&\times e^{-ip_2(x_1 - x_2)} dp'_{01} dp'_{02} P_{x_{01}}(p_{01}, p'_{01}) P_t(p_{02}, p'_{02}) \\
&\times [G_{1,1,\infty}(p'_1) G_{1,j,\infty}(p'_2) - G_{2,2,\infty}(p'_1) G_{2,j,\infty}(p'_2)], \\
& p'_1 = (p'_{01}, \vec{p}_1), \; p'_2 = (p'_{02}, \vec{p}_2),
\end{aligned} \tag{A1}$$

where we have used the projection operator P connecting time-dependent lowest order propagators with time-independent lowest order propagators [27,28]:

$$
\begin{aligned}
&G_t(p_0,\vec{p}) = \int_{-\infty}^{\infty} dp'_0 P_t(p_0,p'_0)G_\infty(p'_0,\vec{p}),\\
&P_t(p_0,p'_0) = \frac{\Theta(t)}{2\pi}\int_{-2t}^{2t} ds_0 e^{is_0(p_0-p'_0)} = \frac{\Theta(t)}{\pi}\frac{\sin 2(p_0-p'_0)t}{(p_0-p'_0)},\\
&\lim_{t\to\infty} P_t(p_0,p'_0) = \delta(p_0-p'_0),\\
&\int_{-\infty}^{\infty} dp_0 e^{-is_0p_0}P_t(p_0,p'_0) = e^{-is_0p'_0}\Theta(t)\Theta(2t-s_0)\Theta(2t+s_0).
\end{aligned} \tag{A2}
$$

Here, G is a bare propagator (matrix propagator or R, A, or K propagator.)
A similar relation holds for lowest order self-energies:

$$
\Sigma_t^1(p_0,\vec{p}) = \int_{-\infty}^{\infty} dp'_0 P_t(p_0,p'_0)\Sigma_\infty^1(p'_0,\vec{p}), \tag{A3}
$$

where Σ_t^1 is the retarded, advanced, or Keldysh self-energy.
By using the above relations, we obtain:

$$
\begin{aligned}
&G_{tad,j}(x_2) = ig\mu^{\kappa/2}\int d^{d-1}x_1\int_0^\infty dx_{01}e^{-ip'_2(x_1-x_2)}\frac{d^dp'_1}{(2\pi)^d}\frac{d^dp'_2}{(2\pi)^d}\\
&\times[G_{1,1,\infty}(p'_1)G_{1,j,\infty}(p'_2) - G_{2,2,\infty}(p'_1)G_{2,j,\infty}(p'_2)],\\
&= ig\mu^{\kappa/2}(2\pi)^{-1}\int\frac{-i}{p'_{02}-i\epsilon}\delta^{(d-1)}(\vec{p}'_2)e^{ip'_{02}x_{02}}\frac{d^dp'_1}{(2\pi)^d}d^dp'_2\\
&\times[G_{1,1,\infty}(p'_1)G_{1,j,\infty}(p'_2) - G_{2,2,\infty}(p'_1)G_{2,j,\infty}(p'_2)],\\
&= ig\mu^{\kappa/2}(2\pi)^{-1}\int\frac{-i}{p'_{02}-i\epsilon}\delta^{(d-1)}(\vec{p}'_2)e^{ip'_{02}x_{02}}\frac{d^dp'_1}{(2\pi)^d}d^dp'_2\\
&\times\frac{1}{2}[-G_{K,\infty}(p'_1)G_{A,\infty}(p'_2) - G_{R,\infty}(p'_1)G_{K,\infty}(p'_2) - G_{A,\infty}(p'_1)G_{K,\infty}(p'_2)\\
&+(-1)^jG_{R,\infty}(p'_1)G_{R,\infty}(p'_2) + (-1)^jG_{A,\infty}(p'_1)G_{R,\infty}(p'_2)],
\end{aligned} \tag{A4}
$$

By taking the fact that tadpoles with G_R and G_A vanish, we obtain:

$$
\begin{aligned}
&G_{tad,j}(x_2) = ig\mu^{\kappa/2}\frac{(2\pi)^{-1}}{2}\int\frac{i}{p'_{02}-i\epsilon}\delta^{(d-1)}(\vec{p}'_2)e^{ip'_{02}x_{02}}\\
&\times\frac{d^dp'_1}{(2\pi)^d}d^dp'_2G_{K,\infty}(p'_1)G_{A,\infty}(p'_2),\\
&= (2\pi)^{-1}\int\frac{i}{p'_{02}-i\epsilon}e^{ip'_{02}x_{02}}G_{A,\infty}(p'_{02},0)dp'_{02}G_{Tad}\\
&G_{Tad} = \frac{ig\mu^{\kappa/2}}{2}\int G_{K,\infty}(p'_1)\frac{d^dp'_1}{(2\pi)^d}.
\end{aligned} \tag{A5}
$$

Thus,

$$G_{tad,j}(x_2) = -G_{A,\infty}(0,0)G_{Tad} + \int \frac{dp'_{02}}{2\pi} \frac{ie^{ip'_{02}x_{02}}}{p'_{02} - i\epsilon}[G_{A,\infty}(p'_{02},0) - G_{A,\infty}(0,0)]G_{Tad}. \tag{A6}$$

The contribution is split into the first, energy-conserving term, and the second term, oscillating with time, in which energy is not conserved at the vertex 1.

References

1. Bollini, C.G.; Giambiagi, J.J. Dimensional Renormalization: The Number of Dimensions as a Regularizing Parameter. *Nuovo Cim. B* **1972**, *12*, 20–26.
2. 't Hooft, G.; Veltman, M.J.G. Regularization and Renormalization of Gauge Fields. *Nucl. Phys. B* **1972**, *44*, 189. [CrossRef]
3. Ashmore, J.F. A Method of Gauge Invariant Regularization. *Nuovo Cim. Lett.* **1972**, *4*, 289. [CrossRef]
4. Cicuta, G.M.; Montaldi, E. Analytic renormalization via continuous space dimension. *Nouvo Cim. Lett.* **1972**, *4*, 329. [CrossRef]
5. Wilson, K.G. Quantum field theory models in less than four-dimensions. *Phys. Rev. D* **1973**, *7*, 2911. [CrossRef]
6. Donoghue, J.F.; Holstein, B.R. Renormalization and Radiative Corrections at Finite Temperature. *Phys. Rev. D* **1983**, *28*, 340. [CrossRef]
7. Donoghue, J.F.; Holstein, B.R. Renormalization and Radiative Corrections at Finite Temperature, Erratum. *Phys. Rev. D* **1984**, *29*, 3004. [CrossRef]
8. Chapman, I.A. Finite temperature wave function renormalization: A Comparative analysis. *Phys. Rev. D* **1997**, *55*, 6287–6291. [CrossRef]
9. Nakkagawa, H.; Yokota, H. Effective potential at finite temperature: RG improvement versus high temperature expansion. *Prog. Theor. Phys. Suppl.* **1997**, *129*, 209–214. [CrossRef]
10. Baacke, J.; Heitmann, K.; Patzold, C. Renormalization of nonequilibrium dynamics at large N and finite temperature. *Phys. Rev. D* **1998**, *57*, 6406–6419. [CrossRef]
11. Esposito, S.; Mangano, G.; Miele, G.; Pisanti, O. Wave function renormalization at finite temperature. *Phys. Rev. D* **1998**, *58*, 105023. [CrossRef]
12. van Hees, H.; Knoll, J. Renormalization in selfconsistent approximation schemes at finite temperature. 3. Global symmetries. *Phys. Rev. D* **2002**, *66*, 025028. [CrossRef]
13. Jakovac, A.; Szep, Z. Renormalization and resummation in finite temperature field theories. *Phys. Rev. D* **2005**, *71*, 105001. [CrossRef]
14. Arrizabalaga, A.; Reinosa, U. Renormalized finite temperature phi**4 theory from the 2PI effective action. *Nucl. Phys. A* **2007**, *785*, 234–237. [CrossRef]
15. Blaizot, J.-P.; Ipp, A.; Mendez-Galain, R.; Wschebor, N. Perturbation theory and non-perturbative renormalization flow in scalar field theory at finite temperature. *Nucl. Phys. A* **2007**, *784*, 376–406. [CrossRef]
16. Blaizot, J.-P.; Wschebor, N. Massive renormalization scheme and perturbation theory at finite temperature. *Phys. Lett. B* **2015**, *741*, 310–315. [CrossRef]
17. Schwinger, J. Brownian motion of a quantum oscillator. *J. Math. Phys.* **1961**, *2*, 407. [CrossRef]
18. Keldysh, L.V. Diagram technique for nonequilibrium processes. *ZH. Eksp. Teor. Fiz.* **1964**, *47*, 1515.
19. Kadanoff, L.P.; Baym, G. *Quantum Statistical Mechanics*; Benjamin: New York, NY, USA, 1962.
20. Danielewicz, P. Quantum Theory Of Nonequilibrium Processes. Ii. Application To Nuclear Collisions. *Ann. Phys.* **1984**, *152*, 239. [CrossRef]
21. Rammer, J.; Smith, H. Quantum field-theoretical methods in transport theory of metals. *Rev. Math. Phys.* **1986**, *58*, 323. [CrossRef]
22. Landsman, N.P.; van Weert, C.G. Real and Imaginary Time Field Theory at Finite Temperature and Density. *Phys. Rep.* **1987**, *145*, 141. [CrossRef]
23. Calzetta, E.; Hu, B.L. Nonequilibrium Quantum Fields: Closed Time Path Effective Action, Wigner Function and Boltzmann Equation. *Phys. Rev. D* **1988**, *37*, 2878. [CrossRef]
24. le Bellac, M. *Thermal Field Theory*; Cambridge University Press: Cambridge, UK, 1996.

25. Brown, D.A.; Danielewicz, P. Partons in phase space. *Phys. Rev. D* **1998**, *58*, 094003. [CrossRef]
26. Blaizot, J.-P.; Iancu, E. The Quark gluon plasma: Collective dynamics and hard thermal loops. *Phys. Rept.* **2002**, *359*, 355–528. [CrossRef]
27. Dadić, I. Out-of-equilibrium thermal field theories: Finite time after switching on the interaction: Fourier transforms of the projected functions. *Phys. Rev. D* **2001**, *63*, 025011. [CrossRef]
28. Dadić, I. Erratum: Out of equilibrium thermal field theories: Finite time after switching on the interaction and Wigner transforms of projected functions. *Phys. Rev. D* **2002**, *66*, 069903. [CrossRef]
29. Dadić, I. Out-of-equilibrium thermal field theories: Finite time after switching on the interaction: Fourier transforms of the projected functions, Erratum. *Nucl. Phys. A* **2002**, *702*, 356. [CrossRef]
30. Bedaque, P.F. Thermalization and pinch singularities in nonequilibrium quantum field theory. *Phys. Lett. B* **1995**, *344*, 23. [CrossRef]
31. Dadić, I. Retarded propagator representation of out-of-equilibrium thermal field theories. *Nucl. Phys. A* **2009**, *820*, 267C–270D. [CrossRef]
32. Kirillov, A.A.; Savelova, E.P. On the possible dynamical realization of the Pauli–Villars regularization. *Phys. Atom. Nucl.* **2015**, *78*, 1069. [CrossRef]
33. Ryder, L.H. *Quantum Field Theory*; Cambridge University Press: Cambridge, UK, 1985.
34. Epstein, H.; Glaser, V. The Role of locality in perturbation theory. *Ann. Inst. Henri Poincare Phys. Theor. A* **1973**, *19*, 211.
35. Scharf, G. *Finite Quantum Electrodynamics—The Causal Approach*; Springer: Berlin/Heidelberg, Germany, 1995.
36. Lazzarini, S.; Gracia-Bondıa, J.M. Improved Epstein-Glaser renormalization in coordinate space. 1. Euclidean framework. *J. Math. Phys.* **2003**, *44*, 3863. [CrossRef]
37. Millington, P.; Pilaftsis, A. Perturbative Non-Equilibrium Thermal Field Theory to all Orders in Gradient Expansion. *Phys. Lett. B* **2013**, *724*, 56–62. [CrossRef]
38. Millington, P.; Pilaftsis, A. Perturbative nonequilibrium thermal field theory. *Phys. Rev. D* **2013**, *88*, 085009. [CrossRef]
39. Dickinson, R.; Forshaw, J.; Millington, P.; Cox, B. Manifest Causality in quantum field theory with sources and detectors. *JHEP* **2014**, *1406*, 049, [CrossRef]
40. Urmossy, K.; Xu, Z. *PoS DIS* **2016**, *265*, 054.
41. Wang, S.-Y.; Boyanovsky, D. Enhanced photon production from quark—gluon plasma: Finite lifetime effect. *Phys. Rev. D* **2001**, *63*, 051702. [CrossRef]
42. Wang, S.-Y.; Boyanovsky, D.; Ng, K.-W. Direct photons: A nonequilibrium signal of the expanding quark gluon plasma at RHIC energies. *Nucl. Phys. A* **2002**, *699*, 819–846. [CrossRef]
43. Arleo, F.; Aurenche, P.; Bopp, F.; Dadic, I.; David, G.; Delagrange, H.; d'Enterria, D.; Eskola, K.J.; Gelis, F.; Guillet, J.-Ph.; et al. Photon Physics in Heavy Ion Collisions at the LHC. 2004. Available online: http://cds.cern.ch/record/815045 (accessed on 30 November 2018).
44. Dadić, I.; Klabučar, D.; Kuić, D. *Direct Photons from Hot Quark Matter in Renormalized Finite-Time-Path QED*. (unpublished).

particles

MDPI

Article

NA61/SHINE Experiment—Program beyond 2020

Ludwik Turko for the NA61/SHINE Collaboration

Institute of Theoretical Physics, University of Wroclaw, pl. M. Borna 9, 50-205 Wroclaw, Poland; ludwik.turko@ift.uni.wroc.pl; Tel.: +48-71-375-9355

Received: 29 October 2018; Accepted: 26 November 2018; Published: 30 November 2018

Abstract: The fixed-target NA61/SHINE experiment (SPS CERN) looks for the critical point (CP) of strongly interacting matter and the properties of the onset of deconfinement. It is a scan of measurements of particle spectra and fluctuations in proton–proton, proton–nucleus, and nucleus–nucleus interactions as a function of collision energy and system size. This gives unique possibilities to researching critical properties of the dense hot hadronic matter created in the collision process. New measurements and their objectives, related to the third stage of the experiment after 2020, are presented and discussed here.

Keywords: QCD matter; phase transition; critical point

---

1. Introduction

The NA61/SHINE, **S**uper Proton Synchrotron (SPS) **H**eavy **I**on and **N**eutrino **E**xperiment, is the continuation and extension of the NA49 [1,2] measurements of hadron and nuclear fragment production properties in fixed-target reactions induced by hadron and ion beams. It has used a similar experimental fixed-target setup as NA49 (Figure 1), but with an extended research program. Beyond an enhanced strong interactions program, there are the measurements of hadron production for neutrino and cosmic ray experiments realized. NA61/SHINE is a collaboration, with about 150 physicists, 33 institutions, and 14 countries being involved.

The strong interaction program of NA61/SHINE is devoted to studying the onset of deconfinement and search for the critical point (CP) of hadronic matter, related to the phase transition between hadron gas (HG) and quark-gluon plasma (QGP). The first order phase boundary between the HG and QGP phase is expected to end at the CP, as seen in Figure 2. At the CP, the sharp first-order phase transition turns into a rapid crossover, resulting in the appearance of large fluctuations of various observables, which are sensitive to the vicinity of the CP. The CP has long been predicted for thermal quantum chromodynamics (QCD) at finite μ_B/T [3–5]. Lattice QCD calculations, which are becoming more and more accurate, have led to the present conclusions that the cross-over region occurs at $T_c(\mu_B = 0) = 154 \pm 9$ MeV [6] and the location of the CP is not expected for $\mu_B/T \leqslant 2$ and $T/T_c(\mu_B = 0) > 0.9$ [7]. A more detailed exploration of the QCD phase diagram would need both new experimental data with extended detection capabilities and improved theoretical models [8].

The NA49 experiment studied hadron production in Pb + Pb interactions, while the NA61/SHINE collects data varying collision energy (13A–158A GeV) and the size of the colliding systems, as shown in Figure 3. This is, in a sense, equivalent to the two-dimensional scan of the NA61/SHINE piece of the hadronic phase diagram in the (T, μ_B) plane, as depicted in Figure 2. Changes in the collision energy lead to different values of the net baryon number chemical potential μ_B and temperature T. Different sizes of colliding systems allow to identify the minimum hadronic volume, which can be excited to the state where statistical physics concepts of HG/QGP phase transition are still meaningful. The research program was initiated in 2009, with the p + p collisions used later on as reference measurements for heavy-ion collisions.

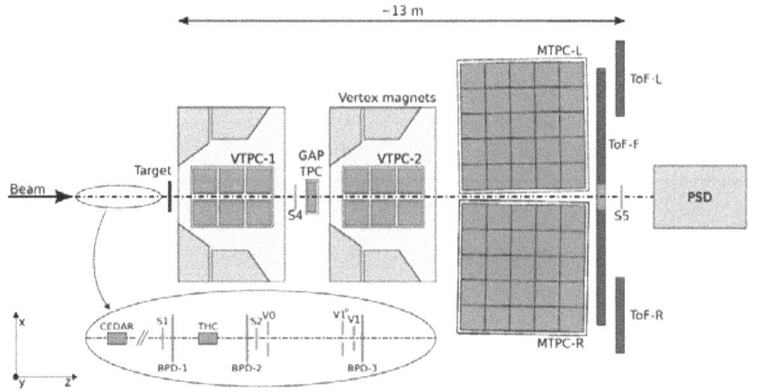

Figure 1. The present NA61/SHINE detector consists of a large acceptance hadron spectrometer, followed by a set of six Time Projection Chambers (TPCs), as well as time-of-flight (ToF) detectors. The high resolution forward calorimeter, the projectile spectator detector (PSD), measures energy flow around the beam direction. For hadron–nucleus interactions, the collision volume is determined by counting the low momentum particles emitted from the nuclear target with the low momentum particle detector (a small TPC) surrounding the target. An array of beam detectors identifies beam particles, secondary hadrons, and nuclei, as well as primary nuclei, and measures precisely their trajectories.

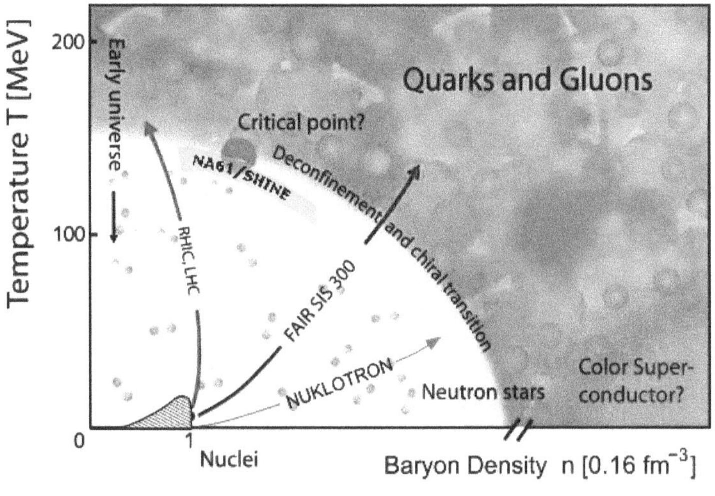

Figure 2. Phase structure of hadronic matter covered by NA61/SHINE (green), compared to present and future heavy ion experiments.

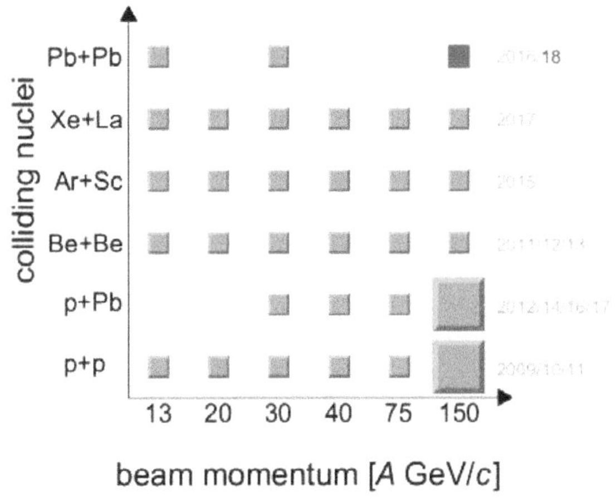

Figure 3. For the program on strong interactions NA61/SHINE scans in the system size and beam momentum. In the plot, the recorded data are indicated in green and the approved future data in red.

Hadron production measurements for neutrino experiments are just reference measurements of p + C interactions for the T2K experiment, since they are necessary for computing initial neutrino fluxes at J-PARC. These measurements have been extended to the production of charged pions and kaons in interactions with thin carbon targets and replicas of the T2K target, to test accelerator neutrino beams [9]. The collection of data began in 2007.

Collected p + C data also allow to better understand nuclear cascades in the cosmic air showers—necessary in the Pierre Auger and KASCADE experiments [10,11]. These are reference measurements of p + C, p + p, π + C, and K + C interactions for cosmic ray physics. The cosmic ray collisions with the Earth's atmosphere produce air shower secondary radiation. Some of the particles produced in such collisions subsequently decay into muons, which are able to reach the surface of the Earth. Cosmic ray induced muon production would allow to reproduce primary cosmic ray composition if the related hadronic interactions are known [12].

As seen in Figure 2, the phase structure of hadronic matter is involved. Progress in the theoretical understanding of the subject and collecting more experimental data will allow to delve into the subject. While the highest energies achieved at LHC and RHIC colliders provide data related to the crossover HG/QGP regions, the SPS fixed-target NA61/SHINE experiment is particularly suited to explore the phase transition line HG/QGP with the CP included.

Results of Initial NA61/SHINE Research

The production properties of light and medium mass hadrons, in particular pions and kaons, have been measured [13] according to the NA61/SHINE proposal [1]. The Be + Be results are close to p + p independently of collision energy. Moreover, the data show a jump between light (p + p, Be + Be) and intermediate, heavy (Ar + Sc, Pb + Pb) systems [14]. The observed rapid change of hadron production properties that starts when moving from Be + Be to Ar + Sc collisions can be interpreted as the beginning of the creation of large clusters of strongly interacting matter—the onset of fireball. One notes that non-equilibrium clusters produced in p + p and Be + Be collisions seem to have similar properties at all beam momenta studied here.

The K^+/π^+ ratio in p + p interactions is below the predictions of statistical models. However, the ratio in central Pb + Pb collisions is close to statistical model predictions for large volume systems [15].

In p + p interactions, and thus also in Be + Be collisions, multiplicity fluctuations are larger than predicted by statistical models. However, they are close to statistical model predictions for large volume systems in central Ar + Sc and Pb + Pb collisions [16].

The two-dimensional scan conducted by NA61/SHINE by varying collision energy and nuclear mass number of colliding nuclei indicates four domains of hadron production separated by two thresholds: The onset of deconfinement and the onset of fireball [17]. The sketch presented in Figure 4 illustrates this preliminary conclusion. Collected Ar + Sc and Xe + La data are being analyzed to provide further information.

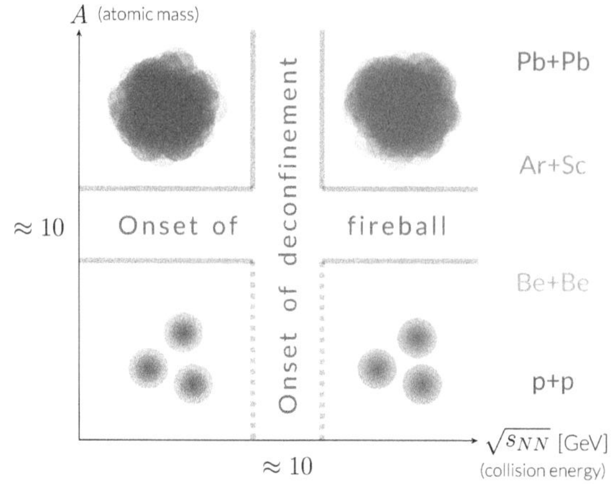

Figure 4. The onset of deconfinement and the onset of fireball. The onset of deconfinement is well established in central Pb + Pb (Au + Au) collisions. Its presence in collisions of low mass nuclei, inelastic p + p interactions in particular, is questionable.

Total production cross-sections and total inelastic cross-sections for reactions π^++C,Al and K^++C,Al at 60 GeV/c and π^++C,Al at 31 GeV/c were measured. These measurements are a key ingredient for neutrino flux prediction from the reinteractions of secondary hadrons in current and future accelerator-based long-baseline neutrino experiments [18].

2. New Measurements Requested

The third stage of the experiment, starting after the Long Shutdown 2 (LS-2) of the CERN accelerator system, would include:

- Measurements of charm hadron production in Pb + Pb collisions for heavy ion physics;
- measurements of nuclear fragmentation cross-section for cosmic ray physics;
- measurements of hadron production in hadron–nucleus interactions for neutrino physics.

The proposed measurements and analysis are requested by heavy ion, cosmic ray, and neutrino communities. A careful analysis of fluctuations and intermittency phenomena in NA61/SHINE data collected so far is necessary to look for the CP [19].

The objective of **charm hadron production measurements** in Pb + Pb collisions is to obtain the first data on the mean number of $\bar{c}c$ pairs produced in the full phase space in heavy ion collisions. Moreover, further new results on the collision energy and system size dependence will be provided. This will help to answer the questions about the mechanism of open charm production, about the relation between the onset of deconfinement and open charm production, and about the behavior of J/ψ in quark-gluon plasma.

The objective of **nuclear fragmentation cross-section measurements** is to provide high-precision data needed for the interpretation of results from current-generation cosmic ray experiments. The proposed measurements are of crucial importance to extract the characteristics of the diffuse propagation of cosmic rays in the Galaxy.

The objectives of **new hadron production measurements for neutrino physics** are to further improve the precision of hadron production measurements for the currently used T2K replica target, to perform measurements for a new target material, both for T2K-II and Hyper-Kamiokande experiments, and to study the possibility of measurements at low incoming beam momenta (below 12 GeV/c), relevant for improved predictions of both atmospheric and accelerator neutrino fluxes.

NA61/SHINE is the only experiment which will conduct such measurements in the near future. Together with other HIC experiments, it creates a full-tone physical picture of QCD in dense medium. Especially concerning the strong interaction heavy-ion program, the NA61/SHINE has unique capabilities in comparison with the other experiments (see Figure 2):

The limitations of other experiments are related to: (i) Limited acceptance, (ii) measurement of open charm not considered in the current program, or (iii) very low cross-section at SIS-100.

Concerning other experiments' capabilities shown at Figure 5:

- LHC and RHIC measurements of open charm at high energies are performed in a limited acceptance due to the collider kinematics and the detector geometry. The NA61/SHINE measurement will not be subject to these limitations [20–23];
- RHIC BES collider ($\sqrt{s_{NN}} = 7.7 - 39$ GeV): Measurement not considered in the current program [24–26];
- RHIC BES fixed-target ($\sqrt{s_{NN}} = 3 - 7.7$ GeV): Measurement not considered in the current program [27];
- NICA ($\sqrt{s_{NN}} < 11$ GeV): Measurements during stage 2 (after 2023) are under consideration [28];
- J-PARC-HI ($\sqrt{s_{NN}} \lesssim 6$ GeV): Under consideration, may be possible after 2025 [29];
- FAIR SIS-100 ($\sqrt{s_{NN}} \lesssim 5$): Not possible due to the very low cross-section at SIS-100, charm measurements are planned with SIS-300 ($\sqrt{s_{NN}} \lesssim 7$ GeV), but not with the start version (timeline is unclear).

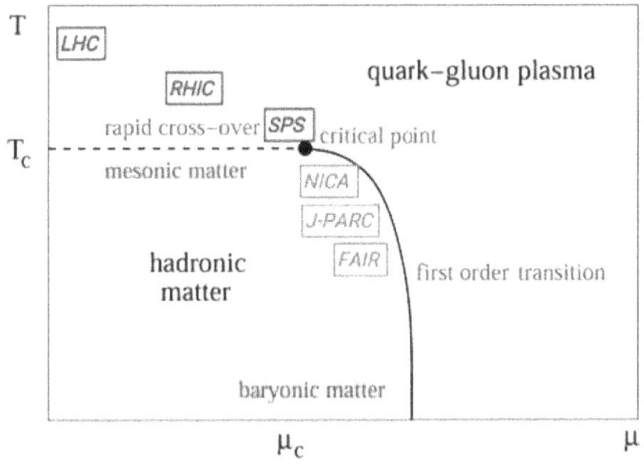

Figure 5. Recent (red) and future (green) heavy ion facilities in the phase diagram of strongly interacting matter.

The beam momentum range provided to NA61/SHINE by the SPS and the H2 beam line is highly important for the heavy ion, neutrino, and cosmic ray communities. It covers:

- Energies at which the transition from confined hadrons to quark gluon plasma in heavy ion collisions takes place—the onset of deconfinement [30];
- proton beams of momenta used to produce neutrino beams at J-PARC, Japan and Fermilab, US [31];
- light nuclei at momenta > 10 A GeV/c, important for the understanding of the propagation of cosmic rays in the Galaxy [32].

Specific Research Goals

The NA61/SHINE charm program addresses questions about the validity and the limits of statistical and dynamical models of high energy collisions in the new domain of quark mass, $m_c \approx 1300$ MeV $\gg T_C \approx 150$ MeV [33]. To answer these questions, knowledge is needed on the mean number of charm–anticharm quark pairs $\langle c\bar{c} \rangle$ produced in the full phase space of heavy ion collisions.

Such data do not exist yet and NA61/SHINE aims to provide them within the coming years. The related preparations have started already. In 2015 and 2016, a Small Acceptance Vertex Detector (SAVD) was constructed and first measurements of open charm production started in 2016—Figure 6. Vertex resolution has appeared precisely enough (30 μm) to distinguish D^0 decay. That was possible due to the fixed-target experiment-specific property, where the Lorenz factor $\beta\gamma \approx 10$ makes short-living D^0 an observable particle, even in such a small acceptance vertex detector.

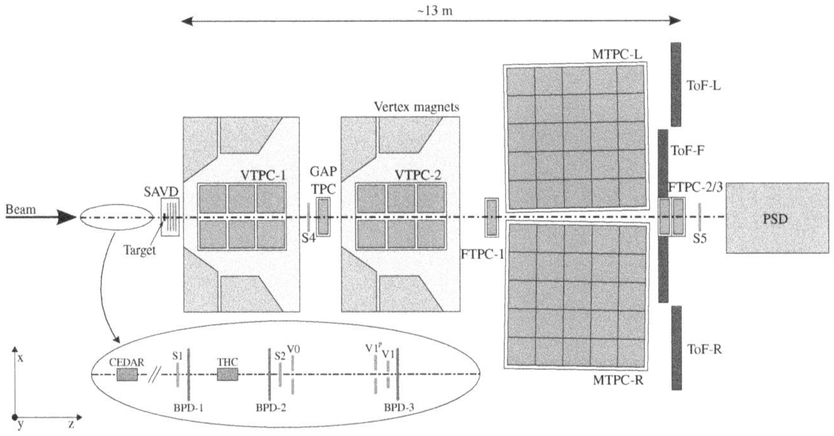

Figure 6. Present NA61/SHINE setup with the SAVD included.

Successful performance of the SAVD in 2016 led to the decision to also use it during the collection of Xe + La data in 2017. About $5 * 10^6$ events of central Xe + La collisions at 150A GeV/c were collected. The Xe + La data are currently under analysis and are expected to lead to physics results in the coming months. One expects to reconstruct several hundreds of D^0 and $\bar{D}^0$ decays. Beyond this, about 4000 D^0 and $\bar{D}^0$ decays can be expected to be reconstructed from the collection of Pb + Pb data in 2018. Further data collection on Pb + Pb collisions and the reconstruction of decays of various open charm mesons are planned by NA61/SHINE for the years 2022–2024. This would be combined with the required detector upgrades, including a full scale, large acceptance vertex detector—now under construction.

Another domain of NA61/SHINE activity will be to measure fragmentation cross-sections relevant for the production of Li, Be, B, C, and N nuclei. These elements are of particular importance for the physics of cosmic rays in the Galaxy. The NA61/SHINE facility has already successfully taken data with light ion beams [34] and can be used with practically no modifications to perform the needed cross-section measurements at isotope level. The ability to separate different isotopes from fragmentation interactions for a given charge was validated with simulations [35].

Funding: The author acknowledges support by the Polish National Science Center under contract No. UMO-2014/15/B/ST2/03752, the COST Actions CA15213 (THOR), CA16117 (ChETEC) and CA16214 (PHAROS) for supporting their networking activities, and the Bogolubov-Infeld Program for supporting the author's stay at JINR Dubna.

Conflicts of Interest: The author declare no conflicts of interest.

Abbreviations

The following abbreviations are used in this manuscript:

CERN	Conseil Europén pour la Recherche Nucléaire
CP	critical point
FAIR	Facility for Antiproton and Ion Research
HG	hadron gas
HIC	heavy-ion collision
J-PARC	Japan Proton Accelerator Research Complex
LHC	Large Hadron Collider
LS	long shutdown
NICA	Nuclotron-based Ion Collider fAcility
QCD	quantum chromodynamics
QGP	quark-gluon plasma
SAVD	small acceptance vertex detector
RHIC	Relativistic Heavy Ion Collider
SPS	Super Proton Synchrotron

References

1. Gazdzicki, M.; Fodor, Z.; Vesztergombi, G. NA49-future Collaboration. In *Study of Hadron Production in Hadron-Nucleus and Nucleus-Nucleus Collisions at the CERN SPS*; Technical Report CERN-SPSC-2006-034; SPSC-P-330; CERN: Geneva, Switzerland, 2006
2. Abgrall, N. NA61/SHINE Collaboration. In *Calibration and Analysis of the 2007 Data*; Technical Report CERN-SPSC-2008-018; CERN: Geneva, Switzerland, 2008
3. Barducci, A.; Casalbuoni, R.; De Curtis, S.; Gatto, R.; Pettini, G. Chiral Symmetry Breaking in QCD at Finite Temperature and Density. *Phys. Lett. B* **1989**, *231*, 463–470. [CrossRef]
4. Halasz, A.M.; Jackson, A.D.; Shrock, R.E.; Stephanov, M.A.; Verbaarschot, J.J.M. Phase diagram of QCD. *Phys. Rev. D* **1998**, *58*, 096007. [CrossRef]
5. Berges, J.; Rajagopal, K. Color superconductivity and chiral symmetry restoration at nonzero baryon density and temperature. *Nucl. Phys. B* **1999**, *538*, 215–232. [CrossRef]
6. Bazavov, A.; Bhattacharya, T.; DeTar, C.; Ding, H.-T.; Gottlieb, S.; Gupta, R.; Hegde, P.; Heller, U.M.; Karsch, F.; Laermann, E.; et al. Equation of state in (2+1)-flavor QCD. *Phys. Rev. D* **2014**, *90*, 094503. [CrossRef]
7. Bazavov, A.; Ding, H.-T.; Hegde, P.; Kaczmarek, O.; Karsch, F.; Laermann, E.; Maezawa, Y.; Ohno, H.; Petreczky, P.H.; Wagner, M.; et al. The QCD Equation of State to $\mathcal{O}(\mu_B^6)$ from Lattice QCD. *Phys. Rev. D* **2017**, *95*, 054504. [CrossRef]
8. Caines, H. The Search for Critical Behavior and Other Features of the QCD Phase Diagram—Current Status and Future Prospects. *Nucl. Phys. A* **2017**, *967*, 121–128. [CrossRef]
9. Abgrall, N.; Aduszkiewicz, A.; Andrieu, B.; Anticic, T.; Antoniou, N.; Argyriades, J.; Asryan, A.G.; Baatar, B.; Blondel, A.; Blumer, J.; et al. (NA61/SHINE Collaboration). Measurements of Cross Sections and Charged Pion Spectra in Proton-Carbon Interactions at 31 GeV/c. *Phys. Rev. C* **2011**, *84*, 034604. [CrossRef]
10. Abraham, J.; Aglietta, M.; Aguirre, I.C.; Albrow, M.; Allard, D.; Allekotte, I.; Allison, P.; Alvarez Muñiz, J.; do Amaral, M.G.; Ambrosio, M.; et al. (Pierre Auger Collaboration). Properties and performance of the prototype instrument for the Pierre Auger Observatory. *Nucl. Instrum. Methods Phys. Res. Sect. A* **2004**, *523*, 50–95. [CrossRef]

11. Antoni, T.; Apel, W.D.; Badea, F.; Bekk, K.; Bercuci, A.; Blümer, H.; Bozdog, H.; Brancus, I.M.; Büttner, C.; Chilingarian, A.; et al. (KASCADE Collaboration). The Cosmic ray experiment KASCADE. *Nucl. Instrum. Methods Phys. Res. Sect. A* **2003**, *513*, 490–510. [CrossRef]
12. Morison, I. *Introduction to Astronomy and Cosmology*; John Wiley & Sons: Hoboken, NJ, USA, 2008; ISBN 978-0-470-03333-3.
13. Turko, L. (NA61/SHINE Collaboration) Looking for the Phase Transition-Recent NA61/SHINE Results. *Universe* **2018**, *4* , 52. [CrossRef]
14. Aduszkiewicz, A. (NA61/SHINE Collaboration Collaboration). In *Report from the NA61/SHINE Experiment at the CERN SPS*; Technical Report CERN-SPSC-2017-038; SPSC-SR-221; CERN: Geneva, Switzerland, 2017.
15. Becattini, F.; Manninen, J.; Gazdzicki, M. Energy and system size dependence of chemical freeze-out in relativistic nuclear collisions. *Phys. Rev.* **2006**, *C73*, 044905. [CrossRef]
16. Begun, V.V.; Gazdzicki, M.; Gorenstein, M.I.; Hauer, M.; Konchakovski, V.P.; Lungwitz, B. Multiplicity fluctuations in relativistic nuclear collisions: Statistical model versus experimental data. *Phys. Rev.* **2007**, *C76*, 024902. [CrossRef]
17. Larsen, D. (NA61/SHINE Collaboration) The onsets of deconfinement and fireball of NA61/SHINE. *arXiv* **2018**, arXiv:1810.02756.
18. Aduszkiewicz, A.; Andronov, E.; Antićić, T.; Antoniou, N.; Baatar, B.; Baszczyk, M.; Bhosale, S.; Blondel, A.; Bogomilov, M.; Brandin, A.; et al. (NA61/SHINE Collaboration) Measurements of total production cross sections for π^++C, π^++Al, K^++C, and K^++Al at 60 GeV/c and π^++C and π^++Al at 31 GeV/c. *Phys. Rev. D* **2018**, *98*, 052001. [CrossRef]
19. Andronov, E. (NA61/SHINE Collaboration) Search for the critical point by the NA61/SHINE experiment. *arXiv* **2018**, arXiv:1807.10737.
20. Meninno, E. (ALICE Collaboration) Open-charm production measurements in pp, 1 p-Pb and Pb-Pb collisions with ALICE at the LHC. *EPJ Web Conf.* **2017**, *137*, 06018. [CrossRef]
21. Hou, G.W.S. (ATLAS, CMS Collaboration) Open charm production and spectroscopy at ATLAS and CMS. *Proc. Sci.* **2016**. [CrossRef]
22. Simko, M. (STAR Collaboration) Measurements of open charm hadrons at the STAR experiment. *J. Phys. Conf. Ser.* **2017**, *832*, 012028. [CrossRef]
23. Nagashima, K. (PHENIX Collaboration) PHENIX measurements of single electrons from charm and bottom decays at midrapidity in Au+Au collisions. *Nucl. Phys.* **2017**, *A967*, 644–647. [CrossRef]
24. Odyniec, G. The RHIC Beam Energy Scan program in STAR and what's next... *J. Phys. Conf. Ser.* **2013**, *455*, 012037. [CrossRef]
25. Yang, C. (STAR Collaboration) The STAR beam energy scan phase II physics and upgrades. *Nucl. Phys.* **2017**, *A967*, 800. [CrossRef]
26. Luo, X.; Xu, N. Search for the QCD Critical Point with Fluctuations of Conserved Quantities in Relativistic Heavy-Ion Collisions at RHIC: An Overview. *Nucl. Sci. Tech.* **2017**, *28*, 112. [CrossRef]
27. Meehan, K.C. (STAR Collaboration) Fixed Target Collisions at STAR. *Nucl. Phys.* **2016**, *A956*, 878. [CrossRef]
28. Kekelidze, V.; Kovalenko, A.; Lednicky, R.; Matveev, V.; Meshkov, I.; Sorin, A.; Trubnikov, G. Feasibility study of heavy-ion collision physics at NICA JINR. *Nucl. Phys. A* **2017**, *967*, 884–887. [CrossRef]
29. Sako, H.; Harada, H.; Sakaguchi, T.; Chujo, T.; Esumi, S.; Gunji, T.; Hasegawa, S.; Hwang, S.H.; Ichikaw, Y.; Imai, K.; et al. (J-PARC Heavy-Ion Collaboration) Studies of high density baryon matter with high intensity heavy-ion beams at J-PARC. *Nucl. Phys. A* **2016**, *956*, 850–853. [CrossRef]
30. Gazdzicki, M.; Gorenstei, M.; Seyboth, P. Onset of deconfinement in nucleus-nucleus collisions: Review for pedestrians and experts. *Acta Phys. Polon. B* **2011**, *42*, 307–351. [CrossRef]
31. Abgrall, N.; Aduszkiewicz, A.; Andronov, E.V.; Antićić, T.; Baatar, B.; Baszczyk, M.; Bhosale, S.; Blondel, A.; Bogomilov, M.; Brandin, A.; et al. (NA61 Collaboration) Measurements of $\pi^{\pm}$, $K^{\pm}$ and proton yields from the surface of the T2K replica target for incoming 31 GeV/c protons with the NA61/SHINE spectrometer at the CERN SPS. *arXiv* **2018**, arXiv:1808.04927.
32. Genolini, Y.; Maurin, D.; Moskalenko, I.V.; Unger, M. Current status and desired accuracy of the isotopic production cross sections relevant to astrophysics of cosmic rays I. Li, Be, B, C, N. *Phys. Rev. C* **2018**, *98*, 034611. [CrossRef]
33. Snoch, A. (NA61/SHINE Collaboration) Charm Program of NA61/SHINE: Motivation and Measurements. *arXiv* **2018**, arXiv:1803.01692.

34. Kaptur, E. (NA61/SHINE Collaboration) Energy scan with Be+Be collisions: Cross-section, centrality determination, pion spectra and mean multiplicities, CPOD2014. *Proc. Sci.* **2015**, 053.
35. Aduszkiewicz, A. (NA61/SHINE Collaboration). In *Feasibility Study for the Measurement of Nuclear Fragmentation Cross Sections with NA61/SHINE at the CERN SPS*; CERN-SPSC-2017-035; SPSC-P-330-ADD-9; CERN: Geneva, Switzerland, 2017.

MDPI
St. Alban-Anlage 66
4052 Basel
Switzerland
Tel. +41 61 683 77 34
Fax +41 61 302 89 18
www.mdpi.com

Particles Editorial Office
E-mail: particles@mdpi.com
www.mdpi.com/journal/particles

Lightning Source UK Ltd.
Milton Keynes UK
UKHW020655090321
379992UK00003B/248

9 783039 368143